PEARSON

ALWAYS LEARNING

Compiled by Darryl Smith • Clare Chua, Ph.D.

Business Statistics

Volume 1

Thirteenth Custom Edition for Ryerson University
Ted Rogers School of Management

With materials from:
Business Statistics: A First Course, Sixth Edition
by David M. Levine, Timothy C. Krehbiel, and Mark L. Berenson

Pearson Education, Inc., 330 Hudson Street, New York, New York 10013
A Pearson Education Company
www.pearsoned.com

Printed in the United States of America

4 17

000200010272057178

RM/AP

ISBN 10: 1-323-50925-9
ISBN 13: 978-1-323-50925-8

Brief Contents

Contents

4 Numerical Descriptive Measures 136

5 Basic Probability 202

6 Discrete Probability Distributions 238

7 The Normal Distribution 278

8 Sampling and Sampling Distributions 316

9 Statistical Applications in Quality Management 352

Business Statistics

1

Type of Data and Measurement Scales

Learning Objectives

In this chapter, you learn:

- How statistics is used in business
- The sources of data used in business
- The types of data used in business
- The basics of Microsoft Excel
- The basics of SPSS

Statistics is the science of collecting, organizing, presenting, analyzing, and interpreting data to assist in making effective decisions. **Descriptive statistics** focuses on collecting, summarizing, presenting, and analyzing a set of data. **Inferential statistics** uses data that have been collected from a small group to draw conclusions about a larger group. A **statistic** is a numerical measure that describes a characteristic of a sample. A **parameter** is a numerical measure that describes a characteristic of a population.

The first course involves descriptive statistics, in which you learn methods of organizing, presenting, and describing a set of data. Before you learn to summarize a given set of data, you must learn about the nature of the data. The techniques to summarize data are governed by the type of data. For example, if you have a set of data containing a bunch of males and females, you can code "male" as 1 and "female" as 2. Suppose your data consists of 5 males and 5 females. The coded data are 1, 1, 1, 1, 1, 2, 2, 2, 2, 2. The average would be $(1+1+1+1+1+2+2+2+2+2)/10=15/10=1.5$. What does the average of 1.5 mean? Does it make sense? Using the average to summarize qualitative data does not provide any significant meaning in this context.

The first chapter begins by discussing what data are, the different types of data, and the four levels of measurements scales. Statistics are applied daily. For example,

- the article "How to get dieters to lose weight? You pay them, obviously" (source: http://www.theglobeandmail.com/life/style/hannah-sung/how-to-get-dieters-to-lose-weight-you-pay-them-obviously/article1867026/) reported that "According to the Canadian Health Measures Survey, almost a quarter of the Canadian population is considered obese."
- the article "Trade deficit drops 'for all the wrong reasons'" (source: http://www.theglobeandmail.com/report-on-business/economy/trade/trade-deficit-drops-for-all-the-wrong-reasons/article1868347/) reported that "Measured in dollars, energy exports shot up 3.2 per cent in November. Exports of industrial goods and materials rose 6.6 per cent."

These examples show that statistics are facts and figures. But in fact, they are something more than that. In the broadest sense, "statistics" refers to a range of techniques and procedures for describing, summarizing, graphically presenting, measuring, and analyzing data. This is the focus of this course.

1.1 What Are Data?

There are many methods of collecting data. Data collection is a process of gathering information using questionnaires, interviews, experiments, and field study. In the business world, information is usually gathered using questionnaires. A questionnaire is a data collection instrument containing sequences of questions to meet a research objective. The purpose of having the questionnaire is to gather information from respondents for various objectives. An example of a survey questionnaire is shown below in Table 1.1.

TABLE 1.1
Survey

> 1. Did you bring your textbook to class today?
> ❑ Yes
> ❑ No
> 2. How much time (in hours) do you usually spend studying per week? _____
> 3. How many courses did you enroll in this semester? _____
> 4. Your Class Year: _____ *(please check your answer below)*
> ❑ Freshman
> ❑ Sophomore
> ❑ Junior
> ❑ Senior
> 5. How did you come to school today?
> ❑ Walk
> ❑ Drive
> ❑ Take public transport
> ❑ Car pool

A random sample of 12 students was asked to fill out the survey questionnaire shown above. The data collected from the 12 students were tabulated in the table displayed in Table 1.2.

TABLE 1.2
Results of the Survey

Student	Did you bring your textbook to class today?	How much time (in hours) do you usually spend studying per week?	How many courses did you enroll in this semester?	Class Year	How did you come to school today?
1	Yes	20.3	3	Freshman	Take public transport
2	Yes	12.5	5	Sophomore	Drive
3	No	10.3	6	Junior	Walk
4	Yes	2.5	4	Junior	Drive
5	No	0.5	5	Senior	Take public transport
6	Yes	7.2	2	Sophomore	Drive
7	Yes	5.5	5	Freshman	Take public transport
8	No	10.0	4	Freshman	Walk
9	No	4.8	4	Freshman	Walk
10	Yes	3.2	3	Freshman	Drive
11	Yes	17.0	5	Senior	Take public transport
12	Yes	4.3	6	Freshman	Take public transport

The responses collected from the question "Did you bring your textbook to class today?" are a collection of "Yes" and "No." The responses collected from the question "How much time (in hours) do you usually spend studying per week?" are a collection of numbers ranging from 0.5 to 20.3. These numbers are elicited by the respondents. Later you will learn to classify these responses by type of data and measurement scale.

Data are a collection of numbers and/or attributes of an entity. The students' responses are called data. You will see that the responses can be expressed either numerically (for example, 3.2 17.0, 3, 5, etc.) or non-numerically (for example, Yes, No, Drive, Walk, etc.). The numeric data is identified as quantitative data, and the non-numeric data is identified as qualitative data.

Examples of data are shown in Examples 1.1 and 1.2. Example 1.1 is a set of consumer price index data that is classified as quantitative data. Example 1.2 is a set of language data that is classified as qualitative data.

EXAMPLE 1.1

A Set of Consumer Price Index Data

Source: *http://www40.statcan.gc .ca/l01/cst01/ECON45A-eng.htm*

TABLE 1.3

All-items	Consumer Price Index, by city (Index)				
	2006	2007	2008	2009	2010
	2002=100				
St. John's (N.L.)	109.1	110.7	114.0	114.7	117.4
Charlottetown and Summerside (P.E.I.)	111.0	113.2	116.9	117.1	119.2
Halifax (N.S.)	109.8	112.0	115.2	115.3	117.6

Saint John (N.B.)	109.2	111.2	113.2	113.7	116.3
Québec (Que.)	108.7	110.1	112.4	113.2	114.8
Montréal (Que.)	108.6	110.3	112.6	113.5	114.8
Ottawa–Gatineau, (Ont. part)	108.6	110.7	113.1	113.7	116.6
Toronto (Ont.)	108.4	110.5	113.1	113.6	116.5
Thunder Bay (Ont.)	106.9	108.1	110.4	110.5	112.8
Winnipeg (Man.)	108.5	110.8	113.3	113.9	114.8
Regina (Sask.)	108.9	111.7	115.2	117.2	118.9
Saskatoon (Sask.)	109.0	112.7	117.1	118.2	119.6
Edmonton (Alta.)	112.0	117.4	121.4	121.6	122.9
Calgary (Alta.)	112.3	118.0	121.8	121.7	122.7
Vancouver (B.C.)	108.0	110.2	112.8	112.9	114.9
Victoria (B.C.)	108.5	109.8	111.8	111.9	113.1
Whitehorse (Y.T.)	106.8	109.5	113.4	113.8	114.7
Yellowknife (N.W.T.)	107.7	110.8	115.2	115.9	117.9

Note: Annual average indexes are obtained by averaging the indexes for the 12 months of the calendar year.
Source: Statistics Canada, CANSIM, table (for fee) 326-0021.
Last modified: 2011-01-24.

EXAMPLE 1.2

A Set of Language Data
Source: *http://www.toronto.ca/ toronto_facts/diversity.htm*

The top five mother tongue languages in 2006 were:

Chinese (420,000);

Italian (195,000);

Punjabi (138,000);

Tagalog/Pilipino (114,000);

Portuguese (113,000).

1.2 Data Collection

As you can see from the examples above, data come in many forms. How do you collect data? Data may be collected from two main sources, namely primary and secondary.

Primary Data

Primary data involves raw data (or original data) that are collected directly from respondents (or participants of a survey) using various instruments such as interviews, surveys (or questionnaires), observations, and laboratory experiments. Collection of data could also involve direct measurement of the item of interest. For example, in the production of a soft drink, the production manager may be interested in measuring the amount of soft drink the machine puts into each bottle.

Secondary Data

Secondary data are collected by another party or source. Secondary data are also recognized as "recycled" data. Examples of secondary data sources are databases from Statistics Canada (http://www.statcan.gc.ca/), CANSIM (Statistics Canada time-series), GDSourcing (Government Data Sourcing), etc.

Definitions

The following are basic statistical terms and definitions you should know.

Variable: a name chosen to describe the data collected. Each variable has a name and a value (also known as a response). The name identifies the variable, and the value relates to the data. For example, the variable for the question "Did you bring your textbook to class today?" could be "textbook." The variable name is usually associated with the question.

Population: includes *all* the items or persons in your study or research. For example, if your study involves the spending habits of the teens in Ontario, the population in your study would include all the teens living in Ontario.

Census: a set of data that includes **all** members of a population.

Sample: a subset of a population.

Sample size: the number of items/persons in a sample. The sample size is denoted as n.

Population size: the number of items/persons in a population. The population size is denoted as N.

1.3 Classification of Data

You can classify data into two types as shown in Figure 1.1.

(1) **Quantitative data (also known as numerical data):** Numeric data resulting from *measuring*.

A set of quantitative data can be either discrete or continuous quantitative data.

(2) **Qualitative data (also known as categorical data):** Usually non-numeric data that describe an attribute or characteristic of the items being studied. For example, yes or no responses, gender, type of car owned, place of birth, etc. Qualitative data can involve numbers. For example, area codes, bank accounts, etc.

FIGURE 1.1
Classification of Data

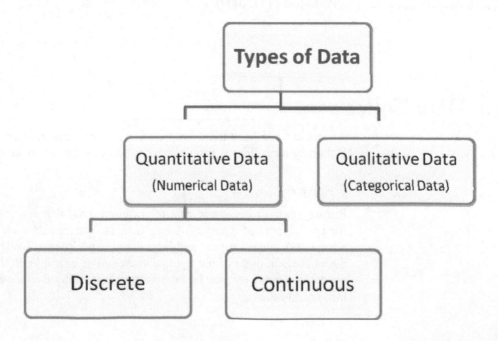

Quantitative Data

Quantitative data consist of data values that can be expressed in numerical values. Numerical values can be either discrete or continuous. Discrete variables have numerical values that arise from a counting process. "The number of premium cable channels subscribed to" is an example of a discrete numerical variable because the response is one of a finite number of integers. You subscribe to zero, one, two, or more channels. "The number of items purchased" is also a discrete numerical variable because you are counting the number of items purchased.

Continuous variables produce numerical responses that arise from a measuring process. The time you wait for teller service at a bank is an example of a continuous numerical variable because the response takes on any value within a continuum, or an interval, depending on the precision of the measuring instrument. For example, your waiting time could be 1 minute, 1.1 minutes, 1.11 minutes, or 1.113 minutes, depending on the precision of the measuring device used. (Theoretically, no two continuous values would ever be identical. However, because no measuring device is perfectly precise, identical continuous values for two or more items or individuals can occur.)

EXAMPLE 1.3
TABLE 1.4

Student	Did you bring your textbook to class today?	How much time (in hours) do you usually spend studying per week?	How many courses did you enroll in this semester?	Class Year	How did you come to school today?
1	Yes	20.3	3	Freshman	Take public transport
2	Yes	12.5	5	Sophomore	Drive
3	No	10.3	6	Junior	Walk
4	Yes	2.5	4	Junior	Drive
5	No	0.5	5	Senior	Take public transport
6	Yes	7.2	2	Sophomore	Drive
7	Yes	5.5	5	Freshman	Take public transport
8	No	10.0	4	Freshman	Walk
9	No	4.8	4	Freshman	Walk
10	Yes	3.2	3	Freshman	Drive
11	Yes	17.0	5	Senior	Take public transport
12	Yes	4.3	6	Freshman	Take public transport

Using the data above, the responses to the question "How much time (in hours) do you usually spend studying per week?" are classified as **quantitative *continuous* data**. Data collected can assume any value within some reasonable range. The values usually result from some form of measurement (e.g., the time it took you to get to class today, the amount of rainfall today, your weight, etc.). Note that the limitations of the measuring instrument are not to be considered when determining whether data is continuous or not. One interesting exception to the general statements above occurs when dealing with money data (such as income and salary). Even though you would think of money as a discrete quantity, this type of data is usually considered continuous.

TABLE 1.5 (A)

These responses are QUANTITATIVE CONTINUOUS data
How much time (in hours) do you usually spend studying per week?
20.3
12.5
10.3
2.5
0.5

The responses to the question "How many courses did you enroll in this semester?" are classified as **quantitative *discrete* data**. The values of the response are whole numbers. **Discrete data** have numerical values that arise from a counting process. "The number of magazines subscribed to" is an example of a discrete numerical variable because the response is one of a finite number of integers. You subscribe to zero, one, two, and so on magazines. The number of items that a customer purchases is also a discrete numerical variable because you are counting the number of items purchased.

TABLE 1.5 (B)

These responses are QUANTITATIVE Discrete data
How many courses did you enroll in this semester?
3
5
6
4
5

Qualitative Data

Qualitative data consist of data values that describe the characteristics or features of an item. Therefore, the data values are non-numeric in nature. For example, a survey asking students to rate an instructor's teaching as excellent, good, fair, or poor gathers qualitative data. "Excellent," "good," "fair," and "poor" are non-numeric values. However, qualitative data can involve numbers (e.g., area codes, bank accounts, etc.).

EXAMPLE 1.4

The responses to the questions "Did you bring your textbook to class today?" and "How did you come to school today?", as well as class year, are classified as **qualitative data**.

TABLE 1.6

These responses are QUALITATIVE data		
Did you bring your textbook to class today?	How did you come to school today?	Class Year
Yes	Take public transport	Freshman
Yes	Drive	Sophomore
No	Walk	Junior
Yes	Drive	Junior
No	Take public transport	Senior
Yes	Drive	Sophomore
Yes	Take public transport	Freshman

Test Your Understanding

Question 1: Which of the following is classified as **qualitative** data?

        A. Data on brand of car (e.g., Honda, Toyota, Dodge, Madza, Chrysler, Ford)
        B. Data on height (meters) (e.g., 1.7, 1.3, 1.5, 1.6, 1.4)
        C. Data on mortgage rate (%) (e.g., 4.2, 2.5, 6.5, 3.6, 4.8, 2.6)
        D. Data on income ($) (e.g., 20,000; 35,000; 40,000; 55,000; 43,000)

Answer: A

Question 2: Which of the following is classified as **quantitative** data?

        A. Data on brand of car (e.g., Honda, Toyota, Dodge, Madza, Chrysler, Ford)
        B. Data on postal code (e.g., N2J-4T3, T3Y-5N4, J5H-2J2)
        C. Data on mortgage rate (%) (e.g., 4.2, 2.5, 6.5, 3.6, 4.8, 2.6)
        D. Data on brand of laptop (e.g., Dell, Acer, Toshiba, Sony, Samsung)

Answer: C

Question 3: Which of the following data are **_not_** discrete quantitive data?

        A. Data on number of child in a family (e.g., 0,1,2,3,4,5,6)
        B. Data on number of correct answers on a test (e.g., 0,1,2,3,4,5,6)
        C. Data on number of times you travelled a year (e.g., 0,1,2,3,4)
        D. Data on income of a household

Answer: D

1.4 Why Do You Classify Your Data?

Data are gathered by using various methods. The most commonly used method in the business field is survey/questionnaires. The questions in a survey are used to collect responses from the respondents. You must learn to classify these response data in order to make informed decisions.

    The type of data often dictates what calculations can be performed and what type of graphical display will be appropriate. One of the primary reasons for classifying data according to their types is to ensure proper use of statistical methodology to analyze the data. There are certain statistical analyses that are only meaningful with a certain type of data. For example, with a set of quantitative data, you can take the average of the values.

1.5 Measurement of Scales

Data can be classified according to the type of measurement scale that is involved. The measurement scale is the set of all the possible values that could result when the data is collected. The type of measurement scale often dictates what calculations can be performed and what type of graphical display will be appropriate.

Classify the Data into Different Types of Scales

TABLE 1.7
Classification of Data

Types of Data	Qualitative (Categorical)		Quantitative (Numerical)	
Measurement Scale	Nominal	Ordinal	Interval	Ratio
Numerical Data Value			Continuous/ Discrete	Continuous/ Discrete

To classify the data, you must first figure out the type of data. There are only two types of data: qualitative (categorical) and quantitative (numerical). **Qualitative** data can be classified into two scales: nominal and ordinal. **Quantitative** data can be classified into two scales: interval and ratio. Table 1.5 summarizes how data are classified.

The four levels of measurement scales are the following:

1. Ratio
2. Interval
3. Ordinal
4. Nominal

The highest level of scale is ratio, followed by interval and ordinal. Nominal scale is the lowest level of scale. Qualitative data are usually associated with either a nominal or ordinal scale. Quantitative data are associated with either a ratio or interval scale.

1.6   Define Measurement Scales

Nominal

These data are qualitative data that have no particular order or ranking in their categories. (Note: Alphabetic order is not a consideration.) The categories may be either numeric or non-numeric. In either case, the data is qualitative.

EXAMPLE 1.5

- **Marital Status:** Single, married, divorced, or widowed. On a survey, the results of this question could be recorded as 1 = single, 2 = married, etc. Even though the data are recorded as numbers, it is still qualitative.
- **Check-out lane used in grocery store:** 1, 2, 3, etc. The checkout lanes could have been labelled A, B, C, or if the store had various colour schemes, the lanes could have been indicated by their colour.
- **Sport:** Tennis, swimming, soccer, etc.
- **Colour of your eyes:** Brown, blue, etc.
- **Postal Code:** N2N 5X8, T3M 5H8, etc.
- **Car brand:** Ford, Mazda, Toyota, etc.
- **Country:** Canada, United States, Norway, etc.

FIGURE 1.2

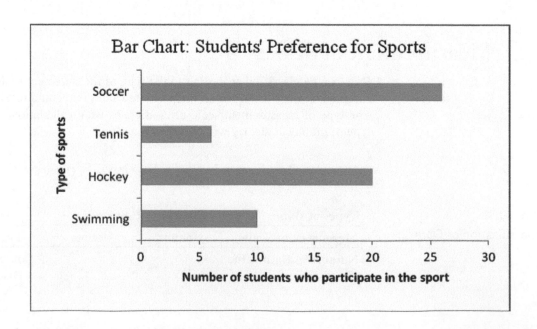

The only calculations that can be performed on nominal data are based on the number of responses in each category. Bar, pie, and Pareto charts (see Chapter 2 for more information on charts) may be useful for displaying the results of this type of data collection. The data on sports (e.g., soccer, tennis, hockey, and swimming) are classified as nominal scale and can be represented graphically in a bar chart as shown in the following figure. Each bar represents the number of students participating in each type of sports.

Ordinal

These data are similar to nominal data in that categories are involved; however, there is a natural order to the categories. We can say that one category is higher or better than another. Again, the categories can be numeric or non-numeric and are considered qualitative. Bar and pie charts are appropriate graphs for displaying results.

EXAMPLE 1.6

•**Professorial rank:** Lecturer, assistant professor, associate professor, and professor
•**Rating of a service:** Excellent, good, average, poor, very poor
•**Letter grades:** A+, A, A-, B+, etc.
•**Medals awarded in Olympic Games:** Gold, Silver, Bronze

Once again, the only type of calculations that can be performed with these data are based on, the number of values in each category.

TABLE 1.8
2010 Winter Olympic Medals Summary Table

(source: http://en.wikipedia.org/wiki/2010 _Winter_Olympics_medal_table_

The variable "medals awarded" is an ordinal scale, and the variable "nation" is a nominal scale.

Rank	Nation	Gold	Silver	Bronze	Total
1	Canada (CAN)	14	7	5	26
2	Germany (GER)	10	13	7	30
3	United States (USA)	9	15	13	37
4	Norway (NOR)	9	8	6	23
5	South Korea (KOR)	6	6	2	14
6	Switzerland (SUI)	6	0	3	9
7	China (CHN)	5	2	4	11
7	Sweden (SWE)	5	2	4	11
9	Austria (AUT)	4	6	6	16
10	Netherlands (NED)	4	1	3	8
11	Russia (RUS)	3	5	7	15
12	France (FRA)	2	3	6	11
13	Australia (AUS)	2	1	0	3
14	Czech Republic (CZE)	2	0	4	6
15	Poland (POL)	1	3	2	6
16	Italy (ITA)	1	1	3	5
17	Belarus (BLR)	1	1	1	3
17	Slovakia (SVK)	1	1	1	3
19	Great Britain (GBR)	1	0	0	1

20	Japan (JPN)	0	3	2	5
21	Croatia (CRO)	0	2	1	3
21	Slovenia (SLO)	0	2	1	3
23	Latvia (LAT)	0	2	0	2
24	Finland (FIN)	0	1	4	5
25	Estonia (EST)	0	1	0	1
25	Kazakhstan (KAZ)	0	1	0	1
	Total	**86**	**87**	**85**	**258**

Interval

The distinguishing feature of interval data, as compared to nominal and ordinal data, is that the data have <u>units of measurement</u>. The data must be numeric and are <u>quantitative</u> (either discrete or continuous). As a result, the interval between data values has a meaning. The other characteristic of significance in interval data is that the value "0" (zero) is only an <u>arbitrary reference point</u>. In other words, a value of zero does not mean that there is no amount of the characteristic being measured.

EXAMPLE 1.7

- **Data on temperature:** $0°$ C does not mean there is no heat.
  The difference between $10°$ C and $11°$ C is the same as the difference between $20°$ C and $21°$ C. If you had a container of water at $10°$ C and a similarly sized container at $20°$ C, then the exact same amount of heat would have to be added to both containers to increase the temperature to $11°$ C and $21°$ C, respectively.
- **Calendar scale:** The date "0" is just a reference point.
  The difference between the dates February 2 and February 9 is 7 days, and this is the same amount of time as the difference between March 21 and March 28.

  Note: Interval data is <u>not</u> of great importance to us in business because other than when measuring temperature, we rarely come across this type of data.

Ratio

Ratio data has the characteristics of interval data, but the "0" value does mean the absence of the characteristic being measured (i.e., 0 = "nothing") and the ratio of data values is meaningful. Ratio data may be continuous or discrete.

Examples of <u>discrete</u> ratio data:

- Number of vacations you have taken in the past 10 years
- Number of part-time employees in your company
- Number of DVD movies you own

Examples of <u>continuous</u> ratio data:

- Size of your house (in square meters)
- Gas price (in cents)
- Sales (in dollars)
- Distance (in km)

How Is the *Ratio* of Data Values Meaningful?

The name "ratio" is appropriate because meaningful results occur when two data values are divided.

For example,
The distance between A and B is 10 km and the distance between C and D is 5 km. Compare the two distances. You have

$$\frac{10\ km}{5\ km} = 2 \quad \text{In other words, the distance of AB is twice the distance of CD.}$$

Also, the same is true for discrete ratio data. Let's consider the variable "number of classes you are currently attending." If you attend 12 classes and your friend attends 6 classes, we can say that you attended twice as many classes as your friend.

All types of calculations can be performed with ratio data. Histograms, polygons, ogives, stem and-leaf displays, and box-whisker plots are all useful graphs of ratio data.

How Do You Differentiate between Interval and Ratio Scales?

Use these two indicators to differentiate between interval and ratio scales. These two indicators are the following:

1. **Using zero**
   For interval scale, "zero" is a reference point, but "zero" is meaningful for ratio scale where zero means "absence of the characteristic." For example, zero textbook means "no textbook." We know that the variable temperature is an interval scale. If your thermometer shows 0° C, does that indicate "absence of temperature" or "no temperature"? You know the answer is no!
2. **Comparing two values**
   Interval scale has meaningful difference between two values, and ratio has meaningful division of two values.

Now consider the following example. The temperature in Location A is 10° C and the temperature in Location B is 5° C. Compare the temperature in the two locations. You have

$$\frac{10°\ C}{5°\ C} = 2 \quad \text{In other words, Location A is twice as hot as Location B. Is this correct?}$$

No! You can say that the temperature difference between the two locations is 5° C. Temperature is measured on an interval scale, so the result of a division is not meaningful.

Example of a ratio scale: Salary
Employee A earns $40,000 and employee B earns $20,000. That means employee A earns twice as much as employee B. $\left(\dfrac{\$40,000}{\$20,000} = 2 \right)$

Test Your Understanding

Question 1. How would you rate the service provided by the Toronto Transit Commission (TTC)?
1. Excellent
2. Good
3. Average
4. Poor

What is the **highest** measurement scale that applies to the set of response data?
A. Nominal
B. Ordinal
C. Interval
D. Ratio – Discrete
E. Ratio – Continuous

Answer: B

Question 2. What are the total sales of your company?
1. less than $200,000
2. between $200,000 and $300,000
3. between $300,000 and $400,000
4. between $400,000 and $500,000
5. between $500,000 and $600,000
6. $600,000 or more

What is the **highest** measurement scale that applies to the set of response data?
  A. Nominal
  B. Ordinal
  C. Interval
  D. Ratio – Discrete
  E. Ratio – Continuous

Answer: E (Note: Although the response data is presented in categories of sales)

Question 3. What is your major in your program?
  1. Accounting
  2. Finance
  3. Human Resources
  4. Management

What is the measurement scale that applies to the set of response data?
  A. Nominal
  B. Ordinal
  C. Interval
  D. Ratio – Discrete
  E. Ratio – Continuous

Answer: A (Note: You cannot rank the program majors in an order.)

Question 4. Which year did you graduate from high school?

What is the measurement scale of the response data?
  A. Ratio
  B. Interval
  C. Ordinal
  D. Nominal
  E. None of the above

Answer: B

1.7 How Do You Transform a Higher-Level Scale to a Lower-Level Scale?

"Downgrading" a scale means transforming a higher-level scale to a lower-level scale. One reason for changing a scale is because of sensitive questions requested in a survey that caused non-response bias. Non-response bias means that respondents will elicit no response. Questions pertaining to age and income may be too personal for respondents to answer. These questions are sensitive questions that respondents may refuse to answer in a survey. By classifying the responses into classes (or categories), the respondents will feel less discomfort when responding to these sensitive questions. For this reason, you may want to transform the data as shown in Examples 1.8 and 1.9. You can downgrade a higher-level scale to the next level of measurement scale. In Example 1.8 of question 1, the age variable is measured on a ratio scale that can be transformed to an ordinal scale by changing the responses to several categories of age as shown in Example 1.8 of question 2.

The possible response categories for the question "What is your age?" are given next:

  [ ] 15–20
  [ ] 20–25
  [ ] 25–30

This "age" variable is now classified as qualitative data because the responses are in categories of age as shown in Example 1.8 of question 2. This age variable is now measured on an ordinal scale because you can order the responses from young to old. So you have "downgraded" quantitative data to qualitative data. By doing so, you lose the ability to summarize the data numerically (e.g., mean, median). It is recommended that you collect data in the highest scale (i.e., ratio scale).

Similarly, in Example 1.9 of question 1, the income variable is measured on a ratio scale that can be downgraded to an ordinal scale by changing the response to categories of income as shown in Example 1.9 of question 2.

EXAMPLE 1.8

Variable: Age	Measurement scale
Question 1: What is your age?_____ years.	Ratio scale
Question 2: What is your age? [ ] 15–20 [ ] 20–25 [ ] 25–30	Ordinal scale

EXAMPLE 1.9

Variable: Salary	Measurement scale
Question 1: What is your salary? $ _____	Ratio scale
Question 2: What is your salary? [ ] 0–10,000 [ ] 10,000–20,000 [ ] 20,000–30,000	Ordinal scale

SUMMARY

Statistics is the collection of methods that help you make better sense of the data used every day to describe and analyze the world. Statistics is a core skill necessary for a complete business education. Businesses use statistics to summarize and reach conclusions from data, to make reliable forecasts, and to improve business processes. In this chapter, you learned the basic vocabulary of statistics and the various types of data used in business. In the next two chapters, you will study data collection and a variety of tables and charts and descriptive measures that are used to present and analyze data.

KEY TERMS

categorical data   6
continuous data   7
descriptive statistics   3
discrete data   8
inferential statistics   3

population   6
primary source   5
qualitative data   6
quantitative data   6
sample   6

statistic   3
parameter   3
secondary source   6
variable   6

PROBLEMS

LEARNING THE BASICS

1.1 Consider the following questions being asked on a survey. The possible responses for each person are given. What is the measurement scale for each response data?

a. What was the rating of the restaurant in which you last had dinner with your partner?
   a) ★
   b) ★★
   c) ★★★

d) ★★★★
e) ★★★★★

b. What is the rating of your favourite television show?
   a) TV-G
   b) TV-PG
   c) TV-14
   d) TV-MA

c. What is your marital status?
   a) Married
   b) Common Law

c) Widowed
d) Divorced
e) Separated
f) Single

d. What is your level of education?
   a) Elementary School
   b) High School
   c) College
   d) University-Undergrad
   e) University-Post Grad

e. What stock-exchange are the majority of your stock investments listed on?
   a) TSX
   b) NYSE
   c) AMEX
   d) NASDAQ
   e) VSE

f. What type of accommodation do you usually choose for your overnight stay when on a car trip?
   a) Hotel
   b) Motel
   c) Bed & Breakfast
   d) Country Inn
   e) Cabin/Cottage

g. What was the rating of the last motel that you stayed in?
   a) ★
   b) ★★

c) ★★★
d) ★★★★
e) ★★★★★

h. What is your postal code? Answer: _____

i. What was the rating of the last movie that you saw in a theatre?
   a) G
   b) PG
   c) PG-13
   d) R
   e) NC-17
   f) X

j. What is your favourite meat?
   a) Beef
   b) Pork
   c) Chicken
   d) Veal
   e) Lamb

1.2 Refer to the following chart, from the autumn 1999 issue of *Canadian Social Trends*, that shows data regarding seniors who have driver's licenses and also a health condition. Many seniors were surveyed and much data were obtained from each respondent. The responses to four questions were used to obtain the data to allow the researchers to construct the chart shown. What type of measurement scale is used for each type of data? Are the values discrete or continuous?

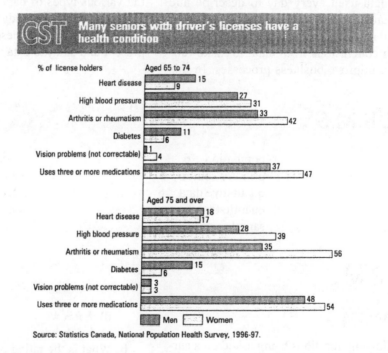

Source: Statistics Canada, National Population Health Survey, 1996-97.

Question	Measurement Scale	Discrete/Continuous

1.3 The responses to two questions in a survey were used by researchers to construct the following bar chart. Assume that this survey was given to the registered nurses employed in the nursing field.

FIGURE 1.3
Proportion of registered nurses employed in the nursing field by age and year

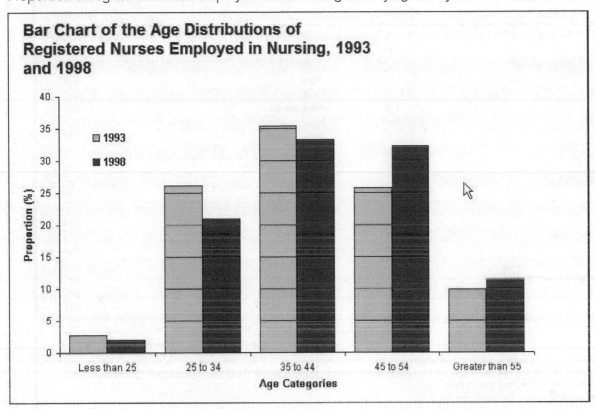

Source: *Registered Nurses Database (RNDB), 1998. (The bar chart appeared on the National Resources Canada's Web site:* http://atlas.nrcan.gc.ca/site/english/maps/health/resources/nursing/nursing_figure7.gif/image_view)

I. What are the two questions?
   Question 1: _____
   Question 2: _____

II. What is the highest measurement scale that applies to the set of response data from the first question?
   a) Nominal
   b) Ordinal
   c) Interval
   d) Ratio – Discrete
   e) Ratio – Continuous

III. What is the highest measurement scale that applies to the set of response data from the second question?
   a) Nominal
   b) Ordinal
   c) Interval
   d) Ratio – Discrete
   e) Ratio – Continuous

1.4 Refer to the table published in *Canadian Social Trends* (CST), that shows data regarding adults aged between 22 and 29 years old with a sense of community and who have higher odds of voting.

Ten questions were asked to obtain data in order to formulate the following table. One of the questions was "What is your gender?" and another was "Did you volunteer in the past year?"

Your task is to identify the remaining eight questions. For each question, identify the type of measurement scale that applies to the set of response data. Use the following measurement scales:
   (a) Nominal
   (b) Ordinal
   (c) Interval - Continuous
   (d) Ratio – Discrete
   (e) Ratio – Continuous

Use the following table to record your answers.

TABLE 1.9

CST	22- to 29-year-olds with a very strong sense of community have higher odds of voting than those with a weaker sense of belonging		
	Odds ratio		**Odds ratio**
Age[1]	1.03	**Region**	
Youth involvement[2]	1.03	*Quebec*	*1.00*
Number of groups of which a member	1.11[3]	Atlantic	0.38*
		Ontario	0.30*
Sex		Prairies	0.32*
Female	*1.00*	British Columbia	0.36*
Male	1.08	**Educational level**	
Place of birth		*University degree*	*1.00*
Foreign-born	*1.00*	Less than high school	0.25*
Canadian-born	4.27*	High school graduate	0.48*
Religious observance		Some post-secondary	0.74
Rarely/never	*1.00*	Diploma or certificate	0.68*
Weekly	0.86	**Main activity**	
Sometimes	1.40*	*Other[4]*	*1.00*
Volunteer in past year		Labour force	1.10
No	*1.00*	Student	0.81
Yes	1.42*	**Household income**	
Sense of belonging to community		*$60,000 or more*	*1.00*
Very weak	*1.00*	Less than $20,000	0.51*
Very strong	1.74*	$20,000 to $29,999	0.74
Somewhat strong	1.30	$30,000 to $39,999	0.75
Somewhat weak	1.26	$40,000 to $49,999	1.00
		$50,000 to $59,999	0.66*

Note: This table presents the odds that a respondent voted in the last election prior to the survey, relative to the odds of a benchmark group when all other variables in the analysis are held constant. Benchmark group is shown in italics.
*   Statistically significant difference from benchmark group ($p < 0.05$).
1. For each additional year, the odds of voting increase by 3%.
2. For each additional activity during youth, the odds of voting increase by 3%.
3. For each additional group, the odds of voting increase by 11%, which is statistically significant ($p < 0.05$).
4. "Other" includes activities such as homemaking, retirement, volunteer work or illness.
Source: Statistics Canada, General Social Survey, 2003.

Source: *Canadian Social Trends*, Issue: Winter 2005, page 5. Web site: http://dsp-psd.tpsgc.gc.ca/Collection-R/Statcan/ 11-008-XIE/0030511-008-XIE.pdf

Question	What is the measurement scale? (a) Nominal (b) Ordinal (c) Interval Continuous (d) Ratio – Discrete (e) Ratio – Continuous
1	
2	
3	
4	
5	
6	
7	
8	

1.5 Refer to the following chart that shows data regarding the majority of young adults who are engaged in at least one non-voting political activity. The chart was produced by ask- ing a question in a survey. What type of measurement scale applies to the set of response data?

FIGURE 1.4

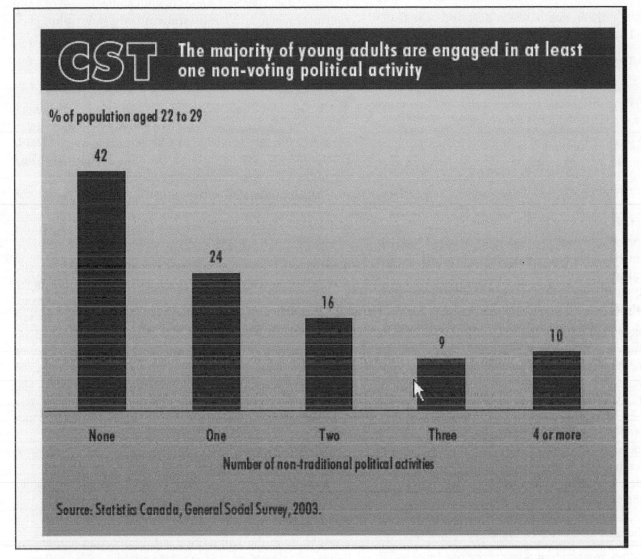

Source: *Canadian Social Trends*, Issue: Winter 2005, page 3. Web site: http://dsp-psd.tpsgc.gc.ca/Collection-R/Statcan/11-008-XIE/0030511-008-XIE.pdf

a) Nominal
b) Ordinal
c) Interval – Continuous
d) Ratio – Discrete
e) Ratio – Continuous

CHECKING YOUR UNDERSTANDING

1.6 What is the difference between a sample and a population?

1.7 What is the difference between a statistic and a parameter?

1.8 What is the difference between descriptive statistics and inferential statistics?

1.9 What is the difference between a categorical variable and a numerical variable?

1.10 What is the difference between a discrete numerical variable and a continuous numerical variable?

1.11 What is an operational definition, and why are operational definitions so important?

1.12 What is the difference between a variable and data?

APPLYING THE CONCEPTS

1.13 Visit the official website for either Excel or Minitab, **www.office.microsoft.com/excel** or **www.minitab.com/products/minitab**. Read about the program you chose and then think about the ways the program could be useful in statistical analysis.

1.14 In 2008, a university in the midwestern United States surveyed its full-time first-year students after they completed their first semester. Surveys were electronically distributed to all 3,727 students, and responses were obtained from 2,821 students. Of the students surveyed, 90.1% indicated that they had studied with other students, and 57.1% indicated that they had tutored another student. The report also noted that 61.3% of the students surveyed came to class late at least once, and 45.8% admitted to being bored in class at least once.
a. Describe the population of interest.
b. Describe the sample that was collected.
c. Describe a parameter of interest.
d. Describe the statistic used to estimate the parameter in (c).

1.15 The Gallup organization releases the results of recent polls at its website, **www.gallup.com**. Visit this site and read an article of interest.
a. Describe the population of interest.
b. Describe the sample that was collected.
c. Describe a parameter of interest.
d. Describe the statistic used to describe the parameter in (c).

1.16 A Gallup poll indicated that 74% of Americans who had yet to retire look to retirement accounts as major funding sources when they retire. Interestingly, 40% also said that they looked to stocks or stock market mutual fund investments as major funding sources when they retire. (data extracted from D. Jacobs, "Investors Look Beyond Social Security to Fund Retirement," **www.gallup.com**, March 28, 2011). The results are based on telephone interviews conducted March 24, 2011, with 1,000 or more adults living in the United States, aged 18 and older.

a. Describe the population of interest.
b. Describe the sample that was collected.
c. Is 74% a parameter or a statistic? Explain.
d. Is 40% a parameter or a statistic?

1.17 The Data and Story Library (DASL) is an online library of data files and stories that illustrate the use of basic statistical methods. Visit **lib.stat.cmu.edu/index.php**, click DASL and explore a data set of interest to you.
a. Describe a variable in the data set you selected.
b. Is the variable categorical or numerical?
c. If the variable is numerical, is it discrete or continuous?

1.18 Download and examine the U.S. Census Bureau's "2007 Survey of Business Owners and Self-Employed Persons," directly available at **bhs.econ.census.gov/BHS/SBO/sbo1_07.pdf** or through the **Get Help with Your Form** link at **www.census.gov/econ/sbo**.
a. Give an example of a categorical variable included in the survey.
b. Give an example of a numerical variable included in the survey.

1.19 Three professors at Northern Kentucky University compared two different approaches to teaching courses in the school of business (M. W. Ford, D. W. Kent, and S. Devoto, "Learning from the Pros: Influence of Web-Based Expert Commentary on Vicarious Learning About Financial Markets," *Decision Sciences Journal of Innovative Education*, January 2007, 5(1), 43–63). At the time of the study, there were 2,100 students in the business school, and 96 students were involved in the study. Demographic data collected on these 96 students included class (freshman, sophomore, junior, senior), age, gender, and major.
a. Describe the population of interest.
b. Describe the sample that was collected.
c. Indicate whether each of the four demographic variables mentioned is categorical or numerical.

1.20 A manufacturer of cat food was planning to survey households in the United States to determine purchasing habits of cat owners. Among the variables to be collected are the following:
  i. The primary place of purchase for cat food
  ii. Whether dry or moist cat food is purchased
  iii. The number of cats living in the household
  iv. Whether any cat living in the household is pedigreed
a. For each of the four items listed, indicate whether the variable is categorical or numerical. If it is numerical, is it discrete or continuous?
b. Develop five categorical questions for the survey.
c. Develop five numerical questions for the survey.

1.21 A sample of 62 undergraduate students answered the following survey:
1. What is your gender? Female _____ Male _____
2. What is your age (*as of last birthday*)? _____

3. What is your current registered class designation?
Freshman _____ Sophomore _____ Junior _____
Senior _____

4. What is your major area of study?
Accounting _____
Computer Information Systems _____
Economics/Finance _____
International Business _____ Management _____
Retailing/Marketing _____
Other _____ Undecided _____

5. At the present time, do you plan to attend graduate school?
Yes _____ No _____ Not sure _____

6. What is your current cumulative grade point average?
_____

7. What is your current employment status?
Full time _____ Part time _____ Unemployed _____

8. What would you expect your starting annual salary (*in $000*) to be if you were to seek full-time employment immediately after obtaining your bachelor's degree?
_____

9. For how many social networking sites are you registered? _____

10. How satisfied are you with the food and dining services on campus? _____

    1   2   3   4   5   6   7
Extremely   Neutral   Extremely
unsatisfied   satisfied

11. About how much money did you spend this semester for textbooks and supplies? _____

12. What type of computer do you prefer to use for your studies?
Desktop _____ Laptop _____
Tablet/notebook/netbook _____

13. How many text messages do you send in a typical week?
_____

14. How much wealth (income, savings, investment, real estate, and other assets) would you have to accumulate (in millions of dollars) before you would say you are rich? _____

  a. Which variables in the survey are categorical?
  b. Which variables in the survey are numerical?
  c. Which variables are discrete numerical variables?

The results of the survey are stored in `UndergradSurvey`

1.22 A sample of 44 graduate students answered the following survey:

1. What is your gender? Female _____ Male _____
2. What is your age (*as of last birthday*)? _____

3. What is your current major area of study?
Accounting _____
Economics/Finance _____
Management _____
Retailing/Marketing _____
Other _____ Undecided _____

4. What is your current graduate cumulative grade point average? _____

5. What was your undergraduate major?
Biological Sciences _____ Business _____
Computers _____
Engineering _____
Other _____

6. What was your undergraduate cumulative grade point average? _____

7. What is your current employment status?
Full time _____ Part time _____ Unemployed _____

8. How many different full-time jobs have you held in the past 10 years? _____

9. What do you expect your annual salary (*in $000*) to be immediately after completion of your graduate studies if you are employed full time? _____

10. About how much money did you spend this semester for textbooks and supplies? _____

11. How satisfied are you with the MBA program advisory services on campus?

    1   2   3   4   5   6   7
Extremely   Neutral   Extremely
unsatisfied   satisfied

12. What type of computer do you prefer to use for your studies?
Desktop _____ Laptop _____ Tablet/notebook/netbook _____

13. How many text messages do you send in a typical week? _____

14. How much wealth (income, savings, investment, real estate, and other assets) would you have to accumulate (in millions of dollars) before you would say you are rich? _____

  a. Which variables in the survey are categorical?
  b. Which variables in the survey are numerical?
  c. Which variables are discrete numerical variables?

The results of the survey are stored in `GradSurvey`

END-OF-CHAPTER CASES

At the end of most chapters, you will find a continuing case study that allows you to apply statistics to problems faced by the management of the Ashland MultiComm Services, a residential telecommunications provider. You will also find a series of Digital Cases that extend many of the Using Statistics scenarios that begin each chapter.

LEARNING WITH THE DIGITAL CASES

People use statistical techniques to help communicate and present important information to others both inside and outside their businesses. Every day, as in these examples, people misuse these techniques. Identifying and preventing misuses of statistics, whether intentional or not, is an important responsibility for all managers. The Digital Cases help you develop the skills necessary for this important task.

A Digital Case asks you to review electronic documents related to a company or statistical issue discussed in the chapter's Using Statistics scenario. You review the contents of these documents, which may contain internal confidential as well as publicly stated facts and claims, seeking to identify and correct misuses of statistics. Unlike a traditional case study, but like many business situations, not all of the information you encounter will be relevant to your task, and you may occasionally discover conflicting information that you have to resolve in order to complete the case.

To assist your learning, each Digital Case begins with a learning objective and a summary of the problem or issue at hand. Each case directs you to the information necessary to reach your own conclusions and to answer the case questions. You can work with the documents for the Digital Cases offline, after downloading them from this book's download page. Or you can work with the Digital Cases online, chapter-by-chapter, at the companion website.

DIGITAL CASE EXAMPLE

This section illustrates learning with a Digital Case. To begin, open the Digital Case file **GTM.pdf**, which contains contents from the Good Tunes & More website. Recall that the privately held Good Tunes & More, the subject of the Using Statistics scenario in this chapter, is seeking financing to expand its business by opening retail locations. Because the managers are eager to show that Good Tunes & More is a thriving business, it is not surprising to discover the "our best sales year ever" claim in the "Good Times at Good Tunes & More" section on the first page.

Click the **our best sales year ever** link to display the page that supports this claim. How would you support such a claim? With a table of numbers? A chart? Remarks attributed to a knowledgeable source? Good Tunes & More has used a chart to present "two years ago" and "latest twelve months" sales data by category. Are there any problems with the choices made on this web page? *Absolutely*!

First, note that there are no scales for the symbols used, so it is impossible to know what the actual sales volumes are. In fact, charts that incorporate symbols in this way are considered examples of *chartjunk* and would never be used by people seeking to properly use graphs.

This important point aside, another question that arises is whether the sales data represent the number of units sold or something else. The use of the symbols creates the impression that unit sales data are being presented. If the data are unit sales, does such data best support the claim being made, or would something else, such as dollar volumes, be a better indicator of sales at the retailer?

Then there are those curious chart labels. "Latest twelve months" is ambiguous; it could include months from the current year as well as months from one year ago and therefore may not be an equivalent time period to "two years ago." But the business was established in 1997, and the claim being made is "best sales year ever," so why hasn't management included sales figures for *every* year?

Are Good Tunes & More managers hiding something, or are they just unaware of the proper use of statistics? Either way, they have failed to properly communicate a vital aspect of their story.

In subsequent Digital Cases, you will be asked to provide this type of analysis, using the open-ended questions in the case as your guide. Not all the cases are as straightforward as this example, and some cases include perfectly appropriate applications of statistics.

REFERENCES

1. Davenport, T., and J. Harris, *Competing on Analytics: The New Science of Winning* (Boston: Harvard Business School Press, 2007).

2. Davenport, T., J. Harris, and R. Morrison, *Analytics at Work* (Boston: Harvard Business School Press, 2010).

3. McCullough, B. D., and D. Heiser, "On the Accuracy of Statistical Procedures in Microsoft Excel 2007," *Computational Statistics and Data Analysis*, 52 (2008), 4568–4606.

4. McCullough, B. D., and B. Wilson, "On the Accuracy of Statistical Procedures in Microsoft Excel 97," *Computational Statistics and Data Analysis*, 31 (1999), 27–37.

5. McCullough, B. D., and B. Wilson, "On the Accuracy of Statistical Procedures in Microsoft Excel 2003," *Computational Statistics and Data Analysis*, 49 (2005), 1244–1252.

6. *Microsoft Excel 2010* (Redmond, WA: Microsoft Corporation, 2010).

7. *Minitab Release 16* (State College, PA: Minitab, Inc., 2010).

8. Nash, J. C., "Spreadsheets in Statistical Practice—Another Look," *The American Statistician*, 60 (2006), 287–289.

9. New York 1964 World's Fair," *National Geographic*, April 1965, p. 526

10. Thompson, C. "What Is I.B.M.'s Watson?". **http://www.nytimes.com/2010/06/20/magazine/20Computer-t.html**, June 20, 2010, p. MM30 of the Sunday Magazine.

2 Graphical Presentation of Qualitative Data

Learning Objectives

In this chapter, you learn:

- To develop tables and charts for categorical data
- To create tables and charts using the Casio Calculator
- The principles of properly presenting graphs

In Chapter 1, you learned to distinguish the types of data and measurement scales. In this chapter, you learn to present qualitative data graphically in the form of a summary table, bar chart, pie chart, and pareto chart.

2.1 How Do You Organize Qualitative Data Graphically?

Qualitative data consist of data values that describe a characteristic or feature of an item. Examples of these types of variables are occupational title, ethnicity, educational level, marital status, types of aircraft, and mode of transportation.

The only calculations that can be performed on **nominal data** and **ordinal data** are based on the number of responses in each category. Bar charts, pie charts, and Pareto charts may be useful for displaying the results of these type of data collection.

EXAMPLE 2.1

A random sample of 100 respondents were asked the question "How do you go to work or school?"

The possible responses to the question are

[　] Bus
[　] Train (GO train or TTC)
[　] Car
[　] Walk
[　] None of the above

The response data are qualitative data that are measured on a nominal scale. The data collected from 100 respondents are displayed in Table 2.1.

TABLE 2.1

The code of "1" denotes "Bus"; "2" denotes "Train (GO train or TTC)", "3" denotes "Car"; "4" denotes "Walk"; and "5" denotes "None of the above"

1	2	4	4	4	4	1	1	4	2	4	4	5	4	4	4	2	4	2	5
2	1	3	4	3	1	4	1	1	1	1	2	3	4	2	4	2	4	2	4
3	2	1	1	3	3	2	3	3	5	3	2	3	2	4	4	3	5	4	4
4	3	2	2	1	5	2	3	2	3	4	2	4	3	2	2	2	4	2	4
4	3	1	2	1	1	2	4	5	4	4	4	4	3	3	3	3	4	4	4

The Summary Table

The data shown in Table 2.1 can be summarized in a summary table. A summary table is made up of two columns, where one column specifies the categories and the other column represents the number of occurrences (known as frequency), which can also be expressed as percentage of occurrence.

The summary table in Table 2.2 is based on the question "How do you go to work or school?"

TABLE 2.2
Summary Table of
"How do you go to
work or school?"

How do you go to work or school?	Number of persons
Bus	15
Train (GO train or TTC)	24
Car	20
Walk	35
None of the above	6
Total	100

Bar Chart

The summary table can be displayed graphically as a bar chart. The rectangle bars in the bar chart represent the frequency (or number of occurrences) for each category. The bars can be shown either vertically or horizontally. The vertical bar chart is a graph with vertical bars. Similarly, a horizontal bar chart is a graph with horizontal bars.

How to construct a bar chart using the CASIO Calculator

EXAMPLE 2.2

Create a horizontal bar chart of "How do you go to work or school?" using the CASIO fx-9750GII calculator.

You will learn to use the CASIO fx-9750GII to create a bar chart for modes of transportation based on the data in Table 2.2 and interpret the results.

Follow the calculator procedures to create a <u>horizontal</u> bar chart.

From the **Main Menu** select **STAT** mode and press **EXE**.
If you have difficulty following the instruction, I recommend that you read the "Calculator Lesson 1" at the end of this chapter.

You may enter the data from Table 2.2 in List 1 as follows:

LIST 1
15 EXE
24 EXE
20 EXE
35 EXE
6 EXE

Use the **F6** key (▷) if necessary to get the following menu choices at the bottom of the display:
To create a bar chart, press the **F1** key to select "**GRPH**."

GRPH	CALC	TEST	INTR	DIST	▷
F1	F2	F3	F4	F5	F6

After you have selected "**GRPH**," you will see the following menu choices at the bottom of the display. Press **F6** key to select "**SET**."

GPH1	GPH2	GPH3	SEL		SET
F1	F2	F3	F4	F5	F6

Then enter the following items:

(Note: Use the cursor ▼ arrow. If you accidentally hit the wrong key, use **AC/ON** or **EXIT** to go back.)

StatGraph1

Graph Type   : **F3**(Bar)   (NOTE: Press F6 for ▷ to change the menu choices at the bottom of the display).

Data1   : **List 1** (Press F1 to change the List number)   ▼

Data2   : **None**

Data3   : **None**

Stick Style   : **Horiz (NOTE: For a vertical bar chart, select F1. For a horizontal bar chart, select F2.)**

Now press **EXE**.
Then press **F1** to select **GPH1**.

The horizontal bar chart will appear on your screen as follows:

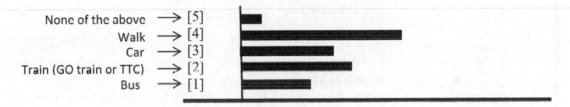

Notations: [1] represents "Bus," [2] represents "Train (GO train or TTC)," [3] represents "Car," [4] represents "Walk," and [5] represents "None of the above."

Interpretation of Results

The most popular mode of transport is walking to work or school, which is the longest bar. The second most popular mode of transport is train (GO train or TTC), which represents the second-longest bar.

EXAMPLE 2.3

Create a vertical bar chart of "How do you go to work or school?" using the CASIO fx-9750GII calculator.

Follow the calculator procedures to create a vertical bar chart.

From the **Main Menu** select **STAT** mode and press **EXE**.
If you have difficulty following the instruction, I recommend that you read the "Calculator Lesson 1" at the end of this chapter.

You may enter the data from Table 2.2 in List 1 as follows:

LIST 1
15 EXE
24 EXE
20 EXE
35 EXE
6 EXE

Use the **F6** key (▷) if necessary to get the following menu choices at the bottom of the display:
To create a bar chart, press the **F1** key to select "**GRPH**."

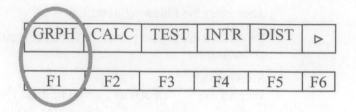

GRPH	CALC	TEST	INTR	DIST	▷
F1	F2	F3	F4	F5	F6

After you have selected "**GRPH**," you get the following menu choices at the bottom of the display. Press the **F6** key to select "**SET**."

GPH1	GPH2	GPH3	SEL		**SET**
F1	F2	F3	F4	F5	F6

Then enter the following items:

(Note: Use the cursor ▼ arrow. If you accidentally hit the wrong key, use **AC/ON** or **EXIT** to go back.)

StatGraph1

Graph Type   : **F3**(Bar)   (NOTE: Press F6 for ▷ to change the menu choices at the bottom of the display.)

Data1   : **List 1** (Press F1 to change the List number.)   ▼

Data2   : **None**

Data3   : **None**

Stick Style   : **Length (NOTE: For a vertical bar chart, select F1. For a horizontal bar chart, select F2.)**

Now press **EXE**.

Then press **F1** to select **GPH1**.

The vertical bar chart will appear on your screen as follows:

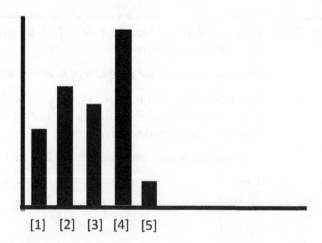

[1]   [2]   [3]   [4]   [5]

Notations: [1] represents "Bus," [2] represents "Train (GO train or TTC)," [3] represents "Car," [4] represents "Walk," and [5] represents "None of the above."

Interpretation of Results

The most popular mode of transport is walking to work or school, which is the tallest bar. The second most popular mode of transport is train (GO train or TTC), which represents the second tallest bar.

Pie Chart

The summary table can be displayed graphically as a pie chart. In a pie chart, the wedges of the pie (also known as pie slides) denote the frequency (or percentage of occurrences) for each category.

EXAMPLE 2.4

Create a pie chart of "How do you go to work or school?" using the CASIO fx-9750GII calculator.

You will learn to use the CASIO fx-9750 GII to create a pie chart for modes of transport based on the data in Table 2.2 and interpret the results.

Follow the calculator procedures to create a pie chart.

From the **Main Menu** select **STAT** mode and press **EXE**.
If you have difficulty following the instruction, I recommend that you read the "Calculator Lesson 1" at the end of this chapter.

You may enter the data from Table 2.2 in List 1 as follows:

LIST 1
15 EXE
24 EXE
20 EXE
35 EXE
6 EXE

Use the **F6** key (▷) if necessary to get the following menu choices at the bottom of the display:
To create a pie chart, press the **F1** key to select "**GRPH**."

GRPH	CALC	TEST	INTR	DIST	▷
F1	F2	F3	F4	F5	F6

After you have selected "**GRPH**," you will see the following menu choices at the bottom of the display. Press the **F6** key to select "**SET**."

GPH1	GPH2	GPH3	SEL		SET
F1	F2	F3	F4	F5	F6

Then enter the following items:

(Note: Use the cursor ▼ arrow. If you accidentally hit the wrong key, use **AC/ON** or **EXIT** to go back.)

StatGraph1

Graph Type   : **F4**(Pie)   (NOTE: Press F6 for ▷ to change the menu choices at the bottom of the display.)

Data 1   : **List 1** (Press F1 to change the List number.)   ▼

Display   : **F2 (Data) : in the form of number of occurrences**

% Sto Mem   : None

Now press **EXE**.

Then press **F1** to select **GPH1**.

The pie chart will appear on your screen as follows:

A   16
B   24
C   20
D   35
E   6

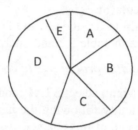

Notations: A represents "Bus," B represents "Train (GO train or TTC)," C represents "Car," D represents "Walk," and E represents "None of the above."

Interpretation of Results

The most popular mode of transportation is walking to school or work, which is the largest wedge of the pie. The second most popular mode of transportation is taking the train (GO train or TTC), which is the second largest wedge of the pie.

Pareto Chart

A Pareto chart is a combination of a bar chart and an OGIVE and is used to analyze attribute data. It is also used to identify and prioritize problem areas. The phrase "Pareto Principle" was coined in the 1950s by Dr. Joseph Juran to focus on his quality management concept of "Vital Few– Useful Many," in which he points out that management should concentrate on the "Vital Few." Juran's work in this area was based on the work of the 19th century Italian economist Vilfredo Pareto, whose research revealed that 80% of the wealth in a country is owned by 20% of the population. This result has been generalized to become the 80/20 rule. **In many instances, management finds that 80% of the problems arise from 20% of the problem sources.**

Pareto charts are often used in *nonmanufacturing applications* of quality improvement methods. Consider the following example:

EXAMPLE 2.5

A quality-improvement team was investigating the purchasing process in a company. The team was particularly interested in errors on purchase orders and hoped to reduce the number of purchase order changes issued by the company. (Each change typically costs around $100, and this company was issuing several hundred purchase order changes each month.)

The team investigated a sample of 2,000 purchase orders and found the following error frequencies.

Type of Error	Frequency
Wrong contract number	74
Wrong part number	14
Wrong price code	60
Wrong schedule date	6
Wrong supplier code	46

To construct the Pareto chart, you first sort the categories in descending order of frequency of occurrence. Then you calculate cumulative percentages. The results are as follows:

Type of Error	Frequency	%	c%
Wrong contract number	74	37	37
Wrong price code	60	30	67
Wrong supplier code	46	23	90
Wrong part number	14	7	97
Wrong schedule date	6	3	100
Total	200	100	

Now you can construct the Pareto chart using SPSS as shown next.

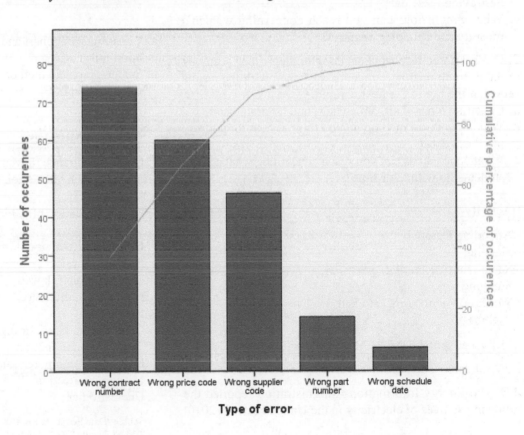

PROBLEMS

APPLYING THE CONCEPTS

2.1 A survey asked 1,264 women who were their most trusted shopping advisers. The survey results were as follows:

Shopping Advisers	Percentage (%)
Advertising	7
Friends/family	45
Manufacturer websites	5
News media	11
Online user reviews	13
Retail websites	4
Salespeople	1
Other	14

Source: Data extracted from "Snapshots," *USA Today*, October 19, 2006, p. 1B.

a. Construct a bar chart, a pie chart, and a Pareto chart.
b. Which graphical method do you think is best for portraying these data?
c. What conclusions can you reach concerning women's most trusted shopping advisers?

2.2 What do college students do with their time? A survey of 3,000 traditional-age students was taken with the results shown at the top of the next column.
a. Construct a bar chart, a pie chart, and a Pareto chart.
b. Which graphical method do you think is best for portraying these data?
c. What conclusions can you reach concerning what college students do with their time?

Activity	Percentage (%)
Attending class/lab	9
Sleeping	24
Socializing, recreating, other	51
Studying	7
Working, volunteering, student clubs	9

Source: Data extracted from M. Marklein, "First Two years of College Wasted?" *USA Today*, January 18, 2011, p. 3A.

2.3 The Energy Information Administration reported the following sources of electricity in the United States in 2010:

Source of Electricity	Percentage (%)
Coal	44
Hydroelectric	7
Natural gas	24
Nuclear	20
Other	5

Source: Energy Information Administration, 2010.

a. Construct a Pareto chart.
b. What percentage of power is derived from coal, nuclear, or natural gas?
c. Construct a pie chart.
d. For these data, do you prefer using a Pareto chart or the pie chart? Why?

2.4 An article discussed radiation therapy and new cures from the therapy, along with the harm that could be done if mistakes were made. The following tables represent the results of the types of mistakes made and the causes of mistakes reported to the New York State Department of Health from 2001 to 2009:

Radiation Mistakes	Number
Missed all or part of intended target	284
Wrong dose given	255
Wrong patient treated	50
Other	32

a. Construct a bar chart and a pie chart for the types of radiation mistakes.
b. Which graphical method do you think is best for portraying these data?

Causes of Mistakes	Number
Quality assurance flawed	355
Data entry or calculation errors by personnel	252
Misidentification of patient or treatment location	174
Blocks, wedges, or collimators misused	133
Patient's physical setup wrong	96
Treatment plan flawed	77
Hardware malfunction	60
Staffing	52
Computer software or digital information transfer malfunction	24
Override of computer data by personnel	19
Miscommunication	14
Unclear/other	8

Source: Data extracted from W. Bogdanich, "A Lifesaving Tool Turned Deadly," *The New York Times*, January 24, 2010, pp. 1, 15, 16.

c. Construct a Pareto chart for the causes of mistakes.
d. Discuss the "vital few" and "trivial many" reasons for the causes of mistakes.

2.5 The following table indicates the percentage of residential electricity consumption in the United States, organized by type of appliance in a recent year:

Type of Appliance	Percentage (%)
Air conditioning	18
Clothes dryers	5
Clothes washers/other	24
Computers	1
Cooking	2
Dishwashers	2
Freezers	2
Lighting	16
Refrigeration	9
Space heating	7
Water heating	8
TVs and set top boxes	6

Source: Data extracted from J. Mouawad, and K. Galbraith, "Plugged-in Age Feeds a Hunger for Electricity," *The New York Times,* September 20, 2009, pp. 1, 28.

a. Construct a bar chart, a pie chart, and a Pareto chart.
b. Which graphical method do you think is best for portraying these data?
c. What conclusions can you reach concerning residential electricity consumption in the United States?

2.6 A study of 1,000 people asked what respondents wanted to grill during barbecue season. The results were as follows:

Type of Food	Percentage (%)
Beef	38
Chicken	23
Fruit	1
Hot dogs	6
Pork	8
Seafood	19
Vegetables	5

Source: Data extracted from "What Folks Want Sizzling on the Grill During Barbecue Season," *USA Today,* March 29, 2009, p. 1A.

a. Construct a bar chart, a pie chart, and a Pareto chart.
b. Which graphical method do you think is best for portraying these data?
c. What conclusions can you reach concerning what folks want sizzling on the grill during barbecue season?

2.7 A survey of 1,085 adults asked "Do you enjoy shopping for clothing for yourself?" The results (data extracted from "Split decision on clothes shopping," *USA Today,* January 28, 2011, p. 1B) indicated that 51% of the females enjoyed shopping for clothing for themselves as compared to 44% of the males. The sample sizes of males and females was not provided. Suppose that the results were as shown in the following table:

a. Construct a side-by-side bar chart of enjoying shopping and gender.
b. What conclusions do you reach from this chart?

Enjoy Shopping for Clothing	Gender		
	Male		Total
Yes	238	276	514
No	304	267	571
Total	542	543	1,085

2.8 Each day at a large hospital, several hundred laboratory tests are performed. The rate at which these tests are done improperly (and therefore need to be redone) seems steady, at about 4%. In an effort to get to the root cause of these nonconformances, tests that need to be redone, the director of the lab decided to keep records over a period of one week. The laboratory tests were subdivided by the shift of workers who performed the lab tests. The results are as follows:

Lab Tests Performed	Shift		
	Day	Evening	Total
Nonconforming	16	24	40
Conforming	654	306	960
Total	670	330	1,000

a. Construct a side-by-side bar chart of nonconformances and shift.
b. What conclusions concerning the pattern of nonconforming laboratory tests can the laboratory director reach?

2.9 Does it take more time to get yourself removed from an email list than it used to? A study of 100 large online retailers revealed the following:

	Need Three or More Clicks to be Removed	
Year	Yes	No
2009	39	61
2008	7	93

Source: Data extracted from "Drill Down," *The New York Times,* March 29, 2010, p. B2.

a. Construct a side-by-side bar chart of year and whether you need to click three or more times to be removed from an email list.
b. What do these results tell you about whether more online retailers were requiring three or more clicks in 2009 than in 2008?

CALCULATOR LESSON 1

**CASIO
fx-9750GII**

Question 1: How do I turn on the calculator?

Press the **AC/ON** key to turn on the calculator.

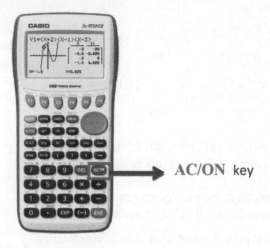

AC/ON key

The diagram is taken from this source: http://www.casio.com/products/Calculators_%26_Dictionaries/Graphing/FX-9750GII/content/Introduction/

Question 2: How do I get to the "Stat" Mode?

Press the **MENU** key. In the main menu, select "**STAT**" by using the cursor keys to move the highlighter to the **STAT** icon and press **EXE**.

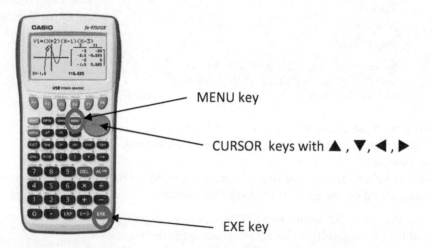

MENU key

CURSOR keys with ▲, ▼, ◄, ►

EXE key

The diagram is taken from this source: http://www.casio.com/products/Calculators_%26_Dictionaries/Graphing/FX-9750GII/content/Introduction/

Question 3: How do I select the Graph function?

Once inside the **STAT** mode, you will see the following screen.

	List 1	List 2	List 3	List 4	
SUB					
1					
2					
3					
4					
GRPH **F1**	**CALC** **F2**	**TEST** **F3**	**INTR** **F4**	**DIST** **F5**	▷ **F6**

Press function key **F1** to select "**GRPH**."

Question 4: How do I sort data?

Once inside the **STAT** mode, you will see the following screen.

	List 1	List 2	List 3	List 4	
SUB					
1					
2					
3					
4					
GRPH **F1**	**CALC** **F2**	**TEST** **F3**	**INTR** **F4**	**DIST** **F5**	▷ **F6**

Press function key **F6** to select " ▷." This brings you to the next screen with the functions TOOL, EDIT, DEL. DEL-A, INS, and ▷ as shown below.

	List 1	List 2	List 3	List 4	
SUB					
1					
2					
3					
4					
TOOL **F1**	**EDIT** **F2**	**DEL** **F3**	**DEL-A** **F4**	**INS** **F5**	▷ **F6**

Selecting "**TOOL**" by selecting **F1** function will bring you to another set of functions (**SRT-A**, **SRT-D**, **TOP**, and **BTM**) as shown below.

	List 1	List 2	List 3	List 4
SUB				
1				
2				
3				
4				
SRT-A	**SRT-D**	**TOP**	**BTM**	
F1	**F2**	**F3**	**F4**	

1. If you wish to sort your data in ascending order, select **F1** (**SRT-A**).
2. If you wish to sort your data in descending order, select **F2** (**SRT-D**).
3. If you wish to go to the TOP of the list, select **F3** (**TOP**).
4. If you wish to go to the BOTTOM of the list, select **F4** (**BTM**).

Press the **EXIT** key to go back to the previous screen.

Question 5: How do I delete data?

Once inside the **STAT** mode, you will see the following screen.

	List 1	List 2	List 3	List 4	
SUB					
1					
2					
3					
4					
GRPH	**CALC**	**TEST**	**INTR**	**DIST**	▷
F1	**F2**	**F3**	**F4**	**F5**	**F6**

Press function key **F6** to select " ▷." This brings you to the next screen with the functions TOOL, EDIT, DEL. DEL-A, INS, and ▷ as shown below.

	List 1	List 2	List 3	List 4	
SUB					
1					
2					
3					
4					
TOOL	**EDIT**	**DEL**	**DEL-A**	**INS**	▷
F1	**F2**	**F3**	**F4**	**F5**	**F6**

1. If you wish to delete a value from a cell, select **F3 (DEL)**.
2. If you wish to delete a list of data, select **F4 (DEL-A)**. The calculator will ask if you want to proceed to delete the whole list. Press **F1** for Yes. Press **F2** for No.

Press the **EXIT** key to go back to the previous screen.

Question 6: How do I insert a value into a list of data?

Once inside the **STAT** mode, you will see the following screen.

	List 1	List 2	List 3	List 4	
SUB					
1					
2					
3					
4					
GRPH	CALC	TEST	INTR	DIST	▷
F1	F2	F3	F4	F5	F6

Press function key **F6** to select "▷." This brings you to the next screen with the functions TOOL, EDIT, DEL. DEL-A, INS, and ▷ as shown below.

	List 1	List 2	List 3	List 4	
SUB					
1	22				
2	13				
3	10				
4	8				
TOOL	EDIT	DEL	DEL-A	INS	▷
F1	F2	F3	F4	F5	F6

If you wish to insert a value into List 1, bring the highlighter to the cell where you want to insert the value. Then select **F5 (INS).**

3 Graphical Presentation of Quantitative Data

Learning Objectives

In this chapter, you learn:

- To construct stem-and-leaf plot
- To construct frequency distribution
- To construct an ogive
- To construct contingency table
- To construct scatter plot

In Chapter 1, you learned the different types of data and scales. In Chapter 2, you learned to present qualitative data in graphical form. In this chapter, you will learn to organize quantitative data in graphical form. Specifically you will learn to group a set of **quantitative** data in the form of the following:

1. Stem-and-leaf plot (section 3.1)
2. Frequency distribution (section 3.6)
3. Histogram
4. Polygon
5. Ogive (cumulative percentage polygon) (section 3.7)
6. Contingency table
7. Scatter plot

How Do You Organize Quantitative Data Graphically?

In this chapter, you can learn to present ratio and interval data using histograms, polygons, Ogives, **stem-and-leaf plots**, frequency distribution, contingency Table and scatter Plot.

3.1 Stem-and-Leaf Plot

Quantitative data can be arranged or summarized either graphically (i.e., charts, graphs, tables) or numerically (i.e., mean, mode, median, standard deviation). In this chapter, you will learn to group the data visually by constructing a stem and leaf plot. The purpose of plotting a stem and-leaf plot is to summarize the distribution (or shape) of a set of quantitative data and at the same time still retain most of the data values (or numbers). A stem-and-leaf plot does look like a bar chart. The advantages of a stem-and-leaf plot are that the plot can be quickly constructed by hand and, most importantly, the values of the individual data can be retrieved from the plot. Stem-and-leaf plots also enable you to find the minimum value, maximum value, and the most frequently occuring value (known as the mode) from just looking at the plot.

A stem-and-leaf plot looks like a horizontal bar chart maintaining most of the original data values. Each data value can be divided into a stem and a leaf.

For example, the value of 84 can be separated into "8" (representing the stem value) and "4" (representing the leaf value).

The stem-and-leaf plot should be considered when the number of data values is not more than 50, which we consider a small set of data.

The following is an example of a stem-and-leaf plot displaying the profits earned by companies in the hospitality industry.

FIGURE 3.1
Stem-and-leaf plot for profits data of the hospitality industry

Hospitality Industry: *Profits ($)*	
Stem (100,000)	**Leaf (10,000)**
1	1234
1	55688
2	2
2	56
3	113
3	79

You must have a title for each stem-and-leaf plot you construct. From the title in Figure 3.1, you know that the data are profits for the hospitality industry. If there is no title provided, the numbers could represent "anything under the sun." So a title is very important because it tells you about the nature of the data. Now, I want you to reverse engineer and give me the list of data values from the stem-and-leaf plot. Each stem is worth 100,000. For stem value 2, we have 200,000. For stem value 3, we have 300,000, and so on. Notice that the first entry has a stem of 1 and a leaf of 1. Since the stem unit is 100,000 and the leaf unit is 10,000, this data value is $1*100,000 + 1*10,000 = 110,000$. Likewise, the second entry has a stem of 1 and a leaf of 2, which corresponds to a value of $1*100,000 + 2*10,000 = 120,000$. Thus, the data can be reconstructed from the entries in the stem-and-leaf plot. Note that if no units are specified for the stem, it should be assumed that the stem unit is 1. While not true in this case, the leaf unit is usually omitted and assumed to be the next single digit after the stem.

Now, let's learn how to construct a stem-and-leaf plot as shown in Figure 3.1.

3.2 Rules and Convention to Construct a Stem-and-Leaf Plot

You must apply these rules to construct a stem-and-leaf plot.

The reasons for applying these rules are (1) to minimize the perception biases and (2) to have an aesthetic appearance graphically.

You will use the following set of rules and conventions.

For the **stems:**
Stem Rules

1. The number of stems should be from 6 to 13 stems.
2. The stem values should be consecutive numbers or repeated numbers. The numbers may each be repeated twice or 5 times.
3. The stem units must be indicated if the stem is not to be taken at face value.
4. There must be at least one leaf associated with the first and last stem.

For the **leaves:**
Leaf Rules

1. The leaf for each data value is the next <u>single</u> digit after the stem. When the stems are repeated twice, the leaves values 0 to 4 go to the first stem and the leaves values 5 to 9 go to the second stem of the same values. This order is reversed when the stems are negative values. When the stems are repeated 5 times, the leaves values 0 and 1 go to the first stem, values 2 and 3 go to the second stem, values 4 and 5 go to the third stem, values 6 and 7 go to the fourth stem, and values 8 and 9 go to the fifth stem. This order is reversed when the stems are negative values.
2. There is no rounding off.
3. The leaf values are written in ascending order when positive and descending order when negative.
4. The leaf values must be evenly spaced.
5. No commas or dashes between the numbers are allowed.

I. Illustration of Stem Rule 1: The number of stems should be from 6 to 13 stems.

Title

Stem (10)	Leaf
1	012
2	567
3	1
4	6789
5	02567
6	01
7	35
8	9

There are **8 stems**, which meets the requirement of stems in the plot.

Title

Stem (10)	Leaf
5	02567
6	01
7	35
8	9

There are **<u>4 stems</u>**, which <u>does not</u> meet the requirement of stems in the plot. What should you do? To increase the number of stems, you should apply **Stem Rule 2**.

II. Illustration of Stem Rule 2: The stem values should be consecutive numbers or repeated numbers. The numbers may each be repeated twice or 5 times.

a.) Illustration of stem values as consecutive numbers.

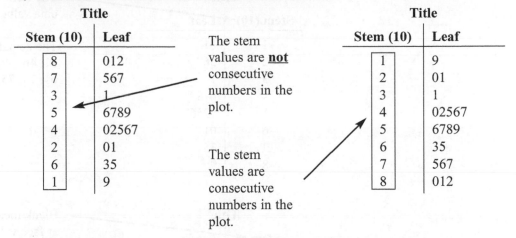

The stem values are **not** consecutive numbers in the plot.

The stem values are consecutive numbers in the plot.

b.) Illustration of few stems and each stem value repeated two times.

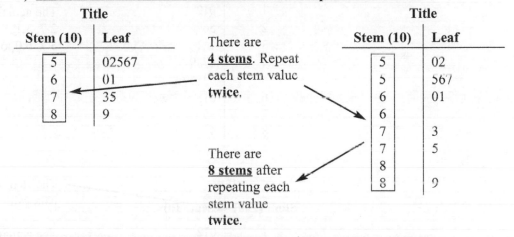

There are **4 stems**. Repeat each stem value **twice**.

There are **8 stems** after repeating each stem value **twice**.

c.) Illustration of few stems and each stem value repeated five times.

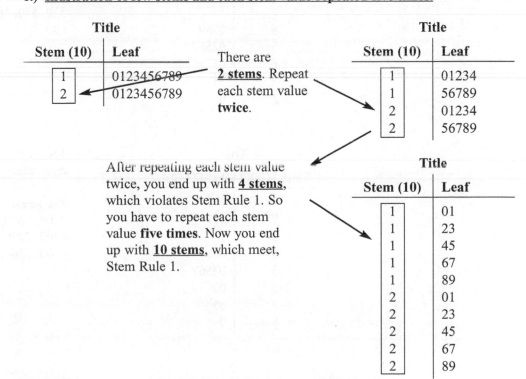

There are **2 stems**. Repeat each stem value **twice**.

After repeating each stem value twice, you end up with **4 stems**, which violates Stem Rule 1. So you have to repeat each stem value **five times**. Now you end up with **10 stems**, which meet, Stem Rule 1.

III. Illustration of Stem Rule 3: The stem units must be indicated if the stem is not to be taken at face value.

Title

Stem (10)	Leaf
1	012
2	567
3	1
4	6789
5	02567
6	01
7	35
8	9

The stem unit must represent the actual data value.

The actual data are 10, 11, 12, 25, 26, 27, 31, 46, 47, 48, 49, 50, 52, 55, 56, 57, 60, 61, 73, 75, 89.

Title

Stem	Leaf
1	012
2	567
3	1
4	6789
5	02567
6	01
7	35
8	9

Blank means that the stem should be taken at face value.

The actual data are 1.0, 1.1, 1.2, 2.5, 2.6, 2.7, 3.1, 4.6, 4.7, 4.8, 4.9, 5.0, 5.2, 5.5, 5.6, 5.7, 6.0, 6.1, 7.3, 7.5, 8.9.

Title

Stem (100)	Leaf (10)
1	012
2	567
3	1
4	6789
5	02567
6	01
7	35
8	9

The stem unit must represent the actual data value.

The actual data are 100, 110, 120, 250, 260, 270, 310, 460, 470, 480, 490, 500, 520, 550, 560, 570, 600, 610, 730, 750, 890.

Title

Stem (1000)	Leaf (100)
1	012
2	567
3	1
4	6789
5	02567
6	01
7	35
8	9

The stem unit must represent the actual data value.

The actual data are 1000, 1100, 1200, 2500, 2600, 2700, 3100, 4600, 4700, 4800, 4900, 5000, 5200, 5500, 5600, 5700, 6000, 6100, 7300, 7500, 8900.

The **stem unit** indicated in the stem-and-leaf plot quantified each stem value.

Stem (100)	Leaf (10)
1	2 3 4 5 6
2	6 6 6 7
3	9
4	1 2 5 5
5	3 3
6	0

The stem is recorded on the left-hand side of the column, which displays the hundreds' place. The stem value is in the hundreds' place. The stem values of 1, 2, 3, 4, 5 and 6 are in fact 100, 200, 300, 400, 500, and 600. The leaf is recorded on the right-hand side of the column, displaying the tens' place. The single digit of the leaf value is in the tens' place. In this way, we retain the original data values, which are 120, 130, 140, 150, 160, etc. We do not usually indicate the leaf unit in the stem-and-leaf plot. Leaf Rule 1 states that "The leaf for each data value is the next single digit after the stem." According to this rule, if the stem value is in hundreds (100), then the leaf values should be in tens (10).

You should not record the stem in hundreds as shown next:

Stem	Leaf
100	2 3 4 5 6
200	6 6 6 7
300	9
400	1 2 5 5
500	3 3
600	0

The previous display contains several errors. There are gaps between stem values. How do you record the leaf value in tens? According to Stem Rule 2, you should record the stem values in consecutive numbers such as 10, 11, 12, 13, etc.; 1.2, 1.3, 1.4, 1.5, etc.; or 100, 101, 102, 103, etc.

IV. Illustration of Stem Rule 4: There must be at least one leaf associated with the first and last stem.

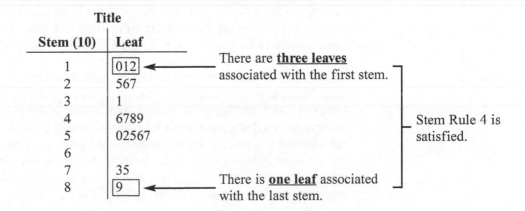

Title

Stem (10)	Leaf
1	012
2	567
3	1
4	6789
5	02567
6	
7	35
8	9

There are **three leaves** associated with the first stem.

Stem Rule 4 is satisfied.

There is **one leaf** associated with the last stem.

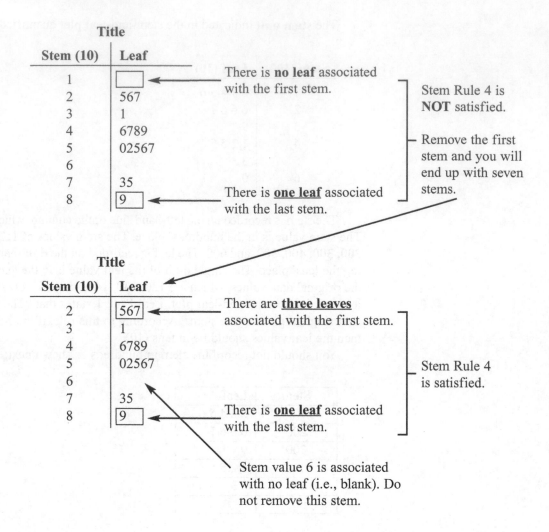

According to Stem Rule 4, there must be at least one leaf associated with the first and last stem.

If the **<u>first stem</u>** has no leaf value (i.e., blank), remove it. *Do not* insert "0," which will give you a data value!

If the **<u>last stem</u>** has no leaf value (i.e., blank), remove it. *Do not* insert "0," which will give you a data value!

For an "intermediate" stem value that is blank (i.e., stem value 6), *do not remove* it.

According to Stem Rule 2, the stem values should be consecutive numbers. Removing this "intermediate" stem value that is blank will violate this rule. If you remove stem value 6, you will end up with stem values 2, 3, 5, 7, and 8. The stem values are not consecutive.

V. Illustration of Leaf Rule 1: The leaf for each data value is the next <u>single</u> digit after the stem. When the stems are repeated twice, the leaves values 0 to 4 go to the first stem and the leaves values 5 to 9 go to the second stem of the same values as shown in Table 3.1. This order is reversed when the stems are negative values as shown in Table 3.2. When the stems are repeated 5 times, the leaves values 0 and 1 go to the first stem, values 2 and 3 go to the second stem, values 4 and 5 go to the third stem, values 6 and 7 go to the fourth stem, and values 8 and 9 go to the fifth stem as shown in Table 3.3. This order is reversed when the stems are negative values as shown in Table 3.4.

TABLE 3.1

Rule for *Positive* Value Stems That Are Repeated Twice

Repeat Stem Twice	Leaves Values	Example: Stem	Leaf
First stem with same value	0 to 4	1	0 1 2 3 4
Second stem with same value	5 to 9	1	5 6 7 8 9
		2	1 1 3 4
		2	5 5 8
		3	0 1 1 4 4
		3	
		4	0 3 3 4
		4	8 9

Note: The stem values are repeated twice.

1. The positive stem is repeated 2 times.
2. Leaves values 0 to 4 go to the first stem.
3. Leaves values 5 to 9 go to the second stem.

Note: For the *positive* stem values, the leaves are arranged in ascending order (i.e., 0, 1, 2, 3, 4, 5, 6, 7, 8, 9)

TABLE 3.2

Rule for *Negative* Value Stems That Are Repeated Twice

Repeat Stem Twice	Leaves Values	Example: Stem	Leaf
First stem with same value	5 to 9	-4	9 8 7 6 5
Second stem with same value	0 to 4	-4	4 3 2 1 0
		-3	
		-3	4 4 2 0 0
		-2	9 8
		-2	4 3 0 0
		-1	9 8 7 6 5
		-1	4 3 2 1 0

Note: The stem values are repeated twice.

1. The negative stem is repeated 2 times.
2. Leaves values 5 to 9 go to the first stem.
3. Leaves values 0 to 4 go to the second stem.

For the *negative* stem values: The leaves are arranged in descending order (i.e., 9, 8, 7, 6, 5, 4, 3, 2, 1, 0)

TABLE 3.3

Rule for *Positive* Value Stems That Are Repeated Five Times

Repeat Stem Five Times	Leaves Values	Example: Stem	Leaf
First stem with same value	0 , 1	5	0 1
Second stem with same value	2 , 3	5	2 3
		5	4 5
Third stem with same value	4 , 5	5	6 7
Fourth stem with same value	6 , 7	5	8 9
		6	0 0 0 0 1
Fifth stem with same value	8 , 9	6	2 2 2 2
		6	4 4 5 5 5
		6	6 6 7
		6	9 9 9 9

Note: The stem values are repeated five times.

Note: For the *positive* stem values, the leaves are arranged in ascending order (i.e., 0, 1, 2, 3, 4, 5, 6, 7, 8, 9)

TABLE 3.4

Rule for *Negative* Value Stems That Are Repeated Five Times

Repeat Stem Five Times	Leaves Values	Example: Stem	Leaf
First stem with same value	8 , 9	−2	9 8
		−2	7 6
Second stem with same value	6 , 7	−2	5 4
		−2	3 2
Third stem with same value	4 , 5	−2	1 0
		−1	9 8
Fourth stem with same value	2 , 3	−1	7 6
		−1	5 4
Fifth stem with same value	0 , 1	−1	3 2
		−1	1 0

Note: The stem values are repeated five times.

For the *negative* stem values: The leaves are arranged in descending order (i.e., 9, 8, 7, 6, 5, 4, 3, 2, 1, 0)

VI. Illustration of Leaf Rule 2: There is no rounding off.

To record value 6786 with a defined stem value of 67, you should record leaf value 8 next to 67. You should not round the leaf value 8 to 9. Otherwise, you will violate Leaf Rule 2.

VII. Illustration of Leaf Rule 3: The leaf values are written in ascending order when positive and descending order when negative.

For the *positive* stem values, the leaves are arranged in ascending order (i.e., 0, 1, 2, 3, 4, 5, 6, 7, 8, 9).

For the *negative* stem values, the leaves are arranged in descending order (i.e., 9, 8, 7, 6, 5, 4, 3, 2, 1, 0).

Refer to Tables 3.1, 3.2, 3.3, and 3.4.

Title

Stem (100,00)	Leaf (10,000)
-0	9 7 5
-0	4 4 3 1
0	0 0 2 4
0	5 5 6 8 8
1	2
1	5 6
2	1 1 3
2	7 9

Corresponds to the negative stem; the leaves are arranged in descending order.

Corresponds to the positive stem; the leaves are arranged in ascending order.

VIII. Illustration of Leaf Rule 4: The leaf values must be evenly spaced.

Title

Stem (10)	Leaf
1	0•——•12
2	56←→7
3	1
4	6←→78•——•9
5	0←→25←→67
6	01
7	35
8	9

These are uneven spaces among the leaves.

IX. Illustration of Leaf Rule 5: No commas or dashes between the numbers are allowed.

Title

Stem (10)	Leaf
1	0,1,2
2	5,6,7
3	1
4	6,7,8,9
5	0,2,5,6,7
6	0,1
7	3,5
8	9

Do not insert commas between leaves.

3.3 How Do You Construct a Stem-and-Leaf Plot Using Data with Positive Values?

EXAMPLE 3.1

Data were taken from http://biz.yahoo.com/p/tops/sf.html.

Refer to Table 3.5, which shows annual returns (in %) of the mutual fund top performers in the financial sector.

TABLE 3.5

Mutual Fund Top Performers

Fund Name	Symbol	Ann. Ret.
Prudential Financial Svcs Z	PFSZX	9.80%
Prudential Financial Svcs A	PFSAX	9.49%
Prudential Financial Svcs B	PUFBX	8.71%
Prudential Financial Svcs C	PUFCX	8.71%
Burnham Financial Industries I	BMFIX	6.87%
Burnham Financial Industries A	BURFX	6.80%
Burnham Financial Industries C	BURCX	6.04%
Royce Financial Services Svc	RYFSX	2.19%
FBR Small Cap Financial I	FBRUX	0.90%
FBR Small Cap Financial Investor	FBRSX	0.79%

Using the data listed in Table 3.5, construct stem-and-leaf displays for the annual returns.

Step 1: Sort the annual return data in ascending order.

By sorting the data, the leaves will fall in either ascending or descending order naturally.

Minimum

Maximum

Use the Casio calculator to sort your data.
To sort your data, follow these calculator steps.

1. Press the **MENU** key; then press **STAT**.
2. Under STAT mode, input your data in List **1**.
3. After you have entered your data in List 1, select **TOOL**, which corresponds to the **F1** function key.
4. Then select **SRT-A**, which corresponds to **F1**. "SRT-A" stands for "sort lists into ascending order."
5. Then a dialog box will prompt you, "How many Lists?" Press **1**, and then press **EXE**. (Select "1" because you have only one list to sort.) Then a dialog box will prompt you, "Select List   List No: **1** <since you enter your data in List **1**>

Step 2: Find the maximum and minimum values.

Minimum = 0.79
Maximum = 9.80

Step 3: Split the minimum and maximum values into stems and leaves.

The value on the left side of the line is the *stem value*, and the value on the right side of the line is the *leaf value*, as shown next.

Minimum	0. 7	9
Maximum	9. 8	0
	Stem	Leaf

The stem values should be consecutive numbers from 0.7 to 9.8. Count the number of stems from values 0.7, 0.8, and 0.9 all the way to 9.8 without skipping any values, as shown next. There is a total of 92 stems. That is too many stems. You have violated Stem Rule 1.

Stem	Value
0.7	1st stem
0.8	2nd stem
0.9	3rd stem
1	4th stem
1.1	5th stem
1.2	6th stem
1.3	7th stem
1.4	8th stem
1.5	9th stem
etc.	etc.
9.2	86th stem
9.3	87th stem
9.4	88th stem
9.5	89th stem
9.6	90th stem
9.7	91st stem
9.8	92nd stem

The numbers of stems from stem values 0.7 to 9.8 is more than 13 stems. When there are too many stems, you must redefine the stem values by moving the vertical line to the left as shown next.

Minimum	0.	7	9
Maximum	9.	8	0

The new set of stem values are from 0 to 9 (i.e., 0, 1, 2, 3, 4, 5, 6, 7, 8, 9). There is a total of 10 stems. According to Stem Rule 1, "The number of stems should be from 6 to 13 stems." You have enough stems to construct the stem-and-leaf plot.

Step 4: Now construct the stem-and-leaf plot.

Annual returns (in %) of the mutual fund

Stem	Leaf
0	
1	
2	
3	
4	
5	
6	
7	
8	
9	

According to Stem Rule 2, the stem values are in ascending and consecutive order.

Note that you have to check the following stem rules:

1. You have 10 stems. Since you have satisfied this Stem Rule 1, you do not have to repeat each stem twice or five times.
2. Per Stem Rule 2, the stem values are in consecutive numbers.
3. Per Stem Rule 3, leave the stem unit blank because the values are taken at face value. What are these true values: 0, 1, 2, 3, 4, 5, 6, 7, 8 and 9? Are they in units, tens, or hundreds? These numbers are in units, and you leave the stem unit under the stem title blank.
4. You are not able to check Stem Rule 4 at this point because you have not recorded the leaves yet. Come back to check this rule after you have done step 5.

Step 5: Record the leaf values

Record the leaf values, which are one digit after the stem value. You must make sure that the minimum value (which is 0.79) is recorded on the first stem and the maximum value (which is 9.80) is recorded on the last stem.

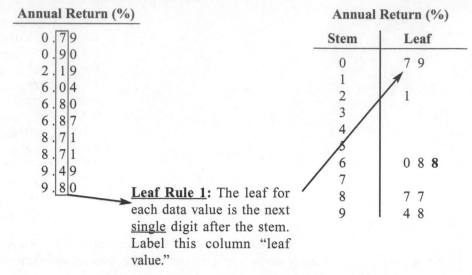

Annual Return (%)

```
0 . 7 9
0 . 9 0
2 . 1 9
6 . 0 4
6 . 8 0
6 . 8 7
8 . 7 1
8 . 7 1
9 . 4 9
9 . 8 0
```

Annual Return (%)

Stem	Leaf
0	7 9
1	
2	1
3	
4	
5	
6	0 8 **8**
7	
8	7 7
9	4 8

Leaf Rule 1: The leaf for each data value is the next single digit after the stem. Label this column "leaf value."

Note that you have to check the following leaf rules:

1. There is no rounding off of the leaf values.
2. The leaf values are written in ascending order when positive and descending order when negative.
3. The leaf values must be evenly spaced.
4. No commas or dashes between the numbers are allowed.

EXAMPLE 3.2

Data were taken from http://finance.yahoo.com/actives?e=us.

TABLE 3.6

U.S. Stock Volume Leaders

Refer to Table 3.6, which shows the volume of company stocks traded in the U.S. stock exchange.

Company	Stock Volume
Intel Corporation	72,621,446
iShares MSCI Emerging Index Fun	72,179,486
Microsoft Corporation	63,114,201
Cisco Systems, Inc.	62,747,101
iShares Russell 2000	49,185,710
iShares MSCI Japan Index Fund	48,722,445
Oracle Corporation	43,176,882
Sirius XM Radio Inc.	42,543,054
Micron Technology, Inc.	39,888,893
JDS Uniphase Corporation	39,836,593
Alcatel-Lucent Common Stock	39,399,448
Sprint Nextel Corporation Comm	38,966,215
General Motors Company Common S	33,074,753
Vanguard Emerging Markets ETF	30,592,552
Office Depot, Inc. Common Stock	30,359,092

Using the data listed in Table 3.6, construct stem-and-leaf displays for the stock volume.

Step 1: Sort the stock volume data in ascending order.

← Minimum

← Maximum

Step 2: Find the maximum and minimum values.

Minimum = 30,359,092
Maximum = 72,621,446

Step 3: Split the minimum and maximum values into stems and leaves.

Minimum	3	0	3	5	9	0	9	2
Maximum	7	2	6	2	1	4	4	6

a) The number of stems from stem values 3035909 to 7262144 is more than 13 stems. There are too many stems, so you have to redefine the stem values again by moving the vertical line to the left.

Minimum	3	0	3	5	9	0	9	2
Maximum	7	2	6	2	1	4	4	6

b) The number of stems from stem values 303590 to 726214 is more than 13 stems. There are too many stems, so you have to redefine the stem values again by moving the vertical line to the left.

Minimum	3	0	3	5	9	0	9	2
Maximum	7	2	6	2	1	4	4	6

c) The number of stems from stem values 30359 to 72621 is more than 13 stems. There are too many stems, so you have to redefine the stem values again by moving the vertical line to the left.

Minimum	3	0	3	5	9	0	9	2
Maximum	7	2	6	2	1	4	4	6

d) The number of stems from stem values 3035 to 7262 is more than 13 stems. There are too many stems, so you have to redefine the stem values again by moving the vertical line to the left.

| Minimum | 3 | 0 | 3 | 5 | 9 | 0 | 9 | 2 |
| Maximum | 7 | 2 | 6 | 2 | 1 | 4 | 4 | 6 |

e) The number of stems from stem values 303 to 726 is more than 13 stems. There are too many stems, so you have to redefine the stem values again by moving the vertical line to the left.

| Minimum | 3 | 0 | 3 | 5 | 9 | 0 | 9 | 2 |
| Maximum | 7 | 2 | 6 | 2 | 1 | 4 | 4 | 6 |

f) The number of stems from stem values 30 to 72 is more than 13 stems. There are too many stems, so you have to redefine the stem values again by moving the vertical line to the left.

| Minimum | 3 | 0 | 3 | 5 | 9 | 0 | 9 | 2 |
| Maximum | 7 | 2 | 6 | 2 | 1 | 4 | 4 | 6 |

The stem values are from 3 to 7 (that is 3, 4, 5, 6, 7). There are a total of 5 stems.

According to Stem Rule 1, "The number of stems should be from 6 to 13 stems." You do not have enough stems to construct the stem-and-leaf plot. According to Stem Rule 2, "The stem values should be consecutive numbers or repeated numbers. The numbers may each be repeated twice or 5 times." Therefore, you have to repeat each stem value twice, that is, 3, 3, 4, 4, 5, 5, 6, 6, 7, 7. You have a total of 10 stems, which satisfies Stem Rule 1. By repeating the stem values, you increase the number of stems so that the distribution does not appear so squeezed or squashed.

Step 4: Now construct the stem-and-leaf plot by repeating each stem value twice.

Per Stem Rule 3, record the stem unit under the stem title in the stem-and-leaf plot. Does stem value 3 represents units (i.e., face value), tens (10), hundreds (100), or thousands (1000). Each stem value is valued at 10,000,000. The stem value of 3 is actually regarded as 30,000,000 (i.e., 3 x 10,000,000), which reflects the original data value (e.g., 30,359,092 etc.). According to Leaf Rule 1, the leaf for each data value is the next <u>single</u> digit after the stem. For value 30,359,092, you record 0 as the leaf value. The rest of the digits after 0 are not recorded.

Stock Volume

Stem (10,000,000)	Leaf
3	
3	
4	
4	
5	
5	A total of 10 stems
6	
6	
7	
7	

Note that you have to check the following stem rules:

1. Per Stem Rule 1, you have 10 stems. Each stem is repeated twice.
2. Per Stem Rule 2, the stem values are consecutive numbers.
3. Per Stem Rule 3, the stem unit is 10,000,000.
4. You are not able to check Stem Rule 4 at this point because you have not recorded the leaves yet. Come back to check this rule after you have done step 5.

Step 5: Record the leaf values.

These values are **not** recorded.

Minimum   3 | 0   3   5   9   0   9   2

Maximum   7 | 2   6   2   1   4   4   6

Stem

According to Leaf Rule 1, record the next *single* digit after the stem.

According to Leaf Rule 2, do not *round off* the single digit of the leaf value.

You have to assign leaf values 0 to 4 to the first stem of the same value. The next leaf values 5 to 9 go to the second stem of the same value.

Record the leaf values, which are one digit after the stem value.

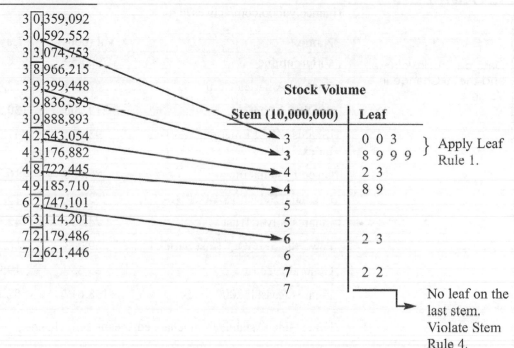

Stock Volume

Stem (10,000,000)	Leaf	
3	0 0 3	} Apply Leaf
3	8 9 9 9	Rule 1.
4	2 3	
4	8 9	
5		
5		
6	2 3	
6		
7	2 2	
7		

No leaf on the last stem. Violate Stem Rule 4.

Note that you have to check the following leaf rules:

1. There is no rounding off with the leaf values.
3. The leaf values are written in ascending order when positive and descending order when negative.
4. The leaf values must be evenly spaced.
5. No commas or dashes between the numbers are allowed.

Stem Rule number 4 "There must be at least one leaf associated with the first and last stem"—is violated. The second stem value 7 has no leaf associated with it, so you have to remove this stem to satisfy Stem Rule 4.

3.4 How Do You Construct a Stem-and-Leaf Plot with Negative and Positive Data Values?

For both positive and negative data values, use positive zero (+0) stem and negative zero (-0) stem to capture the positive and negative values. For example if you have data values -0.8 and +0.9, you would record 9 next to the +0 stem. Where will you record -0.8? If you record 8 next to the +0 stem, you will have a value of +0.8, but the actual value is -0.8. Therefore, you need a -0 to record 8.

Stem	Leaf
-0	8
+0	9

You need both +0 and -0 stems so that you can record 8 next to -0 and 9 next to +0.

EXAMPLE 3.3

Refer to Table 3.7, which shows the stock prices data. The data was taken from http://finance.yahoo.com/actives?e=o.

TABLE 3.7

Data on Stock Volume and the % Change in Volume

Name	Vol (000s)	Last	Change	% Change
Citigroup Inc	790,859	4.42	unch	0.00%
Bank of America Corp	262,174	12.42	−0.4	−3.12%
SPDR S&P 500	210,908	130.56	−1.48	−1.12%
iShares MSCI Emerging Markets Index	93,614	47.9	−1.24	−2.51%
Cisco Systems Inc	86,550	16.73	−0.3	−1.76%
Financial Select Sector SPDR	83,851	15.92	−0.22	−1.36%
iShares Silver Trust	74,937	42.42	0.58	1.38%
PowerShares QQQ Trust Series 1	69,073	56.25	−0.4	−0.71%
General Electric Co	63,659	19.98	−0.06	−0.30%
iShares Russell 2000 Index	58,617	82.13	−1.38	−1.65%

Note: "unch" stands for unchanged, means zero change.

Using the data listed in Table 3.7, construct stem-and-leaf displays for the % change.

Step 1: Sort the % change in ascending order.

% Change	% Change	
0.00%	**−3.12**	◄——————— Minimum
−3.12%	**−2.51**	
−1.12%	**−1.76**	
−2.51%	**−1.65**	
−1.76%	**−1.36**	
−1.36%	**−1.12**	
1.38%	**−0.71**	
−0.71%	**−0.30**	
−0.30%	**0.00**	
−1.65%	**1.38**	◄——————— Maximum

By sorting the data, it is easy to obtain the minimum and maximum values.

Step 2: Find the maximum and minimum values.

Minimum = −3.12
Maximum = 1.38

Step 3: Split the minimum and maximum values into stems and leaves.

Minimum	−	3	.	1	2
Maximum		1	.	3	8

a) The number of stems from stem values −3.1 to 1.3 is more than 13 stems. There are too many stems, so you have to redefine the stem values again by moving the vertical line to the left.

Minimum	−	3	.	1	2
Maximum		1	.	3	8

b) There are 6 stems from stem values −3 to 1: −3, −2, −1, −0, 0, and 1. According to Stem Rule 1, "The number of stems should be from 6 to 13 stems." You have a sufficient number of stems to construct the stem-and-leaf plot.

Step 4: Now construct the stem-and-leaf plot.

% Change

Stem	Leaf
−3	
−2	
−1	
−0	
0	
1	

A total of 6 stems

Note: Insert a negative zero (−0) stem to capture the positive and negative values.

Next, you have to check that your stem-and-leaf plot follows the stem rules.

Step 5: Record the leaf values.

Record the leaf values, which are one digit after the stem value. The stem unit is the face value; therefore, you leave it blank.

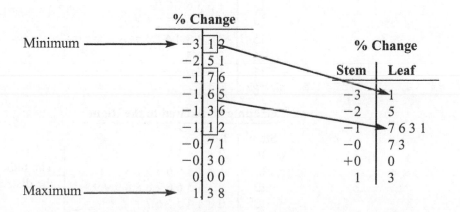

Now you have to check whether the stem and leaf plot follows the following stem rules:

1. The number of stems should be from 6 to 13 stems.

2. The stem values should be consecutive numbers or repeated numbers. The numbers may each be repeated twice or 5 times.
3. The stem units must be indicated if the stem is not to be taken at face value.
4. There must be at least one leaf associated with the first and last stem.

You also have to check the following leaf rules:

1. There is no rounding off with the leaf values.
3. The leaf values are written in ascending order when positive and descending order when negative.
4. The leaf values must be evenly spaced.
5. No commas or dashes between the numbers are allowed.

3.5 Interpretation of Results Using Stem-and-Leaf Plot

A) Using the stem-and-leaf plot to detect the shape of the data distribution.

The symmetry of a data distribution can be classified in three ways: 1) skewed to the left (the bulk of the data is located on the **right** side of the distribution; see Graphic A), (2) symmetrical (the bulk of the data is located in the middle of the distribution; see Graphic B) and (3) skewed to the right (the bulk of the data is located on the **left** side of the distribution; see Graphic C).

Graphic A: Skewed to the Left

Stem	Leaf
10	2
11	1 2
12	3 4 4
13	5 5 6 7 8
14	3 3 5 6 7 7 7
15	2 2 3 3 4 4 5 5 6 7 8
16	2 3 4 5 6 6 7 8 8 8 9 9 9
17	1 5 5 6
18	0 1

The bulk of the data is located on the right side of the distribution.

Graphic B: Symmetrical

Stem	Leaf
10	2
11	1 2
12	3 4 4
13	1 5 5 6 7 8 9
14	3 3 5 6 7 7 7 8 8 9
15	2 2 3 3 4 4
16	2 3 4 5
17	1 5 5
18	0 1

Graphic C: Skewed to the Right

Stem	Leaf
10	2
11	1 2 3 5 6 6 6 7 7 8
12	2 3 4 5 6 6 7 8 8 8 9 9 9
13	0 0 4 4 5 5 6 7
14	3 3 5 6 7 7
15	2 2 3 3
16	3 4 4
17	1 5 8
18	1 2

The bulk of the data is located on the left side of the distribution.

B) Using the stem-and-leaf plot to extract information.

You can extract information from a summarized stem-and-leaf plot. This will be illustrated using the following example.

EXAMPLE 3.4

Hours of Overtime Claimed per Month

A random sample of employees was taken from a technology company, and the hours of overtime claimed per month were recorded and summarized in the following stem-and-leaf plot.

Stem (10)	Leaf
10	2
11	1 2 3 5 6 6 6 7 7 8
12	2 3 4 5 6 6 7 8 8 8 9 9 9
13	0 0 4 4 5 5 6 7
14	3 3 5 6 7 7
15	2 2 3 3
16	3 4 4
17	1 5 8
18	1 2

i. How many employees are being sampled?

Each leaf represents one data value of an employee. Therefore, the sample size is equal to the number of leaves. There are 50 leaves, which means there are 50 employees in this sample.

ii. What percent of employees claimed at least 152 hours per month?

"At least 152" includes the value 152. By counting the values including 152 and greater than 152, you get 12 values. These values are 152, 152, 153, 153, 163, 164, 164, 171, 175, 178, 181, and 182. Each employee has one overtime value. Therefore, 12 values represents 12 employees. Thus, you have (12/50)*100=24% of employees claimed at least 152 hours per month.

iii. What percent of employees claimed less than 130 hours per month?

"Less than 130" does not include the value 130. By counting the values less than 130 and not including 130, you get 24 values. These values are 102, 111, 112, 113, 115, 116, 116, 116, 117, 117, 118, 122, 123, 124, 125, 126, 126, 127, 128, 128, 128, 129, 129, and 129. Each employee has one overtime value. Therefore, 24 values represents 24 employees. Thus, you have (24/50)*100=48% of employees claimed less than 130 hours per month.

iv. What percent of employees claimed more than 163 hours per month?

"More than 163" does not include the value 163. By counting the values more than 163 and not including 163, you get 7 values. These values are 164, 164, 171, 175, 178, 181, and 182. Each employee has one overtime value. Therefore, 7 values represents 7 employees. Thus, you have (7/50)*100 = 14% of employees claimed more than 163 hours per month.

v. What percent of employees claimed at most 115 hours per month?

"At most 115 hours" includes the value 115. By counting the values including 115 and less than 115, you get 5 values. These values are 102, 111, 112, 113, and 115. Each employee has one overtime value. Therefore, 5 values represents 5 employees. Thus, you have (5/50)*100=10% of employees claimed at most 115 hours per month.

Stem and Leaf Plot Problems

3.1 Refer to Table 3.18b (on page 85) that shows data regarding the first 20 companies taken from the FP500 Canada's 500 Largest Corporations table that appeared in the June 2003 issue of *National Post Business*.

Construct stem-and-leaf displays for the following data:
a. Profit rank
b. Asset rank
c. Revenues for 2002
d. Assets for 2002
e. Number of employees
f. Share price Exchange – 1 year percent
g. Profits as a percent of Assets
h. Profits as a percent of Equity

3.2 Refer to Table 3.8, which shows the mutual fund data that appeared in the Canadian Mutual Funds table of the June 3, 2004, issue of the *Globe and Mail*.

Construct stem-and-leaf displays for the following data:
a. Equitable life valuation data
b. Equitable life change data
c. Equitable life percent change data
d. MD management valuation data
e. MD management percent change data

3.3 Refer to Table 3.9 (on page 60), which shows data regarding the first 21 companies taken from the *Financial Post Magazine* Web site (http://www.financialpost.com/magazine/fp500/list.html).

For the 21 companies listed in Table 3.9, construct stem-and-leaf displays for the following data:
a. Revenue amount 2007
b. Profit amount 2007
c. Revenue change
d. Profit change
e. Profit rank

3.4 Refer to Table 3.10 (on page 61), "Telecommunications Industry Annual Ranking of America's Largest Corporations by Revenues, Profits, which appeared in the April 30, 2007, issue of *Fortune* magazine.

Using the data listed in Table 3.10, construct stem-and-leaf displays for the following data:
a. Revenues ($ million)
b. Profits ($ million)
c. Profits % change from 2005
d. Revenues % change from 2005
e. 1000 revenues rank

TABLE 3.8

fund	valuation	chg	% chg
EQUITABLE LIFE			
AIM Cdn Premier 06/01	10.01	+.01	+.07
Accum Income 06/01	23.26	-.03	-.15
American Gwth 06/01	10.48	+.04	+.37
Asian-Pacific 06/01	6.38	+.01	+.17
Asset Allocat 06/01	16.72	-.01	-.06
Dissett Div Inc 06/01	10.19	-.01	-.10
Cdn Bond 06/01	15.55	-.02	-.15
Cdn Stock 06/01	20.17	-.01	-.05
CommonStock 06/01	29.96	-.02	-.05
European Equity 06/01	7.23	-.02	-.22
International 06/01	11.49	+.02	+.17
MB Cdn Eq Value 06/01	18.21	-.04	-.24
Mack US Em Grth 06/01	10.15	+.09	+.84
Templeton Grwth 06/01	9.39	+.02	+.17
Tmplton Glo Bnd 06/01	12.32	+.04	+.36
Trimark Europis 06/01	10.51	+.02	+.15
Trimark Glo Bal 06/01	10.48	+.02	+.17
US Equity 06/01	6.30	+.02	+.32

fund	valuation	chg	% chg
MD MANAGEMENT			
MD Balanced	18.08	-.06	-.33
MD Bnd & Mtg	10.39	-.01	-.10
MD Bond	7.10	-.03	-.42
MD Dividend	16.66	-.03	-.18
MD Equity	19.03	-.03	-.16
MD Glo Bond	11.27	-.03	-.27
MD Glo Equ RSP	7.07	unch	unch
MD Growth	10.37	unch	unch
MD Growth RSP	9.82	unch	unch
MD Int'l Growth	6.64	unch	unch
MD Int'l Value	10.13	unch	unch
MD Intl Gr RSP	6.46	unch	unch
MD Select	15.39	-.04	-.26
MD US LgCpGrRSP	6.07	unch	unch
MD US LrCap Val	8.42	unch	unch
MD US LrCpVIRSP	8.25	unch	unch
MD US Lrg Cp Gr	4.79	unch	unch
MD US Sml Cp Gr	3.68	-.01	-.27
MDPIM Cdn Equ-A	11.01	-.04	-.36
MDPIM US Equ-A	7.39	-.02	-.27

fund	valuation	chg	% chg
MANULIFE MIX FUNDS			
AIM Am MidCp Gw	12.26	-.04	-.33
AIM Cd First Cl	12.25	-.05	-.41
Cd Lg Cap Gw Cl	12.85	-.07	-.54
Cd Lg Cap ValCl	12.12	-.02	-.16
Cd Lg Cp CoreCl	12.05	-.02	-.17
Cdn Equ Val Cl	12.65	-.02	-.16
E&P Gw Opp Cl	14.38	-.04	-.28
E&P US MidCapCl	11.81	-.05	-.42
FI Can DiscEqCl	13.07	-.08	-.61
FI Gwth Amer Cl	11.09	-.03	-.27
FI Intl Port Cl	11.60	-.02	-.17
Global Equ Cl	10.86	-.01	-.09
Global Sect Cl	11.31	-.06	-.53
Global SectCl-H	11.31	-.05	-.44
Global Val Cl	12.48	-.01	-.08
Int'l Growth Cl	11.29	-.01	-.09
Int'l Value Cl	12.27	+.01	+.08
Japanese Class	12.63	-.12	-.94
SM Tot Cd Eq Cl	13.26	+.02	+.15
SM Total Glo Cl	12.00	-.04	-.33
SM Total USEqCl	11.33	-.03	-.26
SMTotal Gl Cl-H	12.00	-.04	-.33
Sht Term Yld Cl	10.21	unch	unch
Str Bond Class	10.30	-.03	-.29
Tri Sel Cdn Cl	12.13	-.03	-.25
Trimark Glo Cl	11.41	+.04	+.35
US Lg Cap Gw Cl	10.40	-.01	-.10
US Lg Cp CoreCl	10.77	-.01	-.09
US Lg Cp Val Cl	10.92	-.02	-.18
US MidCp Val Cl	11.51	-.03	-.26

TABLE 3.8 *(continued)*

fund	valuation	chg	% chg
CI - CLARICA MUTUAL FUNDS			
Alpine CdnRes	10.35	-.08	-.77
Alpine CdnRes A	10.46	-.07	-.66
Alpine GrthEq	13.09	-.04	-.30
Alpine GrthEq A	13.28	-.05	-.38
Cdn Blu Chip Z	11.35	-.04	-.35
Cdn BlueChip	16.34	-.06	-.37
Cdn BlueChip A	16.51	-.07	-.42
Cdn Div Cl Z	10.86	-.04	-.37
Cdn Divers	14.71	-.05	-.34
Cdn Divers A	14.96	-.05	-.33
Cdn Equity	12.80	-.02	-.16
Cdn Equity A	12.82	-.02	-.16
Cdn Lrg Cap Val	10.55	+.01	+.09
Cdn Small/Mid A	21.02	-.04	-.19
Cdn Sml/Mid Cap	18.40	-.03	-.16
Clarica Balance	11.64	-.02	-.17
Glo Lrg Cap Val	10.52	+.04	+.38
Global Bond	9.91	-.04	-.40
Global Bond A	9.91	-.03	-.30
Prem Bond	11.34	-.04	-.35
Prem Bond A	11.49	-.04	-.35
Prem Int'l	12.43	-.03	-.24
Prem Int'l A	12.78	-.03	-.23
Prem Mtg	10.34	-.02	-.19
Prem Mtg A	10.46	-.02	-.19
Slg Corp Bond	9.83	-.02	-.20
Sum Cdn Equ	15.37	-.05	-.32
Sum Cdn Equ A	15.50	-.05	-.32
Sum Div Gwth	15.18	-.02	-.13
Sum Div Gwth A	14.91	-.02	-.13
Sum For Equ	14.46	-.03	-.21
Sum For Equ A	14.96	-.03	-.20
Sum Gwth&inc	14.09	-.03	-.21
Sum Gwth&inc A	14.50	-.03	-.21
US Small Cap	8.44	-.02	-.24
US Small Cap A	8.54	-.01	-.12

fund	valuation	chg	% chg
TRANSAMERICA GROWSAFE3 75/100			
AGF Int Val7510 06/01	4.51	+.00	+.02
AIC AmFoc 7510 06/01	5.07	-.01	-.19
AIC DivCan 7510 06/01	5.38	-.00	-.01
Agg AA GIF 7510	3.63	-.00	-.03
Bal AA GIF 7510	4.47	-.01	-.12
CI Gl Boom 7510 06/01	4.82	-.00	-.10
CI Global 7510 06/01	5.46	-.00	-.01
CanAsian 7510	4.21	-.01	-.14
CanEuro 7510	3.14	+.02	+.75
CanUS 21st 7510	2.86	-.01	-.24
CanUS L Cap7510	4.16	+.02	+.38
Cdn Bal 7510	4.77	-.02	-.46
Cdn Bond 7510	5.91	-.02	-.34
Cdn Equity 7510	3.40	-.03	-.79
Cdn Lg Cap 7510	4.17	-.01	-.35
Cdn MMF 7510	5.29	+.00	+.00
CdnEqVal 7510 06/01	5.62	+.00	+.04
CdnFixPay 7510 06/01	5.67	-.01	-.18
Con AA GIF 7510	4.88	-.01	-.20
Fid Can AA 7510 06/01	5.66	+.03	+.45
Fid IntPort7510 06/01	4.78	-.06	-1.19
Fid TrueNrt7510 06/01	5.75	+.01	+.19
Grow AA GIF7510	4.11	-.00	-.06
MacIvyGwinc7510 06/01	5.68	+.01	+.17
TD Div Inc 7510 06/01	6.12	-.00	-.03
TOP AggrGw 7510 06/01	3.66	+.01	+.24
TOP Bal 7510 06/01	4.50	+.01	+.19
TOP CdnMgr 7510 06/01	5.75	+.00	+.02
TOP Cons 7510 06/01	5.00	+.01	+.14
TOP GloMgr 7510 06/01	4.89	+.01	+.13
TOP GloSect7510 06/01	4.90	+.01	+.29
TOP Growth 7510 06/01	4.24	+.01	+.20
TOP USMgrs 7510 06/01	4.80	+.02	+.39
US EqVal 7510 06/01	5.74	+.03	+.47
US Equity 7510	3.68	-.00	-.01

3.5 Refer to Table 3.11 (on page 61), which shows the stock summary data for companies with names starting with the letter A that were traded on the NASDAQ on May 8, 2008. The data was taken from the *Financial Post Magazine*'s Web site, (*http://www.financialpost.com/markets/market-data/market-nasdaq.html?tmp=nasdaq*).

Using the data listed in Table 3.11, construct stem-and-leaf displays for the following data:

a. Volume
b. High/ask price
c. Low/bid price
d. Close/previous price
e. Net change
f. 52 week high price
g. 52 week low price

TABLE 3.9   FP 500 Ranking of Canada's Companies

FINANCIAL POST
BUSINESS   FP500

Home FP500 Rankings Crown Corps Profit Leaders Largest Subsidiaries Buy the database

Last year's FP500 rankings   **Canada's Top Companies 2008**   *Search*

First · Previous 1 - 50 ▾ Next · Last

Ranking				Revenue		Profit		
2007	2006	Company		Amt. 2007 (x1000)	Change	Amt. 2007 (x1000)	Change	Rank
1	1	Royal Bank of Canada, Toronto (Oc07)	⮥	$41,307,000	14.6%	$5,492,000	16.2%	2
2	2	Manulife Financial Corp., Toronto	⮥	$35,533,000	3.9%	$4,229,000	6.5%	6
▲ 3	4	George Weston Ltd., Toronto	⮥	$32,815,000	2.0%	$563,000	365.3%	61
▼ 4	3	General Motors of Canada Ltd., Oshawa, Ont.	⮥	$31,675,000	-5.0%	-	-	-
5	5	Power Corp. of Canada, Montreal	⮥	$29,408,000	-3.0%	$1,463,000	5.0%	28
6	6	Magna International Inc.*, Aurora, Ont.	⮥	$27,995,958	2.1%	$712,062	18.9%	52
7	7	Alcan Inc.*, Montreal (De06)	⮥	$26,808,894	8.9%	$2,029,860	1199.4%	22
▲ 8	10	The Bank of Nova Scotia, Halifax (Oc07)	⮥	$26,427,000	17.5%	$4,045,000	13.0%	8
▲ 9	11	The Toronto-Dominion Bank, Toronto (Oc07)	⮥	$25,209,000	13.0%	$3,997,000	-13.2%	9
▼ 10	8	Imperial Oil Ltd., Calgary	⮥	$25,069,000	2.3%	$3,188,000	4.7%	12
▲ 11	15	Onex Corp., Toronto	⮥	$23,433,000	25.8%	$228,000	-77.2%	119
▲ 12	13	Canadian Imperial Bank of Commerce, Toronto (Oc07)	⮥	$23,289,000	15.5%	$3,296,000	24.6%	10
▲ 13	16	EnCana Corp.*, Calgary	⮥	$23,033,004	23.9%	$4,251,966	-33.7%	5
14	14	Petro-Canada, Calgary	⮥	$21,710,000	14.8%	$2,733,000	57.1%	15
▼ 15	9	Sun Life Financial Inc., Toronto	⮥	$21,188,000	-12.8%	$2,290,000	6.8%	17
▼ 16	12	Chrysler Canada Inc., Windsor, Ont. (De06)	⮥	$20,534,000	-1.4%	-	-	-
17	17	Bank of Montreal, Montreal (Oc07)	⮥	$20,344,000	12.1%	$2,131,000	-20.0%	20
▲ 18	19	Bombardier Inc.*, Montreal (Ja08)	⮥	$18,538,854	10.1%	$335,703	10.3%	98
▼ 19	18	BCE Inc., Montreal	⮥	$17,866,000	0.9%	$4,057,000	102.1%	7
▲ 20	21	Suncor Energy Inc., Calgary	⮥	$17,212,000	20.0%	$2,832,000	-4.7%	14
▲ 21	27	Husky Energy Inc., Calgary	⮥	$15,518,000	22.5%	$3,214,000	17.9%	11

Source: http://www.financialpost.com/magazine/fp500/list.html

TABLE 3.10   FORTUNE 1,000: Telecommunications Industry Annual Ranking of America's Largest Corporations by Revenues, Profits

Rank	Company	1,000 revenues rank	REVENUES $ millions	REVENUES % change from 2005	PROFITS $ millions	PROFITS % change from 2005
1	Verizon Communications	13	93,221	24	6,197	−16
2	AT&T	27	63,055	44	7,356	54
3	Sprint Nextel	53	43,531	26	1,329	−26
4	Comcast	84	25,700	15	2,533	173
5	DIRECTV Group	160	14,756	12	1,420	323
6	Qwest Communications	178	13,923	0	593	N.A.
7	Echostar Communications	252	9,818	17	608	−60
8	Alltel	256	9,723	2	1,129	−15
9	Liberty Global	340	6,813	29	706	N.A.
10	Virgin Media	347	6,637	83	−984	−228
11	Cablevision Systems	380	6,007	15	−126	−234
12	Charter Communications	409	5,613	7	−1,370	N.A.
13	Level 3 Communications	465	4,778	30	−744	N.A.
14	Telephone & Data Sys.	501	4,266	8	339	52
15	IDT	755	2,452	−1	−179	N.A.
16	CenturyTel	757	2,448	−1	370	11
17	NII Holdings	772	2,371	36	294	68
18	Citizens Communications	825	2,126	−2	345	70

From the April 30th, 2007, issue
Source: http://money.cnn.com/magazines/fortune/fortune500/

TABLE 3.11   Stock Summary Data for Companies with Names Starting with the Letter A That Were Traded on the NASDAQ.

Company	Security	Ticker	Volume	High/ Ask	Low/ Bid	Close/ Previous	Net Change	52 Week High	52 Week Low
A-Power Energy Generation	com	APWR	223,539	10.88	10.09	10.75	+0.73	31.80	3.00
AAON Inc	com	AAON	41,035	21.05	20.62	21.00	+0.50	23.00	12.79
ABIOMED Inc	com	ABMD	93,186	6.98	6.58	6.98	+0.33	20.06	4.67
AC Moore Arts & Crafts	com	ACMR	15,187	3.39	3.26	3.36	−0.01	8.78	0.71
ACADIA Phrmctcls Inc	com	ACAD	84,387	1.94	1.75	1.81	+0.07	8.84	0.73
ACI Worldwide Inc	com	ACIW	194,814	14.33	13.98	14.13	+0.09	22.49	8.86
ADA-ES Inc	com	ADES	900	3.95	3.80	3.86	+0.01	11.98	2.41
ADAM Inc	com	ADAM	3,198	3.33	3.14	3.31	+0.08	7.80	1.96
ADC Telecommuns Inc	com	ADCT	997,080	7.54	7.09	7.43	−0.11	17.45	2.48
ADTRAN Inc	com	ADTN	264,258	20.37	19.56	19.94	+0.19	26.50	12.14
AEP Industries Inc	com	AEPI	15,482	24.63	21.68	23.00	+1.54	28.58	10.43
AEterna Zentaris Inc	com	AEZS	40,060	1.33	1.24	1.32	+0.06	1.48	0.261
AFC Enterprises Inc	com	AFCE	45,533	6.06	5.33	5.62	−0.17	10.14	2.85
AMAG Pharmaceuticals Inc	com	AMAG	155,664	54.65	52.73	54.54	+1.86	55.00	18.33
AMCORE Financial Inc	com	AMFI	12,981	1.40	1.30	1.38	+0.12	14.50	0.59
AMERCO	com	UHAL	14,552	33.45	31.64	33.20	+1.30	59.85	22.01
AMERISAFE Inc	com	AMSF	83,309	17.81	16.85	17.78	+1.00	21.96	12.51
AMICAS Inc	com	AMCS	2,099	2.59	2.44	2.48	+0.01	2.96	1.27
ANADIGICS Inc	com	ANAD	176,563	3.04	2.86	3.04	+0.13	13.94	1.13
ANSYS Inc	com	ANSS	296,247	27.11	26.20	26.65	−0.06	49.81	18.00

Source: http://www.financialpost.com/markets/market-data/commodity-cash_prices.html?tmp=cash_prices

3.6 Frequency Distribution

In this section you will learn to group a set of **quantitative** data into a frequency distribution. Frequency distributions are often used to group data in the form of a table, which gives a general idea of how the data values are being distributed. An advantage of using a frequency distribution is that it can handle a large (typically more than 50) data set. You have to familiarize yourself with the rules and conventions introduced in this chapter to construct your frequency distribution. The guidelines given in this chapter will be useful for a person just learning to make a frequency distribution or for getting a general impression about the distribution of the data. If one has experience and is intimately familiar with the data being organized, several of these general guidelines may not be appropriate.

The following is an example of a frequency distribution displaying the baggage weight for passengers travelling by air.

FIGURE 3.2

Frequency distribution for baggage weight data for passengers travelling by air

Baggage Weight (kg)	Number of passengers
20.0 and under 25.0	4
25.0 and under 30.0	13
30.0 and under 35.0	7
35.0 and under 40.0	4
40.0 and under 45.0	1
45.0 and under 50.0	0
50.0 and under 55.0	1
Total	30

Now, let's learn the general guidelines and how to apply them to construct a frequency distribution as shown in Figure 3.2.

General Guidelines for Constructing a Frequency Distribution

If one has experience and is intimately familiar with the data being organized, several of these general guidelines may not be appropriate.

The frequency distribution for baggage weight data is shown in Figure 3.2 above. The data is grouped into seven **classes** (also known as intervals). The class width for each class is 5 kg. You should know how many classes to use and what class width to apply to your frequency distribution. Before you learn to construct the frequency distribution, you must familiarize yourself with the following guidelines.

1. **Number of classes:** You should not have too few or too **many** classes. For the questions you will solve in this course you should use **5 to 10 classes** in your final constructed frequency distribution.
2. **Notation for indicating classes:** There are several possible notations that are used to designate the classes. In this course we will use the **"and under"** notation (e.g., 260 and under 270). The numerical values used in designating the classes when using the "and under" notation are called **boundaries**.

   You will also likely come across classes that have been set up using the "to" notation (e.g., 260 to 269).

3. **Close-ended classes:** A close-ended class has both a lower and an upper boundary. An open-ended class is missing one of these boundaries. For example, the class "100 and over" is an open-ended class because there is no upper boundary. You should avoid using open-ended classes in this course.

In this course, I do not want you to use "open-ended" classes. I want you to learn the basic rules to construct your frequency distribution—just keep it simple. However, it is not incorrect to use open-ended classes.

Statistics Canada uses open-ended classes in the following frequency distribution of family income by family type.

Family income, by family type (Couple families)					
	2005	2006	2007	2008	2009
	Couple families[1] number of families				
Total, all income groups	7,486,160	7,629,330	7,727,870	7,832,060	7,926,210
Under $10,000	177,840	217,430	198,050	194,670	199,350
$10,000 and over	7,308,320	7,411,900	7,529,820	7,637,400	7,726,860
$15,000 and over	7,180,180	7,291,650	7,416,270	7,527,140	7,613,770
$20,000 and over	6,996,720	7,125,340	7,258,770	7,374,900	7,459,680
$25,000 and over	6,721,450	6,887,120	7,043,530	7,177,060	7,262,910
$30,000 and over	6,370,220	6,552,870	6,734,300	6,876,780	6,958,650
$35,000 and over	6,024,090	6,211,130	6,398,830	6,549,220	6,620,770
$40,000 and over	5,670,370	5,869,210	6,068,570	6,228,650	6,288,200
$45,000 and over	5,313,550	5,524,280	5,734,370	5,900,920	5,949,750
$50,000 and over	4,956,970	5,179,120	5,397,900	5,571,420	5,611,520
$60,000 and over	4,255,720	4,495,550	4,727,730	4,915,080	4,939,370
$70,000 and over	3,589,990	3,838,200	4,077,940	4,277,270	4,292,660
$75,000 and over	3,277,060	3,526,720	3,767,350	3,969,160	3,982,590
$80,000 and over	2,981,070	3,229,670	3,469,550	3,672,840	3,684,990
$90,000 and over	2,443,620	2,684,680	2,915,800	3,119,370	3,129,560
$100,000 and over	1,985,270	2,210,990	2,430,210	2,626,660	2,636,310
$150,000 and over	703,730	824,840	947,310	1,063,240	1,072,990
$200,000 and over	310,260	368,150	424,320	476,110	476,050
$250,000 and over	177,410	209,710	238,760	261,300	256,550

Source: http://www40.statcan.ca/id/cst/FAMIL106A-eng.htm

4. Class width (denoted as CW): A class that has an *upper* and a *lower* boundary has a finite class width. The class width is determined by the following formula:

$$\text{Class Width} = \text{Upper boundary} - \text{Lower boundary}$$

It is best to select a class width that is an "easy" number to work with. The recommended class widths are shown in Table 3.12.

TABLE 3.12

A List of "Nice" Numbers

For narrower classes				For wider classes		
◄— Divide by 10				Multiply by 10 —►		
	0.01	0.1	1	10	100	
	0.02	0.2	2	20	200	
Etc.	0.025	0.25 (if the data has at least 2 decimals)	2.5 (if the data has at least one decimal)	25	250	Etc.
	0.05	0.5	5	50	500	

Note: In this course, when you are asked to construct a frequency distribution, all classes must have the **same class width**.

5. **No gaps between classes:** Classes are mutually exclusive and are not overlapping. In other words, every possible value must fall into exactly one class. There must be **no gaps** between the classes (i.e., the upper boundary of one class will also be the lower boundary of the next class).

6. **All classes must have the same class width:** When working with continuous data, the upper boundary of one class and the lower boundary of the following class reference the same value. Since the boundary value should fall into only one class, the wording "and under" can be used to clarify that the upper boundaries are not included in the classes. This usage is demonstrated in the next example. To keep it simple, use equal class width for each class. The class width in the following frequency distribution is $20 - 10 = 10$. The frequency distribution has 6 classes with a class width of 10 in each class.

Class	Frequency
10 and under 20	2
20 and under 30	1
30 and under 40	3
40 and under 50	11
50 and under 60	16
60 and under 70	7

7. **The first and last class must contain frequencies:** The lowest value (or minimum value) is in the first class, and the highest value (or maximum value) is in the last class.

8. **Boundaries:** There are several guidelines that should be used to determine the actual numerical values of the boundaries.

   a) The boundaries should *look like* the data, that is, have the same number of decimal places as the data. If the data have one decimal point, then the boundaries should have one decimal point. If the data are whole numbers, then the boundaries should be whole numbers. The reason for having this rule is to retain the information about the type of quantitative data. When we grouped the data, we lost the information about the nature of the data. With the grouped data in the form of a frequency distribution, we only know how many values (i.e., frequency) fall in each class.

   b) Each boundary should be a **multiple** of the chosen class width.

   Example: If the class width is 5 then the boundaries should be a multiple of 5. Then the possible values for your boundaries are 0, 5, 10, 15, 20, 25, 30, 35, 40, 45, 50, etc., which are multiples of 5.

   If the class width is 10 then the boundaries should be multiples of 10. Then the possible values for your boundaries are 0, 10, 20, 30, 40, 50, 60, etc., which are multiples of 10.

Pick a Nice Number for the Class Width

"Nice" numbers are listed in Table 3.12. Always start off with this list of 4 numbers: **1, 2, 2.5, 5**. If you want a larger class width, you can multiply each number in the list of **1, 2, 2.5, 5** by 10 and you will have **10, 20, 25, 50**. If you still want a larger class width, multiply again by 10 and you have **100, 200, 250, 500**. If you want a smaller class width, divide each number in the list of **1, 2, 2.5, 5** by 10 and you have **0.1, 0.2 0.25, 0.5**. If you still want a smaller class width, divide again by 10 and you have **0.01, 0.02, 0.025, 0.05**.

Determine Class Width

To figure out the class width in your frequency distribution, you should estimate the class width using the following formula with the highest value (or maximum value) and lowest value (or minimum value) in a date set. Divide the difference by the minimum number of classes specified by the guideline. The minimum number of classes is 5. The value you obtained is called the "estimated class width" because this value rarely turns out to be 1, 2, 2.5 or 5 (the "nice" numbers).

$$\text{Estimated Class Width} = \frac{\text{Highest value} - \text{Lowest value}}{\text{Minimum number of classes recommended}}$$

$$\text{Estimated Class Width} = \frac{\text{Highest value} - \text{Lowest value}}{5}$$

Choose one of the two recommended class widths (i.e., from a list of "nice" numbers) that enclose the estimated class width. For example, if the estimated class width is 15.3, you may choose either 10 or 20. Whichever class width you choose to construct your frequency distribution, you must always check that the number of classes is between 5 and 10 classes.

Demonstration on How to Select a "Nice" Number for the Class Width

You only need two pieces of information to construct the classes in your frequency distribution —the minimum (also known as lowest) and maximum (or highest) values. To construct the frequency column of the frequency distribution, you need the data values.

EXAMPLE 3.5

Given the lowest value 684 and the highest value 1093, calculate the estimated class width using the formula.

$$\textit{Estimated Class Width} = \frac{(1093 - 684)}{5} = 81.8$$

Now let's select the "nice" numbers as shown next.

Start with this list of numbers	Multiply by 10	Multiply by 10 again
1	10	(100)
2	20	200
2.5	25	250
5	(50)	500
Since **81.8** is not in this list, let's move to the next list.	**81.8** is between 50 and 100; thus you will pick either 50 or 100 to construct your classes.	

The estimated class width is **81.8,** and this value falls between two nice numbers, which are 50 and 100. After you have picked the two "nice" numbers from the list, you have to make sure that the number of classes is between 5 and 10. The first class should contain the lowest data value, and the last class should contain the highest data value. To obtain the first class **lower boundary**, find the greatest multiple of the class width that is less than or equal to the minimum data value.

Let's start with the class width of 50 (i.e., CW = 50) to construct the classes. The lower boundary is 650 because 650 is the greatest multiple of 50 that is less than or equal to 684. So the first class would be "650 and under 700."

Using CW = 50, you have the following classes:
650 and under 700 (includes the minimum value) is called the first class.
700 and under 750
750 and under 800
800 and under 850
850 and under 900
900 and under 950
950 and under 1000
1000 and under 1050
1050 and under 1100 (includes the maximum value) is called the last class.

There are a total of 9 classes, which meets the guideline (i.e., number of classes are between 5 and 10).

Now use the class width of 100 (i.e., CW = 100) to construct the classes. The lower boundary is 600 because 600 is the greatest multiple of 100 that is less than or equal to 684. You cannot use 680 because 680 is not a multiple of 100. The first class would be "600 and under 700."

600 and under 700 (includes the minimum value = 684)
700 and under 800
800 and under 900
900 and under 1000
1000 and under 1100 (includes the maximum value = 1093)

There are a total of 5 classes, which meets the guidelines.

The results are summarized in Table 3.13.

TABLE 3.13

Summary of the Classes Using the Same Set of Data with Two Class Widths

No	CW = 50	CW = 100
1	650 and under 700	600 and under 700
2	700 and under 750	700 and under 800
3	750 and under 800	800 and under 900
4	800 and under 850	900 and under 1000
5	850 and under 900	1000 and under 1100
6	900 and under 950	
7	950 and under 1000	
8	1000 and under 1050	
9	1050 and under 1100	

If you use CW = 50, you end up with 9 classes (refer to Table 3.13).
If you use CW = 100, you end up with 5 classes (refer to Table 3.13).

For this set of data, you have two class widths that you can use to group your data. Both resulting frequency distributions are correct.

Issues about Picking the Correct Class Width

Recall the guideline that instructs that the boundaries should *look like* the data. In the basic list of "nice" numbers, there is a class width of **2.5** that has one decimal place, but you should not use this class width for whole number data.

Question: Can I only use a nice number with one decimal place if my data only have one decimal place?

The answer is yes; for example, you may use the following nice numbers for your class width: 0.1, 0.2, 0.5, and 2.5. You may not use 0.25 because the data have one decimal place. However, you can use 0.25 if the data have two decimal places.

Symbols: L = Lowest and H = Highest

EXAMPLE 3.6

How to pick the class width with data that have no decimal.

I.   Data: 3   8   10   11   14

L = 3 and H = 14
Estimated CW = (14 – 3) / 5 = 2.2
Estimated CW = 2.2 falls between 2 and 2.5
You cannot use 2.5 as class width because the data has no decimal; you should pick either 2 or 5. Again, you should check that the class widths comply with the guideline (i.e., number of classes are between 5 and 10).

II. Data: 25   67   87   117   164

L = 25 and H = 164
Estimated CW = (164 – 25) / 5 = 27.8
Estimated CW = 27.8 falls between 25 and 50
You can use either 25 or 50, but you have to check that the class widths comply with the guideline.

EXAMPLE 3.7

How to pick the class width with data that have one decimal place.

I.   Data with one decimal: 1.4   4.6   8.7   11.7   14.9

L = 1.4 and H = 14.9
Estimated CW = (14.9 – 1.4) / 5 = 2.7
Estimated CW = 2.7 falls between 2.5 and 5
You can use either 2.5 or 5. The class width of 5 is a whole number. To comply with the guideline, you show 5.0 instead of 5, but you have to check that the number of classes is between 5 and 10 (according to the guideline).

II. Data with one decimal: 13.4   45.7   87.4   106.5   149.5

L = 13.4 H = 149.5
Estimated CW = (149.5 – 13.4) / 5 = 27.22
Estimated CW = 27.22 falls between 25 and 50
You can use either 25 or 50, but now 25 will be 25.0 and
50 will be 50.0. After you decide which CW to use, you should check that the number of classes are between 5 and 10 (i.e., the boundaries must reflect one decimal, 0.0 and under 25.0). Again, you have to check that the number of classes is between 5 and 10.

EXAMPLE 3.8

How to pick the class width with data that have two decimal places.

I.   Data: 1.34   4.57   8.74   10.65   14.95

L = 1.34 and H = 14.95
Estimated CW = (14.95 – 1.34) / 5 = 2.722
Estimated CW = 2.722 falls between 2.5 and 5

You still can use both 2.5 and 5, but now they are 2.50 and 5.00. Again, you have to check that the number of classes is between 5 and 10.

II. Data with two decimal places: 0.25   0.67   0.87   1.17   1.64

L = 0.25 and H = 1.64
Estimated CW = (1.64 – 0.25) / 5 = 0.278
Estimated CW = 0.278 falls between 0.25 and 0.5
You can use either 0.25 or 0.50, but you have to check that that the number of classes is between 5 and 10.

EXAMPLE 3.9

How to pick the class width with data that have three decimals.

Data: 0.134   0.457   0.874   1.065   1.553

L = 0.134 and H = 1.553
Estimated CW = (1.553 – 0.134) / 5 = 0.2838
Estimated CW = 0.2838 falls between 0.25 and 0.5
You still can use 0.25 and 0.5, but now they are 0.250 and 0.500, respectively. Again, you have to check that the number of classes is between 5 and 10.

Test Your Understanding

In a data set, the lowest value (or minimum value) is 112, and the highest value (or maximum value) is 196.

Question 1: What class width(s) did you use in your completed frequency distribution?

        A. 10
        B. 20
        C. 25
        D. 50
        E. Both a and b

Answer: E

Question 2: What are the number of classes in your completed frequency distribution? Which of the following statements is false?

        A. If you use CW = 10, you would have 9 classes
        B. If you use CW = 20, you would have 5 classes
        C. If you use CW = 25, you would have 5 classes
        D. There is insufficient number of classes if you use CW = 25.

Answer: C

Question 3: Suppose you use CW = 50. What is the first class in your completed frequency distribution?

        A. 0 and under 50
        B. 50 and under 100
        C. 100 and under 150
        D. 110 and under 160
        E. 112 and under 162

Answer: C

Please note that CW = 50 doesn't comply with the guideline. Therefore, you should not use CW = 50 to group your data. This question is only used to test your understanding of obtaining the first class in your data set.

Construct a Frequency Distribution with an Example

Use this example to construct a frequency distribution.

Airlines charge passengers an excess baggage fee for any checked baggage whose weight exceeds a specified limit. A study was conducted to observe how many passengers are being charged with the excess baggage fees. We have taken a random sample of 30 passengers from the airline check-in counter. Their checked baggage weights (measured in kilograms) were recorded as shown next:

25.0 42.9 29.4 25.9 28.7 24.5 30.9 30.5 27.8 28.9 22.8 31.5 23.6 39.5 28.1
31.5 28.1 39.6 27.4 28.9 36.6 25.4 26.9 53.9 33.5 22.5 38.4 26.8 32.4 34.9

The data on baggage weights are classified as quantitative and continuous data. The data have one decimal place.

Next, use the data to construct a frequency distribution by using the following steps.

Step 1: Sort the baggage weights data in ascending order.

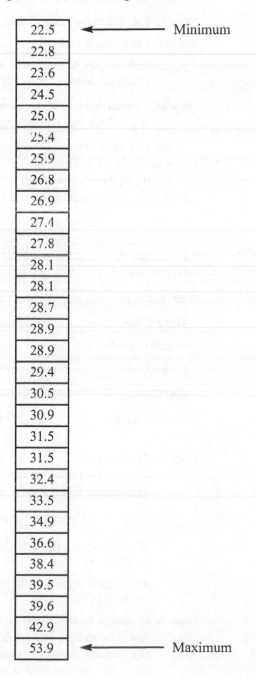

Step 2: Obtain the maximum (highest) and minimum (lowest) values in the data set.

Minimum $= 22.5$
Maximum $= 53.9$

Step 3: Estimate the class width by taking the difference between maximum and minimum values and then dividing it by 5.

$$Estimated\ Class\ Width = \frac{(Maximum - Minimum)}{Minimum\ number\ of\ classes\ recommended}$$

$$Estimated\ Class\ Width = \frac{(53.9 - 22.5)}{5} = 6.28$$

Step 4: Pick two nice numbers from Table 3.12 as class widths to construct the class intervals.

The list of nice numbers is 1, 2, 2.5, 5, 10, 20, 25, 50, etc.

The estimated class width of 6.28 falls between 5 and 10.

Step 5: Use the "nice" class widths to construct the classes and make sure that the number of classes is between 5 and 10.

You can use either 5 or10 to construct the boundaries. Then check that the number of classes is between 5 and 10.

Step 6: To obtain the first class **lower boundary**, pick the greatest multiple of the class width that is less than or equal to the minimum data value.

For a class width of 5, the first class lower boundary is 20, which is less than 22.6. 20 is also a multiple of 5 ($20 \div 5 = 4$, that is, 4 times the class width of 5).

Similarly, for a class width of 10, the first class lower boundary is 20, which is less than 22.6 and is also a multiple of 10 ($20 \div 10 = 2$, that is, 2 times the class width of 10).

TABLE 3.14

Class Intervals for Class Widths 5 and 10

	If you use a class width of 5, then the class intervals are	If you use a class width of 10, then the class intervals are
First Class	20 and under 25	20 and under 30
Second Class	25 and under 30	30 and under 40
Third Class	30 and under 35	40 and under 50
Fourth Class	35 and under 40	50 and under 60
Fifth Class	40 and under 45	
Sixth Class	45 and under 50	
Seventh Class	50 and under 55	

Step 7: To obtain the first class **upper boundary**, add the class width to the lower boundary to form the upper boundary of the first class. At this point check to see that the minimum value is included in the first class interval.

Upper Boundary $=$ Lower Boundary $+$ Class Width

For a class width of 5, the first class upper boundary $= 20 + 5 = 25$ (as shown in Table 3.14)

For a class width of 10, the first class upper boundary $= 20 + 10 = 30$ (as shown in Table 3.14)

Step 8: Continue to construct the rest of the class intervals by adding the class width to the lower boundary. The upper boundary of the first class becomes the lower boundary of the second class and continues to calculate the rest of the boundaries using the formula just shown. Stop when the last class interval includes the maximum value.

As shown in Table 3.14, we have a total of 7 classes with a class width of 5. For a class width of 10, we have a total of 4 classes.

Step 9: Make sure that the class intervals and boundaries meet the guidelines.

Refer to the guidelines to construct a frequency distribution.

1. **Check the number of classes.** The number of classes you should use is between 5 and 10. Therefore, you can only use a class width of 5 because you have 7 classes in total. If you use a class width of 10, you only have 4 classes, which violates the guideline. If you have too few classes, you can narrow the class width to increase the number of classes.

Thus, you have

baggage weights (measured in kilograms)
20 and under 25
25 and under 30
30 and under 35
35 and under 40
40 and under 45
45 and under 50
50 and under 55

2. **Check that you use "and under" for the classes.**
3. **Check that you use close-ended classes.**
4. **Check the class width.** The class width is a nice number. CW=5 is in the list of "nice" numbers.
5. **Check that there is no gap between classes.**
6. **Check that all classes have the same class width.**
7. **Check the boundaries.**
   a) **The boundaries should look like the data.** The data has one decimal point and therefore the boundaries should have one decimal point. Thus, you have

baggage weights (measured in kilograms)
20.0 and under 25.0
25.0 and under 30.0
30.0 and under 35.0
35.0 and under 40.0
40.0 and under 45.0
45.0 and under 50.0
50.0 and under 55.0

   b) **Each boundary must be a multiple of 5** (which is the selected class width to construct your frequency distribution).
   c) **Boundaries between classes have no gaps.** The upper boundary of the first class becomes the lower boundary of the second class. Thus, there is no gap between classes.

Step 10: To construct the frequencies, you have to count the data and put them into the respective class intervals.

Use the sorted data to put the data values into their respective classes as illustrated next.

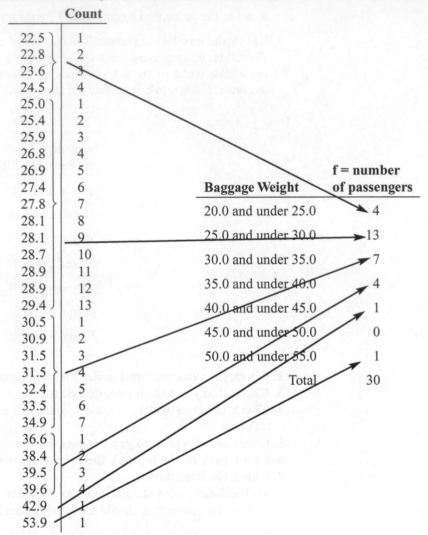

Count	
22.5	1
22.8	2
23.6	3
24.5	4
25.0	1
25.4	2
25.9	3
26.8	4
26.9	5
27.4	6
27.8	7
28.1	8
28.1	9
28.7	10
28.9	11
28.9	12
29.4	13
30.5	1
30.9	2
31.5	3
31.5	4
32.4	5
33.5	6
34.9	7
36.6	1
38.4	2
39.5	3
39.6	4
42.9	1
53.9	1

Baggage Weight	f = number of passengers
20.0 and under 25.0	4
25.0 and under 30.0	13
30.0 and under 35.0	7
35.0 and under 40.0	4
40.0 and under 45.0	1
45.0 and under 50.0	0
50.0 and under 55.0	1
Total	30

Note: It is recommended to total the frequencies.

To recap how you construct the frequency distribution:

Referring back to our baggage weight data, you will see that the frequency distribution shown next follows all the recommended guidelines.

FIGURE 3.3

Frequency distribution of baggage weights measured in kgs

Baggage Weight	f = number of passengers
20.0 and under 25.0	4
25.0 and under 30.0	13
30.0 and under 35.0	7
35.0 and under 40.0	4
40.0 and under 45.0	1
45.0 and under 50.0	0
50.0 and under 55.0	1
Total	30

Note: f denotes "frequency"

Your frequency distribution should have proper titles such as "baggage weight," "number of passengers," "percent of passengers," etc. An observer looking at your frequency distribution would understand what you are presenting without having to ask what "frequency," "percent," and "class" stand for. Any graph or chart that you create must have a proper title. In the future, pay attention to the graphs and charts presented in any magazine or newspaper. You will notice that they have proper titles and labelling to explain the data being presented.

Application of Frequency Distribution

By observing the frequencies in the distribution, you can see that most of the data are close to the target values between 25 and 30 kilograms, and there are fewer and fewer data values as we move farther away from the target on the high and low sides.

Frequency distributions are often used to summarize data and give a general idea of where the data values are located. They also give an indication as to the **"shape"** of a set of data.

EXAMPLE 3.10   Consider the following set of data on the GPA scores for a sample of 98 students:

TABLE 3.15

3.56	3.46	3.48	3.50	3.42	3.43	3.52
3.49	3.44	3.50	3.48	3.56	3.50	3.52
3.47	3.48	3.46	3.50	3.56	3.38	3.41
3.37	3.47	3.49	3.45	3.44	3.50	3.49
3.46	3.46	3.55	3.52	3.44	3.50	3.45
3.44	3.48	3.46	3.52	3.46	3.48	3.48
3.32	3.40	3.52	3.34	3.46	3.43	*3.30*
3.46	3.59	3.63	3.59	3.47	3.38	3.52
3.45	3.48	3.31	3.46	3.40	3.54	3.46
3.51	3.48	3.50	*3.68*	3.60	3.46	3.52
3.48	3.50	3.56	3.50	3.52	3.46	3.48
3.46	3.52	3.56	3.52	3.48	3.46	3.45
3.46	3.54	3.54	3.48	3.49	3.41	3.41
3.45	3.34	3.44	3.47	3.47	3.41	3.48

Step 1: Sort your raw data.

Step 2: Obtain the maximum (highest) and minimum (lowest) values in the data set.

Minimum = 3.30
Maximum = 3.68

Step 3: Estimate the class width by dividing the difference between the maximum and minimum values by the minimum number of classes.

$$Estimated\ Class\ Width = \frac{(Maximum - Minimum)}{Minimum\ number\ of\ classes\ recommended}$$

$$Estimated\ Class\ Width = \frac{(3.68 - 3.30)}{5} = 0.076$$

Step 4: Pick a nice number from Table 3.16 as a class width to construct the class intervals. A list of nice numbers are

TABLE 3.16

"Nice" Class Width		
0.01	(0.1)	1
0.02	0.2	2
0.025	0.25	2.5
(0.05)	0.5	5

The estimated class width of 0.076 falls between 0.05 and 0.1. In the next step, you may use these two nice numbers to construct the classes and then make sure that that the number of classes is between 5 and 10.

Step 5: Use the "nice" class width to construct the classes and make sure that the number of classes is between 5 and 10.

Step 6: To obtain the first class **lower boundary**, find the greatest multiple of the class width that is less than or equal to the minimum data value.

For a class width of 0.05, the first class lower boundary is 3.30, as it is a multiple of 0.05. Similarly, for a class width of 0.1, the first class lower boundary is 3.30, as it is a multiple of 0.1 (3.3 ÷ 0.1 = 33, i.e. 33 times of class width of 0.1).

TABLE 3.17

Class Intervals for Class Widths 0.05 and 0.1

	If you use a class width of 0.05, then the class intervals are	If you use a class width of 0.1, then the class intervals are
First Class	3.30 and under 3.35	3.30 and under 3.40
Second Class	3.35 and under 3.40	3.40 and under 3.50
Third Class	3.45 and under 3.50	3.50 and under 3.60
Fourth Class	3.50 and under 3.55	3.60 and under 3.70
Fifth Class	3.55 and under 3.60	
Sixth Class	3.60 and under 3.65	Note: A total of 4 classes (i.e., not enough classes)
Seventh Class	3.65 and under 3.70	
	Note: A total of 7 classes	

An appropriate frequency distribution would be as follows:

GPA Scores	f = number of students
3.30 and under 3.35	4
3.35 " " 3.40	3
3.40 " " 3.45	15
3.45 " " 3.50	42
3.50 " " 3.55	23
3.55 " " 3.60	8
3.60 " " 3.65	2
3.65 " " 3.70	1

Relative Frequency or Percentage Distributions

Consider the following frequency distributions of manufacturing personnel salaries at ABC Inc. and XYZ Inc.

Salary ($000)	ABC Inc. Number of Employees	XYZ Inc. Number of Employees
20 and under 25	24	10
25 and under 30	41	23
30 and under 35	44	31
35 and under 40	29	14
40 and under 45	15	8
45 and under 50	7	2

Notice that there is a large difference in the number of manufacturing employees in the two companies; therefore, it is difficult to compare the salary distributions by looking at the frequencies.

If you were to set up a **relative frequency** or **percentage** distribution for the two sets of salaries, it would be much easier to make comparisons.

Salary ($000)	ABC Inc.			XYZ Inc.		
	f	rf	%	f	rf	%
20 and under 25	24	0.150	15.0	10	0.114	11.4
25 " " 30	41	0.256	25.6	23	0.261	26.1
30 " " 35	44	0.275	27.5	31	0.352	35.2
35 " " 40	29	0.181	18.1	14	0.159	15.9
40 " " 45	15	0.094	9.4	8	0.091	9.1
45 " " 50	7	0.044	4.4	2	0.023	2.3
Total	160	1.000	100.0	88	1.000	100.0

Notations: f denotes "frequency" (the number of values); rf denotes "relative frequency"

To calculate the relative frequency, use the formula

$$Relative\ Frequency\ (rf) = \frac{Frequency\ (f)}{n}$$

where n denotes sample size (or total number of values).

The relative frequency is also known as proportion of values. The percentage distribution is produced by multiplying the relative frequency in each class by 100.

$$Percentage\ of\ Frequency\ (\%) = \left(\frac{Frequency\ (f)}{n} \right) + 100$$

Note: You will use a maximum of 3 decimals for rf and thus 1 decimal for %.

a) The relative frequency distribution

Use the frequency distribution of baggage weights to create the following relative frequency distribution.

Baggage Weight	f = number of passengers	rf = relative frequency = proportion of passengers
20.0 and under 25.0	4	4/30 = 0.133
25.0 and under 30.0	13	13/30 = 0.433
30.0 and under 35.0	7	7/30 = 0.233
35.0 and under 40.0	4	4/30 = 0.133
40.0 and under 45.0	1	1/30 = 0.033
45.0 and under 50.0	0	0/30 = 0
50.0 and under 55.0	1	1/30 = 0.033
Total	30	

b) The percentage distribution

Use the frequency distribution of baggage weights to create the following percentage distribution.

Baggage Weight	f = number of passengers	Percentage of passengers (%)
20.0 and under 25.0	4	4/30 = 0.133*100 = 13.3
25.0 and under 30.0	13	13/30 = 0.433*100 = 43.3
30.0 and under 35.0	7	7/30 = 0.233*100 = 23.3
35.0 and under 40.0	4	4/30 = 0.133*100 = 13.3
40.0 and under 45.0	1	1/30 = 0.033*100 = 3.3
45.0 and under 50.0	0	0/30 = 0
50.0 and under 55.0	1	1/30 = 0.033*100=3.3
Total	30	

Graphing a Frequency Distribution

I.   Graph a histogram

Histogram: A histogram is a graph of "touching rectangles." The horizontal axis represents the class boundaries. No other values are shown on this axis. The vertical axis shows the class frequencies (or relative frequency or percentage). The above rules only apply to histograms where the classes are all of equal width. We are not concerned in this course with how to draw other types of histograms.

EXAMPLE 3.11

The high-voltage output of a certain power supply that is to be used in copying machines must be 300 ± 50 volts (i.e., from 250 to 350 volts). In setting up a quality control chart, data from a sample of 125 power supplies is to be used. The results are given as follows:

333	297	285	300	279	311	298	300	305	262
289	315	305	302	273	282	313	330	300	271
303	330	290	291	300	290	340	293	309	287
292	312	295	296	302	308	268	296	294	306
295	320	322	328	326	316	290	291	320	315
301	292	291	299	298	308	295	296	325	333
309	304	306	292	327	295	302	302	276	331
293	306	286	310	277	309	307	304	323	288
285	292	342	311	316	297	304	316	305	320
303	296	332	336	313	282	294	341	334	317
296	312	307	328	326	301	309	313	275	328
326	303	308	310	285	317	318	319	314	325
284	289	312	319	298					

A possible frequency distribution for the voltage data is

Power Supply Voltage (Volts)	number of power supplies
260 and under 270	2
270 " " 280	6
280 " " 290	11
290 " " 300	29
300 " " 310	31
310 " " 320	21
320 " " 330	14
330 " " 340	8
340 " " 350	3

Use this frequency distribution to create the following histogram.

Frequency Histogram—Power Supply Voltages (using SPSS version 13)

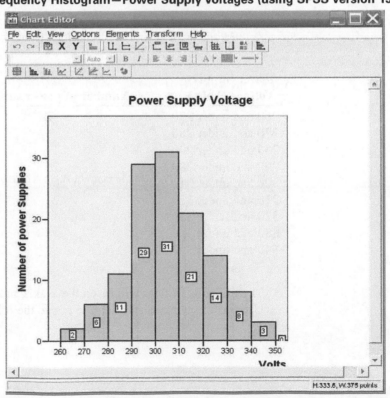

II. Graph a polygon

Polygon: A polygon is a graph in the shape of a many-sided closed figure. (Some texts show a smooth curve, but this is technically not a polygon.) The horizontal axis shows the class **midpoints**. No other values are shown on this axis. The vertical axis shows the class frequencies. In order to close the polygon, an extra class midpoint on the left and right side is used.

The class midpoints may be calculated as follows:

$$m = \frac{lower\ boundary\ +\ upper\ boundary}{2}$$

Notation: m denotes midpoint.

The above rules only apply to polygons where the classes are all of equal width. We are not concerned with how to draw other types of polygons.

EXAMPLE 3.12

The high-voltage output of a certain power supply that is to be used in copying machines must be 300 ± 50 volts (i.e., from 250 to 350 volts). In setting up a quality control chart, data from a sample of 125 power supplies is to be used. The results are given as follows:

333	297	285	300	279	311	298	300	305	262
289	315	305	302	273	282	313	330	300	271
303	330	290	291	300	290	340	293	309	287
292	312	295	296	302	308	268	296	294	306
295	320	322	328	326	316	290	291	320	315
301	292	291	299	298	308	295	296	325	333
309	304	306	292	327	295	302	302	276	331
293	306	286	310	277	309	307	304	323	288
285	292	342	311	316	297	304	316	305	320
303	296	332	336	313	282	294	341	334	317
296	312	307	328	326	301	309	313	275	328
326	303	308	310	285	317	318	319	314	325
284	289	312	319	298					

A possible frequency distribution for the voltage data is

Power Supply Voltage (Volts)	Number of power supplies	Midpoints
260 and under 270	2	(260 + 270) / 2 = 265
270 and under 280	6	(270 + 280) / 2 = 275
280 and under 290	11	(280 + 290) / 2 = 285
290 and under 300	29	(290 + 300) / 2 = 295
300 and under 310	31	(300 + 310) / 2 = 305
310 and under 320	21	(310 + 320) / 2 = 315
320 and under 330	14	(320 + 330) / 2 = 325
330 and under 340	8	(330 + 340) / 2 = 335
340 and under 350	3	(340 + 350) / 2 = 345

The midpoints values will be on the x-axis and the frequency will be on the y-axis. Use this frequency distribution to create the following polygon.

Frequency POLYGON – Power Supply Voltages (using SPSS version 13)

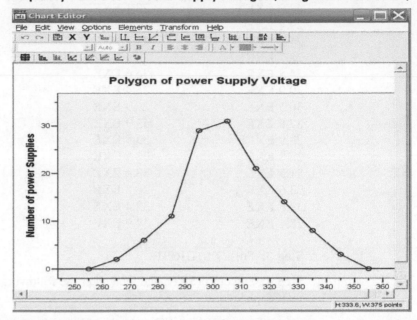

Note: Both graphs, the histogram and the polygon, show that the data has roughly a bell-curve shape.

Using CASIO Calculator to Graph Histogram and Polygon

I. Graph a Histogram Using the CASIO Calculator

The following baggage weight data were used to construct the frequency distribution:

25.0　42.9　29.4　25.9　28.7　24.5　30.9　30.5　27.8　28.9　22.8　31.5　23.6　39.5　28.1
31.5　28.1　39.6　27.4　28.9　36.6　25.4　26.9　53.9　33.5　22.5　38.4　26.8　32.4　34.9

The baggage weight data frequency distribution is needed to construct the histogram.

Baggage Weight	f = number of passengers
20.0 and under 25.0	4
25.0 and under 30.0	13
30.0 and under 35.0	7
35.0 and under 40.0	4
40.0 and under 45.0	1
45.0 and under 50.0	0
50.0 and under 55.0	1
Total	30

CASIO CALCULATOR INSTRUCTIONS:
Follow these steps to draw the histogram.

Step 1: At the Main Menu, select **STAT** Mode by pressing the **EXE** button.

Step 2: Enter raw data into **List 1**.

On the screen, you will only see List 1 to List 4 at first, but if you move the ▶ cursor key you will be able to scroll over to the other lists. Now, take the values from example 2 and input the values one by one in List 1 as follows. After you have entered each value, press the **EXE** button.

25.0 EXE	31.5 **EXE**
42.9 **EXE**	28.1 **EXE**
29.4 **EXE**	39.6 **EXE**
25.9 **EXE**	27.4 **EXE**
28.7 **EXE**	28.9 **EXE**
24.5 **EXE**	36.6 **EXE**
30.9 **EXE**	25.4 **EXE**
30.5 **EXE**	26.9 **EXE**
27.8 **EXE**	53.9 **EXE**
28.9 **EXE**	33.5 **EXE**
22.8 **EXE**	22.5 **EXE**
31.5 **EXE**	38.4 **EXE**
23.6 **EXE**	26.8 **EXE**
39.5 **EXE**	32.4 **EXE**
28.1 **EXE**	34.9 **EXE**

Step 3: Press **F1 (GRPH)**.

Step 4: Select F6(SET), and then enter the following items:
StatGraph1

Graph Type: ▶ (press **F6**) and select **Hist (F1)** and

XList: List (F1) and type **1** (if you input your data in List 1) and

Frequency: 1 (F1)

Now press **EXE**, and then select **GPH1 (F1)** and enter the following items:
Histogram Setting

Start: 20 (the lower boundary of the first class of the frequency distribution)

Width: 5 (choose a "nice" class width in Table 3.8)

Draw:[EXE]

The calculator will now show the histogram. However, there are no major scales on the x-axis. You can refer to the scales from the frequency distribution. That is, the first rectangle will correspond to the first class interval of "20 and under 25."

II. Graph a Polygon Using the CASIO Calculator

The following travel time data were used to construct the frequency distribution:

25.0   42.9   29.4   25.9   28.7   24.5   30.9   30.5   27.8   28.9   22.8   31.5   23.6   39.5   28.1
31.5   28.1   39.6   27.4   28.9   36.6   25.4   26.9   53.9   33.5   22.5   38.4   26.8   32.4   34.9

The frequency distribution of baggage weight data is needed to construct the polygon.

Baggage Weight	f = number of passengers
20.0 and under 25.0	4
25.0 and under 30.0	13
30.0 and under 35.0	7
35.0 and under 40.0	4
40.0 and under 45.0	1
45.0 and under 50.0	0
50.0 and under 55.0	1
Total	30

INSTRUCTIONS:
Follow these steps to draw the polygon.

Step 1: At the Main Menu, select **STAT** Mode by pressing the **EXE** button.

Step 2: Enter raw data into **List 1**.

On the screen, you will only see List 1 to List 4 at first, but if you move the ▶ cursor key you will be able to scroll over to the other lists. Now, take the values from example 2 and input the values one by one in List 1 as follows. After you have entered each value, press the **EXE** button.

25.0 EXE	31.5 **EXE**
42.9 **EXE**	28.1 **EXE**
29.4 **EXE**	39.6 **EXE**
25.9 **EXE**	27.4 **EXE**
28.7 **EXE**	28.9 **EXE**
24.5 **EXE**	36.6 **EXE**
30.9 **EXE**	25.4 **EXE**
30.5 **EXE**	26.9 **EXE**
27.8 **EXE**	53.9 **EXE**
28.9 **EXE**	33.5 **EXE**
22.8 **EXE**	22.5 **EXE**
31.5 **EXE**	38.4 **EXE**
23.6 **EXE**	26.8 **EXE**
39.5 **EXE**	32.4 **EXE**
28.1 **EXE**	34.9 **EXE**

Step 3: Press **F1 (GRPH)**.

Step 4: Select **F6(SET)**, and then enter the following items:
StatGraph1
Graph Type: ▷ (press **F6**) and select **Brkn (F5)**.
XList: List (F1) and type **1** (if you input your data in List 1).
Frequency: 1 (F1)
Now press **EXE**, and then select **GPH1 (F1)** and enter the following items:
Histogram Setting
Start: 15 (the lower boundary of the first class of the frequency distribution with the frequency of zero)
Width: 5 (choose a "nice" class width in Table 3.8)
Draw:[EXE]

The calculator will now show the polygon. However, there are no major scales on the x-axis. You can refer to the midpoint of each class. The lines connect the midpoints of the histogram.

Frequency Distribution Problems

3.6 Refer to Table 3.18a, which shows data regarding the first 32 companies taken from the Top 1000 Ranking by Profits table that appeared in the July 2003 issue of the *Globe and Mail*'s Report on Business.

Construct frequency distributions for the following data:

a. Revenue rank

b. Market capitalization

c. P/E ratio

d. Per share data—price/sales

e. Debt/equity ratio

f. Revenue % change

g. Earnings per share—latest year (Exclude values reported in $US)

h. Number of employees

3.7 Refer to Table 3.9 (on page 60), which shows data regarding the first 21 companies taken from the *Financial Post Magazine* Web site (http://www.financialpost.com/magazine/fp500/list.html).

For the 21 companies listed in Table 3.15, construct frequency distributions for the following data:

a. Revenue amount 2007

b. Profit amount 2007

c. Revenue change

d. Profit change

3.8 Refer to Table 3.11 (on page 61), which shows the stock summary data for companies with names starting with the let-ter A that were traded on the NASDAQ on May 8, 2008. The data was taken from the Financial Post Magazine's Web site (*http://www.financialpost.com/markets/market-data/market-nasdaq.html?tmp=nasdaq*).

Using the data listed in Table 3.11, construct frequency distributions for the following data:

a. Volume

b. High/ask price

c. Low/bid price

d. Close/previous price

e. Net change

f. 52 week High Price

g. 52 week Low Price

3.9 Refer to the mutual fund data in Table 3.19 (on page 86) that appeared in the Canadian Mutual Funds table of the June 3, 2004 issue of The Globe and Mail.

Construct frequency distributions for the following data:

a. Manulife Mix Funds Valuation data

b. Manulife Mix Funds Change data

c. Manulife Mix Funds Percent Change data

d. CI-Clarica Mutual Funds Valuation data

e. Transamerica Growsafe 75/100 Valuation data

f. Transamerica Growsafe 75/100 Percent Change data

TABLE 3.18a

▶Ranking by profits

PROFIT RANK 2002	PROFIT RANK 2001	COMPANY AND YEAR END	PROFIT $000	% CH'GE	REVENUE $000	RANK	%CH'GE	MARKET CAP $ MIL	DIV YIELD %	P/E RATIO	PRICE/ SALES	CASH FLOW
1	1	Royal Bank of Canada(Oc02) ON	2,762,000	15	23,234,000	3	-9	36,197	2.79	13.74	1.58	6.59
2	30	BCE Inc.(De02) QC	2,475,000	382	19,809,000	8	2	26,102	4.21	10.40	1.22	6.04
3	2	Bank of Nova Scotia(Oc02) ON	1,797,000	-17	18,310,000	12	-13	23,129	3.16	13.66	1.26	8.44
4	4	Bell Canada(De02) QC	1,504,000	-5	15,685,000	20	7	nm	nm	nm	nm	13.43
5	5	Bank of Montreal(Oc02) ON	1,417,000	-4	13,059,000	21	-24	18,764	3.15	13.96	1.43	4.45
6	10	Manulife Financial(De02) ON	1,378,000	19	16,532,000	18	2	15,923	1.74	11.86	1.03	4.84
7	7	EnCana Corp.(De02) AB	1,224,000	-5	11,031,000	25	112	23,361	.82	16.71	1.85	9.04
8	8	Imperial Oil(De02) ON	1,210,000	-2	15,821,000	19	-2	16,996	1.87	14.06	1.09	4.64
9	14	Sun Life Financial Services(De02) ON	998,000	13	23,101,000	4	37	16,517	2.10	14.52	.63	9.38
10	15	Power Financial(De02) QC	988,000	12	18,700,000	11	3	12,591	2.87	13.35	.68	5.16
11	12	Petro-Canada(De02) AB	974,000	15	9,917,000	28	14	12,892	.82	13.18	1.30	8.66
12	9	Thomson Corp.(De02) ON[i]	(us)615,000	-21	(us)7,768,000	23	7	27,348	2.64	28.77	2.21	(us)4.32
13	29	Great-West Lifeco(De02) MB	962,000	76	16,632,000	16	4	13,648	2.54	14.72	.84	3.79
14	13	Magna International(De02) ON[i]	(us)554,000	-4	(us)13,044,000	7	17	8,417	2.43	9.62	.38	20.25
15	21	TransCanada PipeLines(De02) AB	805,000	17	5,300,000	48	-1	10,990	4.36	14.69	2.10	3.82
16	20	Husky Energy(De02) AB	804,000	23	6,385,000	40	-3	6.882	2.19	8.76	1.08	(us)5.02
17	39	Suncor Energy(De02) AB	761,000	96	4,913,000	52	17	11,090	.69	15.06	2.26	3.21
18	27	Loblaw Companies(De02) ON	728,000	29	23,099,000	5	7	14,905	.89	20.46	.65	4.05
19	24	George Weston Ltd.(De02) ON	690,000	19	27,464,000	1	11	11,938	1.06	17.87	.43	12.25
20	3	Cdn. Imp. Bank of Commerce(Oc02) ON	653,000	-61	17,055,000	13	-20	13.914	4.13	28.29	.82	4.78
21	23	Power Corp.(De02) QC	645,000	4	19,011.000	10	3	7,997	2.21	12.81	.53	8.61
22	31	Enbridge Inc.(De02) AB	610,100	26	4,830.600	54	13	7,233	3.57	11.84	1.50	4.57
23	44	Alcan Inc.(De02) QC[i]	(us)374,000	nm	(us)12,553,000	9	-1	14,894	2.03	25.65	.76	(us)6.39
24	19	Cdn. Natural Resources(De02) AB	574,800	-12	4,114,900	59	15	6,261	1.07	10.49	1.47	17.71
25	18	Canadian National Railway Co.(De02) QC	571,000	-21	6,173,000	41	8	12,891	1.32	22.74	2.10	8.14
26	11	Shell Canada(De02) AB	561,000	-44	7,314,000	35	-5	13,575	1.63	24.24	1.88	4.45
27	17	Talisman Energy(De02) AB	524,000	-29	5,379,000	47	5	7,450	1.06	15.24	1.42	19.74
28	45	Investors Group(De02) MB	511,759	87	1,940,036	102	10	7,058	3.21	14.35	3.63	3.02
29	41	Canada Life Financial(De02) ON	499,000	46	8,598,000	32	7	6,463	1.49	13.21	.77	4.68
30	36	Canadian Pacific Railway Ltd.(De02) AB	496,000	33	3,692,600	62	-1	4,937	1.64	9.95	1.35	5.98
31	44	Great-West Life Assurance(De02) MB	475,000	68	10,766,000	26	7	nm	nm	nm	nm	1,180.76
32	34	Nexen Inc.(De02) AB	452,000	0	3,102,000	77	1	4,212	.88	10.26	1.36	9.76

DEBT/ EQUITY	LATEST YEAR	PREVIOUS YEAR	2 YEARS AGO	ONE-YEAR %	RANK	FIVE-YEAR %	RANK	NUMBER OF EMPLOYEES	INDUSTRY	MAJOR SHAREHOLDER	PROFIT
0.4	3.96	3.55	3.53	15.96	159	17.16	99	59,770	banks	Widely held	1
1.2	2.74	0.56	7.43	17.99	127	26.69	23	66,266	tele	Widely held	2
0.4	3.36	4.12	3.67	12.85	230	15.64	118	44,633	banks	Widely held	3
1.6	3.90	4.18	4.09	19.00	111	21.38	55	54,258	tele	BCE Inc. 100%	4
0.3	2.73	2.72	3.30	13.37	218	14.92	138	33,912	banks	Widely held	5
0.2	2.90	2.40	2.22	16.17	154	14.74	143	13,000	insur	Widely held	6
0.6	2.92	5.02	4.09	13.94	194	19.13	67	3,646	oilprd	Widely held	7
0.3	3.19	3.15	3.40	25.35	62	22.24	50	6,460	integ	Exxon Mobil Corp. (U.S.) 69.6%	8
0.2	1.84	2.08	1.49	8.82	355	na	nr	14,905	insur	Widely held	9
0.3	2.72	2.44	2.18	17.33	136	18.89	72	10,300	fin	Power Corp. of Canada 67.1%	10
0.5	3.71	3.19	3.28	18.29	123	13.00	180	4,470	integ	Government of Canada 18.74%	11
0.5	(us)0.93	(us)1.19	(us)1.96	7.32	397	15.34	131	44,000	serv	Woodbridge Company Ltd.69%	12
0.2	2.53	1.39	1.72	22.86	74	17.53	96	14,000	insur	Power Financial Corp.64.99%	13
0.1	(us)5.83	(us)6.55	(us)7.04	11.85	262	12.45	195	70,800	auto	Stronach Trust 66.3%	14
1.6	1.56	1.30	1.50	13.37	219	8.63	309	2,767	pipeline	Widely held	15
0.5	1.88	1.49	1.39	16.73	146	nm	nr	2,753	integ	Li Ka-sning 71.5%	16
0.8	1.64	0.79	0.79	28.25	51	17.72	93	3,422	integ	Widely held	17
1.0	2.64	2.04	1.71	18.93	113	15.58	122	122,000	food	George Weston Ltd. 61%	18
1.4	5.05	4.42	3.66	18.27	124	21.10	57	142,850	food	W. Galen Weston 62.13%	19
0.3	1.37	4.19	4.97	5.22	461	12.58	189	42,552	banks	Widely held	20
0.4	2.81	2.74	2.93	13.66	205	15.74	117	19,000	mgt	Paul Desmarais and associates 65%	21
1.8	3.60	2.91	2.54	20.08	101	16.94	103	4,000	pipeline	Widely held	22
0.4	(us)1.15	(us)-0.02	(us)2.45	4.32	486	5.76	373	48,100	mining	Widely held	23
0.8	4.46	5.30	6.70	13.51	211	16.29	107	1,573	oilprd	Widely held	24
0.8	2.87	3.72	3.91	8.93	352	10.29	250	23,190	trans	Widely held	25
0.3	2.03	3.67	3.04	11.45	271	17.54	95	3,825	integ	Shell Investments (1996) Ltd. 78%	26
0.7	3.73	5.25	6.41	12.88	229	11.17	226	1,565	oilprd	Widely held	27
0.5	1.86	1.05	1.35	20.01	103	22.45	48	3,285	fin	Power Financial Corp. 56.2%	28
0.1	3.05	2.13	2.22	13.80	200	nm	nr	6,768	insur	Widely held	29
1.0	3.13	2.35	3.36	15.60	165	11.38	217	16,116	trans	Widely held	30
0.2	na	na	na	14.39	185	12.63	187	7,000	insur	Great-West Lifeco Inc. 100%	31
0.8	3.34	3.40	4.52	29.17	45	26.11	26	2,767	oilprd	Ontario Teachers' Pension Plan 20%	32

Reprinted by permission from "Report on Business," the *Globe and Mail*, 2004.

TABLE 3.18b

FP500 CANADA'S 500 LARGEST CORPORATIONS

RANK BY REVENUE 2002	2001	Company	Industry	REVENUES 2002 $'000s	% Change	% Sales Outside Canada	ASSETS 2002 $'000s	% Change	Rank
1	1	General Motors of Canada Ltd., Oshawa, ON	Vehicle	37,000,000	n.a.	n.a.	n.a.	n.a.	n.a.
2	4	George Weston Ltd., Toronto	Conglom	27,446,000	11.3	n.a.	16,630,000	2.2	34
3	7	Bombardier Inc., Montreal (Ja03)	High-tech	23,664,900	9.4	n.a.	29,009,400	4.5	20
4	8	Ford Motor Co. of Canada, Ltd., Oakville, ON	Vehicle	23,328,700	8.1	n.a.	11,398,000	8.0	48
5	3	Royal Bank of Canada, Montreal (Oc02)	Bank	23,234,000	(9.0)	n.a.	376,956,000	4.9	1
6	18	Sun Life Financial Services of Canada, Toronto	Life	23,101,000	38.4	72	123,438,000	53.7	6
7	5	Onex Corp., Toronto	Conglom	22,653,000	(4.8)	85	19,890,000	(4.7)	27
8	17	Magna International Inc.*, Aurora, ON	Vehicle	20,364,470	19.3	70	16,004,076	27.1	35
9	6	BCE Inc., Montreal	Telecom	19,768,000	(8.9)	n.a.	39,563,000	(27.2)	14
10	13	Alcan Inc.*, Montreal	Mining	19,687,800	0.7	94	27,674,964	(0.4)	21
11	12	DaimlerChrysler Canada Inc., Windsor, ON	Vehicle	19,353,000	(5.2)	n.a.	n.a.	n.a.	n.a.
12	14	Power Corp. of Canada, Montreal	Conglom	19,017,000	3.6	30	70,136,000	2.0	11
13	10	The Bank of Nova Scotia, Toronto (Oc02)	Bank	18,310,000	(13.0)	n.a.	296,380,000	4.2	2
14	9	Canadian Imperial Bank of Commerce, Toronto (Oc02)	Bank	17,055,000	(20.3)	n.a.	273,293,000	(4.9)	4
15	16	Imperial Oil Ltd., Toronto	Energy	16,890,000	(1.5)	13	11,868,000	10.3	44
16	11	The Toronto-Dominion Bank, Toronto (Oc02)	Bank	16,680,000	(20.3)	n.a.	278,040,000	(3.4)	3
17	2	Nortel Networks Corp.*, Brampton, ON	High-tech	16,538,380	(39.1)	n.a.	23,382,804	(27.5)	24
18	19	Manulife Financial Corp., Toronto	Life	16,532,000	1.9	80	81,195,000	3.3	9
19	15	Bank of Montreal, Montreal (Oc02)	Bank	13,059,000	(24.2)	n.a.	252,864,000	5.6	5
20	20	Hydro-Québec, Montreal	Utility	13,002,000	3.4	28	59,078,000	(1.3)	12

PROFITS 2002 $'000s	% Change	Rank	EPS $0.00	PROFITS AS % OF... Revenue	Assets	Equity	GROWTH 5-Year % Profit Growth	Share Price Change 1 Year %	5 Year %	Employees	Symbol	Exchange	Major Shareholder(s)	% Foreign	RANK 2002
n.a.	n.a.	n.a.	n.a.	n.a.	n.a.	n.a.	n.a.	n.a.	n.a.	24,500	(Pr)		General Motors, US	100	1
690,000	18.6	24	5.05	2.5	4.2	17.2	182.8	(19.4)	106.9	139,000	WN	T	W. Galen Weston 62%		2
(615,200)	(257.4)	569	(0.47)	(2.6)	(2.2)	(18.0)	(246.4)	(81.1)	(68.8)	75,000	BBD.B	T	Bombardier family 63%		3
n.a.	n.a.	n.a.	n.a.	n.a.	n.a.	n.a.	n.a.	n.a.	n.a.	15,074	(Pr)		Ford Motor Co., US	100	4
2,762,000	14.6	3	3.96	11.9	0.8	15.0	64.5	9.2	36.7	59,549	RY	T,NY	Widely held	20	5
997,000	13.2	15	1.84	4.3	1.0	8.8	95.1	(17.6)	n.a.	11,800	SLF	T,NY	Widely held		6
(145,000)	(118.2)	546	(0.90)	(0.6)	(0.7)	(8.9)	(366.4)	(36.9)	55.0	98,000	OCX	T	Gerald Schwartz 67% voting		7
869,780	(3.1)	19	9.15	4.3	6.1	11.1	44.1	(32.8)	(26.8)	73,000	MG.A	T,NY	Stronach Trust 58%		8
2,475,000	373.2	4	2.74	12.5	5.3	16.6	259.4	(2.3)	(53.7)	66,266	BCE	T,NY	Widely held	14	9
587,180	7,486.3	31	1.81	3.0	2.1	4.3	(9.4)	(33.1)	(8.5)	50,000	AL	T,NY	Widely held		10
n.a.	n.a.	n.a.	n.a.	n.a.	n.a.	n.a.	n.a.	n.a.	n.a.	n.a.	(Pr)		DaimlerChrysler Corp., US	100	11
645,000	4.4	27	2.81	3.4	0.9	12.8	94.9	(5.9)	31.1	28,000	POW	T	Paul Desmarais Sr. 65%		12
1,797,000	(17.2)	7	3.36	9.8	0.6	12.2	18.7	(0.5)	39.6	49,000	BNS	T,NY	Widely held		13
653,000	(61.3)	26	1.37	3.8	0.2	5.4	(57.9)	(15.7)	(3.3)	42,552	CM	T, NY	Widely held		14
1,210,000	(2.7)	14	3.19	7.2	10.7	25.1	42.9	(0.7)	73.4	6,460	IMO	T,AM	Exxon Mobil Corp., US	70	15
(76,000)	(105.5)	533	(0.25)	(0.5)	n.a.	(0.6)	(107.0)	(24.3)	5.9	42,817	TD	T	Widely held		16
(5,549,950)	86.9	574	(1.43)	(33.6)	(19.9)	(106.6)	n.a.	(56.3)	(86.4)	52,600	NT	T,NY	Widely Held		17
1,370,000	17.4	12	2.90	8.3	1.7	16.1	(65.8)	(18.5)	n.a.	32,400	MFC	T,NY	Widely held		18
1,417,000	(1.7)	11	2.73	10.9	0.6	12.6	8.6	4.9	4.4	33,000	BMO	T,NY	Widely held		19
1,526,000	37.7	9	n.a.	11.7	2.6	10.5	94.1	n.a.	n.a.	20,972	(Cr)		Quebec government		20

TABLE 3.19

fund	valuation	chg	% chg
EQUITABLE LIFE			
AIM Cdn Premier 06/01	10.01	+.01	+.07
Accum Income 06/01	23.26	-.03	-.15
American Gwth 06/01	10.48	+.04	+.37
Asian-Pacific 06/01	6.38	+.01	+.17
Asset Allocat 06/01	16.72	-.01	-.06
Dissett Div Inc 06/01	10.19	-.01	-.10
Cdn Bond 06/01	15.55	-.02	-.15
Cdn Stock 06/01	20.17	-.01	-.05
CommonStock 06/01	29.96	-.02	-.05
European Equity 06/01	7.23	-.02	-.22
International 06/01	11.49	+.02	+.17
MB Cdn Eq Value 06/01	18.21	-.04	-.24
Mack US Em Grth 06/01	10.15	+.09	+.84
Templeton Grwth 06/01	9.39	+.02	+.17
Tmplton Glo Bnd 06/01	12.32	+.04	+.36
Trimark Europls 06/01	10.51	+.02	+.15
Trimark Glo Bal 06/01	10.48	+.02	+.17
US Equity 06/01	6.30	+.02	+.32

fund	valuation	chg	% chg
MD MANAGEMENT			
MD Balanced	18.08	-.06	-.33
MD Bnd & Mtg	10.39	-.01	-.10
MD Bond	7.10	-.03	-.42
MD Dividend	16.66	-.03	-.18
MD Equity	19.03	-.03	-.16
MD Glo Bond	11.27	-.03	-.27
MD Glo Equ RSP	7.07	unch	unch
MD Growth	10.37	unch	unch
MD Growth RSP	9.82	unch	unch
MD Int'l Growth	6.64	unch	unch
MD Int'l Value	10.13	unch	unch
MD Intl Gr RSP	6.46	unch	unch
MD Select	15.39	-.04	-.26
MD US LgCpGrRSP	6.07	unch	unch
MD US LiCap Val	8.42	unch	unch
MD US LrCpVlRSP	8.25	unch	unch
MD US Lrg Cp Gr	4.79	unch	unch
MD US Sml Cp Gr	3.68	-.01	-.27
MDPIM Cdn Equ-A	11.01	-.04	-.36
MDPIM US Equ-A	7.39	-.02	-.27

fund	valuation	chg	% chg
MANULIFE MIX FUNDS			
AIM Am MidCp Gw	12.26	-.04	-.33
AIM Cd First Cl	12.25	-.05	-.41
Cd Lg Cap Gw Cl	12.85	-.07	-.54
Cd Lg Cap ValCl	12.12	-.02	-.16
Cd Lg Cp CoreCl	12.05	-.02	-.17
Cdn Equ Val Cl	12.65	-.02	-.16
E&P Gw Opp Cl	14.38	-.04	-.28
E&P US MidCapCl	11.81	-.05	-.42
FI Can DiscEqCl	13.07	-.08	-.61
FI Gwth Amer Cl	11.09	-.03	-.27
FI Intl Port Cl	11.60	-.02	-.17
Global Equ Cl	10.86	-.01	-.09
Global Sect Cl	11.31	-.06	-.53
Global SectCl-H	11.31	-.05	-.44
Global Val Cl	12.48	-.01	-.08
Int'l Growth Cl	11.29	-.01	-.09
Int'l Value Cl	12.27	+.01	+.08
Japanese Class	12.63	-.12	-.94
SM Tot Cd Eq Cl	13.26	+.02	+.15
SM Total Glo Cl	12.00	-.04	-.33
SM Total USEqCl	11.33	-.03	-.26
SMTotal Gl Cl-H	12.00	-.04	-.33
Sht Term Yld Cl	10.21	unch	unch
Str Bond Class	10.30	-.03	-.29
Tri Sel Cdn Cl	12.13	-.03	-.25
Trimark Glo Cl	11.41	+.04	+.35
US Lg Cap Gw Cl	10.40	-.01	-.10
US Lg Cp CoreCl	10.77	-.01	-.09
US Lg Cp Val Cl	10.92	-.02	-.18
US MidCp Val Cl	11.51	-.03	-.26

fund	valuation	chg	% chg
CI - CLARICA MUTUAL FUNDS			
Alpine CdnRes	10.35	-.08	-.77
Alpine CdnRes A	10.46	-.07	-.66
Alpine GrthEq	13.09	-.04	-.30
Alpine GrthEq A	13.28	-.05	-.38
Cdn Blu Chip Z	11.35	-.04	-.35
Cdn BlueChip	16.34	-.06	-.37
Cdn BlueChip A	16.51	-.07	-.42
Cdn Div Cl Z	10.86	-.04	-.37
Cdn Divers	14.71	-.05	-.34
Cdn Divers A	14.96	-.05	-.33
Cdn Equity	12.80	-.02	-.16
Cdn Equity A	12.82	-.02	-.16
Cdn Lrg Cap Val	10.55	+.01	+.09
Cdn Small/Mid A	21.02	-.04	-.19
Cdn Sml/Mid Cap	18.40	-.03	-.16
Clarica Balance	11.64	-.02	-.17
Glo Lrg Cap Val	10.52	+.04	+.38
Global Bond	9.91	-.04	-.40
Global Bond A	9.91	-.03	-.30
Prem Bond	11.34	-.04	-.35
Prem Bond A	11.49	-.04	-.35
Prem Int'l	12.43	-.03	-.24
Prem Int'l A	12.78	-.03	-.23
Prem Mtg	10.34	-.02	-.19
Prem Mtg A	10.46	-.02	-.19
Sig Corp Bond	9.83	-.02	-.20
Sum Cdn Equ	15.37	-.05	-.32
Sum Cdn Equ A	15.50	-.05	-.32
Sum Div Gwth	15.18	-.02	-.13
Sum Div Gwth A	14.91	-.02	-.13
Sum For Equ	14.46	-.03	-.21
Sum For Equ A	14.96	-.03	-.20
Sum Gwth&Inc	14.09	-.03	-.21
Sum Gwth&Inc A	14.50	-.03	-.21
US Small Cap	8.44	-.02	-.24
US Small Cap A	8.54	-.01	-.12

fund	valuation	chg	% chg
TRANSAMERICA GROWSAFE 75/100			
AGF Int Val7510 06/01	4.51	+.00	+.02
AIC AmFoc 7510 06/01	5.07	-.01	-.19
AIC DivCan 7510 06/01	5.38	-.00	-.01
Agg AA GIF 7510	3.63	-.00	-.03
Bal AA GIF 7510	4.47	-.01	-.12
CI Gl Boom 7510 06/01	4.82	-.00	-.10
CI Global 7510 06/01	5.46	-.00	-.01
CanAsian 7510	4.21	-.01	-.14
CanEuro 7510	3.14	+.02	+.75
CanUS 21st 7510	2.86	-.01	-.24
CanUS L Cap7510	4.16	+.02	+.38
Cdn Bal 7510	4.77	-.02	-.46
Cdn Bond 7510	5.91	-.02	-.34
Cdn Equity 7510	3.40	-.03	-.79
Cdn Lg Cap 7510	4.17	-.01	-.35
Cdn MMF 7510	5.29	+.00	+.00
CdnEqVal 7510 06/01	5.62	+.00	+.04
CdnFixPay 7510 06/01	5.67	-.01	-.18
Con AA GIF 7510	4.88	-.01	-.20
Fid Can AA 7510 06/01	5.66	+.03	+.45
Fid IntPort7510 06/01	4.78	-.06	-1.19
Fid TrueNrt7510 06/01	5.75	+.01	+.19
Grow AA GIF7510	4.11	-.00	-.06
MacIvyGwInc7510 06/01	5.68	+.01	+.17
TD Div Inc 7510 06/01	6.12	-.00	-.03
TOP AggrGw 7510 06/01	3.66	+.01	+.24
TOP Bal 7510 06/01	4.50	+.01	+.19
TOP CdnMgr 7510 06/01	5.75	+.00	+.02
TOP Cons 7510 06/01	5.00	+.01	+.14
TOP GloMgr 7510 06/01	4.89	+.01	+.13
TOP GloSect7510 06/01	4.90	+.01	+.29
TOP Growth 7510 06/01	4.24	+.01	+.20
TOP USMgrs 7510 06/01	4.80	+.02	+.39
US EqVal 7510 06/01	5.74	+.03	+.47
US Equity 7510	3.68	-.00	-.01

Fund Name	Mstar Rating	Fund Type	Fund Sub-Type	Fund Categy	% Ret YrEnd May08	Quart YrEnd May08	% Ret YrEnd May07	Quart YrEnd May07	% Ret YrEnd May06	Quart YrEnd May06	% Ret YrEnd May05	Quart YrEnd May05	% Ret YrEnd May04	Quart YrEnd May04	Exp Ratio	Total Asset $Mill
RBC O'Shaughnessy US Value	5	Equity	US Eq	USEq	-16.5	3	21.4	2	4.9	1	13.4	1	21.5	1	1.57	1271.9
Dynamic Power American Growth Class	5	Equity	US Eq	USEq	9.9	1	17.3	2	0.6	1	13.4	1	27.7	1	2.59	93.9
IG AGF US Growth Class B	5	Equity	US Eq	USEq	-4.2	1	18.8	1	-1	2	-5.2	4	28.6	1	3.29	221.1
Dynamic Power American Growth	5	Equity	US Eq	USEq	8.8	1	17.5	2	-0.5	1	12	1	26.4	1	2.55	198
Dynamic American Value	5	Equity	US Eq	USEq	-2	1	16.9	1	16.7	1	1.6	1	17.9	2	2.55	0
SEI US Large Cap Synthetic Class P	5	Equity	US Eq	USEq	-9.2	1	19.1	1	5.1	1	6.3	1	19.2	1	1.5	119.1
IG AGF US Growth B	5	Equity	US Eq	USEq												
TD US Index Currency Neutral - e	5	Equity	US Eq	USEq	-8.1	1	20.6	1	6.6	1	7.8	4	19	1	0.48	119.1
IG AGF US Growth B	5	Equity	US Eq	USEq	-4.3	1	19.2	1	-0.9	2	-5.2	1	19.2	1	3.14	729.3
TD US Index Currency Neutral - I	5	Equity	US Eq	USEq	-8.4	2	20.2	1	6.2	1	7.3	4	17.9	2	0.85	104.9
McLean Budden American Equity	5	Equity	US Eq	USEq	-10.7	1	19.2	1	-3.9	2	-1.4	2	18.8	2	1.25	349.2
IG AGF US Growth A	5	Equity	US Eq	USEq	-4.2	1	19.4	1	-0.8	1	-5.1	4	18.7	1	2.99	122.6
CI American Value Corporate Class	5	Equity	US Eq	USEq	-5.9	2	19.1	1	-5.9	3	7.4	1	21	1	2.31	313.1
Altamira Precision US Curr Neutral Idx	5	Equity	US Eq	USEq	-8.5	2	20.5	1	6.5	1	7.2	1	23.7	1	0.53	6.2
RBC US Index Currency Neutral	5	Equity	US Eq	USEq	-8.4	2	20	1	6.6	1	7.1	1	16.8	2	0.7	37
Emissary US Small/Mid Cap	4	Equity	US Eq	USEq	-11.5	1	18.5	2	-4.4	2	-4	3	16.8	3	2.93	505.3
IA Clarington Navellier US All Cap A	4	Equity	US Eq	USEq	-9.3	2	10.8	4	10.5	1	-1.4	2	15.6	2	2.88	130
BMO US Equity	4	Equity	US Eq	USEq	-12.5	2	18.7	1	-2.5	2	7	2	20.4	1	2.44	2887
BMO US Equity Index	4	Equity	US Eq	USEq	-11.1	2	18.8	1	2.3	2	4.3	1	21.1	3	1.22	28.2
RBC US Equity	4	Equity	US Eq	USEq	-6.5	1	15.9	3	-1.9	2	-1.1	2	19.7	1	2.02	15.6
RBC US Equity Advisor	4	Equity	US Eq	USEq	-6.5	1	15.8	3	-2.1	2	-1	2	23.1	1	2.2	5.4
GGOF American Equity Ltd Mutual	4	Equity	US Eq	USEq	-7.8	1	20.2	1	-5.3	2	-0.3	2	23.4	1	2.75	16.7
GGOF American Equity Ltd Classic	4	Equity	US Eq	USEq	-19.6	4	20.8	1	-4.8	3	0.3	1	26.6	1	2.21	4
Marquis US Equity Pool	4	Equity	US Eq	USEq	-19.2	4	11.3	4	2.4	1	-8.5	4	20.7	1	2.9	322.5
Mac Universal US Gr Lead (Unhed) CI	4	Equity	US Eq	USEq	-5.1	1	9.8	4	-3.8	2	-1.3	2	19.3	1	2.69	8.2
imaxx US Equity Growth	4	Equity	US Eq	USEq	-7.8	1	8.8	4	2.1	2	0.1	1	13.6	3	2.84	211.6
CI American Equity	4	Equity	US Eq	USEq	-19.6	4	21.8	1	-3	2	-0.6	2	19.3	1	2.31	16
CI American Equity Corporate Class	4	Equity	US Eq	USEq	-19.4	4	21.9	1	-3.1	2	-5.6	4	11.1	1	2.31	317.4
Investors US Large Cap Growth A	4	Equity	US Eq	USEq	-4.5	1	14.5	3	-6.7	4	-3.4	3	25.4	3	2.71	267.1
Franklin Flex Cap Growth Corp Class	4	Equity	US Eq	USEq	-6.8	1	12.4	4	-8.6	4	4.7	1	9.4	1	2.65	27.6
CI American Managers Corporate Class	4	Equity	US Eq	USEq	-14.3	1	15.7	3	-0.5	3	8.7	1	16.8	1	2.31	112.4
CI American Value	4	Equity	US Eq	USEq	-6.1	1	19.9	3	-5.3	1	-1.1	2	16.1	1	2.31	240.6
Marquis US Equity Pool Series V	4	Equity	US Eq	USEq	-2.5	1	14.2	3	5	2	-1.7	2	13.7	3	0.32	1.6
MD American Value	4	Equity	US Eq	USEq	-10.6	2	13.3	3	-1.8	2	-5.3	4	13.7	2	1.72	8.4
IG AGF US Growth C	4	Equity	US Eq	USEq	-4.3	1	19.2	1	-0.9	2	-5.8	4	13.5	1	3.17	1.9
Investors US Large Cap Growth B	4	Equity	US Eq	USEq	-4.6	1	14.3	3	-6.8	4	-6.1	4	13.5	3	2.86	69.7
Investors US Large Cap Growth Class B	4	Equity	US Eq	USEq	-5.2	1	14.2	3	-6.7	4	11.3	1	18.4	1	3.01	77.6
North Growth US Equity	4	Equity	US Eq	USEq	-14.8	3	15.9	3	-7.8	4	0	2	12.6	1	1.2	4.1
Investors US Large Cap Value C	4	Equity	US Eq	USEq	-15.6	3	17.6	2	-3.4	4	3.1	2	11.8	1	2.87	300.9
Middlefield US Growth Class	4	Equity	US Eq	USEq	-3.6	1	10.7	4	-0.1	1	-0.7	2	13.4	1	2.43	14.1
Investors US Opportunities C	4	Equity	US Eq	USEq	-17.4	3	22.7	3	-8.5	4	5.3	3	13.4	4	2.88	16.5
Fidelity American Disciplined Eq Sr T8	4	Equity	US Eq	USEq	-8.3	1	19.7	1	2.2	1	5.5	3			2.65	13.1
Fidelity American Disciplined Eq Sr S8	4	Equity	US Eq	USEq	-8.1	1	19.9	1	2.2	1	5.5	3			2.45	
Fidelity American Disciplined Eq Sr B	4	Equity	US Eq	USEq	-8.1	1	19.9	1	2.4	1	5.4	2			2.45	
Fidelity American Disciplined Eq Sr A	4	Equity	US Eq	USEq	-8.3	1	19.6	1	2	1	-0.7	1			2.65	
Standard Life US Equity Legend Series	4	Equity	US Eq	USEq	-11.2	2	17.7	2	-7.2	4	9.7	1			1.15	
Synergy American	4	Equity	US Eq	USEq	-7.6	1	15.7	3	0.7	1	10	1			2.31	
Synergy American Corporate Class	4	Equity	US Eq	USEq	-7.5	1	15.1	3	0.4	1	5	1			2.31	
Fidelity American Disciplined Eq Cl B	4	Equity	US Eq	USEq	-8.2	1	19.7	1	1.9	1	4.9	1			2.65	
Fidelity American Disciplined Eq Cl A	4	Equity	US Eq	USEq	-8.4	1	19.4	1	1.7	1					2.85	

#				Fund												
4	Equity	US Eq	USEq	IG AGF US Growth Class A	-4.1	1	19	1	-0.9	1	-5.1	4	11	4	3.14	12
4	Equity	US Eq	USEq	TD Dow Jones Industrial Avg Index - I	-12.7	2	19.8	1	-5.3	3	-4.7	4	15.4	3	0.85	43.8
4	Equity	US Eq	USEq	AGF American Growth Class D	-3.4	1	20	4	0.3	1	-4.3	3	12.3	3	2.45	
4	Equity	US Eq	USEq	IG Mackenzie Universal US Gr Leaders CLB	0.3	1	9	4	-3.8	2	-8.8	4	20	1	3.16	27.1
3	Equity	US Eq	USEq	IG Goldman Sachs US Equity C	-19.6	4	10.2	2	-2.1	2	-3.2	3	19.3	1	3.17	43.8
3	Equity	US Eq	USEq	Leith Wheeler US Equity Series B	-21.5	4	17.2	1	-0.3	1	-3.4	3	15.9	2	1.34	16.2
3	Equity	US Eq	USEq	TD Dow Jones Industrial Avg Index - e	-12.3	4	20.3	3	-4.9	3		3	17.2	2		
3	Equity	US Eq	USEq	Emissary US Value	-18.6	4	13	2	-3.4	1	-3.4	3			0.31	137.5
3	Equity	US Eq	USEq	Investors US Opportunities Class B	-17.2	3	22.2	1	-8.4	4	-4.2	2		2	2.92	31.7
3	Equity	US Eq	USEq	Férique American	-16.7	3	18.9	1	-4.9	4	-2.3	2	15.9	2	2.97	741.5
3	Equity	US Eq	USEq	DFA US Value	-22.4	4	16.8	3	3.5	1	-1.2	2			0.96	15.1
3	Equity	US Eq	USEq	TD US Blue Chip Equity - A	-10.8	2	15.9	2	-7.4	4	-1.6	2	17.2	3	1.61	65.1
3	Equity	US Eq	USEq	Professionals Qc American Index	-14.3	3	17.4	3	-5.9	2	5.2	1	17	1	2.44	741.5
3	Equity	US Eq	USEq	PH&N US Growth A	-11.1	2	13.2	3	-2.2	3	-5	4	13.6	3	0.88	0.4
3	Equity	US Eq	USEq	TD US Blue Chip Equity - I	-10.9	2	15.9	2	-7.4	4	-1.6	3	15.7	1	1.22	5.8
3	Equity	US Eq	USEq	Standard Life US Equity E	-11.7	2	16.8	3	-7.9	2	-3.8	2	22.8		2.44	13.1
3	Equity	US Eq	USEq	Counsel Select America	-14.3	3	11.1	4	-5.8	3	-5.1	3	13.6	3	1.91	28.4
3	Equity	US Eq	USEq	TD US Equity Advantage Portfolio-A	-14	2	16.3	2	-5.1	2	-1.2	4	13.6	2	2.83	289.6
3	Equity	US Eq	USEq	Standard Life US Equity A	-12.3	2	16.1	2	-8.4	4	-0.3	3	12.7	2	2.57	32.7
3	Equity	US Eq	USEq	CIBC US Index RRSP	-14.4	3	17.9	3	-5.8	2	-2.1	2	16.7	3	2.43	485.4
3	Equity	US Eq	USEq	SEI US Large Co Equity Class P	-15	3	15	3	-4.4	3	-1.8	3	16.2	4	0.97	13.9
3	Equity	US Eq	USEq	CIBC US Equity Index	-13.7	3	17.3	3	-4.1	2	-1.8	2	16.3	4	2.43	112.9
3	Equity	US Eq	USEq	Investors US Opportunities Class A	-17.1	3	22.3	3	-8.3	4	-0.7	2		4	0.98	
3	Equity	US Eq	USEq	Mac Universal US Blue Chip CI	-7.7	1	12.3	4	0.8	1	-1.1	2	17.9	2	2.82	211.4
3	Equity	US Eq	USEq	Investors US Opportunities B	-17.4	3	22.7	3	-8.5	4	0.6	1	15.8	2	2.43	3.5
3	Equity	US Eq	USEq	Investors US Opportunities A	-17.3	3	22.9	3	-8.3	1	-0.7	2	6.5	4	2.85	2.4
3	Equity	US Eq	USEq	Fidelity American Value Sr A	-20.1	4	14.9	4	-4.5	3	-0.5	2			2.7	
3	Equity	US Eq	USEq	Fidelity American Value Sr B	-19.9	4	15.1	4	-4.4	2	-1.7	2	19.9	1	2.54	150.8
3	Equity	US Eq	USEq	Investors US Large Cap Value Class B	-15.4	3	17.1	3	-3.2	2	-1.7	2	19.9	1	2.34	13.1
3	Equity	US Eq	USEq	Investors US Large Cap Value Class A	-15.2	3	17.3	3	-3	2	-0.4	2	8.9		2.84	22.1
3	Equity	US Eq	USEq	TD US Equity Advantage Portfolio-I	-13.9	3	16.4	2	-5.1	3	-0.3	2		4	2.69	45
3	Equity	US Eq	USEq	Scotia US Value	-9.8	2	9.5	2	-4.4	4	-4.6	3	17.7	2	2.44	359.7
3	Equity	US Eq	USEq	Scotia US Index	-14.4	3	17.5	3	-5.5	2	-1.9	3		2	2.46	
3	Equity	US Eq	USEq	TD US Index - e	-13.7	3	18.4	3	-5.2	2	-1.1	3	16.3	2	0.94	141.1
3	Equity	US Eq	USEq	Investors US Large Cap Value B	-15.5	3	17.6	3	-3.4	2	0.1	2	16.8	2	0.33	88.5
3	Equity	US Eq	USEq	Fidelity Growth America Sr B	-21.2	4	12.7	4	-2.3	4	-1.5	2	12.7	2	2.84	2213.4
3	Equity	US Eq	USEq	Scotia CanAm Index	-14.8	3	17.4	3	-5.3	2	-2.4	3	17.4	3	2.43	5.1
3	Equity	US Eq	USEq	Investors US Large Cap Value A	-15.4	3	17.8	2	-3.2	2	0.2	1	15.7	4	1.02	14.1
3	Equity	US Eq	USEq	National Bank American Index Plus	-15.1	3	15.8	3	-7.9	3	-4.7	2	11.7	4	1.89	359.7
3	Equity	US Eq	USEq	Investors US Large Cap Growth Class A	-5.1	1	14.3	3	-6.5	4	-5.9	2	5.4	4	2.86	19
3	Equity	US Eq	USEq	TD US Index - I	-13.9	3	18.2	2	-5.3	3	-1.3	2	16.6	2	0.53	681.8
3	Equity	US Eq	USEq	Renaissance US Index	-13.6	3	16.7	3	-6	3	-1.6	2	17.2	2	1.82	76.1
3	Equity	US Eq	USEq	TD US Large-Cap Value - A	-17.6	3	18.9	3	-5.4	3	1.4	1	14.7	3	2.44	681.8
3	Equity	US Eq	USEq	Renaissance US Equity Value	-20	4	17.5	3	-4.4	3	-5.1	4	20.4	1	2.62	17.3
3	Equity	US Eq	USEq	TD US Large-Cap Value - I	-17.7	3	19	1	-5.4	2	1.3	3	8		2.44	16.1
3	Equity	US Eq	USEq	Capital Intl-US Equity CI I	-17.4	4	11.8	4	-2	4	-2.3	2	16.1	1	0.08	53.7
3	Equity	US Eq	USEq	Mac Universal US Growth Leaders	0	1	10.4	1	-3.5	2	-8.5	2	15.7	2	2.73	
3	Equity	US Eq	USEq	RBC US Index	-14.2	3	18	2	-5.6	3	-1.6	2	15.7	2	0.85	510.8
3	Equity	US Eq	USEq	TD US Quantitative Equity - I	-17.7	3	15.2	3	-5.4	3	-1.4	3	21.6	3	1.53	18.9
3	Equity	US Eq	USEq	Manulife US Core	-20.8	4	13.4	3	-2.5	3	-1.5	1	15.4	1	2.45	
3	Equity	US Eq	USEq	National Bank American Index	-13	4	19.3	1	-5.3	3	-5	4	15	2	1.24	9
3	Equity	US Eq	USEq	Maritime Life Elite American Eq Pooled	-14.1	2	12.8	3	-3.9	3	-4.5	4	15.4	2	0.44	0.7
3	Equity	US Eq	USEq	Maritime Life Elite US Special Eq Pooled	-10.6	2	14.4	3	-5.8	3	-3.8	3	11.9	3	0.49	0.4

Fund																
HSBC US Equity	3	Equity	US Eq	USEq	-14.9	3	16	3	-5.6	3	-3.3	3	10.4	4	2.33	24.3
IA Clarington American	3	Equity	US Eq	USEq	-12.7	2	17.9	2	-4.3	2	-3.9	3	10.5	4	2.4	29.8
Beutel Goodman American Equity	3	Equity	US Eq	USEq	-11	2	19.6	3	-6.1	3	3.6	1	23.3	1	1.42	1
imaxx TOP US Managers GIP 75/75	3	Equity	US Eq	USEq	-21.6	4	14.4	1	-0.1	1	-2.7	3			3.24	15.3
Quadrus Mac Univ US Growth Leaders	3	Equity	US Eq	USEq	0.1	1	10.4	2	-3.4	2	-8.6	4	7.9	4	2.69	33.6
Mawer US Equity	3	Equity	US Eq	USEq	-6.1	1	12.4	4	-6.9	4	-2.9	3			1.28	8.2
MLI US Large Cap Growth Class GIFe2	3	Equity	US Eq	USEq	-9.3	2	13.4	4	-8.2	4			20.2	1	3.36	31.5
MLI US Large Cap Growth Class GIFe	3	Equity	US Eq	USEq	-9.8	2	12.9	3	-8.7	3					3.9	2
MLI American Equity Index GIFe2	3	Equity	US Eq	USEq	-15.9	3	16.5	2	-7.4	2	-3.9	3	13.7	3	2.76	620.7
AGF American Growth Class	3	Equity	US Eq	USEq	-3.9	1	19.4	1	-0.3	1	-4.7	4	11.8	3	2.95	2.6
imaxx TOP US Managers GIP 75/100	3	Equity	US Eq	USEq	-21.8	2	14.1	3	-0.3	2	-3.1	3			3.49	52.5
Acker Finley Select US Value 50	3	Equity	US Eq	USEq	-27.9	4	18.4	4	15.6	1	12.3	1			1.94	151.7
IG Mackenzie Universal US Gr Leaders CLA	3	Equity	US Eq	USEq	0.5	1	9.2	4	-3.7	4	-8.6	4	7.4	4	3.02	6.9
MLI Renaissance US Basic Value GIFe2	2	Equity	US Eq	USEq	-20.8	3	16.5	2	-5.4	2	-6.1	3			3.52	
IG Fidelity US Equity Class B	2	Equity	US Eq	USEq	-22	4	11.4	3	-2.6	3	-2.9	3			3.21	241.4
IG Goldman Sachs US Equity A	2	Equity	US Eq	USEq	-19.4	4	10.4	4	-2	4	-3	3	14.7	3	2.99	
IG Goldman Sachs US Equity B	2	Equity	US Eq	USEq	-19.5	4	10.2	4	-2.1	4	-3.2	3	15.4	3	3.14	15.4
IG Fidelity US Equity Class A	2	Equity	US Eq	USEq	-21.9	4	11.5	4	-2.4	4	-2.8	3			3.06	10
IG Goldman Sachs US Equity Class A	2	Equity	US Eq	USEq	-20	4	10.2	4	-2.1	4	-0.4	2			3.12	
IG Goldman Sachs US Equity Class B	2	Equity	US Eq	USEq	-20.1	4	10	4	-2.3	4	-0.5	3			3.27	
IG FI US Equity C	2	Equity	US Eq	USEq	-21.9	4	11.5	4	-2.7	4	-2.7	3	15.4	3	3.17	89
IG FI US Equity B	2	Equity	US Eq	USEq	-21.8	4	11.5	4	-2.7	4	-2.7	3			3.14	54.2
IG FI US Equity A	2	Equity	US Eq	USEq	-21.7	4	11.7	4	-2.5	4	-2.5	3			2.99	7.1
IA Clarington US Dividend T	2	Equity	US Eq	USEq	-20.7	1	19.3	1	-6.5	4	-6.5	3			2.66	4.1
Renaissance US Equity Growth	2	Equity	US Eq	USEq	-18.1	3	14.1	3	-8.5	4	-5.7	4	16.2	4	2.62	0.7
AIM Trimark Core American Equity Cl	2	Equity	US Eq	USEq	-13.9	3	12.1	4	-9.6	4	-6.7	4	11.7	4	2.68	10.9
Putnam US Voyager D	2	Equity	US Eq	USEq	-12.2	2	11.1	4	-8.3	4	-6.7	3	12.8	3	1.93	9.5
MLI Renaissance US Basic Value GIFe	2	Equity	US Eq	USEq	-21.2	4	15.9	2	-5.9	2	-6.5	4	18.3	4	4.05	5.8
Putnam US Value D	2	Equity	US Eq	USEq	-27.4	4	17	2	-5.1	3	-1.5	2	15.2	2	1.93	4.5
Franklin Templeton US Rising Div A	2	Equity	US Eq	USEq	-17.3	3	10.9	4	-7.8	4	-4.4	3	11.9	3	2.59	0.5
MLI Fidelity Growth America GIF encore 2	2	Equity	US Eq	USEq	-22.1	2	11.6	4	-3.3	4	-2.4	2	16	4	3.4	8.2
Investors US Large Cap Growth C	2	Equity	US Eq	USEq	-4.7	1	14.3	3	-6.9	3	-5.8	4	6.2	2	2.88	0.3
Fidelity Growth America Sr T8	2	Equity	US Eq	USEq	-21.5	4	13.6	4	-2.5	4	-1.6	2	16.7	4	2.63	47.7
Saxon US Equity Investor Series	2	Equity	US Eq	USEq	-19.5	4	13	3	-5.7	3					1.86	45.8
Fidelity Growth America Sr S8	2	Equity	US Eq	USEq	-21.2	4	12.4	4	-2.3	4	-1.5	2	16.7	3	2.43	1.2
Fidelity Growth America Sr A	2	Equity	US Eq	USEq	-21.5	4	13.1	4	-2.5	4	-1.7	2	16.8	3	2.63	1.5
Scotia US Growth	2	Equity	US Eq	USEq	-11.1	2	12.5	2	-8	4	-2.9	3	10.3	2	2.53	8.5
Fidelity Growth America Cl B	2	Equity	US Eq	USEq	-21.3	4	12.3	4	-2.7	3	-1.8	2	16.2	3	2.58	9.4
Fidelity Growth America Cl A	2	Equity	US Eq	USEq	-21.5	4	11.2	2	-2.8	3	-1.9	2	16.2	3	2.78	0.5
Fidelity American Opportunities Sr B	2	Equity	US Eq	USEq	-12.8	2	11	2	-1.1	3	-3.4	3	6.3	2	2.45	0.8
Fidelity American Opportunities Sr A	2	Equity	US Eq	USEq	-13	2	11	2	-1.3	3	-3.5	3	6.3	2	2.65	
Fidelity American Opportunities Cl B	2	Equity	US Eq	USEq	-13	2	10.8	2	-1.4	3	-3.8	3	5.8	2	2.64	
Fidelity American Opportunities Cl A	2	Equity	US Eq	USEq	-13.1	2	10.6	2	-1.6	3	-3.9	3	5.8	2	2.84	
Ethical American Multi-Strategy	2	Equity	US Eq	USEq	-15.7	3	11	1	1.1	1	-8.1	4	11.3	2	2.31	52.2
MLI Fidelity Growth America GIF encore	2	Equity	US Eq	USEq	-22.5	4	9.3	2	-3.8	2	-2.9	3	15.2	4	3.93	9.8
Emissary US Growth	2	Equity	US Eq	USEq	-13.3	2	12.7	4	-7.4	4	-8.8	4	16.1	3	2.93	12
Trimark US Companies Class	2	Equity	US Eq	USEq	-11.7	2	18	2	-10.5	4			11.8	4	2.86	6.1
Desjardins American Equity Value	2	Equity	US Eq	USEq	-21	4	14.8	3	-6.4	3	-6.3	3			2.49	475
MLI American Equity Index GIFe	2	Equity	US Eq	USEq	-16.4	3	15	3	-7.6	3	-2.1	3	13	3	3.34	3.3
CIBC North American Demographics	2	Equity	US Eq	USEq	-16.8	3	12.9	3	-8.7	3	-4.2	4	10.1	3	2.74	16.4
PH&N US Equity A	2	Equity	US Eq	USEq	-13.7	3	11.2	3	-5.9	3	-7.1	4	15.7	4	1.16	322.5
PH&N US Dividend Income A	2	Equity	US Eq	USEq	-19.1	4	11.2	4	-6.5	4	-3.7	3	18.8	2	1.15	73.7
AGF US Value Class	2	Equity	US Eq	USEq	-34.2	4	19.6	4	2.8	1	-0.2	2	20.5	1	2.85	33.3

Fund														Expense Ratio	Total Asset ($Mill)
MDPIM US Equity Pool	2	Equity	US Eq	USEq	-18.1	3	17.2	2	-3	2	3	9.2	4	1.35	666.1
MD American Growth	2	Equity	US Eq	USEq	-9.9	2	13.7	3	-6.1	3	4	11.4	4	1.44	304.2
Capital Intl-US Equity Cl H	2	Equity	US Eq	USEq	-18	3	11.1	4	-2.8	2	3	18.9	1	0.77	17.3
Capital Intl-US Equity Cl D	2	Equity	US Eq	USEq	-18.6	3	10.3	4	-3.4	2	3	18.4	2	1.47	17.3
Capital Intl-US Equity Cl A	2	Equity	US Eq	USEq	-19	3	9.8	4	-3.9	2	3	13.2	3	1.97	17.3
Manulife US Large Cap Value Class	2	Equity	US Eq	USEq	-20.1	4	17.1	2	-7.3	4	3	13.6	3	2.8	4.4
AIM American Growth	2	Equity	US Eq	USEq	-16.1	3	11.3	4	-8.1	4	4	14.4	3	2.93	18
BMO US Growth	2	Equity	US Eq	USEq	-12.6	2	14.7	3	-11.3	4	1	11.4	4	2.48	71.3
Trimark US Companies	2	Equity	US Eq	USEq	-11.4	2	12.9	3	-10.4	4	4	10.6	4	2.61	76.3
Altamira US Larger Company	2	Equity	US Eq	USEq	-11.9	2	12.9	3	-7.3	4	4	16.1	2	2.67	34.4
imaxx US Equity Value	1	Equity	US Eq	USEq	-27	4	13.6	3	-6.9	4	3	24.6	1	2.74	6
Brandes US Equity	1	Equity	US Eq	USEq	-34.6	4	22.3	1	-6.3	3	3	14.6	3	2.6	69.9
CI Value Trust Corporate CI Shares Cl Z	1	Equity	US Eq	USEq	-34.6	4	23.5	1	-2.2	4	4			2.47	8
AIC Value	1	Equity	US Eq	USEq	-34	4	16.7	2	-9.9	4	2	15.2	3	2.31	77.7
AIC American Focused Corporate Class	1	Equity	US Eq	USEq	-35.2	4	23.1	1	-2.3	2	4	9.1	4	2.52	131.6
CI Value Trust Corporate Class	1	Equity	US Eq	USEq	-39.4	4	6.2	4	8.7	1	2	15.2	3	2.35	37.3
AIC American Focused	1	Equity	US Eq	USEq	-34.1	4	16.4	2	-10.2	4	3	8.6	4	2.57	856.4
Meritas US Equity	1	Equity	US Eq	USEq	-39.5	4	6.1	4	8.3	1	2	11.4	4	2.44	308.4
Northwest US Equity	1	Equity	US Eq	USEq	-17.2	3	13	3	-8.3	4	4	14.3	3	2.87	11.8
Mac Focus America Class	1	Equity	US Eq	USEq	-27.7	4	14.7	4	-5.9	3	1	13.5	3	2.86	16.5
Desjardins CI Value Trust Sector	1	Equity	US Eq	USEq	-11	2	8.1	4	-10.7	4	4			2.43	4.5
Putnam US Value A	1	Equity	US Eq	USEq	-34.2	4	16.3	2	-10.1	4	2	14.4	3	2.75	297.4
First Trust DOW 10 Strategy Trust 2003	1	Equity	US Eq	USEq	-27.9	4	16.3	2	-5.7	3	3	11.6	4	2.62	19.5
Putnam US Voyager A	1	Equity	US Eq	USEq	-23.7	2	23.9	1	-10.7	1	4	12.1	3	2.74	3.1
	1	Equity	US Eq	USEq	-12.9	4	10.4	4	-9	4				2.64	1.4

Expense Ratio: The manager's annual fee for managing and administering the fund, expressed as a percentage of total fund value. Some funds charge additional administrative fees not included in this figure. For full information on management and administrative costs, consult the fund prospectus.

Total Asset ($Mill): the current assets plus non-current assets.

Fund Table: Canadian Balanced and US Equity funds as of May 30, 2008.

Annual Returns: An annual return is the fund or portfolio return, for any 12-month period, including reinvested dividends.

Quartile Rankings: The quartile (1 to 4) in which this fund's "% YrEnd MmmYY" is positioned, relative to all others in its peer group. For example, if a mutual fund has a "Quart YrEnd Nov02" value of "1", that means this fund's rate of return for the 12 months ending November 30, 2002 is in the top 25% of all other mutual funds in its fund category. If it was "4" then this indicates the rate of return is amongst the bottom 25% of all its peers (e.g. Canadian Equity mutual funds or Canadian Bond segregated funds). Quartiles are useful since they indicate how the subject fund performs relative to its peers in its category. Many managers set the first (1) or second (2) quartile as their on-going goal as it indicates that the fund is outperforming the median fund within this category of funds.

3.7 Cumulative Distributions and Ogives

What Is an Ogive?

An *ogive* is a graph of a cumulative frequency distribution. By reading an ogive you can retrieve certain "percentile" information very quickly. This type of information is not readily available from a frequency distribution.

A soft drink manufacturer has to check periodically whether bottles marked as 2 litre actually contain 2 litres. Have you ever noticed that some bottles are filled to the top and some are not? To avoid customers' complaints, the manufacturer has to conduct some investigations to ensure that the bottling machine is working properly and filling the bottles with the right amount. A sample of 255 bottles was taken from the production floor, and the volumes of these 255 bottles were recorded. The data that showed how much soft drink was in each bottle were summarized in the following frequency distribution table:

Amount in a 2-litre bottle (ml)	Number of bottles
1999.00 and under 1999.50	5
1999.50 " " 2000.00	10
2000.00 " " 2000.50	20
2000.50 " " 2001.00	35
2001.00 " " 2001.50	55
2001.50 " " 2002.00	50
2002.00 " " 2002.50	40
2002.50 " " 2003.00	30
2003.00 " " 2003.50	10
Total	255

(Note: 1 litre = 1000 ml)

Suppose this frequency distribution is the only data we have available and we would like to know the answers to the following questions.

a. What percent of the bottles had less than 2000.00 ml?
b. What percent of the bottles had less than 2002.70 ml?
c. What percent of the bottles had at least 2001.25 ml?
d. 30% of the bottles have at most _____ml.
e. 25% of the bottles have at least _____ml.

Question (a) is easy to answer because 2000.00 ml is the upper boundary of the second class and you just add the frequencies of the first and second classes, (i.e. 5 + 10). The answer is 15 bottles, which is (15/255)*100 = 5.9% of the bottles had less than 2000.00 ml.

Question (b) is not easy because 2002.7 ml falls between 2002.50 and 2003.00. Similarly, for question (c) 2001.25 ml falls between 2001.00 and 2001.50.

To answer questions (b) and (c), you must plot an ogive.

The ogive for the volume of a 2000 ml bottle is

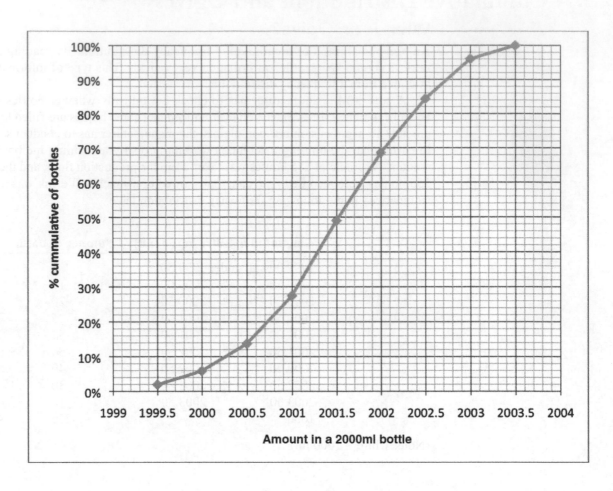

How to Draw an Ogive

Start with a frequency distribution table and add a cumulative frequency column and a cumulative relative frequency column. You may construct two kinds of cumulative relative frequencies. One is the cumulative relative frequency (crf) and the other is the cumulative percentage frequency (c%). Both kinds of cumulative frequency will give you the same answer. However, it is more common to use c% to construct the ogive.

1. Cumulative relative frequency (crf)

crf = relative frequency (rf) of the class + sum of all previous class relative frequencies

Alternatively, crf = Sum of all relative frequencies up to and including the class.

2. Cumulative percentage frequency (c%)

$$c\% = 100 \times \frac{cf}{sum\ of\ all\ frequencies}$$

or

$$c\% = 100 \times crf$$

Amount in a 2 litre bottle (ml)	# of bottles
1999.00 and under 1999.50	5
1999.50 " " 2000.00	10
2000.00 " " 2000.50	20
2000.50 " " 2001.00	35
2001.00 " " 2001.50	55
2001.50 " " 2002.00	50
2002.00 " " 2002.50	40
2002.50 " " 2003.00	30
2003.00 " " 2003.50	10
Total	255

Step 1: Construct the cumulative frequency distribution table as shown.

Amount in a 2 litre bottle (ml)	f = number of bottles	cf = cumulative number of bottles	crf = cumulative proportion of bottles	c% = cumulative percentage of bottles
1999.00 and under 1999.50	5	5	$5 \div 255 = 0.020$	$0.02 \times 100 = 2.0$
1999.50 " " 2000.00	10	$5 + 10 = 15$	$15 \div 255 = 0.059$	$0.059 \times 100 = 5.9$
2000.00 " " 2000.50	20	$5 + 10 + 20 = 35$	$35 \div 255 = 0.137$	$0.137 \times 100 = 13.7$
2000.50 " " 2001.00	35	$5 + 10 + 20 + 35 = 70$	$70 \div 255 = 0.274$	$0.274 \times 100 = 27.4$
2001.00 " " 2001.50	55	125	$125 \div 255 = 0.490$	$0.490 \times 100 = 49.0$
2001.50 " " 2002.00	50	175	$175 \div 255 = 0.686$	$0.686 \times 100 = 68.6$
2002.00 " " 2002.50	40	215	$215 \div 255 = 0.843$	$0.843 \times 100 = 84.3$
2002.50 " " 2003.00	30	245	$245 \div 255 = 0.961$	$0.961 \times 100 = 96.1$
2003.00 " " 2003.50	10	255	$255 \div 255 = 1.000$	$1.00 \times 100 = 100.0$
Total	255			

Step 2: Draw the ogive

To plot the ogive, you need to construct the vertical axis (y-axis) representing the c% and the horizontal axis (x-axis) representing the upper boundary for each class intervals. Start the graph at the first boundary.

The points representing the x-y coordinates on a graph are as follows:

horizontal axis (i.e., x-axis) *upper boundary* for each class	vertical axis (i.e., y-axis) c%
1999.50	2.5
2000.00	5.9
2000.50	13.7
2001.00	27.4
2001.50	49.0
2002.00	68.6
2002.50	84.3
2003.00	96.1
2003.50	100.0

The ogive is plotted as follows:

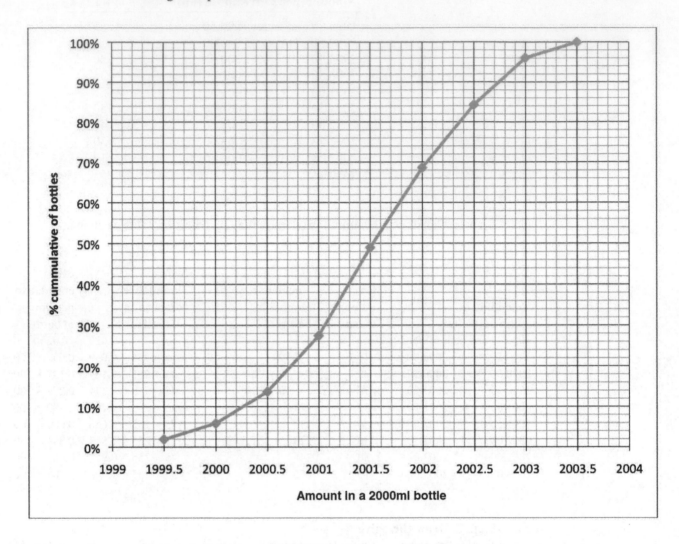

Join the points with a straight line. In the construction of an ogive, an extra upper boundary is added at the beginning so the graph starts with a crf of 0 or 0%.

Use the ogive presented earlier to answer the following questions, part (b) to part (e).

b) What percent of the bottles had less than 2002.70 ml?

To find the "less than 2002.7," go vertically upward at 2002.70 of the x-axis until you hit the ogive line, and then go across to acquire the y value (see A). The y value is 89%; that is, 89% of the bottles had less than 2002.7 ml.

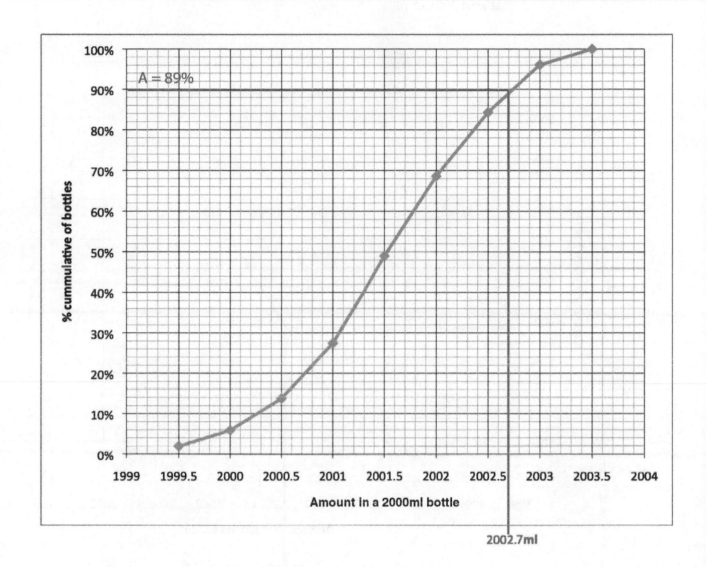

c) What percent of the bottles had at least 2001.25 ml?

To find the "at least 2001.25," go vertically upward at 2001.25 of the x-axis until you hit the ogive line, and then go across to acquire the y value (see B). The y value is 38%. However 38% indicates that 38% of the bottles had less than 2001.25 ml. The question asks for the percent of the bottles that had at least 2001.25 ml. Therefore, 62% (=100%–38%) of bottles had at least 2001.25 ml.

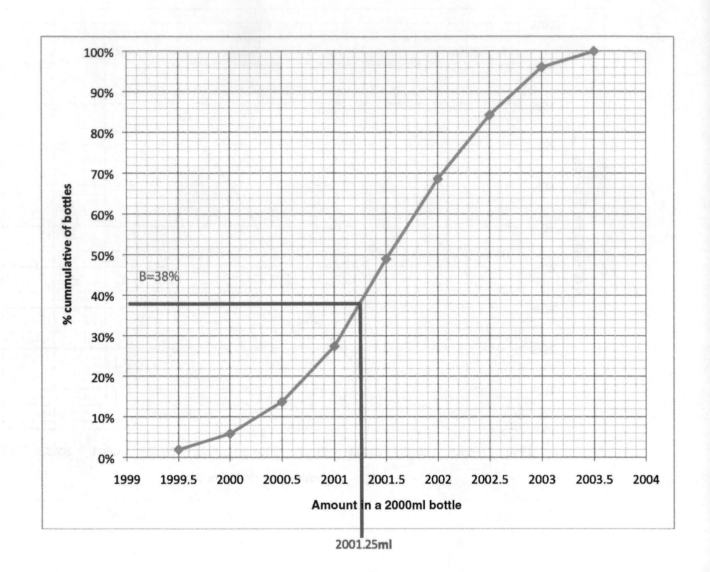

d) 30% of the bottles have at most _____ml.

Go across at 30% of the y-axis until you hit the ogive line, and then go downward to acquire the x value (see C). The x value is 2001.1 ml.

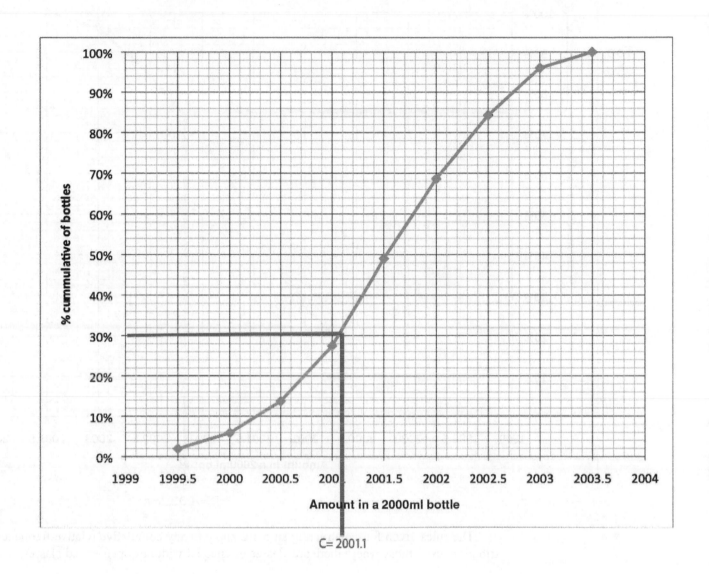

e) 25% of the bottles have at least ____ml.

Go across at 75%(=100%–25%) of the y-axis until you hit the ogive line, and then go downward to acquire the x value (see D). The x value is 2002.2 ml.

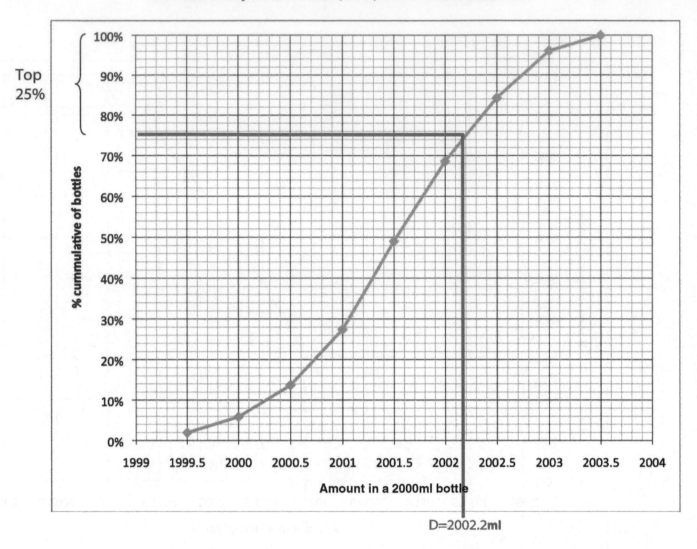

D=2002.2ml

The rules given for constructing an ogive apply to any cumulative relative frequency distribution, even those where there are classes of unequal width or open-ended classes.

EXAMPLE 3.13

A survey of employees in a large company revealed the following results regarding the amount of time employees had been in their current job position. The results were summarized as follows:

Time in Current Position (years)	Percent
less than 1	15.0
1 and under 3	27.4
3 " " 6	22.2
6 " " 10	13.9
10 " " 20	15.5
20 and over	6.0
Total	100

Based on these results:

a) Approximately what percent of quality professionals had been in their current position for 5 years or more?

b) Seventy percent of quality professionals had been in their current position for less than _____ years.

Step 1: Construct the cumulative frequency distribution table as shown.

The calculations necessary to construct a percentage ogive from the given data are shown next.

Time in current position (years)	Percent	Cumulative Percent
less than 1	15.0	15.0
1 and under 3	27.4	15.0 + 27.4 = 42.4
3 " " 6	22.2	15.0 + 27.4 + 22.2 = 64.6
6 " " 10	13.9	15.0 + 27.4 + 22.2 + 13.9 = 78.5
10 " " 20	15.5	15.0 + 27.4 + 22.2 + 13.9 + 15.5 = 94.0
20 and over	6.0	15.0 + 27.4 + 22.2 + 13.9 + 15.5 + 6.0 = 100.0
Total	100	

Step 2: To draw the ogive

To plot the ogive, you need to construct the vertical axis (y-axis) representing the c% and the horizontal axis (x-axis) representing the upper boundary for each class intervals. Start the graph at the first boundary.

The points representing the x-y coordinates on a graph are as follows:

horizontal axis (x-axis) *upper boundary* **for each class**	vertical axis (y-axis) c%
1	15.0
3	42.4
6	64.6
10	78.5
20	94.0

The ogive is plotted as follows:

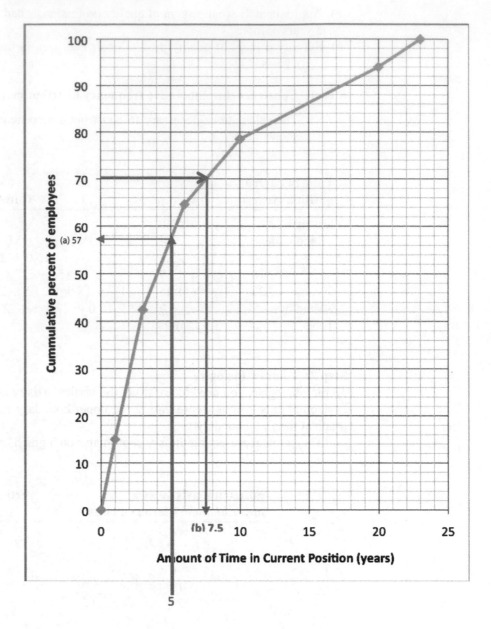

Join the points with straight lines. In the construction of an ogive, an extra upper boundary is added at the beginning so the graph starts with a crf of 0 or 0%.

Use the ogive presented earlier to answer the following questions, part (a) and part (b).

a) Approximately what percent of quality professionals had been in their current position for 5 years or more?

Answer: 100% − 57% = 43%

b) Seventy percent of quality professionals had been in their current position for less than ____ years.

Answer: 7.5 years

Problems for OGIVE

3.10 The National Association of Real Estate Agents has collected the following data on a sample of 170 salespersons. The classes represent their total annual commission.

Total Annual Commission	# people	rf	crf
$ 0 and under $ 5,000	5		
5,000 " " 10,000	9		
10,000 " " 15,000	11		
15,000 " " 20,000	48		
20,000 " " 30,000	62		
30,000 " " 40,000	19		
40,000 " " 50,000	9		
50,000 and over	7		
Total	170		

Construct an ogive that will help you answer the following questions:

a. Approximately what percentage of the salespeople earn more than $27,000?

b. Approximately how much is earned by the "middle" salespeople?

c. Approximately how much would a salesperson have to earn to be in the top 25%?

3.11 A pharmaceutical company sells 78 different products. The distribution of the annual sales amounts last year for these products is as follows:

Annual Sales ($000)	Number of Products
0 and under 10	17
10 " " 50	20
50 " " 100	24
100 " " 150	13
150 " " 250	4
Total	78

Construct an ogive and use it to determine the following:

a. How many products had annual sales of less than $80,000 last year?

b. What percentage of the products had sales of $120,000 or more last year?

3.12 The distribution of a company's stock according to the number of shares held is shown as follows:

Number of Shares Held	% of Shareholders
0 and under 50	25
50 " " 100	19
100 " " 500	41
500 " " 1000	12
1000 " " 2000	3
Total	100

Construct an ogive and use it to determine the following:

a. What percentage of shareholders held 200 or more shares?

b. The 20 percent of shareholders with the most shares each held how many shares or more?

3.8 Measure of Location

In this section, you will learn to estimate percentiles using an ogive. A percentile is the value below which a certain percent of observations fall. So the 30th percentile is the value (or score) below which 30 percent of the observations may be found. There are several ways to analytically determine percentiles, but we will focus on the one used by the calculator.

$$\text{Symbol for Percentile} : P_k = k^{th} \text{ percentile.}$$

The kth percentile in a data set is the value such that at most k% of the data is lower than the value and at most $(100 - k)$% of the data is higher than the value.

There are three steps involved in calculating percentile value.

Step 1: Arrange the data into an *ascending* data array.

Step 2. Calculate the rank of the kth percentile using the following formula:

$$r = Rank\, of\, P_k = Half\, Round\left[n\frac{k}{100} + \frac{1}{2} \right]$$

NOTATION:

n = number of observations in the data set

k = % of observations less than or equal to P_k

"Half round" means round to the nearest half.

The half-round procedure rounds the non-integer rank (e.g., 7.3, 7.4, etc.) to the nearest half.

Example: Half round (2.3) = 2.5,

Half round (3.8) = 4 , Half round (7.7) = 7.5

Round .25 and .75 *down* if k < 50 or

Round .25 and .75 *up* if k > 50

Step 3. Compute P_k.

$$P_k = x_r\, (\textit{if the rank is an integer})\, or = \frac{x_{r-1/2} + x_{r+1/2}}{2}\, (\textit{if the rank is a fractional half})$$

where x denotes the observation value corresponding to the rank (r).

Quartiles:

Some of the percentiles have special names. These are as follows:

First quartile = Q_1 = 25th percentile = P_{25}

Second quartile = Q_2 = Median = 50th percentile = P_{50}

Third quartile = Q_3 = 75th percentile = P_{75}

Summary

If the computed rank is a whole number (e.g., 12) then you looked for the observation value corresponding to the 12th position. That is why you have to arrange your data in ascending order first.

If the computed rank ends with 0.5 (e.g., 10.5) then you take the midpoint (or average) of the corresponding values to rank 10 and 11 because 10.5 is in the middle of 10 and 11.

How to Compute a Percentile

At this point it would be beneficial to demonstrate the calculation of various percentiles by referring to examples 3.14, 3.15, 3.16, and 3.17.

EXAMPLE 3.14   Consider the following data: 4 , 6, 8, 10, 16.

a) Determine Q_1

Step 1: Arrange the data into an *ascending* data array.

4 , 6, 8, 10, 16

Step 2: Calculate the r (rank).

Note: Q_1 is equivalent to the 25th percentile (i.e., P_{25}).

$$r = Half\, Round\left[5\left(\frac{25}{100} \right) + \frac{1}{2} \right] = Half\, Round\, (1.75) \sim 1.5$$

Since the decimal ends with 0.75 and k is less than 50, *round down* to 1.5.

Step 3: Compute P_k.

	x_1	x_2	x_3	x_4	x_5
Data	4	6	8	10	16
Rank	1	2	3	4	5

Note: Rank = 1.5 is between rank 1 and rank 2, so you take the average of the corresponding values of rank 1 and rank 2, which are 4 and 6 as shown next.

$$P_{25} = Q_1 = \frac{(x_1) + (x_2)}{2} = \frac{4 + 6}{2} = 5$$

b) Determine the median.

Step 1: Arrange the data into an *ascending* data array.

4, 6, 8, 10, 16

Step 2: Calculate the r (rank).

Note the median is equivalent to Q_2, which is equivalent P_{50}.

$$r = Half\,Round\left[5\left(\frac{50}{100}\right) + \frac{1}{2}\right] = Half\,Round\,(3) = 3$$

Step 3: Compute P_k.

	x_1	x_2	x_3	x_4	x_5
Data	4	6	8	10	16
Rank	1	2	3	4	5

$$P_{50} = Q_2 = x_3 = 8$$

c) Determine Q_3.

Step 1: Arrange the data into an *ascending* data array.

4, 6, 8, 10, 16

Step 2: Calculate the r (rank).

Note: Q_3 is equivalent to the 75th percentile (i.e., P_{75}).

$$r = Half\,Round\left[5\left(\frac{75}{100}\right) + \frac{1}{2}\right] = Half\,Round\,(4.25) \sim 4.5$$

Since the decimal ends with 0.75 and k is greater than 50, *round up* to 4.5.

Step 3: Compute P_k.

	x_1	x_2	x_3	x_4	x_5
Data	4	6	8	10	16
Rank	1	2	3	4	5

Note: Rank = 4.5 is between rank 4 and rank 5, so you take the average of the corresponding values of rank 4 and rank 5, which are 10 and 16 as shown next.

$$P_{75} = Q_3 = \frac{x_4 + x_5}{2} = \frac{10 + 16}{2} = 13$$

Calculate Percentile Using the CASIO Calculator

CASIO calculator instruction:

You can use the CASIO calculator to obtain Q_1, the median, and Q_3 by following these calculator procedures:

1. From the Main Menu, select the **STAT** mode.
2. Enter data (4, 6, 8, 10, 16) in List 1.
3. Select **CALC** (F2).
4. Select **SET** (F6).

5. Set the following:

1 Var XList : List 1
1 Var Freq : 1

After you have finished, press **EXIT**.

6. Select "**1 Var**" (**F1**) for the results

RESULTS (from CASIO FX-9750GII)

Scroll down until you get to

Q1   : 5
Med : 8
Q3   : 13

EXAMPLE 3.15   Consider the following data: **3, 5, 9, 13, 17, 21**.

a) Determine Q_1.

Step 1: Arrange the data into an *ascending* data array.

3, 5, 9, 13, 17, 21

Step 2: Calculate the r (rank).

Note: Q_1 is equivalent to the 25th percentile (i.e., P_{25}).

$$r = Half\,Round\left[6\left(\frac{25}{100}\right) + \frac{1}{2}\right] = Half\,Round\,(2) = 2$$

Step 3: Compute P_k.

	x_1	x_2	x_3	x_4	x_5	x_6
Data	3	5	9	13	17	21
Rank	1	2	3	4	5	6

$$P_{25} = Q_1 = x_2 = 5$$

b) Determine the median.

Step 1: Arrange the data into an *ascending* data array.

3, 5, 9, 13, 17, 21

Step 2: Calculate the r (rank).

Note the median is equivalent to Q_2, which is equivalent P_{50}.

$$r = Half\,Round\left[6\left(\frac{50}{100}\right) + \frac{1}{2}\right] = Half\,Round\,(3.5) = 3.5$$

Step 3: Compute P_k.

	x_1	x_2	x_3	x_4	x_5	x_6
Data	3	5	9	13	17	21
Rank	1	2	3	4	5	6

Note: Rank = 3.5 is between rank 3 and rank 4, so you take the average of the corresponding values of rank 3 and rank 4, which are 9 and 13 as shown next.

$$P_{50} = Q_2 = \frac{x_3 + x_4}{2} = \frac{9 + 13}{2} = 11$$

c) Determine Q_3.

Step 1: Arrange the data into an *ascending* data array.

3, 5, 9, 13, 17, 21

Step 2: Calculate the r (rank).

Note: Q_3 is equivalent to the 75th percentile (i.e., P_{75}).

$$r = Half\,Round\left[6\left(\frac{75}{100}\right) + \frac{1}{2}\right] = Half\,Round\,(5) = 5$$

Step 3: Compute P_k.

	x_1	x_2	x_3	x_4	x_5	x_{66}
Data	3	5	9	13	17	21
Rank	1	2	3	4	5	6

$P_{75} = Q_3 = x_5 = 17$

Calculate Percentile Using the CASIO Calculator

CASIO calculator instruction:

You can use the CASIO calculator to obtain Q_1, the median, and Q_3 by following these calculator procedures:

1. From the Main Menu, select the **STAT** mode.
2. Enter data **(3, 5, 9, 13, 17, 21)** in List 1.
3. Select **CALC** (F2).
4. Select SET (F6).
5. Set the following:

   1 Var XList : List 1
   1 Var Freq : 1

   After you have finished, press **EXIT**.

6. Select "**1 Var**" **(F1)** for the results

   RESULTS (from casio FX-9750GII)

   Scroll down until you get to

   Q1   : 5

   Med : 11

   Q3   : 17

Calculator versus Formula to Calculate Percentile

The CASIO calculator function "Calc" gives you the following percentiles.

Q1 = 25th percentile = is the value below which (less than) 25 percent of the observations may be found.

Q2 = median = 50th percentile = is the value below which (less than) 50 percent of the observations may be found.

Q3 = 75th percentile = is the value below which (less than) 75 percent of the observations may be found.

If you wish to find any percentile other than the 25th, 50th, or and 75th, you have to use the formula

$$r = Rank\,of\,P_k = Half\,Round\left[n\,\frac{k}{100} + \frac{1}{2}\right]$$

where n= number of elements in the data set or sample size and
k = the kth percentile.

The formula converts the kth percentile to rank (denotes as r) and from rank (r) back to an observation value.

EXAMPLE 3.16

Using Formula
to Obtain the
Percentile

Consider the following data: **6, 8, 9, 16, 19, 23**.

a) Determine P_{20} (20th percentile).

Step 1: Arrange the data into an *ascending* data array.

   6, 8, 9, 16, 19, 23

Step 2: Calculate the r (rank).

$$r = Half\,Round \left[6 \left(\frac{20}{100} \right) + \frac{1}{2} \right] = Half\,Round\,(1.7) \sim 1.5$$

Step 3: Compute P_k.

	x_1	x_2	x_3	x_4	x_5	x_6
Data	6	8	9	16	19	23
Rank	1	2	3	4	5	6

Note: Rank = 1.5 is between rank 1 and rank 2, so you take the average of the corresponding values of rank 1 and rank 2, which are 4 and 6 as shown below.

$$P_{20} = \frac{(x_1 + x_2)}{2} = \frac{6 + 8}{2} = 7$$

b) Determine P_{30} (30th percentile).

Step 1: Arrange the data into an *ascending* data array.

   6, 8, 9, 16, 19, 23

Step 2: Calculate the r (rank).

$$r = Half\,Round \left[6 \left(\frac{30}{100} \right) + \frac{1}{2} \right] = Half\,Round\,(2.3) \sim 2.5$$

Step 3: Compute P_k.

	x_1	x_2	x_3	x_4	x_5	x_6
Data	6	8	9	16	19	23
Rank	1	2	3	4	5	6

Note: Rank = 2.5 is between rank 2 and rank 3, so you take the average of the corresponding values of rank 2 and rank 3, which are 8 and 9 as shown below.

$$P_{30} = \frac{(x_2 + x_3)}{2} = \frac{8 + 9}{2} = 8.5$$

EXAMPLE 3.17

The following data represents the ages, in years, of 20 employees working at a retail outlet. The data has already been arranged in an ascending data array.

   18, 18, 18, 20, 20, 20, 20, 21, 22, 22, 24, 25, 28, 29, 29, 38, 40, 45, 52, 63

a) Determine the 80th percentile.

Step 1: Arrange the data into an *ascending* data array.

18, 18, 18, 20, 20, 20, 20, 21, 22, 22, 24, 25, 28, 29, 29, 38, 40, 45, 52, 63

Step 2: Calculate the r (rank).

$$r = Half\,Round \left[20 \left(\frac{80}{100} \right) + \frac{1}{2} \right] = Half\,Round\,(16.5) = 16.5$$

Step 3: Compute P_k.

	x_1	x_2	x_3	x_4	x_5	x_6	x_7	x_8	x_9	x_{10}	x_{11}	x_{12}	x_{13}	x_{14}	x_{15}	x_{16}	x_{17}	x_{18}	x_{19}	x_{20}
Data	18	18	18	20	20	20	20	21	22	22	24	25	28	29	29	38	40	45	52	63
Rank	1	2	3	4	5	6	7	8	9	10	11	12	13	14	15	16	17	18	19	20

Note: Rank = 16.5 is between rank 16 and rank 17, so you take the average of the corresponding values of rank 16 and rank 17, which are 38 and 40 as shown below.

$$P_{80} = \frac{(x_{16} + x_{17})}{2} = \frac{38 + 40}{2} = 39 \text{ years}$$

b) Determine the 34th percentile.

Step 1: Arrange the data into an *ascending* data array.

18, 18, 18, 20, 20, 20, 20, 21, 22, 22, 24, 25, 28, 29, 29, 38, 40, 45, 52, 63

Step 2: Calculate the r (rank).

$$r = Half\,Round\left[20\left(\frac{34}{100}\right) + \frac{1}{2}\right] = \text{Half Round } (7.3) = 7.5$$

Step 3: Compute P_k.

	x_1	x_2	x_3	x_4	x_5	x_6	x_7	x_8	x_9	x_{10}	x_{11}	x_{12}	x_{13}	x_{14}	x_{15}	x_{16}	x_{17}	x_{18}	x_{19}	x_{20}
Data	18	18	18	20	20	20	20	21	22	22	24	25	28	29	29	38	40	45	52	63
Rank	1	2	3	4	5	6	7	8	9	10	11	12	13	14	15	16	17	18	19	20

Note: Rank = 7.5 is between rank 7 and rank 8, so you take the average of the corresponding values of rank 7 and rank 8, which are 20 and 21 as shown below.

$$P_{34} = \frac{(x_7 + x_8)}{2} = \frac{20 + 21}{2} = 20.5 \text{ years}$$

c) Determine the 61st percentile.

Step 1: Arrange the data into an *ascending* data array.

18, 18, 18, 20, 20, 20, 20, 21, 22, 22, 24, 25, 28, 29, 29, 38, 40, 45, 52, 63

Step 2: Calculate the r (rank).

$$r = Half\,Round\left[20\left(\frac{61}{100}\right) + \frac{1}{2}\right] = \text{Half Round } (12.7) = 12.5$$

Step 3: Compute P_k.

	x_1	x_2	x_3	x_4	x_5	x_6	x_7	x_8	x_9	x_{10}	x_{11}	x_{12}	x_{13}	x_{14}	x_{15}	x_{16}	x_{17}	x_{18}	x_{19}	x_{20}
Data	18	18	18	20	20	20	20	21	22	22	24	25	28	29	29	38	40	45	52	63
Rank	1	2	3	4	5	6	7	8	9	10	11	12	13	14	15	16	17	18	19	20

Note: Rank = 12.5 is between rank 12 and rank 13, so you take the average of the corresponding values of rank 12 and rank 13, which are 25 and 28 as shown below.

$$P_{34} = \frac{(x_{12} + x_{13})}{2} = \frac{25 + 28}{2} = 26.5 \text{ years}$$

We can use the calculator to give us the values of the quartiles.

$$Q_1 = 20 \text{ years}, Q_2 = 23 \text{ years, and } Q_3 = 33.5 \text{ years}$$

Ogive and Percentile

An ogive for the volume of a 2000 ml bottle is shown. Use this ogive to find the first quartile (Q1), the median (Q2), and the third quartile (Q3).

a. To find Q1, you have to know that Q1 is equivalent to the 25th percentile. You can infer that 25% of the bottles are filled less than a certain value, and that value can be found in the ogive. To find the 25th percentile, go across at 25% of the y-axis until you hit the ogive line, and then go downward to acquire the x value (see A). Based on the ogive, 25% of the bottles are filled less than 2000.9 ml (i.e., 25th percentile = 2000.9, so Q1=2000.9).

b. Based on the same reasoning, Q2 is equivalent to the median value, which is the 50th percentile. To find the 50th percentile, go across at 50% of the y-axis until you hit the ogive line, and then go downward to acquire the x value (see B). Based on the ogive, 50% of the bottles are filled less than 2001.5 ml (i.e., the median is 2001.5, which is the same as saying that Q2 is equal to 2001.5).

c. Q3 is equivalent to the 75th percentile. To find the 75th percentile, go across at 75% of the y-axis until you hit the ogive line, and then go downward to acquire the x value (see C). Based on the ogive, 75% of the bottles are filled less than 2002.2 ml (i.e., Q3 = 2002.2).

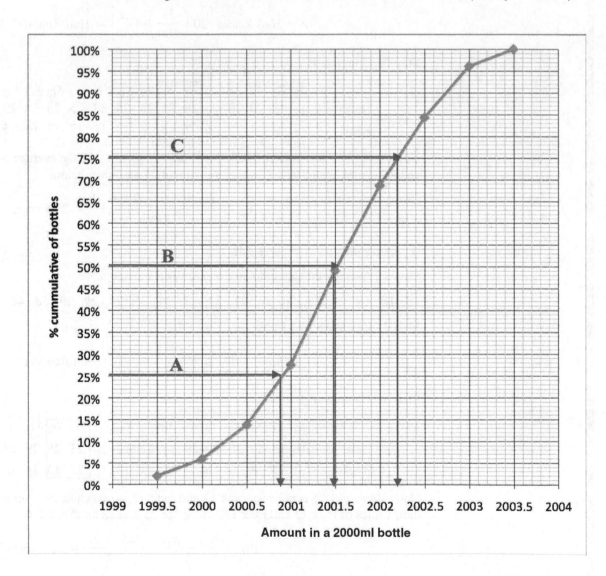

Test Your Understanding

TABLE 3.20

Canadian City Averages

City	Price	Change	Trend
Edmonton, AB	113.748	+0.026	➡
Calgary, AB	116.598	-0.097	➡
Winnipeg, MB	119.718	-0.434	⬇
Victoria, BC	125.717	-0.183	➡
Ottawa, ON	127.247	+1.234	⬆
Abbotsford, BC	127.375	-0.338	⬇
Regina, SK	126.220	+0.185	➡
Saskatoon, SK	126.419	+0.019	➡
London, ON	129.101	+0.329	⬆
Barrie, ON	129.288	-0.068	➡
Hamilton, ON	130.190	+0.316	⬆
Kitchener-Waterloo, ON	130.225	+0.887	⬆
Toronto, ON	131.476	+0.102	➡
Halifax, NS	134.200	-0.014	➡
Quebec City, QC	139.463	+0.030	➡
Montreal, QC	141.103	-0.773	⬇
Vancouver, BC	141.203	+0.592	⬆

Source: http://www.gasbuddy.com/GB_Price_List.aspx

For the gasoline prices in Canadian cities listed in Table 3.20: Canadian City Averages, determine the 43rd percentile value (P_{43}) in cents per litre.

Use the following data for questions 1 and 2.

Question 1: What is the rank for the 43rd percentile value?

        A. 7.81 rounded to 7.5
        B. 7.81 rounded to 8
        C. 7.81 rounded to 7
        D. 7.31 rounded to 7.5
        E. 7.31 rounded to 7

Answer: B

Question 2: What is the 43rd percentile value?

        A. 127.311
        B. 126.419
        C. 126.220
        D. 127.375
        E. None of the above

Answer: D

Problems for Percentile

3.13 Refer to Table 3.21: Divorces by provinces and territories published by Statistics Canada, calculate the following percentiles.

a. For 2002, determine the 25th percentile of number of divorces.

b. For 2002, determine the 50th percentile of number of divorces.

c. For 2002, determine the 75th percentile of number of divorces.

d. For 2002, determine the 80th percentile of number of divorces.

e. For 2002, determine the 43rd percentile of number of divorces.

f. For 2002, determine the 67th percentile of number of divorces.

TABLE 3.21   Divorces by Provinces and Territories

	2000	2001	2002
		number of divorces	
Canada			
Newfoundland and Labrador	1,913	1,755	1,842
Prince Edward Island	1,272	2,246	2,258
Nova Scotia	2,054	2,945	2,990
New Brunswick	2,717	2,570	3,461
Quebéc	7,054	7,094	6,499
Ontario	6,148	6,516	6,170
Manitoba	3,430	3,480	3,396
Saskatchewan	3,194	2,955	3,959
Alberta	9,176	9,252	9,291
British Columbia	11,017	11,115	12,125

Source: Statistics Canada, CANSIM, table 053-0002.
Last modified: 2004-09-02.

3.9 Organizing Categorical Data

You organize categorical data by tallying responses by categories and placing the results in tables. Typically, you construct a summary table to organize the data for a single categorical variable and you construct a contingency table to organize the data from two or more categorical variables.

The Summary Table

A **summary table** presents tallied responses as frequencies or percentages for each category. A summary table helps you see the differences among the categories by displaying the frequency, amount, or percentage of items in a set of categories in a separate column. Table 3.22 shows a summary table (stored in **Bill Payment**) that tallies the responses to a recent survey that asked adults how they pay their monthly bills.

TABLE 3.22

Types of Bill Payment

Form of Payment	Percentage (%)
Cash	15
Check	54
Electronic/online	28
Other/don't know	3

Source: *Data extracted from "How Adults Pay Monthly Bills,"* USA Today, *October 4, 2007, p. 1.*

From Table 3.22, you can conclude that more than half the people pay by check and 82% pay by either check or by electronic/online forms of payment.

EXAMPLE 3.18

Summary Table of Levels of Risk of Bond Funds

The 184 bond funds involved in Part I of the Choice Is Yours scenario are classified according to their risk level, categorized as below average, average, and above average. Construct a summary table of the bond funds, categorized by risk.

SOLUTION From Table 3.23, you can see that about the same number of funds are below average, average, and above average in risk. This means that 69.57% of the bond funds are classified as having an average or above average level of risk.

TABLE 3.23

Frequency and Percentage Summary Table Pertaining to Risk Level for 184 Bond Funds

Fund Risk Level	Number of Funds	Percentage of Funds (%)
Below average	56	30.43%
Average	69	37.50%
Above average	59	32.07%
Total	184	100.00%

The Contingency Table

A **contingency table** allows you to study patterns that may exist between the responses of two or more categorical variables. This type of table cross-tabulates, or tallies jointly, the responses of the categorical variables. In the simplest case of two categorical variables, the joint responses appear in a table such that the category tallies of one variable are located in the rows and the category tallies of the other variable are located in the columns. Intersections of the rows and columns are called **cells**, and each cell contains a value associated with a unique pair of responses for the two variables (e.g., Fee: Yes and Type: Intermediate Government in Table 3.24). Cells can contain the frequency, the percentage of the overall total, the percentage of the row total, or the percentage of the column total, depending on the type of contingency table being used.

In Part I of the Choice Is Yours scenario, you could create a contingency table to examine whether there is any pattern between the type of bond fund (intermediate government or short-term corporate) and whether the fund charges a fee (yes or no). You would begin by tallying the joint responses for each of the mutual funds in the sample of 184 bond mutual funds (stored in **Bond Funds**). You tally a response into one of the four possible cells in the table, depending on the type of bond fund and whether the fund charges a fee. For example, the first fund listed in the sample is classified as an intermediate government fund that does not charge a fee. Therefore, you tally this joint response into the cell that is the intersection of the Intermediate Government row and the No column. Table 3.24 shows the completed contingency table after all 184 bond funds have been tallied.

TABLE 3.24

Contingency Table Displaying Type of Fund and Whether a Fee Is Charged

	FEE		
TYPE	Yes	No	Total
Intermediate government	34	53	87
Short-term corporate	20	77	97
Total	54	130	184

To look for other patterns between the type of bond fund and whether the fund charges a fee, you can construct contingency tables that show cell values as a percentage of the overall total (the 184 mutual funds), the row totals (the 87 intermediate government funds and the 97 short-term corporate bond funds), and the column totals (the 54 funds that charge a fee and the 130 funds that do not charge a fee). Tables 3.25, 3.26, and 3.27 present these contingency tables.

Table 3.25 shows that 47.28% of the bond funds sampled are intermediate government funds, 52.72% are short-term corporate bond funds, and 18.48% are intermediate

TABLE 3.25

Contingency Table Displaying Type of Fund and Whether a Fee Is Charged, Based on Percentage of Overall Total

	FEE		
TYPE	Yes	No	Total
Intermediate government	18.48	28.80	47.28
Short-term corporate	10.87	41.85	52.72
Total	29.35	70.65	100.00

government funds that charge a fee. Table 3.26 shows that 39.08% of the intermediate government funds charge a fee, while 20.62% of the short-term corporate bond funds charge

TABLE 3.26

Contingency Table Displaying Type of Fund and Whether a Fee Is Charged, Based on Percentage of Row Total

	FEE		
TYPE	Yes	No	Total
Intermediate government	39.08	60.92	100.00
Short-term corporate	20.62	79.38	100.00
Total	29.35	70.65	100.00

a fee. Table 3.27 shows that of the funds that charge a fee, 62.96% are intermediate government funds. From the tables, you see that intermediate government funds are much more likely to charge a fee.

TABLE 3.27

Contingency Table Displaying Type of Fund and Whether a Fee Is Charged, Based on Percentage of Column Total

	FEE		
TYPE	Yes	No	Total
Intermediate government	62.96	40.77	47.28
Short-term corporate	37.04	59.23	52.72
Total	100.00	100.00	100.00

Problems for Section 3.9

LEARNING THE BASICS

3.14 A categorical variable has three categories, with the following frequencies of occurrence:

Category	Frequency
A	13
B	28
C	9

a. Compute the percentage of values in each category.
b. What conclusions can you reach concerning the categories?

3.15 The following data represent the responses to two questions asked in a survey of 40 college students majoring in business: What is your gender? (M = male; F = female) and What is your major? (A = Accounting; C = Computer Information Systems; M = Marketing):
a. Tally the data into a contingency table where the two rows represent the gender categories and the three columns represent the academic major categories.
b. Construct contingency tables based on percentages of all 40 student responses, based on row percentages and based on column percentages.

Gender:	M	M	M	F	M	F	F	M	F	M	F	M	M	M	M	F	F	M	F	F
Major:	A	C	C	M	A	C	A	A	C	C	A	A	A	M	C	M	A	A	A	C

Gender:	M	M	M	M	F	M	F	F	M	M	F	M	M	M	M	F	M	F	M	M
Major:	C	C	A	A	M	M	C	A	A	A	C	C	A	A	A	A	C	C	A	C

APPLYING THE CONCEPTS

3.16 The Transportation Security Administration reported that from January 1, 2008, to February 18, 2009, more than 14,000 banned items were collected at Palm Beach International Airport. The categories were as follows:

Category	Frequency
Flammables/irritants	8,350
Knives and blades	4,134
Prohibited tools	753
Sharp objects	497
Other	357

a. Compute the percentage of values in each category.
b. What conclusions can you reach concerning the banned items?

3.17 The following table represents world oil consumption in millions of barrels a day in 2009:

Region	Oil Consumption (millions of barrels a day)
Developed Europe	14.5
Japan	4.4
United States	18.8
Rest of the world	46.7

Source: Energy Information Administration, 2009.

a. Compute the percentage of values in each category.
b. What conclusions can you reach concerning the consumption of oil in 2009?

3.18 Federal obligations for benefit programs and the national debt were $63.8 trillion in 2008. The cost per household ($) for various categories was as follows:

Category	Cost per Household ($)
Civil servant retirement	15,851
Federal debt	54,537
Medicare	284,288
Military retirement	29,694
Social Security	160,216
Other	2,172

Source: Data extracted from "What We Owe," *USA Today*, May 29, 2009, p. 1A.

a. Compute the percentage of values in each category.
b. What conclusions can you reach concerning the benefit programs?

3.19 A survey of 1,085 adults asked "Do you enjoy shopping for clothing for yourself?" The results (data extracted from "Split decision on clothes shopping," *USA Today*, January 28, 2011, p. 1B) indicated that 51% of the females enjoyed shopping for clothing for themselves as compared to 44% of the males. The sample sizes of males and females was not provided. Suppose that the results were as shown in the following table: are summarized in the following table:

ENJOY SHOPPING FOR CLOTHING FOR YOURSELF	GENDER		Total
	Male	Female	
Yes	238	276	514
No	304	267	571
Total	542	543	1,085

a. Construct contingency tables based on total percentages, row percentages, and column percentages.

b. What conclusions do you reach from these analyses?

3.20 Each day at a large hospital, several hundred laboratory tests are performed. The rate at which these tests are done improperly (and therefore need to be redone) seems steady, at about 4%. In an effort to get to the root cause of these nonconformances, tests that need to be redone, the director of the lab decided to keep records over a period of one week. The laboratory tests were subdivided by the shift of workers who performed the lab tests. The results are as follows:

LAB TESTS PERFORMED	SHIFT		
	Day	Evening	Total
Nonconforming	16	24	40
Conforming	654	306	960
Total	670	330	1,000

a. Construct contingency tables based on total percentages, row percentages, and column percentages.

b. Which type of percentage—row, column, or total—do you think is most informative for these data? Explain.

c. What conclusions concerning the pattern of nonconforming laboratory tests can the laboratory director reach?

3.21 Does it take more time to get yourself removed from an email list than it used to? A study of 100 large online retailers revealed the following:

	NEED THREE OR MORE CLICKS TO BE REMOVED	
YEAR	Yes	No
2009	39	61
2008	7	93

Source: Data extracted from "Drill Down," *The New York Times*, March 29, 2010, p. B2.

What do these results tell you about whether more online retailers were requiring three or more clicks in 2009 than in 2008?

3.10 Visualizing Two Numerical Variables

Often you will want to explore possible relationships between two numerical variables. You use a scatter plot as a first step to visualize such relationships. In the special case where one of your variables represents the passage of time, you use a time-series plot.

The Scatter Plot

Often, you have two numerical measurements about the same item or individual. A **scatter plot** can explore the possible relationship between those measurements by plotting the data of one numerical variable on the horizontal, or X, axis and the data of a second numerical variable on the vertical, or Y, axis. For example, a marketing analyst could study the effectiveness of advertising by comparing advertising expenses and sales revenues of 50 stores. Using a scatter plot, a point is plotted on the two-dimensional graph for each store, using the X axis to represent advertising expenses and the Y axis to represent sales revenues.

Table 3.28 presents the revenues and value (both in millions of dollars) for all 30 NBA professional basketball teams that is stored in NBAValues. To explore the possible relationship between the revenues generated by a team and the value of a team, you can create a scatter plot.

TABLE 3.28

Values and Revenues for NBA Teams

Team	Value	Revenues	Team	Value	Revenues
Atlanta	306	103	Milwaukee	254	91
Boston	433	144	Minnesota	268	96
Charlotte	278	96	New Jersey	269	92
Chicago	511	168	New Orleans	267	95
Cleveland	476	159	New York	586	202
Dallas	446	154	Oklahoma City	310	111
Denver	321	115	Orlando	361	107
Detroit	479	171	Philadelphia	344	115
Golden State	315	113	Phoenix	429	148
Houston	470	160	Portland	338	121
Indiana	281	97	Sacramento	305	109
Los Angeles Clippers	295	102	San Antonio	398	133
Los Angeles Lakers	607	209	Toronto	386	133
Memphis	257	88	Utah	343	118
Miami	364	126	Washington	313	110

Source: Data extracted from **www.forbes.com/lists/2009/32/basketball-values-09_NBA-Team-Valuations_Rank.html**.

For each team, you plot the revenues on the X axis and the values on the Y axis. Figure 3.4 presents a scatter plot for these two variables.

FIGURE 3.4

Scatter plot of revenue and value

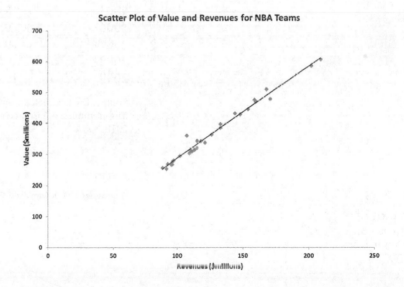

Reviewing Figure 3.4, you see that there appears to be a very strong increasing (positive) relationship between revenues and the value of a team. In other words, teams that generate a smaller amount of revenues have a lower value, while teams that generate higher revenues have a higher value. Notice the straight line that has been superimposed on the plotted data in Figure 3.4. For these data, this line is very close to the points in the scatter plot. This line is a linear regression prediction line that will be discussed in Chapter 15. (In Section 4.5, you will return to this example when you learn about the covariance and the coefficient of correlation.)

Other pairs of variables may have a decreasing (negative) relationship in which one variable decreases as the other increases. In other situations, there may be a weak or no relationship between the variables.

The Time-Series Plot

A **time-series plot** plots the values of a numerical variable on the Y axis and plots the time period associated with each numerical value on the X axis. A time-series plot can help explore trends in data that occur over time. For example, Table 3.29 presents the combined gross (in millions of dollars) of movies released from 1996 to 2009 that is stored in MovieGross. To better visualize this data, you create the time-series plot shown in Figure 3.5.

From Figure 3.5, you see that there was a steady increase in the combined gross of movies between 1996 and 2009. During that time, the combined gross increased from under $6 billion in 1996 to more than $10 billion in 2009.

TABLE 3.29

Combined Gross of Movies

Year	Combined Gross
1996	5,669.20
1997	6,393.90
1998	6,523.00
1999	7,317.50
2000	7,659.50
2001	8,077.80
2002	9,146.10
2003	9,043.20
2004	9,359.40
2005	8,817.10
2006	9,231.80
2007	9,685.70
2008	9,707.40
2009	10,675.60

Source: Data extracted from **www .the-numbers. com/movies**, February 16, 2010.

FIGURE 3.5

Time-series plot of combined gross of movies per year from 1996 to 2009

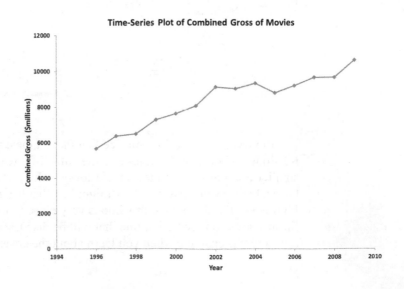

Problems for Section 3.10

LEARNING THE BASICS

3.22 The following is a set of data from a sample of $n = 11$ items:

X:	7	5	8	3	6	0	2	4	9	5	8
Y:	1	5	4	9	8	0	6	2	7	5	4

a. Construct a scatter plot.
b. Is there a relationship between X and Y? Explain.

3.23 The following is a series of annual sales (in millions of dollars) over an 11-year period (2000 to 2010):

Year:	2000	2001	2002	2003	2004	2005	2006	2007	2008	2009	2010
Sales:	13.0	17.0	19.0	20.0	20.5	20.5	20.5	20.0	19.0	17.0	13.0

a. Construct a time-series plot.
b. Does there appear to be any change in annual sales over time? Explain.

APPLYING THE CONCEPTS

3.24 Movie companies need to predict the gross receipts of individual movies once the movie has debuted. The following results, stored in PotterMovies , are the first weekend gross, the U.S. gross, and the worldwide gross (in millions of dollars) of the first six Harry Potter movies.

Title	First Weekend	U.S. Gross	Worldwide Gross
Sorcerer's Stone	90.295	317.558	976.458
Chamber of Secrets	88.357	261.988	878.988
Prisoner of Azkaban	93.687	249.539	795.539
Goblet of Fire	102.335	290.013	896.013
Order of the Phoenix	77.108	292.005	938.469
Half-Blood Prince	77.836	301.460	934.601

Source: Data extracted from **www.the-numbers.com/interactive/comp-Harry-Potter.php**.

a. Construct a scatter plot with first weekend gross on the X axis and U.S. gross on the Y axis.
b. Construct a scatter plot with first weekend gross on the X axis and worldwide gross on the Y axis.

c. What can you say about the relationship between first weekend gross and U.S. gross and first weekend gross and worldwide gross?

3.25 The file VeggieBurger contains data on the calories and total fat (in grams per serving) for a sample of 12 veggie burgers.

Source: Data extracted from *"Healthful Burgers That Taste Good,"* *Consumer Reports,* June 2008, p 8.

a. Construct a scatter plot with calories on the X axis and total fat on the Y axis.
b. What conclusions can you reach about the relationship between the calories and total fat in veggie burgers?

3.26 College basketball is big business, with coaches' salaries, revenues, and expenses in millions of dollars. The file College Basketball contains the coaches' salary and revenue for college basketball at 60 of the 65 schools that played in the 2009 NCAA men's basketball tournament (data extracted from "Compensation for Division 1 Men's Basketball Coaches," *USA Today,* April 2, 2010, p. 8C; and C. Isadore, "Nothing but Net: Basketball Dollars by School," **money.cnn.com/2010/03/18/news/companies/basketball_profits/**).
a. Do you think schools with higher revenues also have higher coaches' salaries?
b. Construct a scatter plot with revenue on the X axis and coaches' salaries on the Y axis.
c. Does the scatter plot confirm or contradict your answer to (a)?

3.27 College football players trying out for the NFL are given the Wonderlic standardized intelligence test. The file Wonderlic contains the average Wonderlic scores of football players trying out for the NFL and the graduation rate for football players at selected schools (data extracted from S. Walker, "The NFL's Smartest Team," *The Wall Street Journal,* September 30, 2005, pp. W1, W10).
a. Construct a scatter plot with average Wonderlic score on the X axis and graduation rate on the Y axis.
b. What conclusions can you reach about the relationship between the average Wonderlic score and graduation rate?

3.28 How have stocks performed in the past? The following table presents the data stored in Stock Performance that shows the performance of a broad measure of stocks (by percentage) for each decade from the 1830s through the 2000s:

Decade	Performance (%)
1830s	2.8
1840s	12.8
1850s	6.6
1860s	12.5
1870s	7.5
1880s	6.0
1890s	5.5
1900s	10.9
1910s	2.2
1920s	13.3
1930s	−2.2
1940s	9.6
1950s	18.2
1960s	8.3
1970s	6.6
1980s	16.6
1990s	17.6
2000s*	−0.5

* Through December 15, 2009.

Source: Data extracted from T. Lauricella, "Investors Hope the '10s" Beat the '00s," *The Wall Street Journal,* December 21, 2009, pp. C1, C2.

a. Construct a time-series plot of the stock performance from the 1830s to the 2000s.
b. Does there appear to be any pattern in the data?

3.29 According to the U.S. Census Bureau, the average price of a new home declined in 2008 and 2009. The file New Home Prices contains the average price paid for a new

home from 1990 to 2010 (extracted from **www.census.gov**, April 1, 2011).

a. Construct a time-series plot of new home prices.
b. What pattern, if any, is present in the data?

3.30 The following data (stored in Movie Attendance) represent the yearly movie attendance (in billions) from 2001 through 2010:

Year	Attendance
2001	1.44
2002	1.60
2003	1.52
2004	1.48
2005	1.38
2006	1.40
2007	1.40
2008	1.36
2009	1.42
2010	1.35

Source: Data extracted from Motion Picture Association of America, **www.mpaa.org**, and S. Bowles, "Ticket Sales Slump at 2010 Box Office," *USA Today,* January 3, 2011, p. 1D.

a. Construct a time-series plot for the movie attendance (in billions).
b. What pattern, if any, is present in the data?

3.31 The file Audits contains the number of audits of corporations with assets of more than $250 million conducted by the Internal Revenue Service (data extracted from K. McCoy, "IRS Audits Big Firms Less Often," *USA Today*, April 15, 2010, p. 1B).

a. Construct a time-series plot.
b. What pattern, if any, is present in the data?

3.11 Misuses and Common Errors in Visualizing Data

Good graphical displays clearly and unambiguously reveal what the data convey. Unfortunately, many graphs presented in the media (broadcast, print, and online) are incorrect, misleading, or so unnecessarily complicated that they should never be used. To illustrate the misuse of graphs, the chart presented in Figure 3.6 is similar to one that was printed in *Time* magazine as part of an article on increasing exports of wine from Australia to the United States.

FIGURE 3.6

"Improper" display of Australian wine exports to the United States, in millions of gallons

Source: *Based on S. Watterson, "Liquid Gold— Australians Are Changing the World of Wine. Even the French Seem Grateful," Time, November 22, 1999, p. 68.*

We're drinking more . . .
Australian wine exports to the U.S.
in millions of gallons

1.04 — 1989
2.25 — 1992
3.67 — 1995
6.77 — 1997

In Figure 3.6, the wineglass icon representing the 6.77 million gallons for 1997 does not appear to be almost twice the size of the wineglass icon representing the 3.67 million gallons for 1995, nor does the wineglass icon representing the 2.25 million gallons for 1992 appear to be twice the size of the wineglass icon representing the 1.04 million gallons for 1989. Part of the reason for this is that the three-dimensional wineglass icon is used to represent the two dimensions of exports and time. Although the wineglass presentation may catch the eye, the data should instead be presented in a summary table or a time-series plot.

In addition to the type of distortion created by the wineglass icons in the *Time* magazine graph displayed in Figure 3.6, improper use of the vertical and horizontal axes leads to distortions. Figure 3.7 presents another graph used in the same *Time* magazine article.

FIGURE 3.7

"Improper" display of amount of land planted with grapes for the wine industry

Source: *Based on S. Watterson, "Liquid Gold—Australians Are Changing the World of Wine. Even the French Seem Grateful," Time, November 22, 1999, pp. 68–69.*

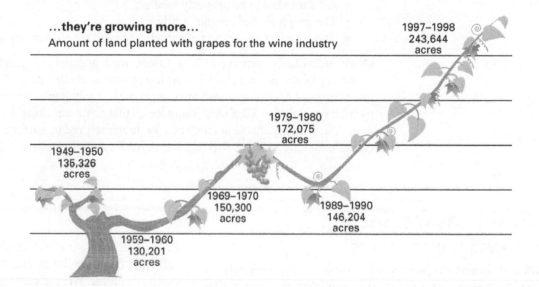

...they're growing more...
Amount of land planted with grapes for the wine industry

1997–1998
243,644
acres

1979–1980
172,075
acres

1949–1950
135,326
acres

1969–1970
150,300
acres

1989–1990
146,204
acres

1959–1960
130,201
acres

There are several problems in this graph. First, there is no zero point on the vertical axis. Second, the acreage of 135,326 for 1949–1950 is plotted above the acreage of 150,300 for 1969–1970. Third, it is not obvious that the difference between 1979–1980 and 1997–1998 (71,569 acres) is approximately 3.5 times the difference between 1979–1980 and 1969–1970 (21,775 acres). Fourth, there are no scale values on the horizontal axis. Years are plotted next to the acreage totals, not on the horizontal axis. Fifth, the values for the time dimension are not properly spaced along the horizontal axis. For example, the value for 1979–1980 is much closer to 1989–1990 than it is to 1969–1970. Other types of eye-catching displays that you typically see in magazines and newspapers often include information that is not necessary and just adds excessive clutter. Figure 3.8 represents one such display.

FIGURE 3.8

"Improper" plot of market share of soft drinks

Source: *Based on Anne B. Carey and Sam Ward, "Coke Still Has Most Fizz," USA Today, May 10, 2000, p. 1B.*

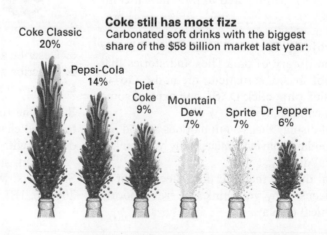

Coke still has most fizz
Carbonated soft drinks with the biggest share of the $58 billion market last year:

Coke Classic
20%

Pepsi-Cola
14%

Diet Coke
9%

Mountain Dew
7%

Sprite
7%

Dr Pepper
6%

The graph in Figure 3.8 shows the products with the largest market share for soft drinks. The graph suffers from too much clutter, although it is designed to show the differences in market share among the soft drinks. The display of the fizz for each soft drink takes up too much of the graph relative to the data. The same information could be better conveyed with a bar chart or pie chart.

The following are some guidelines for developing good graphs:

- A graph should not distort the data.
- A graph should not contain **chartjunk**, unnecessary adornments that convey no useful information.
- Any two-dimensional graph should contain a scale for each axis.
- The scale on the vertical axis should begin at zero.
- All axes should be properly labeled.
- The graph should contain a title.
- The simplest possible graph should be used for a given set of data.

Often individuals unaware of how to construct appropriate graphs violate these guidelines. Some applications, including Excel, tempt you to create "pretty" charts that may be fancy in their designs but that represent unwise choices. For example, making a simple pie chart fancier by adding exploded 3D slices is unwise as this can complicate a viewer's interpretation of the data. Uncommon chart choices such as doughnut, radar, surface, bubble, cone, and pyramid charts may look visually striking, but in most cases they obscure the data.

Problems for Section 3.11

APPLYING THE CONCEPTS

3.32 (Student Project) Bring to class a chart from either a website, newspaper, or magazine published this month that you believe to be a poorly drawn representation of a numerical variable. Be prepared to submit the chart to the instructor with comments about why you believe it is inappropriate. Do you believe that the intent of the chart is to purposely mislead the reader? Also, be prepared to present and comment on this in class.

3.33 (Student Project) Bring to class a chart from either a website, newspaper, or magazine published this month that you believe to be a poorly drawn representation of a categorical variable. Be prepared to submit the chart to the instructor with comments about why you consider it inappropriate. Do you believe that the intent of the chart is to purposely mislead the reader? Also, be prepared to present and comment on this in class.

3.34 (Student Project) The Data and Story Library (DASL) is an online library of data files and stories that illustrate the use of basic statistical methods. Go to **lib.stat.cmu.edu/index.php**, click DASL and explore some of the various graphical displays.
a. Select a graphical display that you think does a good job revealing what the data convey. Discuss why you think it is a good graphical display.
b. Select a graphical display that you think needs a lot of improvement. Discuss why you think that it is a poorly constructed graphical display.

3.35 The following visual display contains an overembellished chart similar to one that appeared in *USA Today*, dealing with the average consumer's Valentine's Day spending ("USA Today Snapshots: The Price of Romance," *USA Today*, February 14, 2007, p. 1B).

a. Describe at least one good feature of this visual display.
b. Describe at least one bad feature of this visual display.
c. Redraw the graph, using the guidelines given above.

3.36 The following visual display contains an overembellished chart similar to one that appeared in *USA Today*, dealing with the estimated number of hours the typical American spends using various media ("USA Today Snapshots: Minding Their Media," *USA Today*, March 2, 2007, p. 1B).

Media Usage
Estimated number of hours the typical American will spend using various media this year.

Listening to music .175

Reading newspapers 175

Using Internet 195

Listening to Radio 974

Watching TV 1555

Courtesy of David Levine

a. Describe at least one good feature of this visual display.
b. Describe at least one bad feature of this visual display.
c. Redraw the graph, using the guidelines given on page 128.

3.37 The following visual display contains an overembellished chart similar to one that appeared in *USA Today*, dealing with which card is safer to use ("USA Today Snapshots: Credit Card vs. Debit Card," *USA Today*, March 14, 2007, p. 1B).

Credit Card vs. Debit Card:
Which one is safer to use?

Don't Mind 49%
Credit Card 32%

a. Describe at least one good feature of this visual display.
b. Describe at least one bad feature of this visual display.
c. Redraw the graph, using the guidelines given on page 128.

3.38 Professor Deanna Oxender Burgess of Florida Gulf Coast University conducted research on annual reports of corporations (see D. Rosato, "Worried About the Numbers? How About the Charts?" *The New York Times*, September 15, 2002, p. B7) and found that even slight distortions in a chart changed readers' perception of the information. Using Internet or library sources, select a corporation and study the most recent annual report. Find at least one chart in the report that you think needs improvement and develop an improved version of the chart. Explain why you believe the improved chart is better than the one included in the annual report.

Choice Is Yours, Part I

I n the Using Statistics scenario, you were hired by the Choice Is Yours investment company to assist clients who seek to invest in mutual funds. A sample of 184 bond mutual funds was selected, and information on the funds and past performance history was recorded. For each of the 184 funds, data were collected on eight variables. With so much information, visualizing all these numbers required the use of properly selected graphical displays.

From bar charts and pie charts, you were able to illustrate that about one-third of the funds were classified as having below-average risk, about one-third had average risk, and about one-third had above-average risk. Cross tabulations of the funds by whether the fund charged a fee and whether the fund invested in intermediate government bonds or short-term corporate bonds revealed that intermediate government bond funds are more likely to charge fees. After constructing histograms on the 2009 return, you were able to conclude that the returns were much higher for the short-term corporate bond funds than for the intermediate government bonds. The return for intermediate government bond funds is concentrated between 0 and 10, whereas the return for the short-term corporate bond funds is concentrated between 5 and 15.

With these insights, you can inform your clients about how the different funds performed. Of course, past performance history does not guarantee future performance. In fact, if you look at returns in 2008, stored in `BondFunds2008`, you will discover that the returns were much *lower* for the short-term corporate bond funds than for the intermediate government bonds!

Using graphical methods such as these is an important first step in summarizing and interpreting data. Although the proper display of data (as discussed in Section 3.12) helps to avoid ambiguity, graphical methods always contain a certain degree of subjectivity. Next, you will need descriptive statistics to further analyze the past performance of the mutual funds. Chapter 4 presents descriptive statistics (e.g., mean, median, and mode).

SUMMARY

Organizing and visualizing data involves using various tables and charts to help draw conclusions about data. In several different chapter examples, tables and charts helped you reach conclusions about how people prefer to pay their bills and about the cost of restaurant meals in a city and its suburbs; they also provided some insights about the sample of bond mutual funds in the Using Statistics scenario.

The tables and charts you use depend on the type of data you have. Table 3.30 summarizes the proper choices for the type of data and the tables and charts discussed in this chapter. In Chapter 4 you will learn about a variety of descriptive statistics useful for data analysis and interpretation.

TABLE 3.30

Selecting Tables and Charts

	Type of Data	
Type of Analysis	**Numerical**	**Categorical**
Organizing data	Ordered array, frequency distribution, relative frequency distribution, percentage distribution, cumulative percentage distribution	Summary table, contingency table (Section 3.10)
Visualizing one variable	Stem-and-leaf display, histogram, percentage polygon, cumulative percentage polygon (ogive)	Bar chart, pie chart, Pareto chart
Visualizing two variables	Scatter plot, time-series plot (Section 3.11)	Side-by-side bar chart
Organizing multidimensional data	Multidimensional tables	Multidimensional tables

KEY EQUATIONS

Determining the Class Interval Width

$$\text{Estimated Class Width} = \frac{\text{maximum} - \text{minimum}}{\text{minimum number of classes recommended}}$$

Computing the Proportion or Relative Frequency

$$\text{Proportion} = \text{relative frequency} = \frac{\text{number of values in each class}}{\text{total number of values}}$$

KEY TERMS

boundaries 62	midpoints 78	stem-and-leaf plot 39
cells 109	OGIVE 89	stem unit 43
chartjunk 118	quantitative 62	summary table 108
classes 62	relative frequency or percentage 75	time-series plot 114
contingency table 109	scatter plot 112	

PROBLEMS

CHECKING YOUR UNDERSTANDING

3.39 How do histograms and polygons differ in their construction and use?

3.40 Why would you construct a summary table?

3.41 What are the advantages and disadvantages of using a bar chart, a pie chart, and a Pareto chart?

3.42 Compare and contrast the bar chart for categorical data with the histogram for numerical data.

3.43 What is the difference between a time-series plot and a scatter plot?

3.44 Why is it said that the main feature of a Pareto chart is its ability to separate the "vital few" from the "trivial many"?

3.45 What are the three different ways to break down the percentages in a contingency table?

3.46 How can a multidimensional table differ from a two variable contingency table?

3.47 What type of insights can you gain from a three-way table that are not available in a two-way table?

APPLYING THE CONCEPTS

3.48 The following summary table presents the breakdown of the price of a new college textbook:

Revenue Category	Percentage (%)	
Publisher	64.8	
Manufacturing costs		32.3
Marketing and promotion		15.4
Administrative costs and taxes		10.0
After-tax profit		7.1
Bookstore	22.4	
Employee salaries and benefits		11.3
Operations		6.6
Pretax profit		4.5
Author	11.6	
Freight	1.2	

Source: Data extracted from T. Lewin, "When Books Break the Bank," *The New York Times*, September 16, 2003, pp. B1, B4.

a. Using the four categories publisher, bookstore, author, and freight, construct a bar chart, a pie chart, and a Pareto chart.

b. Using the four subcategories of publisher and three subcategories of bookstore, along with the author and freight categories, construct a Pareto chart.

c. Based on the results of (a) and (b), what conclusions can you reach concerning who gets the revenue from the sales of new college textbooks? Do any of these results surprise you? Explain.

3.49 The following table represents the market share (in number of movies, gross in millions of dollars, and in number of tickets sold in millions) of each type of movie in 2009:

Type	Number	Gross ($ millions)	Tickets (millions)
Based on book/short story	66	2042.9	272.4
Based on comic/graphic novel	6	376.2	50.2
Based on factual book/article	5	280.7	37.4
Based on game	3	9.2	1.2
Based on musical/opera	1	13.7	1.8
Based on play	8	172.0	22.9
Based on real life events	95	334.9	44.7
Based on toy	1	150.2	20.0
Based on TV	7	267.5	35.7
Compilation	1	0.6	0.1
Original screenplay	203	4,335.7	578.1
Remake	18	422.6	56.3
Sequel	20	2,064.2	275.2
Spin-off	1	179.9	24.0

Source: Data extracted from **www.the-numbers.com/market/Sources2009.php**.

a. Construct a bar chart, a pie chart, and a Pareto chart for the number of movies, gross (in millions of dollars), and number of tickets sold (in millions).
b. What conclusions can you reach about the market share of the different types of movies in 2009?

3.50 A survey was conducted from 665 consumer magazines on the practices of their websites. The results are summarized in a copyediting table and a fact-checking table:

Copyediting as Compared to Print Content	Percentage
As rigorous	41
Less rigorous	48
Not copyedited	11

a. For copyediting, construct a bar chart, a pie chart, and a Pareto chart.
b. Which graphical method do you think is best for portraying these data?

Fact Checking as Compared to Print Content	Percentage
Same	57
Less rigorous	27
Online not fact checked	8
Neither online nor print is fact-checked	8

Source: Data extracted from S. Clifford, "Columbia Survey Finds a Slack Editing Process of Magazine Web Sites," *The New York Times*, March 1, 2010, p. B6.

c. For fact checking, construct a bar chart, a pie chart, and a Pareto chart.
d. Which graphical method do you think is best for portraying these data?
e. What conclusions can you reach concerning copy editing and fact checking of print and online consumer magazines?

3.51 The owner of a restaurant that serves Continental-style entrées has the business objective of learning more about the patterns of patron demand during the Friday-to-Sunday weekend time period. Data were collected from 630 customers on the type of entrée ordered and organized in the following table:

Type of Entrée	Number Served
Beef	187
Chicken	103
Mixed	30
Duck	25
Fish	122
Pasta	63
Shellfish	74
Veal	26
Total	630

a. Construct a percentage summary table for the types of entrées ordered.
b. Construct a bar chart, a pie chart, and a Pareto chart for the types of entrées ordered.
c. Do you prefer using a Pareto chart or a pie chart for these data? Why?
d. What conclusions can the restaurant owner reach concerning demand for different types of entrées?

3.52 Suppose that the owner of the restaurant in Problem 3.51 also wanted to study the demand for dessert during the same time period. She decided that in addition to studying whether a dessert was ordered, she would also study the gender of the individual and whether a beef entrée was ordered. Data were collected from 600 customers and organized in the following contingency tables:

DESSERT ORDERED	GENDER		
	Male	Female	Total
Yes	40	96	136
No	240	224	464
Total	280	320	600

DESSERT ORDERED	BEEF ENTRÉE		
	Yes	No	Total
Yes	71	65	136
No	116	348	464
Total	187	413	600

a. For each of the two contingency tables, construct contingency tables of row percentages, column percentages, and total percentages.
b. Which type of percentage (row, column, or total) do you think is most informative for each gender? For beef entrée? Explain.
c. What conclusions concerning the pattern of dessert ordering can the restaurant owner reach?

3.53 The following data represent the pounds per capita of fresh food and packaged food consumed in the United States, Japan, and Russia in 2009:

FRESH FOOD	COUNTRY		
	United States	Japan	Russia
Eggs, nuts, and beans	88	94	88
Fruit	124	126	88
Meat and seafood	197	146	125
Vegetables	194	278	335

a. For the United States, Japan, and Russia, construct a bar chart, a pie chart, and a Pareto chart for different types of fresh foods consumed.

PACKAGED FOOD	COUNTRY		
	United States	Japan	Russia
Bakery goods	108	53	144
Dairy products	298	147	127
Pasta	12	32	16
Processed, frozen, dried and chilled food, and ready-to-eat meals	183	251	70
Sauces, dressings, and condiments	63	75	49
Snacks and candy	47	19	24
Soup and canned food	77	17	25

Source: Data extracted from H. Fairfield, "Factory Food," *The New York Times,* April 4, 2010, p. BU5.

b. For the United States, Japan, and Russia, construct a bar chart, a pie chart, and a Pareto chart for different types of packaged foods consumed.
c. What conclusions can you reach concerning differences between the United States, Japan, and Russia in the fresh foods and packaged foods consumed?

3.54 In 2000, a growing number of warranty claims on Firestone tires sold on Ford SUVs prompted Firestone and Ford to issue a major recall. An analysis of warranty claims data helped identify which models to recall. A breakdown of 2,504 warranty claims based on tire size is given in the following table:

Tire Size	Number of Warranty Claims
23575R15	2,030
311050R15	137
30950R15	82
23570R16	81
331250R15	58
25570R16	54
Others	62

Source: Data extracted from Robert L. Simison, "Ford Steps Up Recall Without Firestone," *The Wall Street Journal,* August 14, 2000, p. A3.

The 2,030 warranty claims for the 23575R15 tires can be categorized into ATX models and Wilderness models. The type of incident leading to a warranty claim, by model type, is summarized in the following table:

	ATX Model Warranty Claims	Wilderness Warranty Claims
Tread separation	1,365	59
Blowout	77	41
Other/ unknown	422	66
Total	1,864	166

Source: Data extracted from Robert L. Simison, "Ford Steps Up Recall Without Firestone," *The Wall Street Journal,* August 14, 2000, p. A3.

a. Construct a Pareto chart for the number of warranty claims by tire size. What tire size accounts for most of the claims?

b. Construct a pie chart to display the percentage of the total number of warranty claims for the 23575R15 tires that come from the ATX model and Wilderness model. Interpret the chart.

c. Construct a Pareto chart for the type of incident causing the warranty claim for the ATX model. Does a certain type of incident account for most of the claims?

d. Construct a Pareto chart for the type of incident causing the warranty claim for the Wilderness model. Does a certain type of incident account for most of the claims?

3.55 One of the major measures of the quality of service provided by an organization is the speed with which the organization responds to customer complaints. A large family-held department store selling furniture and flooring, including carpet, had undergone a major expansion in the past several years. In particular, the flooring department had expanded from 2 installation crews to an installation supervisor, a measurer, and 15 installation crews. A business objective of the company was to reduce the time between when the complaint is received and when it is resolved. During a recent year, the company received 50 complaints concerning carpet installation. The data from the 50 complaints, stored in **Furniture**, represent the number of days between the receipt of the complaint and the resolution of the complaint:

54	5	35	137	31	27	152	2	123	81	74	27
11	19	126	110	110	29	61	35	94	31	26	5
12	4	165	32	29	28	29	26	25	1	14	13
13	10	5	27	4	52	30	22	36	26	20	23
33	68										

a. Construct a frequency distribution and a percentage distribution.

b. Construct a histogram and a percentage polygon.

c. Construct a cumulative percentage distribution and plot a cumulative percentage polygon (ogive).

d. On the basis of the results of (a) through (c), if you had to tell the president of the company how long a customer should expect to wait to have a complaint resolved, what would you say? Explain.

3.56 The file **DomesticBeer** contains the percentage alcohol, number of calories per 12 ounces, and number of carbohydrates (in grams) per 12 ounces for 145 of the best-selling domestic beers in the United States.
Source: Data extracted from **www.Beer100.com,** April 1, 2011.

a. Construct a percentage histogram for each of the three variables.

b. Construct three scatter plots: percentage alcohol versus calories, percentage alcohol versus carbohydrates, and calories versus carbohydrates.

c. Discuss what you learn from studying the graphs in (a) and (b).

3.57 The file **CigaretteTax** contains the state cigarette tax ($) for each state as of December 31, 2010.

a. Construct an ordered array.

b. Plot a percentage histogram.

c. What conclusions can you reach about the differences in the state cigarette tax between the states?

3.58 The file **CDRate** contains the yields for a one-year certificate of deposit (CD) and a five-year certificate of deposit (CD) for 25 banks in the United States, as of April 4, 2011.
Source: Data extracted from **www.Bankrate.com**, April 4, 2011.

a. Construct a stem-and-leaf display for each variable.

b. Construct a scatter plot of one-year CD versus five-year CD.

c. What is the relationship between the one-year CD rate and the five-year CD rate?

3.59 The file **CEO-Compensation** includes the total compensation (in millions of $) of CEOs of 161 large public companies and the investment return in 2010. For total compensation:
Source: Data extracted from M. Krantz and B. Hansen, "CEO Pay Sours While Workers' Pay Stalls," "Bargains in the Boardroom," *USA Today,* April 1, 2011, pp. 1B, 2B, and **money.usatoday.com**

a. Construct a frequency distribution and a percentage distribution.

b. Construct a histogram and a percentage polygon.

c. Construct a cumulative percentage distribution and plot a cumulative percentage polygon (ogive).

d. Based on (a) through (c), what conclusions can you reach concerning CEO compensation in 2010?

e. Construct a scatter plot of total compensation and investment return in 2010.

f. What is the relationship between the total compensation and investment return in 2010?

3.60 Studies conducted by a manufacturer of Boston and Vermont asphalt shingles have shown product weight to be a major factor in customers' perception of quality.

Moreover, the weight represents the amount of raw materials being used and is therefore very important to the company from a cost standpoint. The last stage of the assembly line packages the shingles before the packages are placed on wooden pallets. The variable of interest is the weight in pounds of the pallet which for most brands holds 16 squares of shingles. The company expects pallets of its Boston brand-name shingles to weigh at least 3,050 pounds but less than 3,260 pounds. For the company's Vermont brand-name shingles, pallets should weigh at least 3,600 pounds but less than 3,800. Data are collected from a sample of 368 pallets of Boston shingles and 330 pallets of Vermont shingles and stored in `Pallet`.

a. For the Boston shingles, construct a frequency distribution and a percentage distribution having eight class intervals, using 3,015, 3,050, 3,085, 3,120, 3,155, 3,190, 3,225, 3,260, and 3,295 as the class boundaries.

b. For the Vermont shingles, construct a frequency distribution and a percentage distribution having seven class intervals, using 3,550, 3,600, 3,650, 3,700, 3,750, 3,800, 3,850, and 3,900 as the class boundaries.

c. Construct percentage histograms for the Boston shingles and for the Vermont shingles.

d. Comment on the distribution of pallet weights for the Boston and Vermont shingles. Be sure to identify the percentage of pallets that are underweight and overweight.

3.61 What was the average price of a room at two-star, three-star, and four-star hotels in cities around the world in the summer of 2010? The file `HotelPrices` contains the prices in English pounds (about US $1.56 as of January 2011). Complete the following for two-star, three-star, and four-star hotels.

Source: Data extracted from **http://www.hotels.com/press/hotel-price-index-summer-2010.html.**

a. Construct a frequency distribution and a percentage distribution.

b. Construct a histogram and a percentage polygon.

c. Construct a cumulative percentage distribution and plot a cumulative percentage polygon (ogive).

d. What conclusions can you reach about the cost of two-star, three-star, and four-star hotels?

e. Construct separate scatter plots of the cost of two-star hotels versus three-star hotels, two-star hotels versus four-star hotels, and three-star hotels versus four-star hotels.

f. What conclusions can you reach about the relationship of the price of two-star, three-star, and four-star hotels?

3.62 The file `Protein` contains calorie and cholesterol information for popular protein foods (fresh red meats, poultry, and fish).

Source: U.S. Department of Agriculture.

a. Construct a percentage histogram for the number of calories.

b. Construct a percentage histogram for the amount of cholesterol.

c. What conclusions can you reach from your analyses in (a) and (b)?

3.63 The file `Natural Gas` contains the monthly average wellhead and residential price for natural gas (dollars per thousand cu. ft.) in the United States from January 1, 2008, to January 1, 2011. For the wellhead price and the residential price:

Source: "Energy Information Administration," **www.eia.doe.gov,** April 4, 2011.

a. Construct a time-series plot.

b. What pattern, if any, is present in the data?

c. Construct a scatter plot of the wellhead price and the residential price.

d. What conclusion can you reach about the relationship between the wellhead price and the residential price?

3.64 The following data (stored in `Drink`) represent the amount of soft drink in a sample of 50 consecutively filled 2-liter bottles. The results are listed horizontally in the order of being filled:

```
2.109 2.086 2.066 2.075 2.065 2.057 2.052 2.044 2.036 2.038
2.031 2.029 2.025 2.029 2.023 2.020 2.015 2.014 2.013 2.014
2.012 2.012 2.012 2.010 2.005 2.003 1.999 1.996 1.997 1.992
1.994 1.986 1.984 1.981 1.973 1.975 1.971 1.969 1.966 1.967
1.963 1.957 1.951 1.951 1.947 1.941 1.941 1.938 1.908 1.894
```

a. Construct a time-series plot for the amount of soft drink on the Y axis and the bottle number (going consecutively from 1 to 50) on the X axis.

b. What pattern, if any, is present in these data?

c. If you had to make a prediction about the amount of soft drink filled in the next bottle, what would you predict?

d. Based on the results of (a) through (c), explain why it is important to construct a time-series plot and not just a histogram.

3.65 The file `Currency` contains the exchange rates of the Canadian dollar, the Japanese yen, and the English pound from 1980 to 2010 where the Canadian dollar, the Japanese yen, and the English pound are expressed in units per U.S. dollar.

a. Construct time-series plots for the yearly closing values of the Canadian dollar, the Japanese yen, and the English pound.

b. Explain any patterns present in the plots.

c. Write a short summary of your findings.

d. Construct separate scatter plots of the value of the Canadian dollar versus the Japanese yen, the Canadian dollar versus the English pound, and the Japanese yen versus the English pound.

e. What conclusions can you reach concerning the value of the Canadian dollar, Japanese yen, and English pound in terms of the U.S. dollar?

3.66 (Class Project) Have each student in the class respond to the question "Which carbonated soft drink do you most prefer?" so that the instructor can tally the results into a summary table.

a. Convert the data to percentages and construct a Pareto chart.

b. Analyze the findings.

3.67 (Class Project) Let each student in the class be cross-classified on the basis of gender (male, female) and current employment status (yes, no) so that the instructor can tally the results.

a. Construct a table with either row or column percentages, depending on which you think is more informative.

b. What would you conclude from this study?

c. What other variables would you want to know regarding employment in order to enhance your findings?

REPORT WRITING EXERCISES

3.68 Referring to the results from Problem 3.60 on pages 121–127 concerning the weight of Boston and Vermont shingles, write a report that evaluates whether the weight of the pallets of the two types of shingles are what the company expects. Be sure to incorporate tables and charts into the report.

3.69 Referring to the results from Problem 3.54 on pages 125–126 concerning the warranty claims on Firestone tires, write a report that evaluates warranty claims on Firestone tires sold on Ford SUVs. Be sure to incorporate tables and charts into the report.

TEAM PROJECT

The file **Bond Funds** contains information regarding nine variables from a sample of 184 mutual funds:

Fund number—Identification number for each bond fund
Type—Bond fund type (intermediate government or short-term corporate)

Assets—In millions of dollars
Fees—Sales charges (no or yes)
Expense ratio—Ratio of expenses to net assets in percentage
Return 2009—Twelve-month return in 2009
Three-year return—Annualized return, 2007–2009
Five-year return—Annualized return, 2005–2009
Risk—Risk-of-loss factor of the mutual fund (below average, average, or above average)

3.70 For this problem, consider the expense ratio.

a. Construct a percentage histogram.

b. Using a single graph, plot percentage polygons of the expense ratio for bond funds that have fees and bond funds that do not have fees.

c. What conclusions about the expense ratio can you reach, based on the results of (a) and (b)?

3.71 For this problem, consider the three-year annualized return from 2007 to 2009.

a. Construct a percentage histogram.

b. Using a single graph, plot percentage polygons of the three-year annualized return from 2007 to 2009 for intermediate government funds and short-term corporate funds.

c. What conclusions about the three-year annualized return from 2007 to 2009 can you reach, based on the results of (a) and (b)?

3.72 For this problem, consider the five-year annualized return from 2005 to 2009.

a. Construct a percentage histogram.

b. Using a single graph, plot percentage polygons of the five-year annualized return from 2005 to 2009 for intermediate government funds and short-term corporate funds.

c. What conclusions about the five-year annualized return from 2005 to 2009 can you reach, based on the results of (a) and (b)?

MANAGING ASHLAND MULTICOMM SERVICES

Recently, Ashland MultiComm Services has been criticized for its inadequate customer service in responding to questions and problems about its telephone, cable television, and Internet services. Senior management has established a task force charged with the business objective of improving customer service. In response to this charge, the task force collected data about the types of customer service errors, the cost of customer service errors, and the cost of wrong billing errors. It found the following data:

Types of Customer Service Errors

Type of Errors	Frequency
Incorrect accessory	27
Incorrect address	42
Incorrect contact phone	31
Invalid wiring	9
On-demand programming error	14
Subscription not ordered	8
Suspension error	15
Termination error	22
Website access error	30
Wrong billing	137
Wrong end date	17
Wrong number of connections	19
Wrong price quoted	20
Wrong start date	24
Wrong subscription type	33
Total	448

Cost of Customer Service Errors in the Past Year

Type of Errors	Cost ($ thousands)
Incorrect accessory	17.3
Incorrect address	62.4
Incorrect contact phone	21.3
Invalid wiring	40.8
On-demand programming errors	38.8
Subscription not ordered	20.3
Suspension error	46.8
Termination error	50.9
Website access errors	60.7
Wrong billing	121.7
Wrong end date	40.9
Wrong number of connections	28.1
Wrong price quoted	50.3
Wrong start date	40.8
Wrong subscription type	60.1
Total	701.2

Type and Cost of Wrong Billing Errors

Type of Wrong Billing Errors	Cost ($ thousands)
Declined or held transactions	7.6
Incorrect account number	104.3
Invalid verification	9.8
Total	121.7

1. Review these data (stored in AMS2-1). Identify the variables that are important in describing the customer service problems. For each variable you identify, construct the graphical representation you think is most appropriate and explain your choice. Also, suggest what other information concerning the different types of errors would be useful to examine. Offer possible courses of action for either the task force or management to take that would support the goal of improving customer service.

2. As a follow-up activity, the task force decides to collect data to study the pattern of calls to the help desk (stored in AMS2-2). Analyze these data and present your conclusions in a report.

DIGITAL CASE

In the Using Statistics scenario, you were asked to gather information to help make wise investment choices. Sources for such information include brokerage firms, investment counselors, and other financial services firms. Apply your knowledge about the proper use of tables and charts in this Digital Case about the claims of foresight and excellence by an Ashland-area financial services firm.

Open **EndRunGuide.pdf,** which contains the EndRun Financial Services "Guide to Investing." Review the guide, paying close attention to the company's investment claims and supporting data and then answer the following.

1. How does the presentation of the general information about EndRun in this guide affect your perception of the business?

2. Is EndRun's claim about having more winners than losers a fair and accurate reflection of the quality of its investment service? If you do not think that the claim is a fair and accurate one, provide an alternate presentation that you think is fair and accurate.

3. Review the discussion about EndRun's "Big Eight Difference" and then open and examine `Mutual Funds`, a sample of mutual funds. Are there any other relevant data from that file that could have been included in the Big Eight table? How would the new data alter your perception of EndRun's claims?

4. EndRun is proud that all Big Eight funds have gained in value over the past five years. Do you agree that EndRun should be proud of its selections? Why or why not?

REFERENCES

1. Huff, D., *How to Lie with Statistics* (New York: Norton, 1954).
2. Levine, D. and D. Stephan, "Teaching Introductory Business Statistics Using the DCOVA Framework," *Decision Sciences Journal of Innovative Education*, 9, September 2011, p. 393–398.
3. *Microsoft Excel 2010* (Redmond, WA: Microsoft Corporation, 2010).
4. *Minitab Release 16* (State College, PA: Minitab, Inc., 2010).
5. Tufte, E. R., *Beautiful Evidence* (Cheshire, CT: Graphics Press, 2006).
6. Tufte, E. R., *Envisioning Information* (Cheshire, CT: Graphics Press, 1990).
7. Tufte, E. R., *The Visual Display of Quantitative Information*, 2nd ed. (Cheshire, CT: Graphics Press, 2002).
8. Tufte, E. R., *Visual Explanations* (Cheshire, CT: Graphics Press, 1997).
9. Wainer, H., *Visual Revelations: Graphical Tales of Fate and Deception from Napoleon Bonaparte to Ross Perot* (New York: Copernicus/Springer-Verlag, 1997).

CALCULATOR LESSON 2A

**CASIO FX-9750G
OR CFX-9850GB
CALCULATOR**

Introduction

To install the batteries and make the initial adjustments follow the instructions on the pink pages inside the front cover of the owner's manual.

The GFX-9850GB has three keyboards:

i. The Primary keyboard
    –indicated on the keys

ii. The **Shift** keyboard
    –indicated in *yellow* above the keys

iii. The **ALPHA** keyboard
    –indicated in *red* above the keys

Common Operations

Clear screen	**AC/ON**
Insert	**SHIFT INS**
Delete	**DEL**
Move cursor	**Use cursor arrows**
Erase the last entry	**Use cursor arrow and typeover**
Power (exponent)	^

The function keys F1, F2 . . . F6 directly under the display are used to select functions shown at the bottom of the display at various times.

Calculations

RUN Mode:

Highlight the RUN icon and press **EXE**

or press **1** when the main menu screen is visible.

Note: If you change your mind about which *mode* you want to select, just press the menu key and this will always return you to the main menu screen.

To calculate the average of 38, 20, 18, and 23:

Enter the following into the calculator:
(38+20+18+23)÷4 EXE   You should get the result 24.75.   Try it.

Correcting errors

Inserting: Suppose we should have entered 148 instead of 18 in the example. Use the replay arrows (◄ or ►) to position the cursor at the end or beginning of the previously entered calculation. Move the cursor until it is located under the 8 in 18. The 8 will flash on and off. Press **SHIFT INS**. A square blank cursor will now be flashing on and off. Press **4** followed by **EXE.**

We now have the following calculation:
(38+20+148+23)÷4 EXE   You should get the result 57.25.   Try it.

Note: You may insert several digits consecutively without pressing **SHIFT INS** each time. The cursor will be in insert mode any time that it appears as a square blank cursor.

Deleting

If, in fact, the original value of 18 is correct, we can delete the 4 as follows. Use the replay cursor followed by any cursor key to position the cursor under the 4. The 4 will flash on and off. Press the **DEL** key followed by **EXE**. We will now get the answer 24.75 of the original calculation.

Using the ANSWER of the Previous Calculation

Suppose we want to add 10 to the previously calculated average. Press + (the word *Ans* will appear on the display) and **10 EXE**. The result 34.75 will appear.

Now suppose we want to calculate 30/34.75. Press **30 ÷ SHIFT Ans EXE** and the result 0.8633093525 appears.

Note: The calculator displayed 10 decimals for the answer above; however, it keeps 15 digits internally in case this number is to be used in further calculations. In this way round off errors are not likely to have occurred in the digits shown on the display.

Note: Suppose the calculator has shut off due to being inactive for several minutes. Use the **AC/ON** key to turn the calculator back on. Choose the RUN icon and press **EXE**. The screen will be blank. Now press the ▲ cursor key followed by **EXE** and the screen will return to the last calculation that was done when the calculator was last on.

Working with DATA LISTS

LIST Mode:

Press the **MENU** key.

Highlight the LIST icon and press **EXE**.

You will now have six blank lists set up on the screen. You can only see the Lists 1 to 4 at first, but if you move the ► cursor key you will be able to scroll over to the other two lists.

You can enter the data from the first example in List 1 as follows:

38 EXE
20 EXE
18 EXE
23 EXE

Note: If you make a mistake, use the following options on the bottom of the display (if you are in **STAT mode**, use the F6 key (▷) to bring up these options):

DEL	DEL-A	INS
F3	F4	F5

Now, if you press **F3** you can *delete* a highlighted data value. If you press **F5** you can create a space to *insert* a data value into the list. All other values will shift downward. To *change* a data value just highlight and type over the old value and then key **EXE**.

Sorting a List

When on the list screen, press the **F1** key if you want to sort a list in ascending order. The calculator will ask you how many lists you want to sort. Answer this and press **EXE.** The calculator will now ask which list(s). Answer this and press **EXE.**

The calculator will immediately sort the list(s) specified.

Deleting a List

To delete a list, place the cursor on any entry in the list and press the **F4** key. The calculator will give you one last chance to change your mind. Delete the highlighted list by answering YES (**F1**).

Error Messages

When you make a syntax error (i.e., you key something that the calculator cannot understand) it tries to point out where the error has occurred. Key in the following:

2 ÷ × 5 − 3 ENTER

The calculator will respond **Syn ERROR** at the bottom of the screen.

Press the left or right cursor arrow and the calculator will return to the calculation and the cursor will be flashing on the entry that is causing the problem.

The SET UP Menu

The SET UP menu allows you to modify the default settings for the calculator. For example, you may want your answer to a series of calculations to have only two decimal places (possibly because the numbers represent dollars and cents). In order to fix the number of decimal places to any calculation result you would go to the main calculation (RUN) screen and press **SHIFT SET UP**, scroll to **DISPLAY** and choose F1 (Fix), and then choose the appropriate number of decimal places, in this case **F3** (for two decimals). Now press the **EXIT** key to return to the previous screen.

Now key in the following calculation: **2 ÷ 3 EXE**. The calculator shows **.67**.

To return to the normal 10 digits with floating point, you will have to reenter the **NORM1** setting from the SET UP menu.

APPENDIX 3.2

CALCULATOR LESSON 2B

CASIO FX-9750GII CALCULATOR

Introduction

Common Operations

Clear screen	**AC/ON**
Insert	**SHIFT INS**
Delete	**DEL**
Move cursor	**Use cursor arrows**
Erase the last entry	**Use cursor arrow and typeover**
Power ON	**AC/ON**
Power OFF	**Shift AC/ON**

The function keys F1, F2 ... F6 directly under the display are used to select functions shown at the bottom of the display at various times.

Calculations

RUN-MAT Mode: Highlight the RUN icon and press **EXE**

or press **1** when the main menu screen is visible.

Note: If you change your mind about which *mode* you want to select, just press the **MENU** key and this will always return you to the main menu screen.

To calculate the average of 54, 36, 27, and 15:

Select **"RUN-MAT"** mode and enter the following into the calculator:
(54+36+27+15)÷4 EXE   You should get the result 33.   Try it.

Correcting Errors

Inserting: Suppose we should have entered 157 instead of 15 in the example. Use the replay arrows (◄ or ►) to position the cursor at the end or beginning of the previously entered calculation. Move the cursor until it is located under the 5 in 15. The 5 will flash on and off. Press **SHIFT INS**. A square blank cursor will now be flashing on and off. Press **4** followed by **EXE.**

We now have the following calculation:
(54+36+27+157)÷4 EXE   You should get the result 68.5.   Try it.

Note: You may insert several digits consecutively without pressing **SHIFT INS** each time. The cursor will be in insert mode any time that it appears as a square blank cursor.

Deleting

If, in fact, the original value of 15 is correct, we can delete the 7 as follows. Use the replay cursor followed by any cursor key to position the cursor under the 7. The 7 will flash on and off. Press the **DEL** key followed by **EXE**. We will now get the answer 33 of the original calculation.

Using the ANSWER of the Previous Calculation

Suppose we want to add 20 to the previously calculated average. Press **+** (the word *Ans* will appear on the display) and **20 and del 4 and type 5**. The result 30.4 will appear.

Now suppose we want to calculate 30/30.4. Press **30 ÷ SHIFT Ans EXE** and the result 0.9868421053 appears.

Note: The calculator displayed 10 decimals for the answer above; however, it keeps 15 digits internally in case this number is to be used in further calculations. In this way round off errors are not likely to have occurred in the digits shown on the display.

Note: Suppose the calculator has shut off due to being inactive for several minutes. Use the **AC/ON** key to turn the calculator back on. Choose the RUN icon and press **EXE**. The screen will be blank. Now press the ▲ cursor key followed by **EXE** and the screen will return to the last calculation that was done when the calculator was last on.

Sort Your Data

STAT MODE   Press the **MENU** key.
                       Highlight the STAT icon and press **EXE**.

You will now have 26 blank lists set up on the screen. You can only see the Lists 1 to 4 at first, but if you move the ► cursor key you will be able to scroll over to the other lists.

You can enter the data from the first example in List 1 as follows:
Note: Key in the number and then press **EXE**.

54 EXE
27 EXE
36 EXE
15 EXE

Note: If you make a mistake, use the following options on the bottom of the display. If you have other options, use the F6 key (▷) to bring up these options.

OPTIONS	TOOL	EDIT	DEL	DEL-A	INS	▶

FUNCTIONS	F1	F2	F3	F4	F5	F6

(1) Option TOOL(F1)

To **sort** the data that was entered in List 1, press **F1 (TOOL)**.
The calculator will show the following options on the bottom of the display.

OPTIONS	SRT-A	SRT-D	TOP	BTM

FUNCTIONS	F1	F2	F3	F4

The option **SRT-A** will sort a list in **A**scending order.

The option **SRT-D** will sort a list in **D**escending order.

The option **TOP** will bring the cursor to the top of the list.

The option **BTM** will bring the cursor to the bottom of the list.

(2) Option EDIT(F2)

If you wish to **change** a data value, place the cursor on the data value you want to change and press **F2 (EDIT)**. Suppose you want to change 15 to 26. Place the cursor on 15, press **DEL** to delete 15, and then enter **26 EXE**.

(3) Option DEL(F3)

If you wish to **delete** a data value, place the cursor on the value you want to delete and press **F3 (DEL)**.

(4) Option DEL-A(F4)

If you wish to **delete** the whole list of data, place the cursor on any entry in the list and press **F4 (DEL-A)**. The calculator will give you one last chance to change your mind. Delete the highlighted list by answering YES **(F1)**. If you do not wish to proceed with the delete procedure, you press **NO (F2)**.

(5) Option INS(F5)

If you wish to **insert** one data value into the list, place the cursor on the value and press **F5 (INS)** to **insert** a data value above the highlighted data value.

Sorting a List

Press the **F1 (SRT-A)** key if you want to sort a list in ascending order. The calculator will ask you how many lists you want to sort. Answer this by entering **1** if you have **one** list to sort and press **EXE**. The calculator will now ask which list(s). Answer this by entering **1** if the data is in List **1**, and press **EXE**.

The calculator will immediately sort the list(s) specified.

4 Numerical Descriptive Measures

Learning Objectives

In this chapter, you learn:

- To describe the properties of central tendency, variation, and shape in numerical data
- To construct and interpret a boxplot
- To compute descriptive summary measures for a population
- To compute the covariance and the coefficient of correlation

@ Choice Is Yours, Part II

The tables and charts you prepared for the sample of 184 bond mutual funds has been useful to the customers of the Choice Is Yours service. However, customers have become frustrated trying to evaluate bond fund performance. Although they know how the 2009 returns are distributed, they have no idea what a typical 2009 rate of return is for a particular category of bond funds, such as intermediate government and short-term corporate bond funds. They also have no idea of the extent of the variability in the 2009 rate of return. Are all the values relatively similar, or do they include very small and very large values? Are there a lot of small values and a few large ones, or vice versa, or are there a similar number of small and large values?

How could you help the customers get answers to these questions so that they could better evaluate the bond funds?

Don Farrall/Getty Images

In this chapter, you will learn to group quantitative data in numerical form. Specifically, you will learn to group a set of quantitative data in the following forms:

1. Central tendency (Section 4.1): mode, median, and mean
2. Variability (Section 4.2): range, interquartile range, variance, standard deviation

Next, you will learn to group the quantitative data graphically in the form of box-whisker plots (Section 4.4).

4.1 Descriptive Statistics I: Measures of Central Tendency

Descriptive statistics are numbers calculated to describe various aspects of a data set. The two most important types of descriptive statistics are the following:

Measures of Central Tendency: A single value to represent the data set

Measures of Variability: A single value to describe how spread out the data are

In this section you will learn how to calculate various measures of central tendency—that is, mode, mean, and median. These measures can be obtained using the function CALC under the STAT mode in the main menu of the recommended calculator.

Mean

I. Arithmetic Mean (Average):

Symbol:	Population Parameter	Sample Statistic
Mean (Average)	μ	$\bar{x}$
Size (Number of items or elements)	N	n

Symbol: Sample Mean: $\bar{x}$ Population Mean: μ

Formula: $\bar{x} = \dfrac{\sum x}{n}$ $\mu = \dfrac{\sum x}{N}$

where: x = a value in the data set
n = sample size
N = population size
$\sum$ = summation   therefore $\sum x$ = add up the data

EXAMPLE 4.1

The Data Are in the Form of Raw Data

A fast food franchise has many outlets across the country. One small restaurant in the city where you live has seven full-time employees who earn $38, 20, 20, 18, 18, 18, and 23 thousand annually. Calculate the average salary of these employees.

SOLUTION

Formula	Casio Calculator
Use the **formula** to obtain the average salary of these employees,	Use the **Casio Calculator** to obtain the average salary of these employees,

Formula

Use the **formula** to obtain the average salary of these employees,

$$\bar{x} = \frac{\sum x}{n} = \frac{38 + 20 + 20 + 18 + 18 + 18 + 23}{7}$$

$$= \$22.1 \text{ thousand per employee}$$

Note: Regarding the form of the answer, use one more figure than those used in the data if the data have one or two figures. Otherwise, the answer should look like the data.

Example: If data are 1.3, 2.4, and 3.6, then
$\bar{x} = 2.43$.

If the data have three or more figures, the answer should look like the data (e.g., if the data are 234, 315, and 484, then $\bar{x} = 344$.

Casio Calculator

Use the **Casio Calculator** to obtain the average salary of these employees,

Now use the calculator to calculate the average salary of these employees. Refer to Calculator Lesson 2.

INSTRUCTIONS:

1. Press the **MENU** key to switch to **STAT** mode. Highlight the **STAT** icon and press **EXE.**

2. You can enter the data from Example 4.1 in List 1 as follows:

38 EXE
20 EXE
20 EXE
18 EXE
18 EXE
18 EXE
23 EXE

3. Press **F2 (CALC).**

4. Press **F6 (SET)**. Highlight **1 Var XList**, press **F1** (List), enter 1 for **List 1**, and press **EXE**. Then highlight **1Var Freq** and choose **1 (F1)**. Now press **EXIT** to return to the display of the data. *Note: Make sure that* 1Var Freq *is set to 1.*

5. Press **F1 (1 VAR)** to obtain a full range of one-variable statistics. The result, $\bar{x} = 22.1428571$, will be at the top of the list.

EXAMPLE 4.2

The Data Are in the Form of Grouped Data

The salaries of all the employees in the outlets in the city where you live are summarized in the following table:

Job Classification	Number of Employees	Annual Salary ($ thousands)
Senior Management	3	52
Middle Management	10	38
Cooking Staff	45	20
Serving Staff	74	18
Maintenance Staff	7	23

Calculate the average salary of these employees.

SOLUTION

Formula	Casio Calculator
Use the **formula** to obtain the average salary of these employees.	Use the **Casio Calculator** to obtain the average salary of these employees.

Formula

Use the **formula** to obtain the average salary of these employees.

In this example the salary figures again need to be averaged. However, we realize that it would be incorrect to add the figures and divide by 5 as this would be correct only if there were an equal number of employees in each category. To take into account the differing number of employees in each category, we must use the **weighted** method to calculate the mean salary. Many textbooks call the result of this calculation, the **weighted mean.**

The formula for the weighted mean is as follows:

$$\bar{x} = \frac{\sum wx}{\sum w}$$

where x = a value in the data set and w = weight of each value—that is, a number to indicate the relative importance of each data value in the overall result.

In this example,
x = the salaries
w = the number of employees

$$\bar{x} = \frac{\sum wx}{\sum w}$$

$$= \frac{(3 \times 52) + (10 \times 38) + (45 \times 20) + (74 \times 18) + (7 \times 23)}{3 + 10 + 45 + 74 + 7}$$

$$= \frac{2929}{139}$$

$$= \$21.1 \text{ thousand per employee}$$

Note: This formula also is 'logical' in that the denominator is 139, which is the total number of employees.

Casio Calculator

Use the **Casio Calculator** to obtain the average salary of these employees.

Now use the calculator to calculate the average salary of these employees. Refer to Calculator Lesson 3.

INSTRUCTIONS

1. Press the **MENU** key to switch to **STAT** mode. Highlight the STAT icon and press **EXE.**

2. You can enter the salaries data, **52 EXE, 38 EXE, 20 EXE, 18 EXE,** and **23 EXE,** in List 1.

Then enter the number of employees (frequencies), **3 EXE, 10 EXE, 45 EXE, 74 EXE,** and **7 EXE,** in List 2.

3. Press **F2 (CALC).**

4. Press **F6 (SET).** Highlight **1 VarXList,** press **F1** (List), enter **1** for **List 1,** and press **EXE.** Then highlight **1Var Freq,** choose **List (F2),** and enter **2** for **List 2.** Now press **EXIT** to return to the display of the data.

5. Press **F1 (1 VAR)** to obtain a full range of one-variable statistics.

The result, $\bar{x}$ = 21.0719424, will appear at the top of the list.

EXAMPLE 4.3

The Data Are in the Form of Grouped Data

A Cruise ship does several week-long cruises during a year. The ship is not always fully occupied. There are three types of cabins on this particular ship: interior (no port hole), deluxe exterior (porthole), and luxury exterior (private balcony). The price for each type of cabin and estimated percent of passengers in each type of cabin for the next cruise is shown below.

Cabin Style	Price per Person ($)	Percent of Passengers
Interior	1900	40
Deluxe exterior	2400	45
Luxury exterior	3200	15

Calculate the average revenue per person earned by the cruise company.

SOLUTION

Formula	Casio Calculator
Use the **formula** to obtain the average revenue per person earned by the cruise company.	Use the **Casio Calculator** to obtain the average revenue per person earned by the cruise company.
In this example,	Now use the calculator to calculate the average revenue per person earned by the cruise company. Refer to Calculator Lesson 3.
x = the price for each person	**INSTRUCTIONS**
w = the percentages	1. Press the **MENU** key to switch to **STAT** mode. Highlight the STAT icon and press **EXE**.
$$\bar{x} = \frac{\sum wx}{\sum w}$$	2. You can enter the price data, **1900 EXE, 2400 EXE**, and **3200 EXE** in **List 1**.
$$= \frac{(40 \times 1900) + (45 \times 2400) + (15 \times 3200)}{40 + 45 + 15}$$	Then enter the percent of passengers (frequencies); **40 EXE, 45 EXE**, and **15 EXE** in **List 2**.
$= \$2,320$ per person	3. Press **F2 (CALC)**.
	4. Press **F6 (SET)**. Highlight **1 VarXList**, press **F1** (List), enter **1** for **List 1**, and press **EXE**. Then highlight **1Var Freq**, choose **List (F2)**, and enter **2** for **List 2**. Now press **EXIT** to return to the display of the data.
	5. Press **F1 (1 VAR)** to obtain a full range of one-variable statistics. The result, $\bar{x} = 2320$, will appear at the top of the list.

There are two other common scenarios in which the weighted mean is necessary.

    a) Data to be averaged are themselves averages.

    b) Data to be averaged are percentages.

EXAMPLE 4.4

The Data Are in the Form of Grouped Data

A car-manufacturing company has assembly lines in four plants. Some data regarding the car production on these assembly lines for the past week are shown below.

Production Line	Number of Cars Produced	Average Time per Car (minutes)
Toronto	134	257
Montréal	105	248
Calgary	97	272
Vancouver	82	286

Calculate the overall average production time for these cars.

SOLUTION

Formula	Casio Calculator
Use the **formula** to obtain the overall average production time for these cars.	Use the **Casio Calculator** to obtain the overall average production time for these cars.

Formula	Casio Calculator
In this example,	Now use the calculator to calculate the overall average production time for these cars. Refer to Calculator Lesson 3.

In this example,

x = the average times

w = the number of cars

$$\bar{x} = \frac{\sum wx}{\sum w}$$

$$= \frac{(134 \times 257) + (105 \times 248) + (97 \times 272) + (82 \times 286)}{134 + 105 + 97 + 82}$$

$$= \frac{110314}{418} = 264 \text{ minutes per car}$$

Casio Calculator side:

Now use the calculator to calculate the overall average production time for these cars. Refer to Calculator Lesson 3.

INSTRUCTIONS

1. Press the **MENU** key to switch to **STAT** mode. Highlight the STAT icon and press **EXE**.

2. You can enter the average times data, **257 EXE, 248 EXE, 272 EXE**, and **286 EXE** in **List 1**.

Then enter the number of cars (frequencies), **134 EXE, 105 EXE, 97 EXE**, and **82 EXE** in **List 2**.

3. Press **F2 (CALC)**.

4. Press **F6 (SET)**. Highlight **1 VarXList**, press **F1** (List), enter **1** for **List 1**, and press **EXE**. Then highlight **Var Freq**, choose **List (F2)**, and enter **2** for **List 2**. Now press **EXIT** to return to the display of the data.

5. Press **F1 (1 VAR)** to obtain a full range of one-variable statistics. The result, $\bar{x} = 263.90909$, will appear at the top of the list.

EXAMPLE 4.5

The Data Are in the Form of Grouped Data

The following data refer to three divisions of a medium-sized business.

Division	Profit Margin (%)	Sales ($ millions)
A	5	10
B	6	5
C	7	35

Calculate the overall average profit margin for the three divisions.

SOLUTION

Formula	Casio Calculator
Use the **formula** to obtain the overall average profit margin for the three divisions	Use the **Casio Calculator** to obtain the overall average profit margin for the three divisions.

In this example,

x = the profit margin

w = the sales

$$\bar{x} = \frac{\sum wx}{\sum w} = \frac{(10 \times 5) + (5 \times 6) + (35 \times 7)}{10 + 5 + 35}$$

$$= \frac{325}{50} = 6.5\% \text{ (per division)}$$

Casio Calculator side:

Now use the calculator to calculate the overall average profit margin for the three divisions. Refer to Calculator Lesson 3.

INSTRUCTIONS

1. Press the **MENU** key to switch to **STAT** mode. Highlight the STAT icon and press **EXE**.

*Note: To delete a list, highlight it and press **F4 (DEL A)**. The whole list will be cleared. It may be necessary to press F6 (|>) for the DEL-A option to show up.*

2. You can enter the profit margin values, **5 EXE**, **6 EXE**, and **7 EXE** in **List 1**.

Then enter the sales values, **10 EXE**, **5 EXE**, and **35 EXE** in **List 2**.

3. Press **F2 (CALC)**.

4. Press **F6 (SET)**. Highlight **1 VarXList**, press **F1** (List), enter **1** for **List 1**, and press **EXE**. Then highlight **1Var Freq**, choose **List (F2)**, and enter **2** for **List 2**. Now press **EXIT** to return to the display of the data.

5. Press **F1 (1 VAR)** to obtain a full range of one-variable statistics. The result, $\bar{x} = 6.5$, will appear at the top of the list.

One final scenario involving the calculating of a mean is also common.

II: Another Type of Mean

EXAMPLE 4.6

In a particular province there are three provincial parks. The Ministry of Natural Resources is interested in the concentration of moose in these parks. The results of a survey yielded the following data.

Provincial Park	Number of Moose	Area of Park (km^2)
Moose Forest	134	2575
Moose Swamp	105	2037
Moosonee	97	2892

Calculate the overall average number of moose per square kilometre.

SOLUTION

$$\bar{x} = \frac{\sum moose}{\sum area} = \frac{134 + 105 + 97}{2575 + 2037 + 2892}$$

$$= \frac{336}{7504} = 0.0448 \text{ moose per km}^2.$$

Note: When no other rule applies to the result of a particular calculation, we will use a general rule of **three significant digits** (or more if the zeros are to the left of the decimal point).

The arithmetic mean is by far the most important measure of central tendency.

III: Grouped Data: Mean

Suppose the only data available to us are in the form of a frequency or relative frequency (or percentage) distribution. Then in order to estimate the mean of the data, we need to use the **class midpoints** to represent the values in each class. We then use the weighted method to calculate the mean, where the frequencies or relative frequencies will be the appropriate weights.

EXAMPLE 4.7

On a particular Saturday, the amount paid for parking in a small downtown parking lot was as summarized in the following table:

Cost of Parking ($)	Number of Cars (f)	%	Midpoint (m)
2.00 and under 4.00	20	18.3	3.00
4.00 " " 6.00	37	33.9	5.00
6.00 " " 10.00	29	26.6	8.00
10.00 " " 15.00	15	13.8	12.50
15.00 " " 20.00	8	7.3	17.50
Total	109	99.9	

Estimate the mean amount paid for parking.

SOLUTION: a) Using the frequencies as weights (note the symbols in the formula),

$$\bar{x} = \frac{\sum fm}{\sum f} = \frac{(20 \times 3.00) + (37 \times 5.00) + (29 \times 8.00) + (15 \times 12.50) + (8 \times 17.50)}{20 + 37 + 29 + 15 + 8}$$

$$= \frac{804.50}{109} = \$7.38 \text{ per customer}$$

b) Using the percentages as weights,

$$\bar{x} = \frac{\sum \%m}{\sum \%}$$

$$= \frac{(18.3 \times 3.00) + (33.9 \times 5.00) + (26.6 \times 8.00) + (13.8 \times 12.50) + (7.3 \times 17.50)}{18.3 + 33.9 + 26.6 + 13.8 + 7.3}$$

$$= \frac{737.45}{99.9} = \$7.38 \text{ per customer}$$

CASIO CALCULATOR

Now use the calculator to calculate the mean amount paid for parking. Refer to Calculator Lesson 3 on page 145.

INSTRUCTIONS

1. Press the **MENU** key to switch to **ST**AT mode. Highlight the STAT icon and press **EXE**.

*Note: To delete a list, highlight it and press **F4 (DEL A)**. The whole list will be cleared. It may be necessary to press F6 (|>) in order for the DEL-A option to show up.*

2. You can enter the midpoints of cost of parking data, **3 EXE, 5 EXE, 8 EXE, 12.5 EXE,** and **17.5 EXE** in **List 1**.

Then enter the number of cars (frequencies), **20 EXE, 37 EXE, 29 EXE, 15 EXE, 8 EXE** in **List 2**.

Note: Instead you may use percentages as the weights (or frequencies) by entering 18.3 EXE, 33.9 EXE, 26.6 EXE, 13.8 EXE, and 7.3 EXE in List 2 (or whichever list you wish to use).

3. Press **F2 (CALC)**.

4. Press **F6 (SET)**. Highlight **1 Var XList**, press **F1** (List), enter **1** for **List 1**, and press **EXE**. Then highlight **1Var Freq**, choose **List (F2)**, and enter **2** for **List 2**. Now press **EXIT** to return to the display of the data.

5. Press **F1 (1 VAR)** to obtain a full range of one-variable statistics. The result, $\bar{x} =$ 7.38073394, will appear at the top of the list.

CALCULATOR LESSON 3

CASIO FX-9750GII CALCULATOR

Lesson 3—Calculations using STAT mode

STAT Mode: Press the **MENU** key.

Use the cursor keys to move the highlighting to the **STAT** icon and press **EXE**.

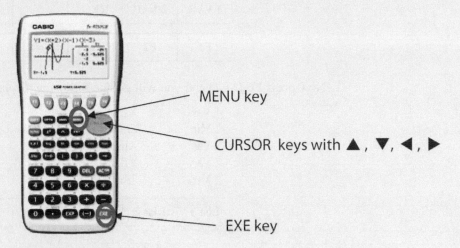

MENU key

CURSOR keys with ▲, ▼, ◀, ▶

EXE key

Source: http://www.casio.com/products/Calculators_%26_Dictionaries/Graphing/FX-750GII/content/Introduction/

You will now have 26 blank lists set up on the screen. You can see only List 1 to List 4 at first, but if you move the ▶ cursor key you will be able to scroll over to the other lists.

You can enter the data from Example 4.1 in the introductory handout in List 1 as follows:

38 EXE
20 EXE
20 EXE
20 EXE
18 EXE
18 EXE
23 EXE

EXAMPLE 1 (revisited)

To calculate the average of the salary data, use the **F6** key (▷) if necessary to get the following menu choices at the bottom of the display:

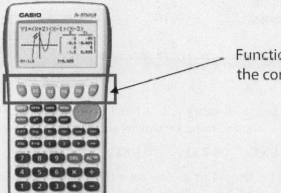

Function keys with F1, F2, F3, F4, F5, F6 to access the commands in the menu bar.

Source: http://www.casio.com/products/Calculators_%26_Dictionaries/Graphing/FX-9750GII/content/Introduction/

GRPH	CALC	TEST	INTR	DIST	▷
F1	F2	F3	F4	F5	F6

Now press **F2** (CALC) and you will get the following on-screen menu items:

1 VAR	2 VAR	REG			SET
F1	F2	F3			F6

Now press **F6** (SET) and you will get the following display:

1 Var	XList	:	List1
1 Var	Freq	:	1
2 Var	Xlist	:	List1
2 Var	YList	:	List2
2 Var	Freq	:	1

List 1	List 2	List 3	List 4	List 5	List 6

The first row will be highlighted. To select the desired list for your **1Var XList**, press **F1** (List). The calculator will now ask which list(s). Answer this question (by entering **1** if the data are in List **1**) and press **EXE**.

You also want to have the 1Var Freq as **F1 (1)**.

Now press **EXIT** to return to the display of the data.

Now press **F1 (1 VAR)** and a full range of one-variable statistics will appear. The result, $\bar{x} = 22.4285714$, will be at the top of the list.

Now press **EXIT** to return to the data list display.

Weighted Data

Recall from the Measures of Central Tendency lecture notes that in Example 4.2 we needed to calculate the mean salary for the following group of people:

TABLE 4.1

Job Classification	Number of Employees	Annual Salary ($ thousands)
Senior Management	3	52
Middle Management	10	38
Cooking Staff	45	20
Serving Staff	74	18
Maintenance Staff	7	23

Enter the values for the annual salary in List 1 and the corresponding values for the number of employees in List 2. The following keystrokes will calculate the **weighted** statistics:

Enter the salaries, **52 EXE, 38 EXE, 20 EXE, 18 EXE,** and **23 EXE** under List 1.

Position the cursor at the top of List 2. Now enter the weights (frequencies), **3 EXE, 10 EXE, 45 EXE, 74 EXE,** and **7 EXE**.

Now press **F2** (CALC) **F6** (SET).

Highlight 1Var XList, press **F1** (List), enter **1** for List 1, and press **EXE**. Then highlight 1Var Freq, choose List (**F2**), and enter **2** for List 2. Now press **EXIT**.

Press **F1** (1 VAR) and a full range of one-variable weighted statistics will appear. The result, $\bar{x} = 21.0719424$, will be at the top of the list—that is, the average salary is $21.1 thousand, as we saw in the notes on measures of central tendency.

The Median

The **median** is the middle value in an ordered array of data that have been ranked from smallest to largest. Half the values are smaller than or equal to the median, and half the values are larger than or equal to the median. The median is not affected by extreme values, so you can use the median when extreme values are present.

MEDIAN:

Symbol: sample or population $- \tilde{x}$

The technical definition of the median is that it is the value such that at most 50% of the data values are smaller than the median and at most 50% of the data values are larger than the median. In other words, the median occupies the *middle position* of the data after they are sorted into **an ordered array**, either ascending or descending.

Let **i** denote the position of the median.

To calculate i (position), we use the formula $i = \dfrac{n+1}{2}$.

Once **i** is calculated, there are two possibilities regarding how to determine the median of a data set.

EXAMPLE 4.8

There Is An *Even* Number of Data Values

The following data represent the ages, in years, of 20 employees working at a retail outlet.

$$63, 52, 38, 20, 21, 18, 29, 28, 45, 40, 24, 25, 22, 20, 29, 20, 18, 20, 18, 22$$

The corresponding **data array** in ascending order is the following:

$$18, 18, 18, 20, 20, 20, 20, 21, 22, 22, 24, 25, 28, 29, 29, 38, 40, 45, 52, 63$$

Calculate the median age of the employees.

The **position** of the median is $i = \dfrac{n+1}{2} = \dfrac{20+1}{2} = 10.5^{\text{th}}$ position

Therefore, the median is $\tilde{x} = \dfrac{10^{\text{th}} \text{ value} + 11^{\text{th}} \text{ value}}{2} = \dfrac{22+24}{2} = 23$ years

Note: The mean is $\bar{x} = 28.6$ years. The mean is higher than the median because most of the data are in the 18-to-29 range, with a few larger values that will have the effect of increasing the mean.

Calculator Method to Obtain the Median

The **"CALC"** function provides the median as well as the mean.

Use the calculator to calculate the median age of the employees. Refer to Calculator Lesson 3.

INSTRUCTIONS:

1. Press the **MENU** key to switch to **STAT** mode. Highlight the **STAT** icon and press **EXE**.

2. You can enter the age data, **63 EXE, 52 EXE, 38 EXE, 20 EXE, 21 EXE, 18 EXE, 29 EXE, 28 EXE, 45 EXE, 40 EXE, 24 EXE, 25 EXE, 22 EXE, 20 EXE, 29 EXE, 20 EXE, 18 EXE, 20 EXE, 18 EXE,** and **22 EXE** in **List 1**.

3. Press **F2 (CALC)**.

4. Press **F6 (SET)**. Highlight **1 VarXList**, and press **F1** (List), enter **1** for **List 1**, and press **EXE**. Then highlight **1Var Freq** and choose **1 (F1)**. Now press **EXIT** to return to the display of the data. *Note: Make sure that* 1Var Freq *is set to 1.*

5. Press **F1 (1 VAR)** to obtain a full range of one-variable statistics. The result, $\bar{x} = 28.6$, will be at the top of the list. Scroll down the screen to obtain $\tilde{x} = 23$.

EXAMPLE 4.9

There Is An *Odd* Number of Data Values

The following data represents the ages, in years, of 17 employees working at a retail outlet.

$$63, 52, 38, 20, 21, 18, 29, 28, 45, 40, 24, 25, 22, 20, 29, 20, 18$$

The corresponding **data array** in ascending order is the following:

$$18, 18, 20, 20, 20, 21, 22, 24, 25, 28, 29, 29, 38, 40, 45, 52, 63$$

The **position** of the median is: $i = \dfrac{n + 1}{2} = \dfrac{17 + 1}{2} = 9^{\text{th}}$ position

Therefore, the median is: $\tilde{x} = 9^{\text{th}}$ value $= 25$ years

Calculator Method to Obtain the Median

The **CALC** function provides the median as well as the mean.

Use the calculator to calculate the median age of the employees. Refer to Calculator Lesson 3.

INSTRUCTIONS:

1. Press the **MENU** key to switch to **STAT** mode. Highlight the **STAT** icon and press **EXE**.

2. You can enter the age data, **63 EXE, 52 EXE, 38 EXE, 20 EXE, 21 EXE, 18 EXE, 29 EXE, 28 EXE, 45 EXE, 40 EXE, 24 EXE, 25 EXE, 22 EXE, 20 EXE, 29 EXE, 20 EXE,** and **18 EXE**.

3. Press **F2 (CALC)**.

4. Press **F6 (SET)**. Highlight **1 VarXList**, press **F1** (List), enter **1** for **List 1**, press **EXE**. Then highlight **1Var Freq** choose **1 (F1)**. Now press **EXIT** to return to the display of the data. *Note: Make sure that* 1Var Freq *is set to 1.*

5. Press **F1 (1 VAR)** to obtain a full range of one-variable statistics. The result, $\bar{x} = 30.117647$, will be at the top of the list. Scroll down the screen to obtain $\tilde{x} = 25$.

Which Is a Better Measure of Central Tendency? The Mean or the Median?

The following examples show situations in which the median might be the preferred measure of central tendency to represent a data set (i.e., when the median is preferred over the mean).

EXAMPLE 4.10   The following data represent the prices of houses sold last week in a particular neighbour-hood. The data have been put into an array.

$200,000 $205,000 $210,000 $220,000 $225,000

a) If you read that the mean house price in this neighbourhood was

$$\bar{x} = \$212,000$$

then you would get a certain impression as to the size and type of the typical house in the neighbourhood.

b) If you read that the median house price in this neighbourhood was

$$\tilde{x} = \$210,000$$

then you would get the same impression as to the size and type of the typical house in the neighbourhood.

Conclusion: If the mean and median are **close**, then the **mean** will give the correct impression and is the preferred measure. How do you measure or evaluate the *closeness* of mean and median? *Closeness* means that the mean is approximately close (or equal) to the median. We proposed a heuristics rule, known as the 10% rule, to evaluate the *closeness*.

EXAMPLE 4.11   The following data represents the prices of houses sold last week in a particular neighbour-hood. The data have been put into an array.

$200,000 $205,000 $210,000 $220,000 $425,000

a) If you read that the mean house price in this neighbourhood was

$$\bar{x} = \$252,000$$

then you would get a certain impression as to the size and type of the typical house in the neighbourhood.

b) If you read that the median house price is this neighbourhood was

$$\tilde{x} = \$210,000$$

then you would get a different impression as to the size and type of the typical house in the neighbourhood.

Conclusion: If the mean and median are **not close**, then the **median** will give the correct impression. The reason why the mean and the median are not close is that the data set has **unbalanced extreme values.** *Not close* means that the median is not equal to the mean. Use the 10% rule to evaluate the closeness of mean and median.

Use the 10% rule to evaluate the two values (mean and median) to determine which is the better measure of central tendency (**median** or **mean** (average)) to describe a set of data. Examples 4.10 and 4.11 demonstrate this point.

The following procedure is used to determine whether mean or median is a better measure:

1. Compute the mean.
2. Compute the median.
3. Apply the heuristic rule, which is the 10% rule, to determine if the mean has the same value as or a different value from the median.
4. Select either mean or median to summarize your data based on the heuristic 10% rule.

10% RULE:

To help you determine if the mean and median are really different, use the following rule:

Calculate the *difference* between the mean and median.

Calculate *10% of the smaller value,* be it the mean or median.

Compare the two values, *difference* and *10% of the smaller value* using the following decision rule below.

The decision rules are the following:

If the difference is less than 10% of the smaller value, you conclude that the mean is approximately equal to the median, in which case the *mean* is the preferred measure. This decision also tells you that the distribution is symmetrical. Given a symmetrical distribution, the mean would be a preferred measure of central tendency.

If the difference is greater than 10% of the smaller value, you conclude that the mean is *not equal* to the median, in which case the *median* is the preferred measure. This decision also tells you that the distribution is skewed. Given a skewed distribution, the median would be a preferred measure of central tendency.

Example 4.10: Difference = 2,000, which is **less than** 10% of the smaller value, or 21,000, and you conclude that mean price is a better measure to describe the data set.

Example 4.11: Difference = 42,000, which is **greater than** 10% of the smaller value, or 21,000, and you conclude that median price is a better measure to describe the data set.

The Mode

The **mode** is the value in a set of data that appears most frequently. Like the median and unlike the mean, extreme values do not affect the mode. Often, there is no mode or there are several modes in a set of data. For example, consider the time-to-get-ready data shown as follows:

$$29 \quad 31 \quad 35 \quad 39 \quad 39 \quad 40 \quad 43 \quad 44 \quad 44 \quad 52$$

There are two modes, 39 minutes and 44 minutes, because each of these values occurs twice.

EXAMPLE 4.12

Determining the Mode

A systems manager in charge of a company's network keeps track of the number of server failures that occur in a day. Determine the mode for the following data, which represent the number of server failures a day for the past two weeks:

$$1 \quad 3 \quad 0 \quad 3 \quad 26 \quad 2 \quad 7 \quad 4 \quad 0 \quad 2 \quad 3 \quad 3 \quad 6 \quad 3$$

SOLUTION The ordered array for these data is

$$0 \quad 0 \quad 1 \quad 2 \quad 2 \quad 3 \quad 3 \quad 3 \quad 3 \quad 3 \quad 4 \quad 6 \quad 7 \quad 26$$

Because 3 appears five times, more times than any other value, the mode is 3. Thus, the systems manager can say that the most common occurrence is having three server failures in a day. For this data set, the median is also equal to 3, and the mean is equal to 4.5. The value 26 is an extreme value. For these data, the median and the mode better measure central tendency than the mean.

A set of data has no mode if none of the values is "most typical." Example 4.13 presents a data set with no mode.

EXAMPLE 4.13

Data with no Mode

The bounced check fees ($) for a sample of 10 banks is

$$26 \quad 28 \quad 20 \quad 21 \quad 22 \quad 25 \quad 18 \quad 23 \quad 15 \quad 30$$

Compute the mode.

SOLUTION These data have no mode. None of the values is most typical because each value appears once.

Problems for Section 4.1

4.1 A company has invited its entire human resources staff from each office across the country to attend a conference at the head office in Toronto. The following information is available:

Office	Return Airfare	# of Offices	# of HR Staff per Office
Calgary	$400	2	4
Halifax	350	1	2
Montréal	330	2	3
Ottawa	300	2	3
Vancouver	500	3	5

a. What is the median return airfare per office?
b. What is the mean return airfare per person?

4.2 The following sample data were obtained at 8:00 p.m. at a popular downtown restaurant. There were 15 tables occupied at that time.

Number of Guests at the Table	Food Bill for the Table ($)	Liquor Bill for the Table ($)
2	48.75	15.75
2	36.75	26.00
4	90.55	22.90
4	87.45	42.45
2	41.25	14.00
4	83.30	29.75
6	109.40	44.05
4	88.25	21.55
4	93.45	22.00
2	36.50	16.45
2	42.60	18.00
4	105.80	37.57
4	84.65	18.95
5	110.35	43.95
4	83.55	22.50

a. What is the 40th percentile table liquor bill?
b. What was the average food bill for the 15 tables?

c. How much did the average guest spend on food?
d. In order to be in the top 32% of the amount spent on food, a table would have to spend at least what amount?

4.3 A referendum was held on a particular issue affecting the GTA Megacity. The following table shows the results.

Municipality	Number of Votes	% in Favour
City of Toronto	482,000	45
East York	152,000	63
North York	365,000	27
Etobicoke	298,000	48
Scarborough	456,000	33

What was the overall percent in favour of the issue?

4.4 A specialty bookstore concentrates mainly on selling used books and magazines. Paperbacks sell for $1.00 each, hardcover books are $5.00 each, and magazines sell for $0.50 each. Of the 50 books sold on Tuesday, 40 were paperback and the remainder were hardcover. The bookstore also sold 15 magazines. What was the mean price per item sold?

4.5 Rye Pizza sells soft drinks in three sizes: small, medium, and large. The small size costs $0.75, the medium is $0.90, and the large is $1.15 . On a typical weekday, 25% of the soft drinks sold are small, 45% are medium, and 30% are large. What is the typical daily mean price per soft drink sold?

4.6 A particular oak dining table requires time in three manufacturing stages: 2 hours of cutting, 4 hours of assembly, and 6 hours of finishing. The wood-cutters are paid $10 per hour, the assemblers get $15 per hour, and the finishers get $20 per hour. What is the average hourly labour cost to manufacture one table?

4.7 The personnel director at Recovery Hospital wanted a study made of overtime hours and associated costs of the nurses. Ten (10) nurses were randomly selected and the following data were obtained for August.

Nurse	O/T Hours	Pay ($/hr)	Nurse	O/T Hours	Pay ($/hr)
1	13	35	6	15	25
2	13	35	7	5	30
3	12	20	8	12	35
4	15	25	9	6	30
5	7	30	10	7	25

a. What was the average number of hours of overtime worked per nurse?
b. What was the average hourly overtime pay rate per nurse?
c. What was the average pay rate per hour of overtime?

4.8 The following table shows some data regarding the top four chains of toy stores.

Chain	# of Stores	Average Sales/ Store ($ thousands)
Toys 'R' Us	144	7,236
Child World	79	3,582
Kay bee	361	507
Lionel	56	3,232

a. What is the average sales of a toy store?
b. What is the mean sales of the four toy store chains?
c. Data regarding several retail chains are shown in the table below. What is the overall percent gain in sales for the chains shown?

Company/ Chain	Sales (000,000)	% Gain (Loss)	Number of Stores	% Gain (Loss)
Radio Shack	$1,515	28	4,398	7
Mervyn's	1,336	26	92	15
Toys 'R' Us	1,042	33	144	20
Marshall's	830	35	137	27
Saks Fifth Avenue	710	2	34	6
Lerners	682	(4)	790	3
Nordstrom	613	17	36	6

4.9 The table below shows data dealing with product liability.

			Status of Injured Persons/Parties		
Liability Category Claim	Injured Party	# of Persons Receiving Payment	% of Persons Receiving Payment	% of Total Payment	Average Payment per Person
Bodily Injury	Employee	875	10.6	42.0	$97,884
	Purchaser	5,562	67.5	28.7	10,544
	User	1,441	17.5	22.5	31,836
	Other	364	4.4	6.8	38,016

Property Damage	Employee	12	0.2	0.0	$ 325
	Purchaser	3,928	78.7	64.3	4,372
	User	359	7.2	22.8	22,468
	Employee	695	3.9	12.9	6,176

a. What was the average payment to a person who suffered bodily injury?
b. What was the average payment to a purchaser involved in all types of claims?

4.10 An extensive study was conducted to determine whether there are differences in the characteristics of holiday travellers that are less than 50 years old as compared to those that are more than 50 years old. One of the items of interest was the amount spent for a one-day trip. The results are shown below:

Cost of One-Day Trip	Under 50 Years Old (n = 480)	Over 50 Years Old (n = 325)
$ 0 and under 50	2%	1%
50 " " 100	7	5
100 " " 200	12	9
200 " " 300	20	13
300 " " 400	29	20
400 " " 500	18	17
500 " " 750	6	14
750 " " 1000	3	10
1000 " " 2000	2	7
2000 " " 3000	1	4

a. For which group of travellers, if any, would the median be a better measure of central tendency than the mean?
b. For the under–50 group, 360 of those surveyed would have spent less than $___.

4.11 Based on the data in the following table:
a. What is the overall average tobacco sales revenue per person?
b. What is the mean amount of federal tax per state?
c. Would the mean or median better represent the state tobacco taxes?
d. Which state(s) had the 60th percentile federal tobacco taxes?

		Under-Age Smoking		
	Number of Smokers under 18 Years Old	State Tobacco Taxes ($ millions)	Federal Tobacco Taxes ($ millions)	Sales Revenue ($ millions)
California	300,000	20.6	11.8	125.0
New York	190,000	14.6	7.4	78.2
Texas	200,000	16.6	8.0	76.0
Illinois	130,000	7.8	5.2	49.2
Florida	125,000	8.4	5.0	49.2
Pennsylvania	130,000	8.0	5.2	47.8
Ohio	125,000	4.6	5.0	43.6

Michigan	110,000	5.6	4.4	41.0
New Jersey	85,000	6.6	3.4	33.2
Alabama	50,000	2.8	3.4	31.4

4.12 The following is a portion of a table that appeared in the December 1, 2002 issue of the Toronto Star.

Cancer Surgery Wait Times

In 2002, the average wait time for cancer surgery at the Princess Margaret Hospital and University Health Network was 54 days. This is an increase from 43 days in 2000.

Average wait time from the decision to operate to the date of surgery:

Hospital	Days	Cases
Princess Margaret Hospital	35	144
Toronto General Hospital	33	537
Toronto Western Hospital	5	10

What is the overall average wait time per patient for the three hospitals shown?

4.13 Based on the following table that appeared in *The Globe and Mail*, Classroom Edition, of March 1994, answer the questions:

a. Was the overall mean price per room higher for three star hotels than for two-star hotels?

b. What is the median number of rooms for all the hotels in the table?

c. It would be reported that 40% of the hotels had a selling price higher than $___ .

Eastern Canada

Hotel	Level of quality	Location	Number of rooms	Selling price $million	Buyer origin
Hotel Strata, Mississauga	2-star	Toronto	129	$2.7	Domestic
Royal Connaught	3-star	Hamilton	206	$4.5	Domestic
Chestnut Park	3-star	Toronto	522	$20.4	Hong Kong
Carlton Place	2-star	Toronto	528	$8.5	Indonesia/Singapore
Howard Johnson, Scarborough	2-star	Toronto	192	$5.6	China
Howard Johnson	2-star	Ottawa	108	$3.7	Domestic
Best Western, Rose City Inn	1-star	Windsor	147	$2.5	Domestic
Sutton Place	4-star	Toronto	280*	$29.2	Hong Kong
Hotel Aurora	2-star	Aurora	98	$3.5	Domestic
Rock Haven Motor Inn	1-star	Peterborough	86	$1.0	Iranian
Skyline Triumph	2-star	Toronto	380	$9.5	Domestic

Western Canada

Hotel	Level of quality	Location	Number of rooms	Selling price $million	Buyer origin
Delta River Inn	4-star	Vancouver	416	$30.0	Domestic/Hong Kong
Skyline Hotel	3-star	Calgary	385	$26.0	Domestic
Cherrywood Inn	2-star	Edmonton	136	$2.9	Domestic
Coast Lakeside Inn	3-star	Penticton	200	$13.5	Domestic
Best Western, Port O'Call	3-star	Calgary	201	$8.5	East African

*Plus 161 apartment units.

Source: Colliers Macaulay Nicolis

4.14 The following data came from the Sales & Marketing Management, Survey of Buying Power, 1998. For the states shown in the table below, answer the following questions:

a. What is the projected overall average retail sales per household in 2002?

b. What is the projected overall percent increase in the number of households from 1998 to 2003?

Survey of Buying Power (Regional and State Summaries for 5-year Projections)

REGION STATE	POPULATION					RETAIL SALES	
	1/1/98 TOTAL POP. (000s)	1/1/2003 TOTAL POP. (000s)	% CHANGE 1998–2003	1/1/2003 TOTAL HSHLDS. (000s)	% CHANGE 1998–2003	2002 TOTAL RETAIL SALES ($000)	% CHANGE 1997–2002
NEW ENGLAND							
Connecticut	3,271.1	3,275.2	.1	1,246.1	1.4	39,848,761	15.0
Maine	1,243.7	1,260.1	1.3	496.2	3.5	13,998,071	12.2
Massachusetts	6,133.5	6,241.1	1.8	2,384.6	3.3	66,722,629	12.6
New Hampshire	1,179.1	1,242.3	5.4	472.5	7.0	17,284,399	18.6
Rhode Island	987.0	978.5	–.9	372.5	.1	8,590,400	9.4
Vermont	590.4	601.6	1.9	235.4	4.3	6,407,914	11.4

4.15 A survey of 300 prize winners of a certain contest revealed the following results:

a. What was the mean prize value?

b. How many won prizes of less than $500?

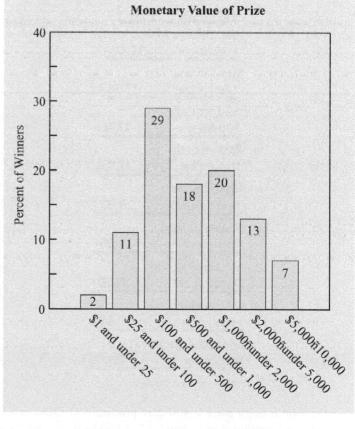

4.16 Based on the following table, what is the mean size of institutions that make extensive use of TQM (Total Quality Management)?

Breakdown by Size of Institution				
Student Population	Number of Institutions Responding	Percent of Institutions Responding	Number of Institutions Extensively Using TQM	Percent of Institutions Extensively Using TQM
0 and under 2,000	19	8	3	7
2,000 " " 5,000	58	24	7	17
5,000 " " 10,000	65	27	13	31
10,000 " " 15,000	41	17	6	14
15,000 " " 25,000	35	14	9	22
25,000 " " 35,000	15	6	3	7
35,000 " " 50,000	10	4	1	2

4.17 The following table appeared in the June 19, 2003 issue of the *Toronto Star*.

Auto productivity

Top 10 assembly plants in North America by labour-hours per vehicle.

Nissan, Smyrna, Tenn.
Midsize car   **15.74**

GM, Oshawa #1
Midsize car   **16.44**

GM, Oshawa #2
Midsize car   **17.08**

Ford, Chicago
Midsize car   **17.71**

Ford, Atlanta
Midsize car   **17.78**

Nissan, Smyrna
Small pickup   **18.23**

Nissan, Smyrna
Small SUV   **18.35**

GM, Lansing, Mich
Compact car   **18.59**

GM, Lansing
Midsize car   **18.64**

Toyota Georgetown #1
Midsize car   **20.06**

SOURCE: Harbour and Associates

Last month there were 2,400 cars produced at Oshawa #1, 3,000 cars produced at Oshawa #2, 1,800 midsize cars produced at Lansing, and 1,500 compact cars produced at Lansing. What was the overall average labour hours per car for these four GM plants?

4.18 The following is a portion of a chart that appeared in the May 25, 2003 issue of the *Toronto Star*.

By the numbers

Housing outlook... Ontario home starts will jump 3 per cent this year to 86,000, but fall back to 80,000 in 2004.

Home sales... Existing-home sales in Canada's 25 major markets declined less than 1 per cent in April, but the average price rose.

Seasonally adjusted

	Apr. 2003	Mar. 2003	% change
Dollar volume (billions)	$4.6	$4.8	-3.6%
Sales	21,905	22,085	-0.8%
Average price	$217,073	$203,589	6.6%
New listings	35,247	34,611	1.8%

What was the overall average price of houses sold in Canada's 25 major markets for March and April 2003?

4.19 The table below appeared in the *Financial Post* of December 2, 1998.

World oil giants

		Profit US$billion	Rev. per employee US$	Employees
1	Exxon Corp./Mobil Corp. (U.S.)	11.8	96,170	122,700
2	Royal Dutch/Shell Group (Britain/Netherlands)	7.8	74,286	105,000
3	British Petroleum/Amoco (Britain)	4.0	70,859	56,450
4	Total SA/Petrofina SA (France)	2.9	67.391	69,066
5	Texaco Inc. (U.S.)	2.7	92,109	29,313
6	Elf Aquitaine (France)	0.96	11,469	83,700
7	ENI (Italy)	3.0	37,417	80,178
8	Chevron Corp. (U.S.)	3.3	84,615	39,362
9	PDVSA (Venezuela)	4.8	84,818	56,592
10	SK (South Korea)	0.125	4,086	30,595

SOURCE: COMPANY REPORTS

a. For the 10 companies shown, what is the mean profit per company?

b. What is the overall mean revenue per employee for the 10 companies shown?

c. What is the overall mean profit per employee?

4.2 Descriptive Statistics II: Measures of Variability

Descriptive statistics comprises numbers calculated to describe various aspects of a data set. The two most important types of descriptive statistics are the following:

Measures of Central Tendency: A single value to represent the data set

Measures of Variability: A single value to describe how spread out the data are

In this section you will learn how to calculate various measures of variability or dispersion. The most common measures of the variability of the data are range, interquartile range, standard deviation, and variance.

We will use the following three data sets to demonstrate the concepts and calculations of variability measures:

Data set A: 1, 2, 3, 4, 5

Data set B: 1, 1, 3, 3, 5, 5

Data set C: 1, 1, 1, 5, 5, 5

It should be noted that for each data set: mean = median = 3.

In other words, the most important measures of central tendency are the same for all three data sets, but the data sets themselves are different; therefore, there must be some other aspect of them that is different. It is the fact that they have different amounts of **variability**.

Range (R)

Symbol: R for sample or population range

Formula: $R = Maximum - Minimum$ **(4.1)**

EXAMPLE 4.14

Data set A: $R = 5 - 1 = 4$

Data set B: $R = 5 - 1 = 4$

Data set C: $R = 5 - 1 = 4$

These results would seem to indicate that the three data sets had the same amount of variability. This would appear not to be true, since our intuition would seem to indicate that the three data sets would have different amounts of variability.

From this example we can see why the range has limited use. It considers only the high and low values of a data set and ignores the values in between. These in-between values should have some input in determining the variability of a data set.

It should be noted, however, that the range can be useful to measure variability in some cases. For many years the range has been the preferred way to measure variability when setting up quality control charts, which are used to monitor the mean and the variability of repeated processes.

In this course, you will calculate the range only if you are told to do so.

EXAMPLE 4.15

Computing the Range in the 2003 Return of Small Cap High-Risk Mutual Funds

The 184 mutual funds that are part of the "Using Statistics" scenario (see page 137) are classified according to the risk level of the mutual funds (low, average, and high) and type (small cap, mid cap, and large cap). Compute the range of the 2003 return for the small cap mutual funds with high risk.

SOLUTION: Ranked from the smallest to the largest, the 2003 return for the nine small cap mutual funds with high risk is the following:

37.3   39.2   44.2   44.5   53.8   56.6   59.3   62.4   66.5

Therefore, using Equation (4.1), the range = 66.5 − 37.3 = 29.2.

The largest difference between any two returns for the small cap mutual funds with high risk is 29.2.

The range measures the *total spread* in the set of data. Although the range is a simple measure of total variation in the data, it does not take into account *how* the data are distributed between the smallest and largest values. In other words, the range does not indicate if the values are evenly distributed throughout the data set, clustered near the middle, or clustered near one or both extremes. Thus, using the range as a measure of variation when at least one value is an extreme value is misleading.

Interquartile Range (IQR)

Symbol: IQR for sample or population

Formula: $IQR = Q_3 - Q_1$ **(4.2)**

EXAMPLE 4.16

Data set A: $IQR = 4.5 - 1.5 = 3$

Data set B: $IQR = 5 - 1 = 4$

Data set C: $IQR = 5 - 1 = 4$

These results would seem to indicate that data set A has less variability than data sets B and C. This is an improvement over the previous results based on the range (as we shall see shortly). However, data sets B and C do not have the same amount of variability.

The interquartile range is often preferred over the range as a measure of variability since the range can easily be influenced by one extreme value.

Consider the following example:

EXAMPLE 4.17

Data set D: 1, 3, 3, 4, 4, 4, 5, 5, 5, 5, 6, 6, 6, 7, 7, 7, 8, 8, 9, 10

Data set E: 1, 3, 3, 4, 4, 4, 5, 5, 5, 5, 6, 6, 6, 7, 7, 7, 8, 8, 9, 20

Suppose we use the *range* to measure the variability of these two data sets:

Data set D: $R = 10 - 1 = 9$ Data set E: $R = 20 - 1 = 19$

Intuitively, we would not expect that data set E would have twice as much variability as data set D (i.e., the range does not seem to be a good measure of variability in this case).

Now, suppose we use the *interquartile range* to measure the variability:

Data set D: $IQR = 7 - 4 = 3$ Data set E: $IQR = 7 - 4 = 3$

Intuitively, we would not say that both data sets have exactly the same variability. However, this appears to be closer to the truth than the conclusion that the range results lead us to. The IQR is not affected by one or two extreme values as the range is.

EXAMPLE 4.18

Computing the Interquartile Range for the 2003 Return of Small Cap High-Risk Mutual Funds

The 184 mutual funds that are part of the "Using Statistics" scenario (see page 137) are classified according to the risk level of the mutual funds (low, average, and high) and type (small cap, mid cap, and large cap). Compute the interquartile range of the 2003 return for the small cap mutual funds with high risk.

SOLUTION: Ranked from smallest to largest, the 2003 return for the nine small cap mutual funds with high risk is the following:

37.3   39.2   44.2   44.5   53.8   56.6   59.3   62.4   66.5

Using Equation (4.2) and the earlier results, $Q_1 = 41.7$ and $Q_3 = 60.85$.

Interquartile range $= 60.85 - 41.7 = 19.15$

Therefore, the interquartile range in the 2003 return is 19.15.

Because the interquartile range does not consider any value smaller than Q_1 or larger than Q_3, it is not affected by a limited number of extreme values. Summary measures such as the median, Q_1, Q_3, and the interquartile range, which are not easily influenced by extreme values, are called **resistant measures**.

Variance

Symbol	Population Parameter	Sample Statistic
Variance	σ^2	s^2
Standard Deviation	$\sqrt{\sigma^2} = \sigma$	$\sqrt{s^2} = s$
Size (Number of items or elements)	N	n

The symbol we use to denote the sample variance is s^2, as shown in the table above. The symbol we use to denote the population variance is σ^2.

The formula to calculate the variance if you are given **sample** data is $s^2 = \dfrac{\sum (x - \bar{x})^2}{n - 1}$

The formula to calculate the variance if you are given **population** data is $\sigma^2 = \dfrac{\sum (x - \mu)^2}{N}$

Note: *For the first time, we will get a different result for a descriptive measure if the data are a sample instead of a population. Previously, only the symbol was different (if anything was different).*

We now have a measure of variability that considers *all* the values in a data set.

EXAMPLE 4.19

How to Calculate the Variance Using a Formula?

I.   Data set A: 1, 2, 3, 4, 5

x	$x - \bar{x}$ or $x - \mu$	$(x - \bar{x})^2$ or $(x - \mu)^2$
1	−2	4
2	−1	1
3	0	0
4	1	1
5	2	4
		10 ⟵ $\sum (x - mean)^2 = 10$

If the data are from a **sample**, the sample variance is the following:

$$s^2 = \frac{\sum (x - \bar{x})^2}{n - 1} = \frac{10}{5 - 1} = 2.5$$

If the data are from a **population**, the population variance is the following:

$$\sigma^2 = \frac{\sum (x - \mu)^2}{N} = \frac{10}{5} = 2$$

II.   Data set B: 1, 1, 3, 3, 5, 5

x	$x - \bar{x}$ or $x - \mu$	$(x - \bar{x})^2$ or $(x - \mu)^2$
1	−2	4
1	−2	4
3	0	0
3	0	0
5	2	4
5	2	4
		16 ⟵ $\sum (x - mean)^2 = 16$

If the data are from a **sample**, the sample variance is the following:

$$s^2 = \frac{\sum (x - \bar{x})^2}{n - 1} = \frac{16}{6 - 1} = 3.2$$

If the data are from a **population**, the population variance is the following:

$$\sigma^2 = \frac{\sum (x - \mu)^2}{N} = \frac{16}{6} = 2.67$$

III.   Data set C: 1, 1, 1, 5, 5, 5

x	$x - \bar{x}$ or $x - \mu$	$(x - \bar{x})^2$ or $(x - \mu)^2$
1	−2	4
1	−2	4
1	−2	4
5	2	4
5	2	4
5	2	4
		24 ⟵ $\sum (x - mean)^2 = 24$

If the data are from a **sample**, the sample variance is the following:

$$s^2 = \frac{\sum (x - \bar{x})^2}{n - 1} = \frac{24}{6 - 1} = 4.8$$

If the data are from a population, the population variance is the following:

$$\sigma^2 = \frac{\sum (x - \mu)^2}{N} = \frac{24}{6} = 4$$

Conclusion: Based on these results, data set A has the least amount of variability, while data set C has the most. These results are reasonable when we understand that variability in statistics has nothing to do with how many different values there are but instead has to do with whether the data seem to be close to the mean or they tend to be further from the mean.

Variance is a good measure of variability in that it takes into account all values. However, variance has a major practical disadvantage: the units don't make sense. The units of variance are (data units)^2. For example, if the data in data set A are \$, then the variance is 2.5\$^{2}. If the data are people, the variance is 2.5 people^2. Because of this problem, variance does not have a *practical* interpretation. In statistics, variance is used almost exclusively in the theoretical development of formulas.

Standard Deviation

Symbol: Sample standard deviation s Population standard deviation σ

Formula: Sample standard deviation: $s = \sqrt{s^2} = \sqrt{\dfrac{\sum(x - \bar{x})^2}{n - 1}}$

Population standard deviation: $\sigma = \sqrt{\sigma^2}$

EXAMPLE 4.20

Data set A: If the data are from a sample, the sample standard deviation is $s = \sqrt{s^2}$ $= \sqrt{2.5} = 1.58$.

In Example 4.19, we found $s^2 = \dfrac{\sum(x - \bar{x})^2}{n - 1} = \dfrac{10}{5 - 1} = 2.5$.

Data set B: If the data are from a sample, the sample standard deviation is $s = \sqrt{s^2}$ $= \sqrt{3.2} = 1.79$.

In Example 4.19, we found $s^2 = \dfrac{\sum(x - \bar{x})^2}{n - 1} = \dfrac{16}{6 - 1} = 3.2$.

Data set C: If the data are from a sample, the sample standard deviation is $s = \sqrt{s^2}$ $= \sqrt{4.8} = 2.19$.

In Example 4.19, we found $s^2 = \dfrac{\sum(x - \bar{x})^2}{n - 1} = \dfrac{24}{6 - 1} = 4.8$.

We can see that the conclusions regarding which data set is the most variable and which is the least variable is the same as when we compared variances.

The main advantage of standard deviation, for practical purposes, is that the units are the *same* as the data.

Rounding Rule for Standard Deviation

Regarding the form of the answer when calculating standard deviation (when rounding is obviously necessary), use three (3) figures or a number that looks like the data, whichever has more figures. This rule also applies to the use of standard deviation in further calculations, although it is sometimes easier to use results stored in the memory of your calculator or computer.

Example 1: If data are 10,   11,   13,   15,   then $s = 2.22$.
Example 2: If data are 2,315,   4,156,   7,542,   9,587,   then $s = 3,275$.
Example 3: If data are 2,315,   2,320,   2,325,   2,330,   then $s = 6.45$.
Example 4: If data are 23.46,   56.82,   83.47,   92.61,   then $s = 31.05$.

Calculator Method to Obtain the Standard Deviation

The **CALC** function provides the mean, median, and standard deviation.

Use the calculator to calculate the standard deviation. Refer to **Data set A: 1, 2, 3, 4, 5**. Follow these steps to obtain the standard deviation:

INSTRUCTIONS
1. From the Main Menu, select the **STAT** mode.
2. Enter data set A (1,2,3,4,5) in List 1.
3. Select **CALC** (F2).
4. Select **SET** (F6).
5. Set the following:
   1 VarXList : List 1

1 VarFreq : "1"
After you are done, press **EXIT**.
6. Select "**1Var**" (F1) for the results.

RESULTS (with Casio FX-9750GII):

σ_x = 1.41421356 (where σ_x is the value of population standard deviation).

s_x = 1.58113883 (where s_x is the value of sample standard deviation).

The Casio calculator does not provide variance. The calculator presents the two standard deviation values: (1) sample standard deviation (with symbols "s_x" or "s_{n-1}" shown in your calculator) and (2) population standard deviation (with symbols" σ_x" or "σ_n" shown in your calculator). To obtain the variance, you square the standard deviation. The calculator symbols for standard deviation are presented below.

	CALCULATORS MODELS			
	Casio fx 9750 plus		Casio fx 9750 GII	
	Population	Sample	Population	Sample
Standard Deviation	$x\sigma_n$	$x\sigma_{n-1}$	σ_x	S_x

However, you must use the standard statistical symbols: σ (for population standard deviation), s (for sample standard deviation), σ^2 (for population variance) and s^2 (for sample variance).

EXAMPLE 4.21

Computing the Variance and Standard Deviation of the 2003 Return of Small Cap High-Risk Mutual Funds

The 184 mutual funds that are part of the "Using Statistics" scenario (see page 137) are classified according to the risk level of the mutual funds (low, average, and high) and type (small cap, mid cap, and large cap). Compute the variance and standard deviation of the 2003 return for the small cap mutual funds with high risk.

SOLUTION: Table 4.2 illustrates the computation of the variance and standard deviation of the return in 2003 for the small cap mutual funds with high risk. Using the equation below,

$$
S^2 = \frac{\sum_{i=1}^{n}(X_i - \overline{X})^2}{n - 1}
$$

$$
= \frac{(44.5 - 51.53)^2 + (39.2 - 51.53)^2 + \cdots + (66.5 - 51.53)^2}{9 - 1}
$$

$$
= \frac{891.16}{8}
$$

$$
= 111.395
$$

Using the equation below, the sample standard deviation S is

$$
S = \sqrt{S^2} = \sqrt{\frac{\sum_{i=1}^{n}(X_i - \overline{X})^2}{n - 1}} = \sqrt{111.395} = 10.6\%
$$

TABLE 4.2

Computing the Variance of the 2003 Return for the Small Cap Mutual Funds with High Risk

$\overline{X} = 51.5333$

Return 2003	Step 1: $(X_i - \overline{X})$	Step 2: $(X_i - \overline{X})^2$
44.5	−7.0333	49.4678
39.2	−12.3333	152.1111
62.4	10.8667	118.0844
59.3	7.7667	60.3211
56.6	5.0667	25.6711
53.8	2.2667	5.1378
37.3	−14.2333	202.5878
44.2	−7.3333	53.7778
66.5	14.9667	224.0011
	Step 3: Sum:	Step 4: Divide by ($n-1$):
	891.16	111.395

The following summarizes the characteristics of the range, interquartile range, variance, and standard deviation.

- The more spread out, or dispersed, the data are, the larger the range, interquartile range, variance, and standard deviation.
- The more concentrated, or homogeneous, the data are, the smaller the range, interquartile range, variance, and standard deviation.
- If the values are all the same (so that there is no variation in the data), the range, interquartile range, variance, and standard deviation will all equal zero.
- None of the measures of variation (the range, interquartile range, standard deviation, and variance) can *ever* be negative.

Coefficient of Variation

All of the above measures of variability are *absolute* measures. It is often better (i.e., you get more meaningful results) to compare factors using *relative* measures. The coefficient of variation is a relative measure of variability.

The symbol for the coefficient of variation is CV.

The formulae to compute the coefficient of variation are

With a sample data: $CV = \dfrac{s}{\overline{x}} \times 100\%$

With a population data: $CV = \dfrac{\sigma}{\mu} \times 100\%$

CV is expressed in percentage.

Examples 4.22, 4.23, and 4.24 demonstrate how to determine the coefficient of variation.

EXAMPLE 4.22

TABLE 4.3

The following information for four stocks is to be analyzed.

Stock	Price	Dividend
ABC Company	$25	$0.70
DEF Company	47	1.50
HIJ Company	78	2.00
XYZ Company	92	3.00

Compare the variability of the prices and dividends.

SOLUTION: Since the sizes of the numbers in the two data sets are quite a bit different, it will be best to use a relative measure to compare the variability.

$$\text{Price:} \qquad CV = \frac{s}{\bar{x}} \times 100\% = \frac{30.23}{60.50} \times 100\% = 50\%$$

$$\text{Dividend:} \quad CV = \frac{s}{\bar{x}} \times 100\% = \frac{0.963}{1.80} \times 100\% = 53\%$$

Conclusion: Since $CV_{\text{dividend}} = 54\%$ is greater than $CV_{\text{price}} = 50\%$, the dividends are relatively more variable than the prices.

Note: If we had just looked at the standard deviation, we would have concluded (rather obviously because of the size of the numbers) that the prices were more variable.

Rounding rule for CV One decimal if $< 10\%$. No decimals if $> 10\%$.

EXAMPLE 4.23

The following table shows data for the houses that are being built on a short street in a new subdivision.

TABLE 4.4

House Number	Size Square ft.	Price ($ thousands)
1002	2400	269
1004	2650	289
1006	2200	225
1008	2150	219
1010	2500	249

Compare the variability of the sizes and the prices.

SOLUTION: Since the *units* of the data are *different*, the only way to compare the variability of these two sets of data is to use the coefficient of variation.

$$\text{Size:} \quad CV = \frac{s}{\bar{x}} \times 100\% = \frac{208}{2380} \times 100\% = 8.7\%$$

$$\text{Price:} \quad CV = \frac{s}{\bar{x}} \times 100\% = \frac{29.4}{250} \times 100\% = 12\%$$

Conclusion: Since $CV_{\text{price}} = 12\%$ is greater than $CV_{\text{size}} = 8.7\%$, the prices are relatively more variable than the sizes.

EXAMPLE 4.24

Comparing Two Coefficients of Variation When Two Variables Have Different Units of Measurement

The operations manager of a package delivery service is deciding on whether to purchase a new fleet of trucks. When packages are stored in the trucks in preparation for delivery, you need to consider two major constraints—the weight (in pounds) and the volume (in cubic feet) for each item.

The operations manager samples 200 packages and finds that the mean weight is 26.0 pounds, with a standard deviation of 3.9 pounds, and the mean volume is 8.8 cubic feet, with a standard deviation of 2.2 cubic feet. How can the operations manager compare the variation of the weight and the volume?

SOLUTION: Because the measurement units differ for the weight and volume constraints, the operations manager should compare the relative variability in the two types of measurements.

For weight, the coefficient of variation is

$$CV_W = \left(\frac{3.9}{26.0}\right) 100\% = 15\%$$

For volume, the coefficient of variation is

$$CV_V = \left(\frac{2.2}{8.8}\right)100\% = 25\%$$

Since $CV_V = 25\% > CV_W = 15\%$, the package volume is much more variable than the package weight.

Problems for Section 4.2

4.20 Last year's travel expenditures ($) by the 12 members of a university's business council were as follows:

        0   0   173   378   441   733   759
      857 958 985 1434 2063

a. Calculate the mean travel expenditure per member.
b. Determine the median travel expenditure per member.
c. Determine the 80th percentile of these data.
d. Determine the range and the interquartile range of the data.
e. Calculate the coefficient of variation of the data.

4.21 The number of defective items in 12 recent production lots of 1,000 items, each from Plant A, were as follows:

      3   1   0   2 21   4   1   1   0   2   5

a. Calculate the mean number of defective items per lot.
b. The mean number of defectives per lot in a group of 16 lots from Plant B was 3.5. What was the total number of defective items in these 16 lots?
c. What is the median number of defective items per lot?
d. Why does the median differ substantially from the mean of these data?
e. The median number of defectives per lot for 20 lots from Plant C was 4. What was the total number of defectives in these 20 lots?
f. What is the standard deviation of the number of defectives per lot for Plant A?

4.22 The change in enrollment between this year and last year in seven programs at a particular university are as follows:

      -614 -103   41   258   313   387   490

a. Calculate the mean enrollment change per program. Does the fact that the mean is positive imply that the combined total enrollment in the seven programs has increased? Explain.
b. Determine the median enrollment change per program.
c. Calculate the standard deviation of enrollment change. Does the fact that the standard deviation is positive relate to the fact that the mean was positive? Explain.

4.23 Refer to Problem 4.2 in Descriptive Statistics Exercises—Set 1:
What is the standard deviation of the liquor bill for a table?

4.24 Refer to Problem 4.8 in Descriptive Statistics Exercises—Set 1:

What is the standard deviation of the sales of a toy store?

4.25 Refer to Problem 4.10 in Descriptive Statistics Exercises—Set 1:
What is the standard deviation of the cost of a one-day trip for people under 50 years old?

4.26 Refer to Problem 4.15 in Descriptive Statistics Exercises—Set 1:
What is the standard deviation of the monetary value of the prizes?

4.27 Refer to Problem 4.17 in Descriptive Statistics Exercises—Set 1:
What is the standard deviation of the labour hours per car for the four GM plants?

4.28 Refer to Problem 4.19 in Descriptive Statistics Exercises—Set 1:
What is the standard deviation of the company profits?

4.29 A suburban farm grows strawberries in a large field where prospective customers go to pick-their-own. A survey of 200 customers showed that 30% picked one basket, 50% picked two baskets, and the remainder picked three baskets. What is the mean number of baskets of strawberries per customer? What is the standard deviation?

4.30 The means and standard deviations of revenue per farm ($ thousands) and volume harvested per farm (thousands of kg.) for two farm products in Western Canada are as follows:

Grain	Revenue per Farm		Volume per Farm	
	Mean	**Std. Dev.**	**Mean**	**Std. Dev.**
Wheat	12.56	4.03	76.7	22.9
Barley	14.49	5.89	106.3	35.4

Is revenue or volume relatively more variable for wheat? Is the same true for barley?

4.31 The table below appeared in the May 1995 issue of *Report on Business*.
a. What is the overall average selling space per store for all 469 stores?
b. What is the overall average sales per store for all 469 stores?

Can Brooks Catch Up

Coutu's current stores outperform its newly acquired Brooks outlets

Coutu stores averaged sales of $6 million in 94

Number of franchises 227
Selling space per store .... 7,700 sq.ft.
System-wide retail sales 1994 .... $1.34 billion

...and the U.S. Maxi outlets averaged $4 million

Number of stores 21
Selling space per store .... 12,000 sq.ft.
1994 sales .... $85 million

...while Brooks lagged far behind at $1.9 million

Number of stores 221
Selling space per store .... 6,000 sq.ft.
1994 sales .... $425.8 million

4.32 The percentage distribution of hourly earnings for the 2,100 plant employees of the ABC Corp. is shown below:

Hourly Earnings ($)	Percent of Employees
14.00 and under 16.00	12
16.00 " " 18.00	24
18.00 " " 20.00	44
20.00 " " 25.00	15
25.00 " " 30.00	5

Calculate the mean and standard deviation of hourly earnings of the employees at ABC Corp.

4.33 Refer to the table 'Who works the hardest' and determine if the five countries indicated were more variable in terms of average hours worked or gross domestic product in 2000.

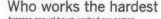

Who works the hardest

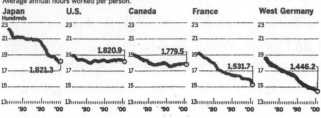

Buying power

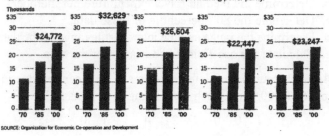

SOURCE: Organization for Economic Co-operation and Development

4.3 Descriptive Statistics III

Shape

Shape is the pattern of the distribution of data values throughout the entire range of all the values. A distribution is either symmetrical or skewed. In a **symmetrical** distribution, the values below the mean are distributed in exactly the same way as the values above the mean. In this case, the low and high values balance each other out. In a **skewed** distribution, the values are not symmetrical around the mean. This skewness results in an imbalance of low values or high values.

Shape also can influence the relationship of the mean to the median. In most cases:

- Mean < median: negative, or left-skewed
- Mean = median: symmetric, or zero skewness
- Mean > median: positive, or right-skewed

Figure 4.1 depicts three data sets, each with a different shape.

FIGURE 4.1

A comparison of three data sets that differ in shape

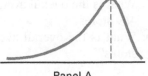

Panel A
Negative, or left-skewed

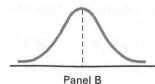

Panel B
Symmetrical

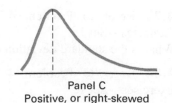

Panel C
Positive, or right-skewed

The data in Panel A are negative, or **left-skewed**. In this panel, most of the values are in the upper portion of the distribution. A long tail and distortion to the left is caused by some extremely small values. These extremely small values pull the mean downward so that the mean is less than the median.

The data in Panel B are symmetrical. Each half of the curve is a mirror image of the other half of the curve. The low and high values on the scale balance, and the mean equals the median.

The data in Panel C are positive, or **right-skewed**. In this panel, most of the values are in the lower portion of the distribution. A long tail on the right is caused by some extremely large values. These extremely large values pull the mean upward so that the mean is greater than the median.

Problems for Section 4.3

LEARNING THE BASICS

4.34 The following set of data is from a sample of $n = 5$:

$$7 \quad 4 \quad 9 \quad 8 \quad 2$$

a. Compute the mean, median, and mode.
b. Compute the range, variance, standard deviation, and coefficient of variation.
c. Compute the Z scores. Are there any outliers?
d. Describe the shape of the data set.

4.35 The following set of data is from a sample of $n = 6$:

$$7 \quad 4 \quad 9 \quad 7 \quad 3 \quad 12$$

a. Compute the mean, median, and mode.
b. Compute the range, variance, standard deviation, and coefficient of variation.
c. Compute the Z scores. Are there any outliers?
d. Describe the shape of the data set.

4.36 The following set of data is from a sample of $n = 7$:

$$12 \quad 7 \quad 4 \quad 9 \quad 0 \quad 7 \quad 3$$

a. Compute the mean, median, and mode.
b. Compute the range, variance, standard deviation, and coefficient of variation.
c. Compute the Z scores. Are there any outliers?
d. Describe the shape of the data set.

4.37 The following set of data is from a sample of $n = 5$:

$$7 \quad -5 \quad -8 \quad 7 \quad 9$$

a. Compute the mean, median, and mode.
b. Compute the range, variance, standard deviation, and coefficient of variation.
c. Compute the Z scores. Are there any outliers?
d. Describe the shape of the data set.

APPLYING THE CONCEPTS

4.38 A survey conducted by the American Statistical Association reported the following results for the salaries of professors teaching statistics in research universities with four to five years in the rank of associate professor and professor.

Title	Median
Associate professor	81,600
Professor	120,000

Source: Data extracted from **magazine.amstat.org/blog/2010/12/01/academic-salary-survey**.

Interpret the median salary for the associate professors and professors.

4.39 The operations manager of a plant that manufactures tires wants to compare the actual inner diameters of two grades of tires, each of which is expected to be 575 millimeters. A sample of five tires of each grade was selected, and the results representing the inner diameters of the tires, ranked from smallest to largest, are as follows:

Grade X	Grade Y
568 570 575 578 584	573 574 575 577 578

a. For each of the two grades of tires, compute the mean, median, and standard deviation.
b. Which grade of tire is providing better quality? Explain.
c. What would be the effect on your answers in (a) and (b) if the last value for grade Y were 588 instead of 578? Explain.

4.40 According to the U.S. Census Bureau, in 2010, the median sales price of new houses was $221,000 and the mean sales price was $272,400 (extracted from **www.census.gov**, April 4, 2011).
a. Interpret the median sales price.
b. Interpret the mean sales price.
c. Discuss the shape of the distribution of the price of new houses.

✓ SELF Test **4.41** The file **FastFood** contains the amount that a sample of nine customers spent for lunch ($) at a fast-food restaurant:

4.20 5.03 5.86 6.45 7.38 7.54 8.46 8.47 9.87

a. Compute the mean and median.
b. Compute the variance, standard deviation, range, and coefficient of variation.

c. Are the data skewed? If so, how?
d. Based on the results of (a) through (c), what conclusions can you reach concerning the amount that customers spent for lunch?

4.42 The file Sedans contains the overall miles per gallon (MPG) of 2011 family sedans:

24 21 25 22 23 34 34
20 20 22 44 32 20 20

Source: Data extracted from "Ratings," *Consumer Reports*, April 2011, pp. 30–31.

a. Compute the mean, median, and mode.
b. Compute the variance, standard deviation, range, coefficient of variation, and *Z* scores.
c. Are the data skewed? If so, how?
d. Compare the results of (a) through (c) to those of Problem 4.43 (a) through (c) that refer to the miles per gallon of small SUVs.

4.43 The file SUV contains the overall miles per gallon (MPG) of 2011 small SUVs:

20 24 22 23 20 22 21 22 22
19 22 22 26 19 19 23 24 21
21 19 21 22 22 16 16

Source: Data extracted from "Ratings," *Consumer Reports*, April 2011, pp. 35–36.

a. Compute the mean, median, and mode.
b. Compute the variance, standard deviation, range, coefficient of variation, and *Z* scores.
c. Are the data skewed? If so, how?
d. Compare the results of (a) through (c) to those of Problem 4.42 (a) through (c) that refer to the miles per gallon of family sedans.

4.44 The file ChocolateChip contains the cost (in cents) per 1-ounce serving for a sample of 13 chocolate chip cookies. The data are as follows:

54 22 25 23 36 43 7 43 25 47 24 45 44

Source: Data extracted from "Chip, Chip, Hooray," *Consumer Reports*, June 2009, p. 7.

a. Compute the mean, median, and mode.
b. Compute the variance, standard deviation, range, coefficient of variation, and *Z* scores. Are there any outliers? Explain.
c. Are the data skewed? If so, how?
d. Based on the results of (a) through (c), what conclusions can you reach concerning the cost of chocolate chip cookies?

4.45 The file DarkChocolate contains the cost per ounce ($) for a sample of 14 dark chocolate bars:

0.68 0.72 0.92 1.14 1.42 0.94 0.77
0.57 1.51 0.57 0.55 0.86 1.41 0.90

Source: Data extracted from "Dark Chocolate: Which Bars Are Best?" *Consumer Reports*, September 2007, p. 8.

a. Compute the mean, median, and mode.
b. Compute the variance, standard deviation, range, coefficient of variation, and *Z* scores. Are there any outliers? Explain.
c. Are the data skewed? If so, how?
d. Based on the results of (a) through (c), what conclusions can you reach concerning the cost of dark chocolate bars?

4.46 Is there a difference in the variation of the yields of different types of investments? The file CDRate contains the yields for a one-year certificate of deposit (CD) and a five-year certificate of deposit (CD), for 23 banks in the United States, as of April 4, 2011.

Source: Data extracted from **www.Bankrate.com**, April 4, 2011.

a. For one-year and five-year CDs, separately compute the variance, standard deviation, range, and coefficient of variation.
b. Based on the results of (a), do one-year or five-year CDs have more variation in the yields offered? Explain.

4.47 The file HotelUK contains the average room price (in English pounds) paid in six British cities in 2010:

110 98 78 70 76 62

Source: Data extracted from **www.hotels.com/press/hotel-price-index-summer-2010.html**.

a. Compute the mean, median, and mode.
b. Compute the range, variance, and standard deviation.
c. Based on the results of (a) and (b), what conclusions can you reach concerning the room price (in English pounds) in 2010?
d. Suppose that the first value was 160 instead of 110. Repeat (a) through (c), using this value. Comment on the difference in the results.

4.48 A bank branch located in a commercial district of a city has the business objective of developing an improved process for serving customers during the noon-to-1:00 P.M. lunch period. The waiting time, in minutes, is defined as the time the customer enters the line to when he or she reaches the teller window. Data are collected from a sample of 15 customers during this hour. The file Bank1 contains the results, which are also listed here:

4.21 5.55 3.02 5.13 4.77 2.34 3.54 3.20
4.50 6.10 0.38 5.12 6.46 6.19 3.79

a. Compute the mean and median.
b. Compute the variance, standard deviation, range, coefficient of variation, and *Z* scores. Are there any outliers? Explain.
c. Are the data skewed? If so, how?
d. As a customer walks into the branch office during the lunch hour, she asks the branch manager how long she can expect to wait. The branch manager replies, "Almost certainly less than five minutes." On the basis of the results of (a) through (c), evaluate the accuracy of this statement.

4.49 Suppose that another bank branch, located in a residential area, is also concerned with the noon-to-1 P.M. lunch hour. The waiting time, in minutes, collected from a sample of 15 customers during this hour, is contained in the file Bank2 and listed here:

9.66 5.90 8.02 5.79 8.73 3.82 8.01 8.35
10.49 6.68 5.64 4.08 6.17 9.91 5.47

a. Compute the mean and median.
b. Compute the variance, standard deviation, range, coefficient of variation, and Z scores. Are there any outliers? Explain.
c. Are the data skewed? If so, how?
d. As a customer walks into the branch office during the lunch hour, he asks the branch manager how long he can expect to wait. The branch manager replies, "Almost certainly less than five minutes." On the basis of the results of (a) through (c), evaluate the accuracy of this statement.

4.4 Box-Whisker Plot

A. What Is the Five-Number Summary?

Sections 4.1 and 4.2 discussed the measures of central tendency and measures of variability.

You can graphically display these two measures in a box-whisker plot. The box-whisker plot gives an overall picture of a set of numerical data. You can summarize the numerical data by means of a five-number summary. The "five-number" summarizes the various positions of a set of data. The five-number summary contains the following:

1. Minimum (value)
2. First quartile (Q1)
3. Median (Q2)
4. Third quartile (Q3)
5. Maximum (value)

You can use the five-number summary to construct a box-whisker plot.

B. How to Construct a Box-Whisker Plot

A box-whisker plot is a diagram that can be constructed using the following steps (if it has no outliers values):

1. Draw an evenly spaced scale that covers all of the data values.
2. Using the scale as a reference, draw the box with the *first quartile* (Q_1) and *third quartile* (Q_3) as the sides of the box (see A_1 and A_2 in Figure 4.2). Join the two vertical sides with horizontal sides to form a box.
3. Using the scale as a reference, draw a vertical line across the box to represent the *median* (see **B** in Figure 4.2).
4. Using the scale as a reference, draw a horizontal line linking Q_1 (which is the left-hand side of the box) to the minimum (see **C** in Figure 4.2). The horizontal line from Q_1 to minimum is called the *left whisker*.

FIGURE 4.2
The Box-Whisker Plot

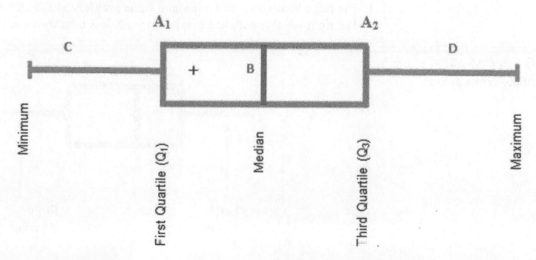

5. Using the scale as a reference, draw a horizontal line linking Q_3 (which is the right-hand side of the box) to the maximum (see **D** in Figure 4.2). The horizontal line from Q_3 to maximum is called the *right whisker*.
6. Similarly, indicate the mean with a '+' sign on the diagram (see Figure 4.2).

The box-whisker plot shown in Figure 4.2 resembles the five-number summary.

However, you have to check whether the minimum and maximum values are either suspect outliers or outliers.

C. How Do You Determine the Suspect Outliers and Outliers?

Suspect Outliers are defined as data values that lie between the inner and outer fences. Suspect outliers are plotted individually using a special symbol, 'o'.

Outliers are defined as data values that lie outside the outer fences. The outliers are plotted individually using a special symbol, '*'.

How to determine the inner and outer fences?
There are four fences, namely

1. Right Inner Fence (RIF) is a value that lies on the right-hand side of the box (see Figure 4.2).
2. Right Outer Fence (ROF) is a value that lies on the right-hand side of the box.
3. Left Inner Fence (LIF) is a value that lies on the left-hand side of the box.
4. Left Outer Fence (LOF) is a value that lies on the left-hand side of the box.

The left and right fences are then calculated but are *not* plotted on the diagram.
The formulae to calculate the fences are as follows:

1. $RIF = Q_3 + (1.5 \times IQR)$
2. $ROF = RIF + (1.5 \times IQR)$
3. $LIF = Q_1 - (1.5 \times IQR)$
4. $LOF = LIF - (1.5 \times IQR)$

Note: IQR stands for *Interquartile Range*. $IQR = Q_3 - Q_1$, where Q_3 is the third quartile and Q_1 is the first quartile.

What happens if the minimum and maximum values are identified as either suspect outliers or outliers? In this case, you have to redefine the whiskers on both sides of the box.

D. How to Determine the Whiskers

There are two whiskers, one on each side of the box (as shown in Figure 4.3)
There are two rules to determine the whiskers. Each whisker is as long as possible, but

- the whiskers cannot go past the inner fence.
- the whiskers must end at a data point (or value).

Applying these two rules, you have the following:

1. The left whisker ends at a minimum value **greater** than the left inner fence (LIF).
2. The right whisker ends at a maximum value **less** than the right inner fence (RIF).

FIGURE 4.3
The Box-Whisker Plot

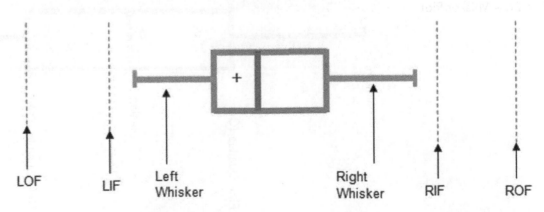

Note:

- The box-whisker plot is not drawn to scale
- The **inner and outer fences** are plotted in this diagram for illustrative purposes.

EXAMPLE 4.25

The following data show the number of days absent from work for 50 employees in a large company. The data have been arranged into an ascending data array.

1	2	4	4	5	5	5	10	10	11
12	13	13	14	19	20	22	23	25	26
26	26	27	27	27	28	29	29	29	30
31	31	32	33	35	35	36	52	54	61
68	74	81	84	95	123	126	137	152	173

The following statistics have been calculated using the CASIO CFX-9850GB calculator.

Mean:	40.7	Min:	1
Median:	27.5	Max:	173
Q1:	13		
Q3:	52		
IQR:	39		

The first step in drawing the box-whisker plot is to lay out an appropriate horizontal scale.

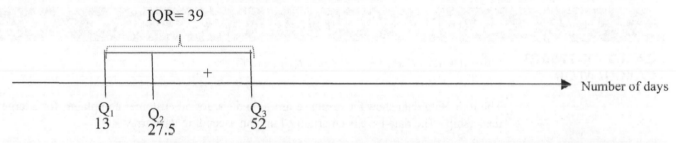

The box is then formed with the first and third quartiles determining the location of the sides. The *mean* may be indicated with a '+' sign. The *median* is indicated by a line across the box.

The **inner left and right fences** are then calculated but are not plotted on the diagram.

The formulae to calculate the **left inner fence (LIF)** and **right inner fence(RIF)** are as followed:

$$\text{LIF} = Q_1 - (1.5 \times \text{IQR}) \qquad \text{RIF} = Q_3 + (1.5 \times \text{IQR})$$

The whiskers may now be drawn using the following procedure:

i. Imagine plotting all the data between the edge of the box and the inner fences (including data that fall on the fence) as points.
ii. Two (2) rules now apply for the whiskers. Each whisker is as long as possible, but
   a) it can't go past the inner fence.
   b) it must end at a data point.

Now we can calculate the location of the **left outer fence (LOF)** and **right outer fence (ROF)** as follows:

$$\text{LOF} = \text{LIF} - (1.5 \times \text{IQR}) \qquad \text{ROF} = \text{RIF} + (1.5 \times \text{IQR})$$

All data values that fall between the fences are called **suspect outliers** and are plotted individually using a special symbol. SPSS uses an 'o' symbol to indicate **suspect outliers**. Suspect outliers are values that are *somewhat unusual* in that they lie away from the majority of the data.

All data values that lie beyond the outer fences are called **outliers** and are also plotted using a special symbol. SPSS uses an '*' symbol to indicate outliers. Outliers are *unusual* values that are often of extreme interest to the statistical analyst.

Using the data in Example 4.25, the values of the fences are calculated as followed:

$$LIF = Q_1 - (1.5 \times IQR) = 13 - (1.5 \times 39) = -45.5$$
$$LOF = LIF - (1.5 \times IQR) = -45.5 - (1.5 \times 39) = -104$$
$$RIF = Q_3 + (1.5 \times IQR) = 52 + (1.5 \times 39) = 110.5$$
$$ROF = RIF + (1.5 \times IQR) = 110.5 + (1.5 \times 39) = 169$$

The complete box-whisker plot is shown below.

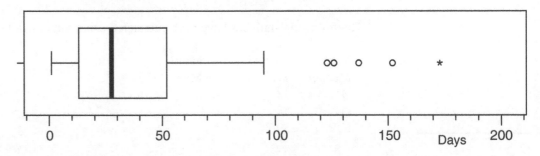

Note: In the diagram, the suspect outliers are indicated by the 'o' symbol. The outliers are indicated by the '*' symbol.

CALCULATOR LESSON 4

CASIO FX-9750GII CALCULATOR

Lesson 4—Graph a Box-Whisker Plot

The following data show the response times, in days, for 50 customer complaints for a large car dealership. The data have been arranged into an ascending data array.

1	2	4	4	5	5	5	10	10	11
12	13	13	14	19	20	22	23	25	26
26	26	27	27	27	28	29	29	29	30
31	31	32	33	35	35	36	52	54	61
68	74	81	84	95	123	126	137	152	173

Follow these steps to draw the box-whisker plot.

Step 1: From the **Main Menu,** select **STAT mode.**

Step 2: Enter data into **List 1**.

Step 3: Press **F1 (GRPH)**.

Step 4: Select F6(SET) and then enter the following items:

StatGraph1
Graph Type   : ▶ (press **F6**) and select **BOX (F2)**
XList   : List (F1) and type **1** (if you input your data in List 1)
Frequency   : 1 (F1)
Outlier   : ON (F1)

Now press **EXE**, and then select **GPH1 (F1)**.

The calculator will now show the box-whisker plot.

To obtain a full range of one-variable statistics, press **F1 (1 VAR)** at the bottom left-hand corner of the screen. The result is the following:

$$\bar{x} = 40.7$$
$$\Sigma x = 2035$$
$$\Sigma x^2 = 164603$$
$$\sigma x = 40.4421809$$
$$sx = 40.8527719$$
$$n = 50$$
$$\text{minx} = 1$$
$$Q1 = 13$$
$$\text{Med} = 27.5$$
$$Q3 = 52$$
$$\text{maxX} = 173$$
$$\text{Mod} = 5$$
$$\text{Mod} = 26$$
$$\text{Mod} = 27$$
$$\text{Mod} = 29$$
$$\text{Mod:n} = 4$$
$$\text{Mod:F} = 3$$

To go back to view the plot, press **F6(DRAW)**.

The Five-Number Summary

A **five-number summary**, which consists of the following, provides a way to determine the shape of a distribution:

$$X_{\text{smallest}} \quad Q_1 \quad \text{Median} \quad Q_3 \quad X_{\text{largest}}$$

Table 4.5 explains how the relationships among these five numbers allow you to recognize the shape of a data set.

To further analyze the sample of 10 times to get ready in the morning, you can compute the five-number summary. For these data, the smallest value is 29 minutes, and the largest value is 52 minutes. Calculations done show that the median $= 39.5, Q_1 = 35$, and $Q_3 = 44$. Therefore, the five-number summary is as follows:

$$29 \quad 35 \quad 39.5 \quad 44 \quad 52$$

The distance from X_{smallest} to the median $(39.5 - 29 = 10.5)$ is slightly less than the distance from the median to $X_{\text{largest}} (52 - 39.5 = 12.5)$. The distance from X_{smallest} to $Q_1 (35 - 29 = 6)$ is slightly less than the distance from Q_3 to $X_{\text{largest}} (52 - 44 = 8)$. The distance from Q_1 to the median $(39.5 - 35 = 4.5)$ is the same as the distance from the median to $Q_3 (44 - 39.5 = 4.5)$. Therefore, the getting-ready times are slightly right-skewed.

TABLE 4.5

Relationships Among the Five-Number Summary and the Type of Distribution

	Type of Distribution		
Comparison	**Left-Skewed**	**Symmetric**	**Right-Skewed**
The distance from $X_{smallest}$ to the median versus the distance from the median to $X_{largest}$.	The distance from $X_{smallest}$ to the median is greater than the distance from the median to $X_{largest}$.	The two distances are the same.	The distance from $X_{smallest}$ to the median is less than the distance from the median to $X_{largest}$.
The distance from $X_{smallest}$ to Q_1 versus the distance from Q_3 to $X_{largest}$.	The distance from $X_{smallest}$ to Q_1 is greater than the distance from Q_3 to $X_{largest}$.	The two distances are the same.	The distance from $X_{smallest}$ to Q_1 is less than the distance from Q_3 to $X_{largest}$.
The distance from Q_1 to the median versus the distance from the median to Q_3.	The distance from Q_1 to the median is greater than the distance from the median to Q_3.	The two distances are the same.	The distance from Q_1 to the median is less than the distance from the median to Q_3.

EXAMPLE 4.26

Computing the Five-Number Summary of the Number of Calories in Cereals

Nutritional data about a sample of seven breakfast cereals (stored in Cereals) includes the number of calories per serving. Compute the five-number summary of the number of calories in cereals.

SOLUTION From previous computations for the number of calories in cereals, you know that the median $= 110, Q_1 = 100,$ and $Q_3 = 190$.

In addition, the smallest value in the data set is 80, and the largest value is 200. Therefore, the five-number summary is as follows:

$$80 \ \ 100 \ \ 110 \ \ 190 \ \ 200$$

The three comparisons listed in Table 4.5 are used to evaluate skewness. The distance from $X_{smallest}$ to the median $(110 - 80 = 30)$ is less than the distance $(200 - 110 = 90)$ from the median to $X_{largest}$. The distance from $X_{smallest}$ to Q_1 $(100 - 80 = 20)$ is the more than the distance from Q_3 to $X_{largest}$ $(200 - 190 = 10)$. The distance from Q_1 to the median $(110 - 100 = 10)$ is less than the distance from the median to Q_3 $(190 - 110 = 80)$. Two comparisons indicate a right-skewed distribution, whereas the other indicates a left-skewed distribution. Therefore, given the small sample size and the conflicting results, the shape is not clearly determined.

EXAMPLE 4.27

The Boxplots of the 2006 Returns of Growth and Value Mutual Funds

The 868 mutual funds (Mutual Funds) that are part of the Using Statistics scenario are classified according to whether the mutual funds are growth or value funds. Construct the boxplot of the 2006 returns for growth and value mutual funds.

SOLUTION Figure 4.4 shows the 2006 return for the growth and value mutual funds and Figure 4.5 illustrates Minitab boxplots. The median return, the quartiles, and the minimum and maximum returns are much higher for the value funds than for the growth funds. Both the growth and value funds appear to be fairly symmetrical between the quartiles, but the value funds seem to have more extremely high returns.

FIGURE 4.4

PHStat2 boxplots of the
2006 return for growth
and value mutual funds

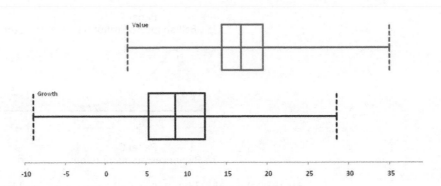

Boxplots for the Growth and Value Funds
2006 Return

FIGURE 4.5

Minitab boxplots of the
2006 return for growth
and value mutual funds

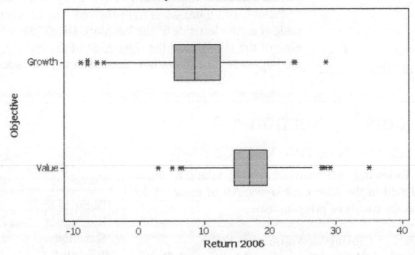

Boxplot of Return 2006

Notice that in Figure 4.5, several * appear in the boxplots. This indicates outliers that are more than 1.5 times the interquartile range beyond the quartiles.

Figure 4.6 demonstrates the relationship between the boxplot and the polygon for four different types of distributions. (*Note:* The area under each polygon is split into quartiles corresponding to the five-number summary for the boxplot.)

Panels A and D of Figure 4.6 are symmetrical. In these distributions, the mean and median are equal. In addition, the length of the left tail is equal to the length of the right tail, and the median line divides the box in half.

Panel B of Figure 4.6 is left-skewed. The few small values distort the mean toward the left tail. For this left-skewed distribution, there is a heavy clustering of values at the high end of the

FIGURE 4.6

Boxplots and corresponding polygons for four distributions

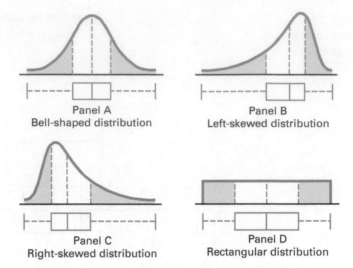

Panel A
Bell-shaped distribution

Panel B
Left-skewed distribution

Panel C
Right-skewed distribution

Panel D
Rectangular distribution

scale (i.e., the right side); 75% of all values are found between the left edge of the box (Q_1) and the end of the right tail ($X_{largest}$). There is a long left tail that contains the smallest 25% of the values, demonstrating the lack of symmetry in this data set.

Panel C of Figure 4.6 is right-skewed. The concentration of values is on the low end of the scale (i.e., the left side of the boxplot). Here, 75% of all values are found between the beginning of the left tail and the right edge of the box (Q_3). There is a long right tail that contains the largest 25% of the values, demonstrating the lack of symmetry in this data set.

Problems for Section 4.4

PROBLEMS FOR BOX-WHISKER PLOT

4.50 The following data were obtained by taking a sample of stocks listed in the *Financial Times*. All of these stocks have had recent trends of price increases.

Stock	Closing Price	Volume ($ hundreds)	Yield %	P/E Ratio
Abitibi-Price	20.25	31435	0.7	67.5
Agnico Eagle	19.38	7529	na	55.4
Air Canada	7.75	13010	na	na
Alberta Energy	20.75	9934	1.9	15.6
Arbor Me	18.50	770	0.3	21.8
Atlantis	1.90	3896	na	14.6
Brascan Cl	19.38	2616	5.4	57.5
Brunswick	11.12	749	3.1	na
Canadex j	33.30	62	na	20.6
Donohue Sv	16.75	1938	1.6	23.8
Electrohom	10.38	920	1.0	7.7
Finning	21.62	1658	1.5	19.3
Gennum	18.50	4	0.4	14.6
Hemlo gold	15.38	3091	1.3	24.4
Ipsco	26.25	1873	1.8	17.5
Jordan Petrol	10.62	356	na	31.3
Kerr Addison	24.50	292	2.5	37.1
Lynx Energy	11.00	10	na	13.6
MDS Helth	14.38	60	1.0	13.2
Noranda	27.50	26426	3.6	32.5
Okanaga	3.30	46	0.6	33.0

Stock	Closing Price	Volume ($ hundreds)	Yield %	P/E Ratio
Pagurian nv	4.50	3898	6.7	13.6
Rio Algom	25.75	24697	2.3	21.6
Shaw Ind	13.75	557	1.0	16.0
Tombill A	5.50	2	3.3	7.6
Versa Services	10.12	699	2.2	21.5
Wetsmin	5.62	388	3.5	na
XL Foods	0.78	1315	na	7.8

a. Draw the box-whisker plot for the Volume data.
b. Draw the box-whisker plot for the Yield data.

4.51 Refer to Problem 4.20 in Descriptive Statistics Exercises—Set 2:

Draw the box-whisker plot for the travel expense data.

4.52 Refer to Problem 4.21 in Descriptive Statistics Exercises—Set 2:

Draw the box-whisker plot for the number of defectives data.

4.53 Refer to Problem 4.22 in Descriptive Statistics Exercises—Set 2:

Draw the box-whisker plot for the university enrollment data.

LEARNING THE BASICS

4.54 The following is a set of data from a sample of $n = 7$:

12   7   4   9   0   7   3

a. Compute the first quartile (Q_1), the third quartile (Q_3), and the interquartile range.
b. List the five-number summary.
c. Construct a boxplot and describe its shape.
d. Compare your answer in (c) with that from Problem 4.36 (d) on page 165. Discuss.

4.55 The following is a set of data from a sample of $n = 6$:

7   4   9   7   3   12

a. Compute the first quartile (Q_1), the third quartile (Q_3), and the interquartile range.
b. List the five-number summary.
c. Construct a boxplot and describe its shape.
d. Compare your answer in (c) with that from Problem 4.35 (d) on page 165. Discuss.

4.56 The following is a set of data from a sample of $n = 5$:

7   4   9   8   2

a. Compute the first quartile (Q_1), the third quartile (Q_3), and the interquartile range.
b. List the five-number summary.
c. Construct a boxplot and describe its shape.
d. Compare your answer in (c) with that from Problem 4.34 (d) on page 165. Discuss.

4.57 The following is a set of data from a sample of $n = 5$:

7   −5   −8   7   9

a. Compute the first quartile (Q_1), the third quartile (Q_3), and the interquartile range.
b. List the five-number summary.
c. Construct a boxplot and describe its shape.
d. Compare your answer in (c) with that from Problem 4.37 (d) on page 165. Discuss.

APPLYING THE CONCEPTS

4.58 The file ChocolateChip contains the cost (in cents) per 1-ounce serving, for a sample of 13 chocolate chip cookies. The data are as follows:

54   22   25   23   36   43   7   43   25   47   24   45   44

Source: Data extracted from "Chip, Chip, Hooray," *Consumer Reports,* June 2009, p. 7.

a. Compute the first quartile (Q_1), the third quartile (Q_3), and the interquartile range.
b. List the five-number summary.
c. Construct a boxplot and describe its shape.

SELF Test **4.59** The file Dark Chocolate contains the cost ($) per ounce for a sample of 14 dark chocolate bars:

0.68   0.72   0.92   1.14   1.42   0.94   0.77   0.57   1.51
0.57   0.55   0.86   1.41   0.90

Source: Data extracted from "Dark Chocolate: Which Bars Are Best?" *Consumer Reports,* September 2007, p. 8.

a. Compute the first quartile (Q_1), the third quartile (Q_3), and the interquartile range.
b. List the five-number summary.
c. Construct a boxplot and describe its shape.

4.60 The file HotelUK contains the average room price (in English pounds) paid in six British cities in 2010:

110   98   78   70   76   62

Source: Data extracted from **www.hotels.com/press/hotel-price-index-summer-2010.html**.

a. Compute the first quartile (Q_1), the third quartile (Q_3), and the interquartile range.
b. List the five-number summary.
c. Construct a boxplot and describe its shape.

4.61 The file SUV contains the overall miles per gallon (MPG) of 2011 small SUVs:

20   24   22   23   20   22   21   22   22
19   22   22   26   19   19   23   24   21
21   19   21   22   22   16   16

Source: Data extracted from "Ratings," *Consumer Reports,* April 2011, pp. 35–36.

a. Compute the first quartile (Q_1), the third quartile (Q_3), and the interquartile range.
b. List the five-number summary.
c. Construct a boxplot and describe its shape.

4.62 The file CD Rate contains the yields for a one-year certificate of deposit (CD) and a five-year CD, for 23 banks in the United States, as of April 4, 2011.

Source: Data extracted from **www.Bankrate.com**, April 4, 2011.

For each type of account:
a. Compute the first quartile (Q_1), the third quartile (Q_3), and the interquartile range.
b. List the five-number summary.
c. Construct a boxplot and describe its shape.

4.63 A bank branch located in a commercial district of a city has the business objective of developing an improved process for serving customers during the noon-to-1:00 P.M. lunch period. The waiting time, in minutes, is defined as the time the customer enters the line to when he or she reaches the teller window. Data are collected from a sample of

15 customers during this hour. The file Bank1 contains the results, which are listed here:

4.21   5.55   3.02   5.13   4.77   2.34   3.54   3.20
4.50   6.10   0.38   5.12   6.46   6.19   3.79

Another bank branch, located in a residential area, is also concerned with the noon-to-1 P.M. lunch hour. The waiting times, in minutes, collected from a sample of 15 customers during this hour, are contained in the file Bank2 and listed here:

9.66   5.90   8.02   5.79   8.73   3.82   8.01   8.35
10.49   6.68   5.64   4.08   6.17   9.91   5.47

a. List the five-number summaries of the waiting times at the two bank branches.
b. Construct boxplots and describe the shapes of the distributions for the two bank branches.
c. What similarities and differences are there in the distributions of the waiting times at the two bank branches?

4.64 For this problem, use the data in Bond Funds2008.
a. Construct a multidimensional table of the mean 2008 return by type and risk.
b. Construct a multidimensional table of the standard deviation of the 2008 return by type and risk.
c. What conclusions can you reach concerning differences between the type of bond funds (intermediate government and short-term corporate) based on risk factor (low, average, and high)?
d. Compare the results in (a)–(c) to the 2009 returns (stored in Bond Funds).

4.65 For this problem, use the data in Bond Funds2008.
a. Construct a multidimensional table of the mean three-year return by type and risk.

b. Construct a multidimensional table of the standard deviation of the three-year return by type and risk.
c. What conclusions can you reach concerning differences between the type of bond funds (intermediate government and short-term corporate) based on risk factor (low, average, and high)?
d. Compare the results in (a)–(c) to the three-year returns from 2007–2009 (stored in Bond Funds).

4.66 For this problem, use the data in Bond Funds2008.
a. Construct a multidimensional table of the mean five-year return by type and risk.
b. Construct a multidimensional table of the standard deviation of the five-year return by type and risk.
c. What conclusions can you reach concerning differences between the type of bond funds (intermediate government and short-term corporate) based on risk factor (low, average, and high)?
d. Compare the results in (a)–(c) to the five-year returns from 2005–2009 (stored in Bond Funds).

4.67 For this problem, use the data in Bond Funds2008.
a. Construct a multidimensional table of the mean 2008 return by type, fees, and risk.
b. Construct a multidimensional table of the standard deviation of the 2008 return by type, fees, and risk.
c. What conclusions can you reach concerning differences between the type of bond funds (intermediate government and short-term corporate) based on fees (yes or no) and risk factor (low, average, and high)?
d. Compare the results in (a)–(c) to the 2009 returns (stored in Bond Funds).

4.5 The Covariance and the Coefficient of Correlation

In Section 3.10, you used scatter plots to visually examine the relationship between two numerical variables. This section presents two measures of the relationship between two numerical variables: the covariance and the coefficient of correlation.

The Covariance

The **covariance** measures the strength of the linear relationship between two numerical variables (X and Y). Equation (4.3) defines the **sample covariance**, and Example 4.28 illustrates its use.

SAMPLE COVARIANCE

$$\text{cov}(X, Y) = \frac{\sum_{i=1}^{n}(X_i - \bar{X})(Y_i - \bar{Y})}{n - 1} \tag{4.3}$$

The Coefficient of Correlation

The **coefficient of correlation** measures the relative strength of a linear relationship between two numerical variables. The values of the coefficient of correlation range from -1 for a perfect negative correlation to $+1$ for a perfect positive correlation. *Perfect* in this case means that if the points were plotted on a scatter plot, all the points could be connected with a straight line.

When dealing with population data for two numerical variables, the Greek letter ρ (*rho*) is used as the symbol for the coefficient of correlation. Figure 4.8 illustrates three different types of association between two variables.

EXAMPLE 4.28

Computing the
Sample Covariance

You constructed a scatter plot that showed the relationship between the value and the annual revenue of the 30 teams that make up the National Basketball Association (NBA) (extracted from **www.forbes.com/lists/2009/32/basketball-values-09_NBA-Team-Valuations_Rank.html**; stored in NBAValues). Now, you want to measure the association between the value of a franchise and annual revenue by computing the sample covariance.

SOLUTION Table 4.6 below provides the value and the annual revenue of the 30 teams.

Figure 4.7 contains a worksheet that computes the covariance for these data. The Calculations Area section of Figure 4.7 breaks down Equation (4.3) into a set of smaller calculations. From cell F9, or by using Equation (4.3) directly, you find that the covariance is 3,115.7241:

$$\text{cov}(X, Y) = \frac{90,356}{30 - 1}$$
$$= 3,115.7241$$

The covariance has a major flaw as a measure of the linear relationship between two numerical variables. Because the covariance can have any value, you are unable to use it to determine the relative strength of the relationship. In other words, you cannot tell whether the value 3,115.7241 indicates a strong relationship or a weak relationship. To better determine the relative strength of the relationship, you need to compute the coefficient of correlation.

TABLE 4.6

Values and Annual Revenues of the 30 NBA Teams (in millions of dollars)

Team	Value	Revenue	Team	Value	Revenue
Atlanta	306	103	Milwaukee	254	91
Boston	433	144	Minnesota	268	96
Charlotte	278	96	New Jersey	269	92
Chicago	511	168	New Orleans	267	95
Cleveland	476	159	New York	586	202
Dallas	446	154	Oklahoma City	310	111
Denver	321	115	Orlando	361	107
Detroit	479	171	Philadelphia	344	115
Golden State	315	113	Phoenix	429	148
Houston	470	160	Portland	338	121
Indiana	281	97	Sacramento	305	109
Los Angeles Clippers	295	102	San Antonio	398	133
Los Angeles Lakers	607	209	Toronto	386	133
Memphis	257	88	Utah	343	118
Miami	364	126	Washington	313	110

FIGURE 4.7

Excel worksheet to compute the covariance between the value and the annual revenue of the 30 NBA teams

	A	B	C	D	E	F
1	Covariance Analysis					
2						
3	Revenue	Value	(X-XBar)(Y-YBar)			
4	103	306	1415.2000		Calculations Area	
5	144	433	1174.8000		XBar	126.2000
6	96	278	2687.8000		YBar	367
7	168	511	6019.2000		n-1	29
8	159	476	3575.2000		Σ(X-XBar)(Y-YBar)	90356.0000
9	154	446	2196.2000		Covariance	3115.7241
10	115	321	515.2000			
11	171	479	5017.6000			
12	113	315	686.4000			
13	160	470	3481.4000			
14	97	281	2511.2000			
15	102	295	1742.4000			
16	209	607	19872.0000			
17	88	257	4202.0000			
18	126	364	0.6000			
19	91	254	3977.6000			
20	96	268	2989.8000			
21	92	269	3351.6000			
22	95	267	3120.0000			
23	202	586	16600.2000			
24	111	310	866.4000			
25	107	361	115.2000			
26	115	344	257.6000			
27	148	429	1351.6000			
28	121	338	150.8000			
29	109	305	1066.4000			
30	133	398	210.8000			
31	133	386	129.2000			
32	118	343	196.8000			
33	110	313	874.8000			

In Panel A of Figure 4.8, there is a perfect negative linear relationship between X and Y. Thus, the coefficient of correlation, ρ, equals -1, and when X increases, Y decreases in a perfectly predictable manner. Panel B shows a situation in which there is no relationship between X and Y. In this case, the coefficient of correlation, ρ, equals 0, and as X increases, there is no tendency for Y to increase or decrease. Panel C illustrates a perfect positive relationship where ρ equals $+1$. In this case, Y increases in a perfectly predictable manner when X increases.

Correlation alone cannot prove that there is a causation effect—that is, that the change in the value of one variable caused the change in the other variable. A strong correlation can be produced simply by chance, by the effect of a third variable not considered in the calculation of the correlation, or by a cause-and-effect relationship. You would need to perform addi-

FIGURE 4.8

Types of association between variables

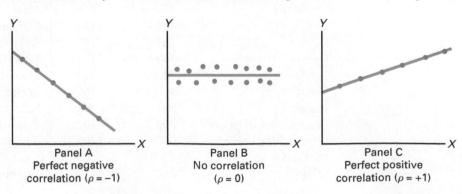

Panel A	Panel B	Panel C
Perfect negative correlation ($\rho = -1$)	No correlation ($\rho = 0$)	Perfect positive correlation ($\rho = +1$)

tional analysis to determine which of these three situations actually produced the correlation. Therefore, you can say that *causation implies correlation, but correlation alone does not imply causation*.

Equation (4.4) defines the **sample coefficient of correlation (*r*)**.

SAMPLE COEFFICIENT OF CORRELATION

$$r = \frac{\text{cov}(X, Y)}{S_X S_Y} \tag{4.4}$$

where

$$\text{cov}(X, Y) = \frac{\sum_{i=1}^{n} (X_i - \bar{X})(Y_i - \bar{Y})}{n - 1}$$

$$S_X = \sqrt{\frac{\sum_{i=1}^{n} (X_i - \bar{X})^2}{n - 1}}$$

$$S_Y = \sqrt{\frac{\sum_{i=1}^{n} (Y_i - \bar{Y})^2}{n - 1}}$$

When you have sample data, you can compute the sample coefficient of correlation, *r*. When using sample data, you are unlikely to have a sample coefficient of correlation of exactly +1, 0, or −1. Figure 4.9 presents scatter plots along with their respective sample coefficients of correlation, *r*, for six data sets, each of which contains 100 values of *X* and *Y*.

In Panel A, the coefficient of correlation, *r*, is −0.9. You can see that for small values of *X*, there is a very strong tendency for *Y* to be large. Likewise, the large values of *X* tend to be paired with small values of *Y*. The data do not all fall on a straight line, so the association between *X* and *Y* cannot be described as perfect. The data in Panel B have a coefficient of correlation equal to −0.6, and the small values of *X* tend to be paired with large values of *Y*. The linear relationship between *X* and *Y* in Panel B is not as strong as that in Panel A. Thus, the coefficient of correlation in Panel B is not as negative as that in Panel A. In Panel C, the linear relationship between *X* and *Y* is very weak, *r* = −0.3, and there is only a slight tendency for the small values of *X* to be paired with the large values of *Y*. Panels D through F depict data sets that have positive coefficients of correlation because small values of *X* tend to be paired with small values of *Y* and large values of *X* tend to be associated with large values of *Y*. Panel D shows weak positive correlation, with *r* = 0.3. Panel E shows stronger positive correlation with *r* = 0.6. Panel F shows very strong positive correlation, with *r* = 0.9.

FIGURE 4.9

Six scatter plots and their sample coefficients of correlation, *r*

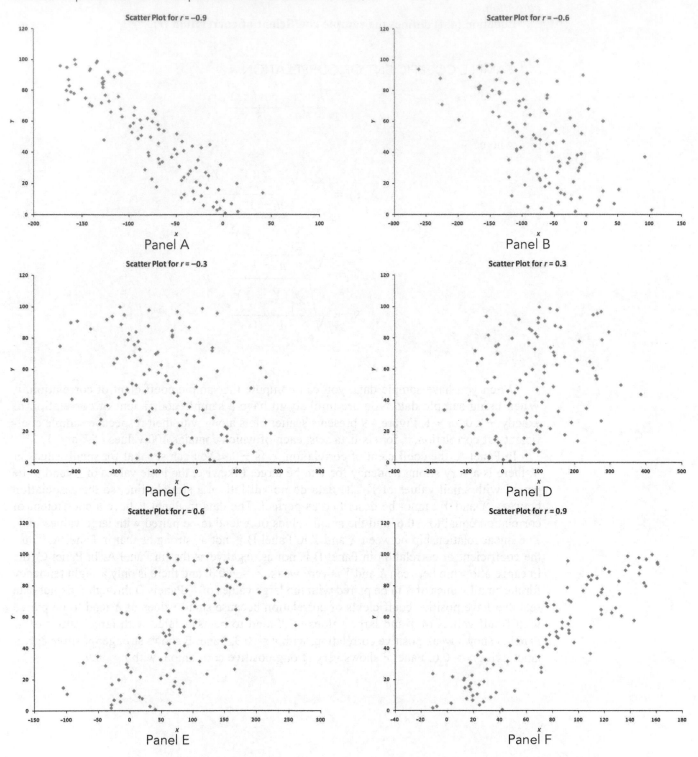

EXAMPLE 4.29

Computing the Sample Coefficient of Correlation

In Example 4.28 on page 177, you computed the covariance of the values and revenues of 30 NBA basketball teams. Using Figure 4.10 and Equation (4.4) on page 179, compute the sample coefficient of correlation.

FIGURE 4.10

Excel worksheet to compute the sample coefficient of correlation, r, between the values and revenues of 30 NBA teams

	A	B	C	D	E	F
1	Coefficient of Correlation Calculations					
2						
3	Revenue	Value	(X-XBar)(Y-YBar)		Calculations Area	
4	103	306	1415.2000		XBar	126.2000
5	144	433	1174.8000		YBar	367.0000
6	96	278	2687.8000		Σ(X-XBar)²	30550.8000
7	168	511	6019.2000		Σ(Y-YBar)²	272410.0000
8	159	476	3575.2000		Σ(X-XBar)(Y-YBar)	90356.0000
9	154	446	2196.2000		n-1	29
10	115	321	515.2000			
11	171	479	5017.6000		Results	
12	113	315	686.4000		Covariance	3115.7241
13	160	470	3481.4000		Sₓ	32.4573
14	97	281	2511.2000		S_Y	96.9198
15	102	295	1742.4000		r	0.9905
16	209	607	19872.0000			
17	88	257	4202.0000			
18	126	364	0.6000			
19	91	254	3977.6000			
20	96	268	2989.8000			
21	92	269	3351.6000			
22	95	267	3120.0000			
23	202	586	16600.2000			
24	111	310	866.4000			
25	107	361	115.2000			
26	115	344	257.6000			
27	148	429	1351.6000			
28	121	338	150.8000			
29	109	305	1066.4000			
30	133	398	210.8000			
31	133	386	129.2000			
32	118	343	196.8000			
33	110	313	874.8000			

SOLUTION

$$r = \frac{cov(X, Y)}{S_X S_Y}$$

$$= \frac{3,115.7241}{(32.4573)(96.9198)}$$

$$= 0.9905$$

The value and revenue of the NBA teams are very highly correlated. The teams with the lowest revenues have the lowest values. The teams with the highest revenues have the highest values. This relationship is very strong, as indicated by the coefficient of correlation, r = 0.9905.

In general you cannot assume that just because two variables are correlated, changes in one variable caused changes in the other variable. However, for this example, it makes sense to conclude that changes in revenue would cause changes in the value of a team.

In summary, the coefficient of correlation indicates the linear relationship, or association, between two numerical variables. When the coefficient of correlation gets closer to +1 or −1, the linear relationship between the two variables is stronger. When the coefficient of correlation is near 0, little or no linear relationship exists. The sign of the coefficient of correlation indicates whether the data are positively correlated (i.e., the larger values of X are typically paired with the larger values of Y) or negatively correlated (i.e., the larger values of X are typically paired with the smaller values of Y). The existence of a strong correlation does not imply a causation effect. It only indicates the tendencies present in the data.

Problems for Section 4.5

LEARNING THE BASICS

4.68 The following is a set of data from a sample of $n = 11$ items:

X	7	5	8	3	6	10	12	4	9	15	18
Y	21	15	24	9	18	30	36	12	27	45	54

a. Compute the covariance.
b. Compute the coefficient of correlation.
c. How strong is the relationship between X and Y? Explain.

APPLYING THE CONCEPTS

4.69 A study of 218 students at Ohio State University suggests a link between time spent on the social networking site Facebook and grade point average. Students who rarely or never used Facebook had higher grade point averages than students who use Facebook.

Source: Data extracted from M. B. Marklein, "Facebook Use Linked to Less Textbook Time," **www.usatoday.com**, April 14, 2009.

a. Does the study suggest that time spent on Facebook and grade point average are positively correlated or negatively correlated?
b. Do you think that there might be a cause-and-effect relationship between time spent on Facebook and grade point average? Explain.

SELF Test 4.70 The file Cereals lists the calories and sugar, in grams, in one serving of seven breakfast cereals:

Cereal	Calories	Sugar
Kellogg's All Bran	80	6
Kellogg's Corn Flakes	100	2
Wheaties	100	4
Nature's Path Organic Multigrain Flakes	110	4
Kellogg's Rice Krispies	130	4
Post Shredded Wheat Vanilla Almond	190	11
Kellogg's Mini Wheats	200	10

a. Compute the covariance.
b. Compute the coefficient of correlation.
c. Which do you think is more valuable in expressing the relationship between calories and sugar—the covariance or the coefficient of correlation? Explain.

d. Based on (a) and (b), what conclusions can you reach about the relationship between calories and sugar?

4.71 Movie companies need to predict the gross receipts of individual movies after a movie has debuted. The following results, listed in PotterMovies, are the first weekend gross, the U.S. gross, and the worldwide gross (in millions of dollars) of the six Harry Potter movies that debuted from 2001 to 2009:

Title	First Weekend	U.S. Gross	Worldwide Gross
Sorcerer's Stone	90.295	317.558	976.458
Chamber of Secrets	88.357	261.988	878.988
Prisoner of Azkaban	93.687	249.539	795.539
Goblet of Fire	102.335	290.013	896.013
Order of the Phoenix	77.108	292.005	938.469
Half-Blood Prince	77.836	301.460	934.601

Source: Data extracted from **www.the-numbers.com/interactive/comp-Harry-Potter.php**.

a. Compute the covariance between first weekend gross and U.S. gross, first weekend gross and worldwide gross, and U.S. gross and worldwide gross.
b. Compute the coefficient of correlation between first weekend gross and U.S. gross, first weekend gross and worldwide gross, and U.S. gross and worldwide gross.
c. Which do you think is more valuable in expressing the relationship between first weekend gross, U.S. gross, and worldwide gross—the covariance or the coefficient of correlation? Explain.
d. Based on (a) and (b), what conclusions can you reach about the relationship between first weekend gross, U.S. gross, and worldwide gross?

4.72 College basketball is big business, with coaches' salaries, revenues, and expenses in millions of dollars. The file College Basketball contains the coaches' salaries and revenues for college basketball at 60 of the 65 schools that played in the 2009 NCAA men's basketball tournament

Source: Data extracted from "Compensation for Division 1 Men's Basketball Coaches," *USA Today*, April 2, 2010, p. 8C; and C. Isadore, "Nothing but Net: Basketball Dollars by School," **money.cnn.com/2010/03/18/news/companies/basketball_profits/**.

a. Compute the covariance.

b. Compute the coefficient of correlation.

c. Based on (a) and (b), what conclusions can you reach about the relationship between coaches' salaries and revenues?

4.73 College football players trying out for the NFL are given the Wonderlic standardized intelligence test. The file Wonderlic contains the average Wonderlic score of football players trying out for the NFL and the graduation rate for football players at selected schools.

Source: Data extracted from S. Walker, "The NFL's Smartest Team," *The Wall Street Journal,* September 30, 2005, pp. W1, W10.

a. Compute the covariance.

b. Compute the coefficient of correlation.

c. Based on (a) and (b), what conclusions can you reach about the relationship between the average Wonderlic score and graduation rate?

4.6 Numerical Descriptive Statistics: Pitfalls and Ethical Issues

This chapter describes how a set of numerical data can be characterized by the statistics that measure the properties of central tendency, variation, and shape. In business, descriptive statistics such as the ones you have learned about are frequently included in summary reports that are prepared periodically.

The volume of information available on the Internet, in newspapers, and in magazines has produced much skepticism about the objectivity of data. When you are reading information that contains descriptive statistics, you should keep in mind the quip often attributed to the famous nineteenth-century British statesman Benjamin Disraeli: "There are three kinds of lies: lies, damned lies, and statistics."

For example, in examining statistics, you need to compare the mean and the median. Are they similar, or are they very different? Or, is only the mean provided? The answers to these questions will help you determine whether the data are skewed or symmetrical and whether the median might be a better measure of central tendency than the mean. In addition, you should look to see whether the standard deviation or interquartile range for a very skewed set of data has been included in the statistics provided. Without this, it is impossible to determine the amount of variation that exists in the data.

Ethical considerations arise when you are deciding what results to include in a report. You should document both good and bad results. In addition, when making oral presentations and presenting written reports, you need to give results in a fair, objective, and neutral manner. Unethical behavior occurs when you selectively fail to report pertinent findings that are detrimental to the support of a particular position.

© Steve Cole / iStockphoto.com

USING STATISTICS @ Choice Is Yours, Part II Revisited

In Part II of the Choice Is Yours scenario, you were hired by the Choice Is Yours investment company to assist investors interested in bond mutual funds. A sample of 184 bond mutual funds included 87 intermediate government funds and 97 short-term corporate bond funds. By comparing these two categories, you were able to provide investors with valuable insights.

The 2009 returns for both the intermediate government funds and the short-term corporate bond funds were right-skewed, as indicated by the boxplots. The descriptive statistics allowed you to compare the central tendency and variability of returns of the intermediate government funds and the short-term corporate bond funds. The mean indicated that the intermediate government funds returned an average of 4.4529, and the median indicated that half of the funds had returns of 4.4 or more. The short-term corporate bond funds' central tendencies were much higher than those of the intermediate government funds—they had an average of 9.5959, and half the funds had returns above 9.1. The intermediate government funds showed slightly less variability than the short-term corporate funds with a standard deviation of 5.36 as compared to 5.69. An interesting insight is that while 25% of the intermediate government funds had returns of 6.5 or higher ($Q_3 = 6.5$), 75% of the short-term corporate bond funds had returns of 5.7 or higher ($Q_1 = 5.7$). Although past performance is no assurance of future performance, in 2009, the short-term corporate funds greatly outperformed the intermediate government funds. (To see a situation where the opposite was true, open the Bond Funds2008 file.)

SUMMARY

In this chapter and the previous chapter, you studied descriptive statistics—how you can visualize data through tables and charts and how you can use different statistics to help analyze the data and reach conclusions. In Chapters 2 and 4, you were able to visualize data by constructing bar and pie charts, histograms, and other charts. In this chapter, you learned how descriptive statistics such as the mean, median, quartiles, range, and standard deviation are used to describe the characteristics of central tendency, variability, and shape.

In addition, you constructed boxplots to visualize the distribution of the data. You also learned how the coefficient of correlation is used to describe the relationship between two numerical variables. Table 4.7 provides a list of the descriptive statistics covered in this chapter.

In the next chapter, the basic principles of probability are presented in order to bridge the gap between the subject of descriptive statistics and the subject of inferential statistics.

TABLE 4.7

Summary of Descriptive Statistics

Type of Analysis	Numerical Data
Describing central tendency, variation, and shape of a numerical variable	Mean, median, mode, quartiles, range, interquartile range, variance, standard deviation, coefficient of variation, Z scores, boxplot (Sections 4.1 through 4.4)
Describing the relationship between two numerical variables	Covariance, coefficient of correlation (Section 4.5)

KEY EQUATIONS

Sample Mean

$$\bar{X} = \frac{\sum_{i=1}^{n} X_i}{n}$$

Median

$$\text{Median} = \frac{n+1}{2} \text{ ranked value}$$

Range

$$\text{Range} = X_{\text{largest}} - X_{\text{smallest}}$$

Sample Variance

$$S^2 = \frac{\sum_{i=1}^{n}(X_i - \bar{X})^2}{n-1}$$

Sample Standard Deviation

$$S = \sqrt{S^2} = \sqrt{\frac{\sum_{i=1}^{n}(X_i - \bar{X})^2}{n-1}}$$

Coefficient of Variation

$$CV = \left(\frac{S}{\bar{X}}\right)100\%$$

Z Score

$$Z = \frac{X - \bar{X}}{S}$$

Interquartile Range

$$\text{Interquartile range} = Q_3 - Q_1$$

Population Mean

$$\mu = \frac{\sum\limits_{i=1}^{N} X_i}{N}$$

Population Variance

$$\sigma^2 = \frac{\sum\limits_{i=1}^{N} (X_i - \mu)^2}{N}$$

Population Standard Deviation

$$\sigma = \sqrt{\frac{\sum\limits_{i=1}^{N} (X_i - \mu)^2}{N}}$$

Sample Covariance

$$\text{cov}(X, Y) = \frac{\sum\limits_{i=1}^{n} (X_i - \bar{X})(Y_i - \bar{Y})}{n - 1}$$

Sample Coefficient of Correlation

$$r = \frac{\text{cov}(X, Y)}{S_X S_Y}$$

KEY TERMS

arithmetic mean   136
boxplot   171
central tendency   136
coefficient of correlation   175
coefficient of variation   159
covariance   174
extreme value   147
five-number summary   169
interquartile range   154
left-skewed   163
mean   136
median   145

mode   148
outlier   166
population mean   136
population standard deviation   157
population variance   155
Q_1: first quartile   165
Q_2: second quartile   165
Q_3: third quartile   165
quartile   165
range   153
resistant measure   155
right-skewed   163

sample coefficient of
   correlation (r)   177
sample covariance   174
sample mean   136
sample standard deviation   157
sample variance   155
shape   162
skewed   162
spread   154
standard deviation   157
symmetrical   162
variance   155

PROBLEMS

REVIEW PROBLEMS

4.74 The following table appeared in the May 28th, 1998 issue of the *Toronto Star*.

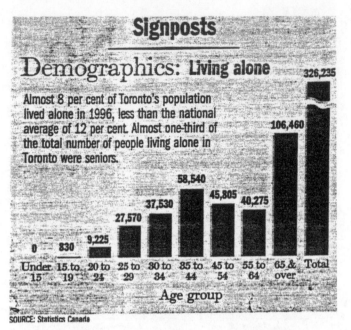

Signposts

Demographics: Living alone

Almost 8 per cent of Toronto's population lived alone in 1996, less than the national average of 12 per cent. Almost one-third of the total number of people living alone in Toronto were seniors.

SOURCE: Statistics Canada

In 1996, excluding seniors (aged 65 and over), what was the average age of people who lived alone in Toronto?

4.75 The following ad appeared in the Feb. 7th, 1997 issue of the *Real Estate News*. It shows the rental costs for various condos in Harbour Square.

HARBOUR SQUARE RENTALS

250 Queens Quay W.#806 2br	$1,200 mo.	
270 Queens Quay W.#1301 1br	$1,295 mo.	
270 Queens Quay W.#602 1br	$1,295 mo.	
270 Queens Quay W.#2302 1br Furnished	$1,595 mo.	
77 Harbour Sq. #2611 1br	$1,500 mo.	
401 Queens Quay W.#204 1br	$1,950 mo.	
105 Victoria #305 1br	$1,150 mo.	
#306 2br	$1,450 mo.	
#807 1br	$1,200 mo.	
#1007 1br	$1,200 mo.	

Carrie Bynford 203-6636.
Harry Stinson R.E. Ltd.

What is the mean monthly rent for an unfurnished one-bedroom condo?

4.76 Ryerson Memorial Hospital wants to compare its annual patient turnover rate per bed with those of other similar hospitals. The turnover rates for a sample of 80 beds at Ryerson were summarized and organized in the following frequency distribution. (An annual turnover of 21 per bed indicates that, during the year, 21 patients occupied the same hospital bed.)

Annual Turnover Rate Patients per Bed	Number of Beds
10 and under 15	4
15 " " 20	9
20 " " 25	13
25 " " 30	25
30 " " 35	15
35 " " 40	7
40 " " 50	5
50 " " 60	2

a. What is the mean turnover rate?
b. What is the median turnover rate?
c. What is the standard deviation of the turnover rate?

4.77 The following table shows room rates for a resort hotel in Nova Scotia for the time period January 1 to December 31, 2003.

2003 Room Rates	1/1– 7/3	8/3– 30/3	31/3– 31/5	1/6– 30/6	1/7– 1/9	2/9– 8/10	9/10– 1/12	2/12– 20/12	21/12– 31/12
A Oceanfront 1 double bed	75	125	85	100	150	95	85	75	125
B Oceanfront 2 double beds	85	135	95	110	160	105	95	85	135
C Oceanfront Effic. 2 double beds	105	155	115	130	180	125	115	105	155
D 2 room suite 3 double beds	120	175	130	150	200	140	130	120	175
E Oceanfront Suite 3 double beds	140	200	150	175	225	165	150	140	200
Extra Person	5	8	5	5	10	7	5	5	10

a. For the nine time periods, what was the mean extra person rate?
b. This hotel has 20% type A rooms, 15% type B, 30% type C, 25% type D and the remainder are type E. If the hotel was fully booked (with no extra people in any room) on October 1, then what was the mean revenue per room? What was the standard deviation?
c. On April 20, the only rooms occupied were 25 type A, 13 type B, and 5 type E. What was the average revenue per bed on that day? If every bed was occupied by two people, what was the mean and standard deviation of the number of people per rented room on that day?

4.78 The following data refer to the OAC average grades of students being accepted into first year of several Ontario universities.

University	60–70	70–75	75–80	80–85	85–90	≥ 90
Brock	5.8	22.1	26.7	26.0	13.1	6.3
Guelph	0	0.2	27.6	37.9	21.4	12.9
McMaster	0.1	10.5	24.2	32.4	19.7	13.1
Queen's	0	0.2	3.2	21.9	36.8	37.9
Ryerson	0.5	23.0	31.0	29.3	12.4	3.8
Toronto	0	1.2	8.9	26.0	36.6	27.3

Grade Distribution of New 1st Year Students

a. Based on the above data, is the average entering grade higher for Brock or Ryerson, or is the average about the same? How do the standard deviations compare?

b. What about Ryerson compared to Queen's?

4.79 The table below appeared in the April 9, 1998 edition of *The Globe and Mail*.

Municipal salary comparisons

	Mayor's salary	Councillor's salary
Barrie	$45,000	$11,705
Brantford	$54,758	$11,000
Burlington	$56,000	$27,000
Cambridge	$47,000	$14,500
Gloucester	$69,020	$21,585
Kingston	$52,000	$13,000
Kitchener	$54,440	$22,640
Markham	$60,669	$34,287
Nepean	$72,603	$24,146
Oakville	$45,000	$17,000
Oshawa	$49,610	$18,540
Richmond Hill	$53,074	$29,185
St. Catharines	$51,759	$10,664
Thunder Bay	$57,342	$26,343
Toronto	$101,084	$63,915
Vaughan	$62,792	$38,126
Windsor	$88,236	$26,645
AVERAGE	$60,023	$24,134

Source: KPMG

a. Which are more variable, the mayors' salaries or the councillors' salaries for the 17 cities shown?

b. Draw a box-whisker diagram for the mayors' salaries.

c. Is the mean or median a better indication of the typical councillor's salary?

4.80 The following table and graphical display appeared in the March 21, 1998 issue of *The Globe and Mail*.

Major English-language specialty channels

Year ended Aug. 31, 1997	Total subscribers	Cable revenue per subscriber per month	Advertising revenue per subscriber per month	Profit margin before interest and taxes
TSN	6,401,276	$1.25	$0.66	36.0%
MuchMusic	6,048,240	0.11	0.26	27.5
YTV	7,150,000	0.29	0.32	21.0
Weather	8,167,204	0.22	0.04	19.2
Vision*	6,115,792	0.07	0.02	4.2
Newsworld	7,316,000	0.46	0.14	0.4
WTN	4,676,286	0.32	0.07	14.0
Discovery	4,584,298	0.39	0.15	1.9
Showcase	3,644,440	0.34	0.15	15.7
Life	3,793,871	0.31	0.16	11.5
CMT	6,290,810	0.05	0.08	14.0
Bravo!	3,947,159	0.26	0.05	12.5

* Almost half of Vision's total revenue of $12.5-million a year comes from other revenue such as donations.

Note: Does not include latest tier of channels as pay period started Jan. 18, 1998

Source: Canadian Radio-television and Telecommunications Commission

The growth of specialty TV channels

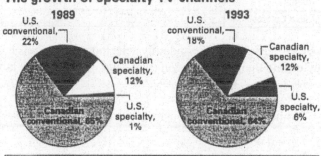

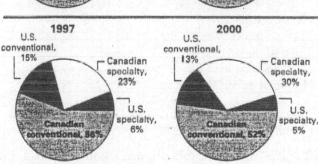

Source: Nielsen People Meter data plus Initiative Media estimates

a. Which factor is more uniform over the 12 stations: (i) cable revenue per subscriber or (ii) advertising revenue per subscriber?

b. Draw the box-whisker plot for the "Advertising revenue per subscriber" data.

c. If the total advertising revenue per channel is $20 per conventional Canadian channel, $15 million per specialty Canadian channel, $12 million per conventional U.S. channel, and $10 million per U.S. specialty channel, will the overall average advertising revenue per channel in the year 2000 be higher or lower than the average was in 1989?

4.81 The following table shows the number of unemployed persons by province for the months of October 1995 and October 1996. Were the numbers of unemployed persons across the provinces relatively more variable in 1995 or 1996?

	Unemployment	(x 1,000)
	October 1995	October 1996
Newfoundland	150	118
P. E. I.	25	31
New Brunswick	75	69
Nova Scotia	79	63
Quebec	250	278
Ontario	300	280
Manitoba	85	85
Saskatchewan	95	87
Alberta	63	43
British Columbia	105	81

4.82 A survey of 137 randomly selected students was conducted and their annual incomes are summarized in the table below.

Annual Income ($ thousands)	# of Students
0.0 and under 2.5	36
2.5 and under 5.0	43
5.0 and under 7.5	18
7.5 and under 10.0	19
10.0 and under 15.0	16
15.0 and under 20.0	5

What is the mean income of the 137 students? What is the standard deviation?

4.83 The following table appeared in the April 1995 *Report on Business Magazine*.

Most Respected: the Top Five

Canada's best corporations excel in profitability, innovation and global reach

Rank	Company	Revenues	Net income
		($ millions)	
1	Royal Bank of Canada (Oc94) financial services	13,434	1,169
2	BCE (De94) telecommunications	21,670	1,178
3	Bombardier (Ja94) aviation, mass transit eqpt.	4,769	176
4	Bank of Montreal (Oc94) financial services	9,108	825
5	Northern Telecom (De94) telecommunications eqpt.	8,874	408

Are the five most respected companies more similar in terms of Revenues or Net Incomes?

4.84 A wholesale appliance distributing firm is studying its accounts receivables for two successive months. Two samples of 50 accounts were selected and the amount of receivables for each has been summarized in the table below.

Accounts Receivables ($)	# of Accounts in March	# of Accounts in April
0 and under 2,000	6	10
2,000 and under 5,000	13	14
5,000 and under 10,000	17	13
10,000 and under 15,000	10	10
15,000 and under 25,000	0	3
25,000 and under 50,000	4	0
Total	50	50

In which month were the accounts receivable amounts more variable?

4.85 The following display appeared in the March 23, 1995 edition of *USA Today*. For all the films made from 1989 to 1994, what was the overall average production cost per movie?

Big picture for film industry

The movie business is thriving despite competition from broadcast and cable TV, home video and other forms of entertainment:

Theater admissions are growing

in millions

1989	1.26
1990	1.19
1991	1.14
1992	1.17
1993	1.24
1994	1.29

Major studios are making more films . . .

Films made

1989	157
1990	158
1991	150
1992	141
1993	156
1994	168

Films to be made in 1995[1]

Buena Vista	25
Warner Bros.	35
Sony	30
Paramount	25
Universal	20
Fox	25
New Line	25

. . . and, on average, each one is more expensive

Total cost, in millions

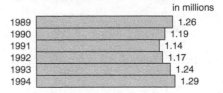

$32.7	$38.8	$38.1	$42.4	$44	$50.4
1989	1990	1991	1992	1993	1994

Average production cost, in millions

$23.5	$26.8	$26.1	$28.9	$29.9	$34.3

Average advertising and print costs, in millions

$9.2	$12.0	$12.0	$13.5	$14.1	$16.1

1 Estimates
Sources: Motion Picture Association of America, Merrill Lynch

4.86 The following table appeared in the March 26, 1998 edition of *The Globe and Mail*.

Average work days lost per year

	Total	For illness	Personal or family
All employees	7.4	6.2	1.2
Men	6.3	5.3	0.9
Men with preschoolers	5.9	4.2	1.8
Women	9.1	7.6	1.5
Women with preschoolers	11.7	7.5	4.2
Company size			
Under 20 employees	6.2	4.9	1.3
Over 500 employees	9.0	7.8	1.2
Union status			
Union member	10.7	9.4	1.3
Non-union member	5.6	4.5	1.1
Job status			
Permanent	7.6	6.4	1.2
Non-permanent	5.4	4.2	1.2

Source: Statistics Canada

The following data are applicable to a new division being set up by the Statistics Consulting Company.

	% Employees	Average Daily Salary
Men	8	$400
Men with preschoolers	62	250
Women	20	320
Women with preschoolers	10	200

a. What is the average number of days lost per employee due to illness during the first year of operation of the new division? What is the standard deviation?

b. What is the difference in the average daily salary between the men and the women of this new division?

c. What is the standard deviation of the daily salary for the men?

4.87 The following chart appeared in the Royal Bank's Business Report of January 1995.

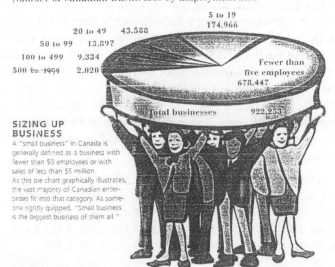

Number of Canadian Businesses by Employment Size

SIZING UP BUSINESS
A "small business" in Canada is generally defined as a business with fewer than 50 employees or with sales of less than $5 million. As this pie chart graphically illustrates, the vast majority of Canadian enterprises fit into that category. As someone rightly quipped, "Small business is the biggest business of them all."

a. What is the average employment size of a Canadian business? (Assume that the data cover all Canadian businesses.)

b. What is the standard deviation of employment size?

4.88 The following table appeared in the December 8, 1995 issue of the *Toronto Star*.

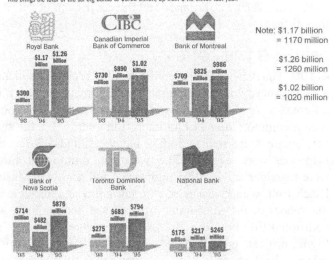

The banks' record haul

The Canadian Imperial Bank of Commerce yesterday reported record 1995 profits of $1.02 billion. This brings the total of the six big banks to $5.18 billion, up from $4.3 billion last year.

Note: $1.17 billion = 1170 million
$1.26 billion = 1260 million
$1.02 billion = 1020 million

a. Did the median profit increase or decrease in 1994 compared to 1993?

b. For the sample of six banks shown above, were bank profits relatively more variable in 1994 or 1995?

c. In 1993 there were 215 branches of the Royal Bank, 427 branches of CIBC, 385 branches of the Bank of Montreal, 453 branches of the Bank of Nova Scotia, 288 branches of the Toronto Dominion Bank, and 154 branches of the National Bank. What was the overall average profit and per branch in 1993? What was the standard deviation?

CHECKING YOUR UNDERSTANDING

4.89 What are the properties of a set of numerical data?

4.90 What is meant by the property of central tendency?

4.91 What are the differences among the mean, median, and mode, and what are the advantages and disadvantages of each?

4.92 How do you interpret the first quartile, median, and third quartile?

4.93 What is meant by the property of variation?

4.94 What does the Z score measure?

4.95 What are the differences among the various measures of variation, such as the range, interquartile range, variance, standard deviation, and coefficient of variation, and what are the advantages and disadvantages of each?

4.96 How does the empirical rule help explain the ways in which the values in a set of numerical data cluster and distribute?

4.97 How do the empirical rule and the Chebyshev rule differ?

4.98 What is meant by the property of shape?

4.99 How do the covariance and the coefficient of correlation differ?

APPLYING THE CONCEPTS

4.100 The American Society for Quality (ASQ) conducted a salary survey of all its members. ASQ members work in all areas of manufacturing and service-related institutions, with a common theme of an interest in quality. For the survey, emails were sent to 56,052 members, and 5,743 valid responses were received. The two most common job titles were manager and quality engineer. Another title is Master Black Belt, who is a person who takes a leadership role as the keeper of the Six Sigma process (see Section 9.4). An additional title is Green Belt, someone who works on Six Sigma projects part-time. Descriptive statistics concerning salaries for these four titles are given in the following table:

Title	Sample Size	Minimum	Maximum	Standard Deviation	Mean	Median
Green Belt	15	24,000	137,000	29,000	75,917	70,000
Manager	1,438	10,400	212,000	26,455	88,993	86,000
Quality Engineer	831	25,000	175,000	19,878	76,239	75,000
Master Black Belt	86	60,000	185,000	26,466	113,276	112,650

Source: Data extracted from J. Seaman and I. Allen, "Revealing Answers," *Quality Progress*, December 2010, p. 31.

Compare the salaries of Green Belts, managers, quality engineers, and Master Black Belts.

4.101 In New York State, savings banks are permitted to sell a form of life insurance called savings bank life insurance (SBLI). The approval process consists of underwriting, which includes a review of the application, a medical information bureau check, possible requests for additional medical information and medical exams, and a policy compilation stage, during which the policy pages are generated and sent to the bank for delivery. The ability to deliver approved policies to customers in a timely manner is critical to the profitability of this service to the bank. During one month, a random sample of 27 approved policies was selected, and the following were the total processing times in days (stored in **Insurance**):

```
73  19  16  64  28  28  31  90  60  56  31  56  22  18
45  48  17  17  17  91  92  63  50  51  69  16  17
```

a. Compute the mean, median, first quartile, and third quartile.
b. Compute the range, interquartile range, variance, standard deviation, and coefficient of variation.
c. Construct a boxplot. Are the data skewed? If so, how?
d. What would you tell a customer who enters the bank to purchase this type of insurance policy and asks how long the approval process takes?

4.102 One of the major measures of the quality of service provided by an organization is the speed with which it responds to customer complaints. A large family-held department store selling furniture and flooring, including carpet, had undergone a major expansion in the past several years. In particular, the flooring department had expanded from 2 installation crews to an installation supervisor, a measurer, and 15 installation crews. The business objective of the company was to reduce the time between when the complaint is received and when it is resolved. During a recent year, the company received 50 complaints concerning carpet installation. The data from the 50 complaints, organized in **Furniture** , represent the number of days between the receipt of a complaint and the resolution of the complaint:

```
54    5   35  137  31  27  152    2  123  81  74  27  11
19  126  110  110  29  61   35   94   31  26   5  12   4
165   32   29   28  29  26   25    1   14  13  13  10   5
27    4   52   30  22  36   26   20   23  33  68
```

a. Compute the mean, median, first quartile, and third quartile.
b. Compute the range, interquartile range, variance, standard deviation, and coefficient of variation.
c. Construct a boxplot. Are the data skewed? If so, how?
d. On the basis of the results of (a) through (c), if you had to tell the president of the company how long a customer should expect to wait to have a complaint resolved, what would you say? Explain.

4.103 A manufacturing company produces steel housings for electrical equipment. The main component part of the housing is a steel trough that is made of a 14-gauge steel coil. It is produced using a 250-ton progressive punch press with a wipe-down operation and two 90-degree forms placed in the flat steel to make the trough. The distance from one side of the form to the other is critical because of weatherproofing in outdoor applications. The company requires that the width of the trough be between 8.31 inches and 8.61 inches. Data are collected from a sample of 49 troughs and stored in **Trough** , which contains the widths of the troughs in inches as shown here:

```
8.312 8.343 8.317 8.383 8.348 8.410 8.351 8.373 8.481 8.422
8.476 8.382 8.484 8.403 8.414 8.419 8.385 8.465 8.498 8.447
8.436 8.413 8.489 8.414 8.481 8.415 8.479 8.429 8.458 8.462
8.460 8.444 8.429 8.460 8.412 8.420 8.410 8.405 8.323 8.420
8.396 8.447 8.405 8.439 8.411 8.427 8.420 8.498 8.409
```

a. Compute the mean, median, range, and standard deviation for the width. Interpret these measures of central tendency and variability.

b. List the five-number summary.

c. Construct a boxplot and describe its shape.

d. What can you conclude about the number of troughs that will meet the company's requirement of troughs being between 8.31 and 8.61 inches wide?

4.104 The manufacturing company in Problem 4.99 also produces electric insulators. If the insulators break when in use, a short circuit is likely to occur. To test the strength of the insulators, destructive testing is carried out to determine how much force is required to break the insulators. Force is measured by observing how many pounds must be applied to an insulator before it breaks. Data are collected from a sample of 30 insulators. The file Force contains the strengths, as follows:

1,870 1,728 1,656 1,610 1,634 1,784 1,522 1,696 1,592 1,662
1,866 1,764 1,734 1,662 1,734 1,774 1,550 1,756 1,762 1,866
1,820 1,744 1,788 1,688 1,810 1,752 1,680 1,810 1,652 1,736

a. Compute the mean, median, range, and standard deviation for the force needed to break the insulator.

b. Interpret the measures of central tendency and variability in (a).

c. Construct a boxplot and describe its shape.

d. What can you conclude about the strength of the insulators if the company requires a force of at least 1,500 pounds before breakage?

4.105 The file VeggieBurger contains data on the calories and total fat (in grams per serving) for a sample of 12 veggie burgers.

Source: Data extracted from "Healthful Burgers That Taste Good," *Consumer Reports*, June 2008, p 8.

a. For each variable, compute the mean, median, first quartile, and third quartile.

b. For each variable, compute the range, interquartile range, variance, standard deviation, and coefficient of variation.

c. For each variable, construct a boxplot. Are the data skewed? If so, how?

d. Compute the coefficient of correlation between calories and total fat.

e. What conclusions can you reach concerning calories and total fat?

4.106 A quality characteristic of interest for a tea-bag-filling process is the weight of the tea in the individual bags. If the bags are underfilled, two problems arise. First, customers may not be able to brew the tea to be as strong as they wish. Second, the company may be in violation of the truth-in-labeling laws. For this product, the label weight on the package indicates that, on average, there are 5.5 grams of tea in a bag. If the mean amount of tea in a bag exceeds the label weight, the company is giving away product. Getting an exact amount of tea in a bag is problematic because of variation in the temperature and humidity inside the factory, differences in the density of the tea, and the extremely fast filling operation of the machine (approximately 170 bags per minute). The file Teabags, as shown below, contains the weights, in grams, of a sample of 50 tea bags produced in one hour by a single machine:

5.65 5.44 5.42 5.40 5.53 5.34 5.54 5.45 5.52 5.41
5.57 5.40 5.53 5.54 5.55 5.62 5.56 5.46 5.44 5.51
5.47 5.40 5.47 5.61 5.53 5.32 5.67 5.29 5.49 5.55
5.77 5.57 5.42 5.58 5.58 5.50 5.32 5.50 5.53 5.58
5.61 5.45 5.44 5.25 5.56 5.63 5.50 5.57 5.67 5.36

a. Compute the mean, median, first quartile, and third quartile.

b. Compute the range, interquartile range, variance, standard deviation, and coefficient of variation.

c. Interpret the measures of central tendency and variation within the context of this problem. Why should the company producing the tea bags be concerned about the central tendency and variation?

d. Construct a boxplot. Are the data skewed? If so, how?

e. Is the company meeting the requirement set forth on the label that, on average, there are 5.5 grams of tea in a bag? If you were in charge of this process, what changes, if any, would you try to make concerning the distribution of weights in the individual bags?

4.107 The manufacturer of Boston and Vermont asphalt shingles provides its customers with a 20-year warranty on most of its products. To determine whether a shingle will last as long as the warranty period, accelerated-life testing is conducted at the manufacturing plant. Accelerated-life testing exposes a shingle to the stresses it would be subject to in a lifetime of normal use via an experiment in a laboratory setting that takes only a few minutes to conduct. In this test, a shingle is repeatedly scraped with a brush for a short period of time, and the shingle granules removed by the brushing are weighed (in grams). Shingles that experience low amounts of granule loss are expected to last longer in normal use than shingles that experience high amounts of granule loss. In this situation, a shingle should experience no more than 0.8 gram of granule loss if it is expected to last the length of the warranty period. The file Granule contains a sample of 170 measurements made on the company's Boston shingles and 140 measurements made on Vermont shingles.

a. List the five-number summaries for the Boston shingles and for the Vermont shingles.

b. Construct side-by-side boxplots for the two brands of shingles and describe the shapes of the distributions.

c. Comment on the ability of each type of shingle to achieve a granule loss of 0.8 gram or less.

4.108 The file Restaurants contains the cost per meal and the ratings of 50 city and 50 suburban restaurants on their food, décor, and service (and their summated ratings). Complete the following for the urban and suburban restaurants.

Source: Data extracted from *Zagat Survey 2009 New York City Restaurants* and *Zagat Survey 2009–2010 Long Island Restaurants*.

a. Construct the five-number summary of the cost of a meal.

b. Construct a boxplot of the cost of a meal. What is the shape of the distribution?

c. Compute and interpret the correlation coefficient of the summated rating and the cost of a meal.

4.109 The file `Protein` contains calories, protein, and cholesterol of popular protein foods (fresh red meats, poultry, and fish).

Source: U.S. Department of Agriculture.

a. Compute the correlation coefficient between calories and protein.

b. Compute the correlation coefficient between calories and cholesterol.

c. Compute the correlation coefficient between protein and cholesterol.

d. Based on the results of (a) through (c), what conclusions can you reach concerning calories, protein, and cholesterol?

4.110 The file `HotelPrices` contains the average price of a room at two-star, three-star, and four-star hotels in cities around the world in 2010 in English pounds (about US$1.56 as of January 2011). Complete the following for two-star, three-star, and four-star hotels.

Source: Data extracted from **www.hotels.com/press/hotel-price-index-summer-2010.html**.

a. Compute the mean, median, first quartile, and third quartile.

b. Compute the range, interquartile range, variance, standard deviation, and coefficient of variation.

c. Interpret the measures of central tendency and variation within the context of this problem.

d. Construct a boxplot. Are the data skewed? If so, how?

e. Compute the covariance between the average price at two-star and three-star hotels, between two-star and four-star hotels, and between three-star and four-star hotels.

f. Compute the coefficient of correlation between the average price at two-star and three-star hotels, between two-star and four-star hotels, and between three-star and four-star hotels.

g. Which do you think is more valuable in expressing the relationship between the average price of a room at two-star, three-star, and four-star hotels—the covariance or the coefficient of correlation? Explain.

h. Based on (f), what conclusions can you reach about the relationship between the average price of a room at two-star, three-star, and four-star hotels?

4.111 The file `PropertyTaxes` contains the property taxes per capita for the 50 states and the District of Columbia.

a. Compute the mean, median, first quartile, and third quartile.

b. Compute the range, interquartile range, variance, standard deviation, and coefficient of variation.

c. Construct a boxplot. Are the data skewed? If so, how?

d. Based on the results of (a) through (c), what conclusions can you reach concerning property taxes per capita, in thousands of dollars, for each state and the District of Columbia?

4.112 The file `CEO-Compensation` includes the total compensation (in millions of $) of CEOs of 161 large public companies and the investment return in 2010. Complete the following for the total compensation (in millions of $).

Source: Data extracted from M. Krantz and B. Hansen, "CEO Pay Soars While Workers' Pay Stalls," *USA Today*, April 1, 2011, pp. 1B, 2B and **money.usatoday.com**.

a. Compute the mean, median, first quartile, and third quartile.

b. Compute the range, interquartile range, variance, standard deviation, and coefficient of variation.

c. Construct a boxplot. Are the data skewed? If so, how?

d. Based on the results of (a) through (c), what conclusions can you reach concerning the total compensation (in millions of $) of CEOs?

e. Compute the correlation coefficient between compensation and the investment return in 2010.

f. What conclusions can you reach from the results of (e)?

4.113 You are planning to study for your statistics examination with a group of classmates, one of whom you particularly want to impress. This individual has volunteered to use Excel or Minitab to get the needed summary information, tables, and charts for a data set containing several numerical and categorical variables assigned by the instructor for study purposes. This person comes over to you with the printout and exclaims, "I've got it all—the means, the medians, the standard deviations, the boxplots, the pie charts—for all our variables. The problem is, some of the output looks weird—like the boxplots for gender and for major and the pie charts for grade point average and for height. Also, I can't understand why Professor Krehbiel said we can't get the descriptive stats for some of the variables; I got them for everything! See, the mean for height is 68.23, the mean for grade point average is 2.76, the mean for gender is 1.50, the mean for major is 4.33." What is your reply?

REPORT WRITING EXERCISES

4.114 The file `DomesticBeer` contains the percentage of alcohol, number of calories per 12 ounces, and number of carbohydrates (in grams) per 12 ounces for 145 of the best-selling domestic beers in the United States.

Your task is to write a report based on a complete descriptive evaluation of each of the numerical variables—percentage of alcohol, number of calories per 12 ounces, and number of carbohydrates (in grams) per 12 ounces. Appended to your report should be all appropriate tables, charts, and numerical descriptive measures.

Source: Data extracted from **www.Beer100.com**, April 1, 2011.

TEAM PROJECTS

The file `Bond Funds` contains information regarding nine variables from a sample of 184 bond funds:

Fund number—Identification number for each bond fund

Type—Type of bonds comprising the bond fund (intermediate government or short-term corporate)

Assets—In millions of dollars

Fees—Sales charges (no or yes)

Expense ratio—Ratio of expenses to net assets

Return 2009—Twelve-month return in 2009

Three-year return—Annualized return, 2007–2009

Five-year return—Annualized return, 2005–2009

Risk—Risk-of-loss factor of the mutual fund (low, average, or high)

4.115 Complete the following for expense ratio in percentage, three-year return, and five-year return.

a. Compute the mean, median, first quartile, and third quartile.

b. Compute the range, interquartile range, variance, standard deviation, and coefficient of variation.

c. Construct a boxplot. Are the data skewed? If so, how?

d. Based on the results of (a) through (c), what conclusions can you reach concerning these variables?

4.116 You want to compare bond funds that have fees to those that do not have fees. For each of these two groups, use the variables expense ratio, return in 2009, three-year return, and five-year return and complete the following.

a. Compute the mean, median, first quartile, and third quartile.

b. Compute the range, interquartile range, variance, standard deviation, and coefficient of variation.

c. Construct a boxplot. Are the data skewed? If so, how?

d. Based on the results of (a) through (c), what conclusions can you reach about differences between bond funds that have fees and those that do not have fees?

4.117 You want to compare intermediate government to short-term corporate bond funds. For each of these two groups, use the variables expense ratio, three-year return, and five-year return and complete the following.

a. Compute the mean, median, first quartile, and third quartile.

b. Compute the range, interquartile range, variance, standard deviation, and coefficient of variation.

c. Construct a boxplot. Are the data skewed? If so, how?

d. Based on the results of (a) through (c), what conclusions can you reach about differences between intermediate government and short-term corporate bond funds?

4.118 You want to compare bond funds based on risk. For each of these three levels of risk (below average, average,

above average), use the variables expense ratio, return 2009, three-year return, and five-year return and complete the following.

a. Compute the mean, median, first quartile, and third quartile.

b. Compute the range, interquartile range, variance, standard deviation, and coefficient of variation.

c. Construct a boxplot. Are the data skewed? If so, how?

d. Based on the results of (a) through (c), what conclusions can you reach about differences between bond funds based on risk?

STUDENT SURVEY DATABASE

4.119 Problem 1.21 on page 20 describes a survey of 62 undergraduate students (stored in UndergradSurvey). For these data, for each numerical variable, complete the following.

a. Compute the mean, median, first quartile, and third quartile.

b. Compute the range, interquartile range, variance, standard deviation, and coefficient of variation.

c. Construct a boxplot. Are the data skewed? If so, how?

d. Write a report summarizing your conclusions.

4.120 Problem 1.21 on page 20 describes a survey of 62 undergraduate students (stored in UndergradSurvey).

a. Select a sample of undergraduate students at your school and conduct a similar survey for those students.

b. For the data collected in (a), repeat (a) through (d) of Problem 4.115.

c. Compare the results of (b) to those of Problem 4.115.

4.121 Problem 1.22 on page 21 describes a survey of 44 MBA students (stored in GradSurvey). For these data, for each numerical variable, complete the following.

a. Compute the mean, median, first quartile, and third quartile.

b. Compute the range, interquartile range, variance, standard deviation, and coefficient of variation.

c. Construct a boxplot. Are the data skewed? If so, how?

d. Write a report summarizing your conclusions.

4.122 Problem 1.22 on page 21 describes a survey of 44 MBA students (stored in GradSurvey).

a. Select a sample of graduate students from your MBA program and conduct a similar survey for those students.

b. For the data collected in (a), repeat (a) through (d) of Problem 4.117.

c. Compare the results of (b) to those of Problem 4.117.

MANAGING ASHLAND MULTICOMM SERVICES

For what variable in the Chapter 3 "Managing Ashland MultiComm Services" case (see page 129) are numerical descriptive measures needed?

1. For the variable you identify, compute the appropriate numerical descriptive measures and construct a boxplot.

2. For the variable you identify, construct a graphical display. What conclusions can you reach from this other plot that cannot be made from the boxplot?

3. Summarize your findings in a report that can be included with the task force's study.

DIGITAL CASE

Apply your knowledge about the proper use of numerical descriptive measures in this continuing Digital Case from Chapter 3.

Open **EndRunGuide.pdf**, the EndRun Financial Services "Guide to Investing." Reexamine EndRun's supporting data for the "More Winners Than Losers" and "The Big Eight Difference" and then answer the following:

1. Can descriptive measures be computed for any variables? How would such summary statistics support EndRun's claims? How would those summary statistics affect your perception of EndRun's record?

2. Evaluate the methods EndRun used to summarize the results presented on the "Customer Survey Results" page. Is there anything you would do differently to summarize these results?

3. Note that the last question of the survey has fewer responses than the other questions. What factors may have limited the number of responses to that question?

REFERENCES

1. Kendall, M. G., A. Stuart, and J. K. Ord, *Kendall's Advanced Theory of Statistics*, *Volume 1: Distribution Theory*, 6th ed. (New York: Oxford University Press, 1994).

2. *Microsoft Excel 2010* (Redmond, WA: Microsoft Corporation, 2010).

3. *Minitab Release 16* (State College, PA: Minitab, Inc., 2010).

Microsoft Excel

Analysis ToolPak Use **Descriptive Statistics** to create a list that contains measures of variation and shape along with central tendency.

For example, to create a worksheet that presents descriptive statistics for the 2009 return for the intermediate government and short-term corporate bond funds, open to the **RETURN2009 worksheet** of the **Bond Funds workbook** and:

1. Select **Data → Data Analysis**.

2. In the Data Analysis dialog box, select **Descriptive Statistics** from the **Analysis Tools** list and then click **OK**.

In the Descriptive Statistics dialog box (shown below):

3. Enter **A1:B98** as the **Input Range**. Click **Columns** and check **Labels in First Row**.

4. Click **New Worksheet Ply**, check **Summary statistics**, and then click **OK**.

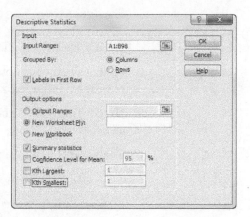

In the new worksheet:

5. Select column C, right-click, and click **Delete** in the shortcut menu (to eliminate the duplicate row labels).

6. Adjust the column headings and cell formatting. (See Appendix B for help with these adjustments.)

To add the coefficient of variation to this worksheet, first enter **Coefficient of variation** in cell **A16**. Then, enter the formula **=B7/B3** in cell **B16** and then copy it to cell **C16**. Finally, format cells B16 and C16 for percentage display.

APPENDIX 4.2

SPSS—Version 15 Lesson 1

Descriptive Statistics

INDEPENDENT READING

At this stage you should read the following help features. Cancel the SPSS opening window. Now look at the following tutorial.

Help / Tutorial / Table of contents (if necessary) / **Working With Output / Next** (as often as necessary)

The tutorial will take you through

    Using the Viewer

Stop when this part is finished.

Example 1: The following data show the response times, in days, for 50 customer complaints for a large car dealership. The data have been arranged into an ascending data array.

1	2	4	4	5	5	5	10	10	11
12	13	13	14	19	20	22	23	25	26
26	26	27	27	27	28	29	29	29	30
31	31	32	33	35	35	36	52	54	61
68	74	81	84	95	123	126	137	152	173

Create a SPSS data file where the above raw data are entered and save it as **Lesson 3 - Ex.1.sav.**

Define the variable and fix data at zero decimal places. Give the variable the label **Response Time - Days.**

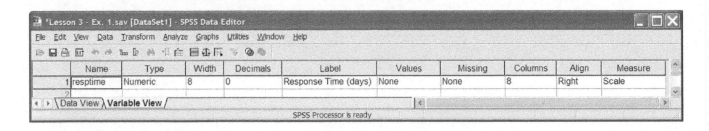

Explore Procedure

Now return to the SPSS Data Editor window. Make the following menu selections:

Analyze / Descriptive Statistics / Explore... / Response Time - Days (Highlight) ▶ (for Dependent List)/ **Statistics** (for Display)/ **Statistics** / check **Percentiles / Continue / OK**

At this point you will get a set of exploratory information about the data in the SPSS Viewer window. The first table will be a *Case Processing Summary*. This table allows you to check to see how much data were used to produce the results that follow it. This table is of interest only to the researcher and would never be included in any report.

The next table is called *Descriptives* (shown below) and includes several statistics, including measures of centre and measures of variability.

Descriptives

			Statistic	Std. Error
Response Time (days)	Mean		40.70	5.777
	95% Confidence	Lower Bound	29.09	
	Interval for Mean	Upper Bound	52.31	
	5% Trimmed Mean		36.37	
	Median		27.50	
	Variance		1668.949	
	Std. Deviation		40.853	
	Minimum		1	
	Maximum		173	
	Range		172	
	Interquartile Range		40	
	Skewness		1.731	.337
	Kurtosis		2.444	.662

You can customize this table to suit your needs. One way would be by deleting any items that you are not interested in. First activate the table by double-clicking on it so that a fuzzy border appears around the table. (Close the Pivot Trays window.) Then just **Highlight** and **Delete** any items you don't want. You can easily produce the edited table shown below.

Descriptives

		Statistic
Response Time (days)	Mean	40.70
	Median	27.50
	Variance	1668.949
	Std. Deviation	40.853
	Minimum	1
	Maximum	173
	Range	172
	Interquartile Range	39.50
	Skewness	1.731

The next table (shown below) is a table of *Percentiles* that was asked for by checking off the percentiles box.

Percentiles

| | | Percentiles | | | | |
		5	10	25	50	75
Weighted Average (Definition1)	Response Time (days)	3.10	5.00	13.00	27.50	52.50
Turkey's Hinges	Response Time (days)			13.00	27.50	52.00

Percentiles

| | Percentiles | |
	90	95
Weighted Average (Definition 1)	120.20	143.75

Note: **Tukey's Hinges** are the quartiles calculated with a different formula than the weighted average (definition 1) formula.

Descriptives Procedure

For another method that can be used to calculate descriptive statistics (without the graphing options), choose the following from the SPSS Data Editor window:

Analyze / Descriptive Statistics / Descriptives... / Response Time - Days (Highlight) ▶ (for Variables) **/ Options /** check **Mean, Std. deviation, Range / Continue / OK**

The output for this procedure is shown below:

Descriptive Statics

	N	Range	Mean	Std. Deviation
Response Time (days)	50	172	40.70	40.853
Valid N (listwise)	50			

Note: This procedure is useful when you know what you want and you don't want a table with a lot of extra items.

Frequencies Procedure

You may also calculate descriptive statistics by using the following procedure:

Analyze / Descriptive Statistics / Frequencies... / Response Time - Days (Highlight) ▶ (for Variables) **/ Statistics /** check **Mean, Median, Std. deviation, Range, Quartiles / Cut points for /** key 5 in the equal groups box **/ Percentiles /** key 33 in the percentiles box **/ Add /** key 67 in the percentiles box **Add / Continue /** Now verify that the Display frequency tables option is not selected. **OK**

The Frequencies: Statistics window is shown below.

Frequencies: Statistics

Percentile Values
- ☑ Quartiles
- ☑ Cut points for: `5` equal groups
- ☑ Percentile(s): `___`
  - Add
  - Change
  - Remove
  - 33
  - 67

Central Tendency
- ☑ Mean
- ☑ Median
- ☐ Mode
- ☐ Sum

☐ Values are group midpoints

Dispersion
- ☑ Std. deviation   ☐ Minimum
- ☐ Variance   ☐ Maximum
- ☑ Range   ☐ S.E. mean

Distribution
- ☐ Skewness
- ☐ Kurtosis

- Continue
- Cancel
- Help

The 'Frequencies' output is shown below.

Statistics

Response Time (days)

N	Valid		50
	Missing		0
Mean			40.70
Median			27.50
Std. Deviation			40.853
Range			172
Percentiles	20		11.20
	25		13.00
	33		21.66
	40		26.00
	50		27.50
	60		30.60
	67		33.34
	75		52.50
	80		66.60

You may now want to save the results as they appear in the SPSS Viewer window.

File / Save as / Lesson 3 – Ex.1.spo / File / Close / File / Exit

Subgroups of one variable

Recall the file **Lesson – Ex. 1a.sav.**

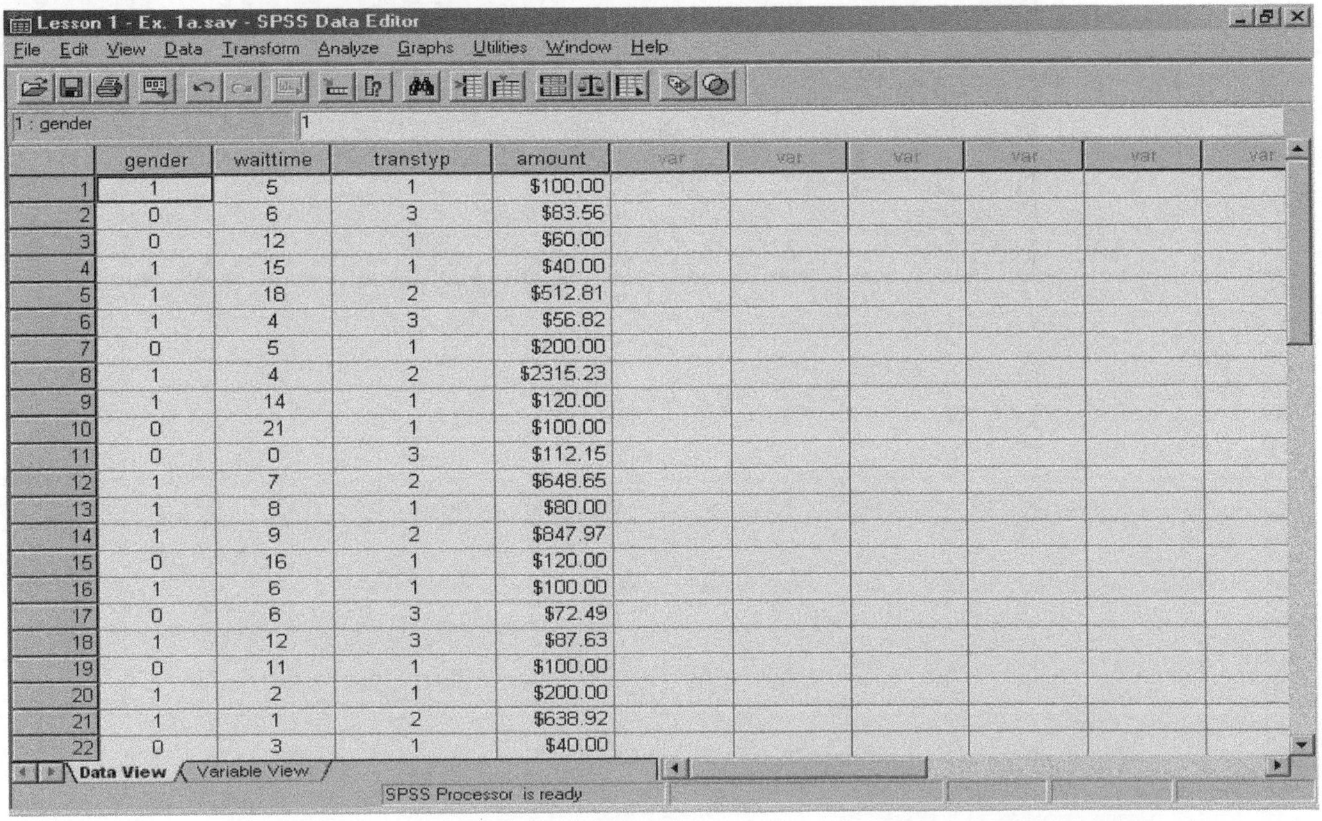

	gender	waittime	transtyp	amount
1	1	5	1	$100.00
2	0	6	3	$83.56
3	0	12	1	$60.00
4	1	15	1	$40.00
5	1	18	2	$512.81
6	1	4	3	$56.82
7	0	5	1	$200.00
8	1	4	2	$2315.23
9	1	14	1	$120.00
10	0	21	1	$100.00
11	0	0	3	$112.15
12	1	7	2	$648.65
13	1	8	1	$80.00
14	1	9	2	$847.97
15	0	16	1	$120.00
16	1	6	1	$100.00
17	0	6	3	$72.49
18	1	12	3	$87.63
19	0	11	1	$100.00
20	1	2	1	$200.00
21	1	1	2	$638.92
22	0	3	1	$40.00

Suppose we want to calculate the mean and standard deviation of the waiting times for the females and males separately.

Choose **Data / Split file...** and fill in the following window as shown on the next page:

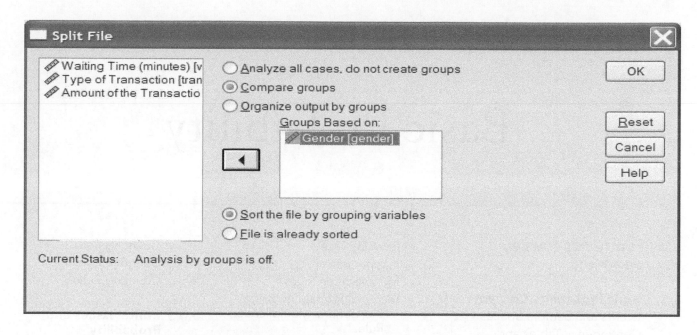

Important note: The **Split file** procedure will cause your, input data file to be sorted by the 'Groups Based on:' variable. Usually you want your original data file *not* to be sorted, therefore *do not save* the sorted data file when you close the file. If you do want the sorted file, then save it under a different name.

Now choose **Analyze / Descriptive Statistics / Frequencies... /** Waiting time (minutes) (Highlight) ▶ (for Variables / **Statistics** check **Mean Std. deviation / Continue / OK**

The results are shown below:

Statistics

Waiting Time (minutes)

Female	N	Valid	10
		Missing	0
	Mean		8.90
	Std. Deviation		6.297
Male	N	Valid	15
		Missing	0
	Mean		8.13
	Std. Deviation		5.303

Note: You may also use the **Descriptives** or **Explore** procedures to get similar results in different layouts. You can also include the 'Gender' variable in the **Factor List:** box of the **Explore** procedure.

5

Basic Probability

Learning Objectives

In this chapter, you learn:

- Basic probability concepts
- Conditional probability
- Bayes' theorem to revise probabilities
- Various counting rules

© Alan Levenson / Corbis

@ M&R Electronics World

As the marketing manager for M&R Electronics World, you are analyzing the survey results of an intent-to-purchase study. This study asked the heads of 1,000 households about their intentions to purchase a big-screen television sometime during the next 12 months. As a follow-up, you plan to survey the same people 12 months later to see whether they purchased televisions. In addition, for households purchasing big-screen televisions, you would like to know whether the television they purchased had a faster refresh rate (120 Hz or higher) or a standard refresh rate (60 Hz), whether they also purchased a Blu-ray disc (BD) player in the past 12 months, and whether they were satisfied with their purchase of the big-screen television.

You are expected to use the results of this survey to plan a new marketing strategy that will enhance sales and better target those households likely to purchase multiple or more expensive products. What questions can you ask in this survey? How can you express the relationships among the various intent-to-purchase responses of individual households?

In previous chapters, you learned descriptive methods to summarize categorical and numerical variables. In this chapter, you will learn about probability to answer questions such as the following:

- What is the probability that a household is planning to purchase a big-screen television in the next year?
- What is the probability that a household will actually purchase a big-screen television?
- What is the probability that a household is planning to purchase a big-screen television and actually purchases the television?
- Given that the household is planning to purchase a big-screen television, what is the probability that the purchase is made?
- Does knowledge of whether a household *plans* to purchase the television change the likelihood of predicting whether the household *will* purchase the television?
- What is the probability that a household that purchases a big-screen television will purchase a television with a faster refresh rate?
- What is the probability that a household that purchases a big-screen television with a faster refresh rate will also purchase a Blu-ray disc player?
- What is the probability that a household that purchases a big-screen television will be satisfied with the purchase?

With answers to questions such as these, you can begin to make decisions about your marketing strategy. Should your strategy for selling more big-screen televisions target those households that have indicated an intent to purchase? Should you concentrate on selling televisions that have faster refresh rates? Is it likely that households that purchase big-screen televisions with faster refresh rates can be easily persuaded to also purchase Blu-ray disc players?

Ljupco Smokovski / Shutterstock

The principles of probability help bridge the worlds of descriptive statistics and inferential statistics. Reading this chapter will help you learn about different types of probabilities, how to compute probabilities, and how to revise probabilities in light of new information. Probability principles are the foundation for the probability distribution, the concept of mathematical expectation, and the binomial and Poisson distributions, topics that are discussed in Chapter 6.

5.1 Basic Probability Concepts

What is meant by the word *probability*? A **probability** is the numeric value representing the chance, likelihood, or possibility that a particular event will occur, such as the price of a stock increasing, a rainy day, a defective product, or the outcome five dots in a single toss of a die. In all these instances, the probability involved is a proportion or fraction whose value ranges between 0 and 1, inclusive. An event that has no chance of occurring (the **impossible event**) has a probability of 0. An event that is sure to occur (the **certain event**) has a probability of 1.

There are three types of probability:

- *A priori*
- Empirical
- Subjective

In *a priori* **probability**, the probability of an occurrence is based on prior knowledge of the process involved. In the simplest case, where each outcome is equally likely, the chance of occurrence of the event is defined in Equation (5.1).

PROBABILITY OF OCCURRENCE

$$\text{Probability of occurrence} = \frac{X}{T} \tag{5.1}$$

where

X = number of ways in which the event occurs

T = total number of possible outcomes

Consider a standard deck of cards that has 26 red cards and 26 black cards. The probability of selecting a black card is $26/52 = 0.50$ because there are $X = 26$ black cards and $T = 52$ total cards. What does this probability mean? If each card is replaced after it is selected, does it mean that 1 out of the next 2 cards selected will be black? No, because you cannot say for certain what will happen on the next several selections. However, you can say that in the long run, if this selection process is continually repeated, the proportion of black cards selected will approach 0.50. Example 5.1 shows another example of computing an *a priori* probability.

EXAMPLE 5.1

Finding *A Priori* Probabilities

A standard six-sided die has six faces. Each face of the die contains either one, two, three, four, five, or six dots. If you roll a die, what is the probability that you will get a face with five dots?

SOLUTION Each face is equally likely to occur. Because there are six faces, the probability of getting a face with five dots is 1/6.

The preceding examples use the *a priori* probability approach because the number of ways the event occurs and the total number of possible outcomes are known from the composition of the deck of cards or the faces of the die.

In the **empirical probability** approach, the probabilities are based on observed data, not on prior knowledge of a process. Surveys are often used to generate empirical probabilities. Examples of this type of probability are the proportion of individuals in the Using Statistics scenario who actually purchase big-screen televisions, the proportion of registered voters who prefer a certain political candidate, and the proportion of students who have part-time jobs. For example, if you take a survey of students, and 60% state that they have part-time jobs, then there is a 0.60 probability that an individual student has a part-time job.

The third approach to probability, **subjective probability,** differs from the other two approaches because subjective probability differs from person to person. For example, the development team for a new product may assign a probability of 0.60 to the chance of success for the product, while the president of the company may be less optimistic and assign a probability of 0.30. The assignment of subjective probabilities to various outcomes is usually based on a combination of an individual's past experience, personal opinion, and analysis of a particular situation. Subjective probability is especially useful in making decisions in situations in which you cannot use *a priori* probability or empirical probability.

Events and Sample Spaces

The basic elements of probability theory are the individual outcomes of a variable under study. You need the following definitions to understand probabilities.

EVENT

Each possible outcome of a variable is referred to as an **event**.
A **simple event** is described by a single characteristic.

For example, when you toss a coin, the two possible outcomes are heads and tails. Each of these represents a simple event. When you roll a standard six-sided die in which the six faces of the die contain either one, two, three, four, five, or six dots, there are six possible simple events. An event can be any one of these simple events, a set of them, or a subset of all of them. For example, the event of an *even number of dots* consists of three simple events (i.e., two, four, or six dots).

JOINT EVENT

A **joint event** is an event that has two or more characteristics.

Getting two heads when you toss a coin twice is an example of a joint event because it consists of heads on the first toss and heads on the second toss.

COMPLEMENT

The **complement** of event A (represented by the symbol A') includes all events that are not part of A.

The complement of a head is a tail because that is the only event that is not a head. The complement of five dots on a die is not getting five dots. Not getting five dots consists of getting one, two, three, four, or six dots.

SAMPLE SPACE

The collection of all the possible events is called the **sample space**.
The sample space for tossing a coin consists of heads and tails. The sample space when rolling a die consists of one, two, three, four, five, and six dots. Example 5.2 demonstrates events and sample spaces.

EXAMPLE 5.2

Events and Sample Spaces

TABLE 5.1

Purchase Behavior for Big-Screen Televisions

The Using Statistics scenario on page 203 concerns M&R Electronics World. Table 5.1 presents the results of the sample of 1,000 households in terms of purchase behavior for big-screen televisions.

| PLANNED | ACTUALLY PURCHASED | | |
TO PURCHASE	Yes	No	Total
Yes	200	50	250
No	100	650	750
Total	300	700	1,000

What is the sample space? Give examples of simple events and joint events.

SOLUTION The sample space consists of the 1,000 respondents. Simple events are "planned to purchase," "did not plan to purchase," "purchased," and "did not purchase." The complement of the event "planned to purchase" is "did not plan to purchase." The event "planned to purchase and actually purchased" is a joint event because in this joint event the respondent must plan to purchase the television *and* actually purchase it.

Contingency Tables and Venn Diagrams

There are several ways in which you can view a particular sample space. One way involves using a **contingency table** (see Section 3.9) such as the one displayed in Table 5.1. You get the values in the cells of the table by subdividing the sample space of 1,000 households according to whether someone planned to purchase and actually purchased a big-screen television set. For example, 200 of the respondents planned to purchase a big-screen television set and subsequently did purchase the big-screen television set.

A second way to present the sample space is by using a **Venn diagram**. This diagram graphically represents the various events as "unions" and "intersections" of circles. Figure 5.1 presents a typical Venn diagram for a two-variable situation, with each variable having only two events (A and A', B and B'). The circle on the left (the red one) represents all events that are part of A.

The circle on the right (the yellow one) represents all events that are part of B. The area contained within circle A and circle B (center area) is the intersection of A and B (written as $A \cap B$), since it is part of A and also part of B. The total area of the two circles is the union of A and B (written as $A \cup B$) and contains all outcomes that are just part of event A, just part of event B, or part of both A and B. The area in the diagram outside of $A \cup B$ contains outcomes that are neither part of A nor part of B.

You must define A and B in order to develop a Venn diagram. You can define either event as A or B, as long as you are consistent in evaluating the various events. For the big-screen television example, you can define the events as follows:

$$A = \text{planned to purchase} \qquad B = \text{actually purchased}$$
$$A' = \text{did not plan to purchase} \qquad B' = \text{did not actually purchase}$$

In drawing the Venn diagram (see Figure 5.2), you must determine the value of the intersection of A and B so that the sample space can be divided into its parts. $A \cap B$ consists of all 200 households who planned to purchase and actually purchased a big-screen television set.

FIGURE 5.1

Venn diagram for events
A and B

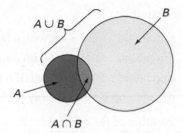

FIGURE 5.2

Venn diagram for the
M&R Electronics World
example

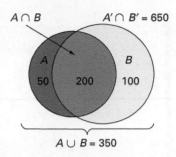

The remainder of event *A* (planned to purchase) consists of the 50 households who planned to purchase a big-screen television set but did not actually purchase one. The remainder of event *B* (actually purchased) consists of the 100 households who did not plan to purchase a big-screen television set but actually purchased one. The remaining 650 households represent those who neither planned to purchase nor actually purchased a big-screen television set.

Simple Probability

Now you can answer some of the questions posed in the Using Statistics scenario. Because the results are based on data collected in a survey (refer to Table 5.1), you can use the empirical probability approach.

As stated previously, the most fundamental rule for probabilities is that they range in value from 0 to 1. An impossible event has a probability of 0, and an event that is certain to occur has a probability of 1.

Simple probability refers to the probability of occurrence of a simple event, *P(A)*. A simple probability in the Using Statistics scenario is the probability of planning to purchase a big-screen television. How can you determine the probability of selecting a household that planned to purchase a big-screen television? Using Equation (5.1) on page 204:

$$\text{Probability of occurrence} = \frac{X}{T}$$

$$P(\text{Planned to purchase}) = \frac{\text{Number who planned to purchase}}{\text{Total number of households}}$$

$$= \frac{250}{1,000} = 0.25$$

Thus, there is a 0.25 (or 25%) chance that a household planned to purchase a big-screen television. Example 5.3 illustrates another application of simple probability.

EXAMPLE 5.3

Computing the
Probability That the
Big-Screen Television
Purchased Had a
Faster Refresh Rate

In the Using Statistics follow-up survey, additional questions were asked of the 300 households that actually purchased big-screen televisions. Table 5.2 indicates the consumers' responses to whether the television purchased had a faster refresh rate and whether they also purchased a Blu-ray disc (BD) player in the past 12 months.

Find the probability that if a household that purchased a big-screen television is randomly selected, the television purchased had a faster refresh rate.

TABLE 5.2

Purchase Behavior
Regarding Purchasing
a Faster Refresh Rate
Television and Blu-ray
Disc (BD) Player

REFRESH RATE OF	PURCHASED BD PLAYER		
TELEVISION PURCHASED	Yes	No	Total
Faster	38	42	80
Standard	70	150	220
Total	108	192	300

SOLUTION   Using the following definitions:

$$A = \text{purchased a television with a faster refresh rate}$$
$$A' = \text{purchased a television with a standard refresh rate}$$
$$B = \text{purchased a Blu-ray disc (BD) player}$$
$$B' = \text{did not purchase a Blu-ray disc (BD) player}$$

$$P(\text{faster refresh rate}) = \frac{\text{Number of faster refresh rate televisions}}{\text{Total number of televisions}}$$

$$= \frac{80}{300} = 0.267$$

There is a 26.7% chance that a randomly selected big-screen television purchased has a faster refresh rate.

Joint Probability

Whereas simple or marginal probability refers to the probability of occurrence of simple events, **joint probability** refers to the probability of an occurrence involving two or more events. An example of joint probability is the probability that you will get heads on the first toss of a coin and heads on the second toss of a coin.

In Table 5.1 on page 206, the group of individuals who planned to purchase and actually purchased a big-screen television consist only of the outcomes in the single cell "yes—planned to purchase *and* yes—actually purchased." Because this group consists of 200 households, the probability of picking a household that planned to purchase *and* actually purchased a big-screen television is

$$P(\text{Planned to purchase } and \text{ actually purchased}) = \frac{\text{Planned to purchase } and \text{ actually purchased}}{\text{Total number of respondents}}$$

$$= \frac{200}{1,000} = 0.20$$

Example 5.4 also demonstrates how to determine joint probability.

EXAMPLE 5.4

Determining the Joint Probability That a Household Purchased a Big-Screen Television with a Faster Refresh Rate and a Blu-ray Disc Player

In Table 5.2, the purchases are cross-classified as having a faster refresh rate or having a standard refresh rate and whether the household purchased a Blu-ray disc player. Find the probability that a randomly selected household that purchased a big-screen television also purchased a television that had a faster refresh rate and purchased a Blu-ray disc player.

SOLUTION   Using Equation (5.1) on page 204,

$$P\left(\begin{array}{c}\text{television with a faster refresh}\\ \text{rate } and \text{ Blu-ray disc player}\end{array}\right) = \frac{\begin{array}{c}\text{Number that purchased a television with a faster}\\ \text{refresh rate } and \text{ a Blu-ray disc player}\end{array}}{\text{Total number of big-screen television purchasers}}$$

$$= \frac{38}{300} = 0.127$$

Therefore, there is a 12.7% chance that a randomly selected household that purchased a big-screen television purchased a television that had a faster refresh rate and a Blu-ray disc player.

Marginal Probability

The **marginal probability** of an event consists of a set of joint probabilities. You can determine the marginal probability of a particular event by using the concept of joint probability just discussed. For example, if B consists of two events, B_1 and B_2, then $P(A)$, the probability of event A, consists of the joint probability of event A occurring with event B_1 and the joint probability of event A occurring with event B_2. You use Equation (5.2) to compute marginal probabilities.

MARGINAL PROBABILITY

$$P(A) = P(A \text{ and } B_1) + P(A \text{ and } B_2) + \cdots + P(A \text{ and } B_k) \qquad \textbf{(5.2)}$$

where $B_1, B_2, \ldots, B_k$ are k mutually exclusive and collectively exhaustive events, defined as follows:

Two events are **mutually exclusive** if both the events cannot occur simultaneously.
A set of events is **collectively exhaustive** if one of the events must occur.

Heads and tails in a coin toss are mutually exclusive events. The result of a coin toss cannot simultaneously be a head and a tail. Heads and tails in a coin toss are also collectively exhaustive events. One of them must occur. If heads does not occur, tails must occur. If tails does not occur, heads must occur. Being male and being female are mutually exclusive and collectively exhaustive events. No person is both (the two are mutually exclusive), and everyone is one or the other (the two are collectively exhaustive).

You can use Equation (5.2) to compute the marginal probability of "planned to purchase" a big-screen television:

$$P(\text{Planned to purchase}) = P(\text{Planned to purchase } and \text{ purchased})$$
$$+ P(\text{Planned to purchase } and \text{ did not purchase})$$

$$= \frac{200}{1,000} + \frac{50}{1,000}$$

$$= \frac{250}{1,000} = 0.25$$

You get the same result if you add the number of outcomes that make up the simple event "planned to purchase."

General Addition Rule

How do you find the probability of event "A or B"? You need to consider the occurrence of either event A or event B or both A and B. For example, how can you determine the probability that a household planned to purchase or actually purchased a big-screen television? The event "planned to purchase or actually purchased" includes all households that planned to purchase and all households that actually purchased a big-screen television. You examine each cell of the contingency table (Table 5.1 on page 206) to determine whether it is part of this event. From Table 5.1, the cell "planned to purchase and did not actually purchase" is part of the event because it includes respondents who planned to purchase. The cell "did not plan to purchase and actually purchased" is included because it contains respondents who actually purchased. Finally, the cell "planned to purchase and actually purchased" has both characteristics of interest. Therefore, one way to calculate the probability of "planned to purchase or actually purchased" is

$$P(\text{Planned to purchase } or \text{ actually purchased}) = P(\text{Planned to purchase } and \text{ did}$$
$$\text{not actually purchase}) + P(\text{Did not plan to}$$
$$\text{purchase } and \text{ actually purchased}) + P(\text{Planned}$$
$$\text{to purchase } and \text{ actually purchased})$$

$$= \frac{50}{1,000} + \frac{100}{1,000} + \frac{200}{1,000}$$

$$= \frac{350}{1,000} = 0.35$$

Often, it is easier to determine $P(A \text{ or } B)$, the probability of the event A or B, by using the **general addition rule**, defined in Equation (5.3).

GENERAL ADDITION RULE

The probability of A or B is equal to the probability of A plus the probability of B minus the probability of A and B.

$$P(A \text{ or } B) = P(A) + P(B) - P(A \text{ and } B) \qquad (5.3)$$

Applying Equation (5.3) to the previous example produces the following result:

$$
\begin{aligned}
P(\text{Planned to purchase } or \text{ actually purchased}) &= P(\text{Planned to purchase}) \\
&\quad + P(\text{Actually purchased}) - P(\text{Planned to} \\
&\quad \text{purchase } and \text{ actually purchased}) \\
&= \frac{250}{1{,}000} + \frac{300}{1{,}000} - \frac{200}{1{,}000} \\
&= \frac{350}{1{,}000} = 0.35
\end{aligned}
$$

The general addition rule consists of taking the probability of A and adding it to the probability of B and then subtracting the probability of the joint event A and B from this total because the joint event has already been included in computing both the probability of A and the probability of B. Referring to Table 5.1 on page 206, if the outcomes of the event "planned to purchase" are added to those of the event "actually purchased," the joint event "planned to purchase and actually purchased" has been included in each of these simple events. Therefore, because this joint event has been double-counted, you must subtract it to provide the correct result. Example 5.5 illustrates another application of the general addition rule.

EXAMPLE 5.5

Using the General Addition Rule for the Households That Purchased Big-Screen Televisions

In Example 5.3 on page 207, the purchases were cross-classified in Table 5.2 as televisions that had a faster refresh rate or televisions that had a standard refresh rate and whether the household purchased a Blu-ray disc (BD) player. Find the probability that among households that purchased a big-screen television, they purchased a television that had a faster refresh rate or a BD player.

SOLUTION Using Equation (5.3),

$$
\begin{aligned}
P(\text{Television had a faster refresh} \atop \text{rate } or \text{ purchased a BD player}) &= {P(\text{Television had a faster refresh rate}) \atop + P(\text{purchased a BD player}) - P(\text{Television} \atop \text{had a faster refresh rate } and \text{ purchased a BD player})} \\
&= \frac{80}{300} + \frac{108}{300} - \frac{38}{300} \\
&= \frac{150}{300} = 0.50
\end{aligned}
$$

Therefore, of those households that purchased a big-screen television, there is a 50.0% chance that a randomly selected household purchased a television that had a faster refresh rate or purchased a BD player.

Problems for Section 5.1

LEARNING THE BASICS

5.1 Two coins are tossed.
a. Give an example of a simple event.
b. Give an example of a joint event.
c. What is the complement of a head on the first toss?
d. What does the sample space consist of?

5.2 An urn contains 12 red balls and 8 white balls. One ball is to be selected from the urn.
a. Give an example of a simple event.
b. What is the complement of a red ball?
c. What does the sample space consist of?

5.3 Consider the following contingency table:

	B	B'
A	10	20
A'	20	40

What is the probability of event
a. A?
b. A'?
c. A and B?
d. A or B?

5.4 Consider the following contingency table:

	B	B'
A	10	30
A'	25	35

What is the probability of event
a. A'?
b. A and B?
c. A' and B'?
d. A' or B'?

APPLYING THE CONCEPTS

5.5 For each of the following, indicate whether the type of probability involved is an example of *a priori* probability, empirical probability, or subjective probability.
a. The next toss of a fair coin will land on heads.
b. Italy will win soccer's World Cup the next time the competition is held.
c. The sum of the faces of two dice will be seven.
d. The train taking a commuter to work will be more than 10 minutes late.

5.6 For each of the following, state whether the events created are mutually exclusive and collectively exhaustive.
a. Registered voters in the United States were asked whether they are registered as Republicans or Democrats.

b. Each respondent was classified by the type of car he or she drives: sedan, SUV, American, European, Asian, or none.
c. People were asked, "Do you currently live in (i) an apartment or (ii) a house?"
d. A product was classified as defective or not defective.

5.7 Which of the following events occur with a probability of zero? For each, state why or why not.
a. A voter in the United States is registered as a Republican and as a Democrat.
b. A voter in the United States is female and registered as a Republican.
c. An automobile is a Ford and a Toyota.
d. An automobile is a Toyota and was manufactured in the United States.

5.8 Does it take more time to be removed from an email list than it used to take? A study of 100 large online retailers revealed the following:

	NEED THREE OR MORE CLICKS TO BE REMOVED	
YEAR	**Yes**	**No**
2009	39	61
2008	7	93

Source: Data extracted from "More Clicks to Escape an Email List," *The New York Times*, March 29, 2010, p. B2.

a. Give an example of a simple event.
b. Give an example of a joint event.
c. What is the complement of "Needs three or more clicks to be removed from an email list"?
d. Why is "Needs three or more clicks to be removed from an email list in 2009" a joint event?

5.9 Referring to the contingency table in Problem 5.8, if a large online retailer is selected at random, what is the probability that
a. you needed three or more clicks to be removed from an email list?
b. you needed three or more clicks to be removed from an email list in 2009?
c. you needed three or more clicks to be removed from an email list or were a large online retailer surveyed in 2009?
d. Explain the difference in the results in (b) and (c).

5.10 Do people of different age groups differ in their response to email messages? A survey by the Center for the Digital Future of the University of Southern California (data extracted from A. Mindlin, "Older E-mail Users Favor Fast Replies," *The New York Times*, July 14, 2008, p. B3) reported that 70.7% of users over 70 years of age believe that email messages should be answered quickly, as compared to

53.6% of users 12 to 50 years old. Suppose that the survey was based on 1,000 users over 70 years of age and 1,000 users 12 to 50 years old. The following table summarizes the results:

ANSWERS QUICKLY	AGE OF RESPONDENTS		
	12–50	Over 70	Total
Yes	536	707	1,243
No	464	293	757
Total	1,000	1,000	2,000

a. Give an example of a simple event.
b. Give an example of a joint event.
c. What is the complement of a respondent who answers quickly?
d. Why is a respondent who answers quickly and is over 70 years old a joint event?

5.11 Referring to the contingency table in Problem 5.10, if a respondent is selected at random, what is the probability that
a. he or she answers quickly?
b. he or she is over 70 years old?
c. he or she answers quickly *or* is over 70 years old?
d. Explain the difference in the results in (b) and (c).

SELF Test **5.12** According to a Gallup Poll, the extent to which employees are engaged with their workplace varies from country to country. Gallup reports that the percentage of U.S. workers engaged with their workplace is more than twice as high as the percentage of German workers. The study also shows that having more engaged workers leads to increased innovation, productivity, and profitability, as well as reduced employee turnover. The results of the poll are summarized in the following table:

ENGAGEMENT	COUNTRY		
	United States	Germany	Total
Engaged	550	246	796
Not engaged	1,345	1,649	2,994
Total	1,895	1,895	3,790

Source: Data extracted from M. Nink, "Employee Disengagement Plagues Germany," *Gallup Management Journal*, **gmj.gallup.com**, April 9, 2009.

If an employee is selected at random, what is the probability that he or she
a. is engaged with his or her workplace?
b. is a U.S. worker?
c. is engaged with his or her workplace *or* is a U.S. worker?
d. Explain the difference in the results in (b) and (c).

5.13 What is the preferred way for people to order fast food? A survey was conducted in 2009, but the sample sizes were not reported. Suppose the results, based on a sample of 100 males and 100 females, were as follows:

DINING PREFERENCE	GENDER		
	Male	Female	Total
Dine inside	21	12	33
Order inside to go	19	10	29
Order at the drive-through	60	78	138
Total	100	100	200

Source: Data extracted from **www.qsrmagazine.com/reports/drive-thru_time_study/2009/2009_charts/whats_your_preferred_way_to_order_fast_food.html**.

If a respondent is selected at random, what is the probability that he or she
a. prefers to order at the drive-through?
b. is a male *and* prefers to order at the drive-through?
c. is a male *or* prefers to order at the drive-through?
d. Explain the difference in the results in (b) and (c).

5.14 A survey of 1,085 adults asked "Do you enjoy shopping for clothing for yourself?" The results (data extracted from "Split decision on clothes shopping," *USA Today*, January 28, 2011, p. 1B) indicated that 51% of the females enjoyed shopping for clothing for themselves as compared to 44% of the males. The sample sizes of males and females were not provided. Suppose that the results indicated that of 542 males, 238 answered yes. Of 543 females, 276 answered yes. Construct a contingency table to evaluate the probabilities. What is the probability that a respondent chosen at random
a. enjoys shopping for clothing for themself?
b. is a female *and* enjoys shopping for clothing for herself?
c. is a female *or* is a person who enjoys shopping for clothing?
d. is a male *or* a female?

5.15 Each year, ratings are compiled concerning the performance of new cars during the first 90 days of use. Suppose that the cars have been categorized according to whether a car needs warranty-related repair (yes or no) and the country in which the company manufacturing a car is based (United States or not United States). Based on the data collected, the probability that the new car needs a warranty repair is 0.04, the probability that the car was manufactured by a U.S.-based company is 0.60, and the probability that the new car needs a warranty repair *and* was manufactured by a U.S.-based company is 0.025. Construct a contingency table to evaluate the probabilities of a warranty-related repair. What is the probability that a new car selected at random
a. needs a warranty repair?
b. needs a warranty repair *and* was manufactured by a U.S.-based company?
c. needs a warranty repair *or* was manufactured by a U.S.-based company?
d. needs a warranty repair *or* was not manufactured by a U.S.-based company?

5.2 Conditional Probability

Each example in Section 5.1 involves finding the probability of an event when sampling from the entire sample space. How do you determine the probability of an event if you know certain information about the events involved?

Computing Conditional Probabilities

Conditional probability refers to the probability of event A, given information about the occurrence of another event, B.

CONDITIONAL PROBABILITY

The probability of A given B is equal to the probability of A *and* B divided by the probability of B.

$$P(A \mid B) = \frac{P(A \text{ and } B)}{P(B)}$$

(5.4a)

The probability of B given A is equal to the probability of A *and* B divided by the probability of A.

$$P(B \mid A) = \frac{P(A \text{ and } B)}{P(A)}$$

(5.4b)

where

$$P(A \text{ and } B) = \text{joint probability of } A \text{ and } B$$

$$P(A) = \text{marginal probability of } A$$

$$P(B) = \text{marginal probability of } B$$

Referring to the Using Statistics scenario involving the purchase of big-screen televisions, suppose you were told that a household planned to purchase a big-screen television. Now, what is the probability that the household actually purchased the television? In this example, the objective is to find P(Actually purchased | Planned to purchase). Here you are given the information that the household planned to purchase the big-screen television. Therefore, the sample space does not consist of all 1,000 households in the survey. It consists of only those households that planned to purchase the big-screen television. Of 250 such households, 200 actually purchased the big-screen television. Therefore, based on Table 5.1 on page 206, the probability that a household actually purchased the big-screen television given that they planned to purchase is

$$P(\text{Actually purchased} \mid \text{Planned to purchase}) = \frac{\text{Planned to purchase } and \text{ actually purchased}}{\text{Planned to purchase}}$$

$$= \frac{200}{250} = 0.80$$

You can also use Equation (5.4b) to compute this result:

$$P(B \mid A) = \frac{P(A \text{ and } B)}{P(A)}$$

where

$$A = \text{planned to purchase}$$
$$B = \text{actually purchased}$$

then

$$P(\text{Actually purchased}|\text{Planned to purchase}) = \frac{200/1{,}000}{250/1{,}000}$$
$$= \frac{200}{250} = 0.80$$

Example 5.6 further illustrates conditional probability.

EXAMPLE 5.6

Finding the Conditional Probability of Purchasing a Blu-ray Disc Player

Table 5.2 on page 207 is a contingency table for whether a household purchased a television with a faster refresh rate and whether the household purchased a Blu-ray disc player. If a household purchased a television with a faster refresh rate, what is the probability that it also purchased a Blu-ray disc player?

SOLUTION Because you know that the household purchased a television with a faster refresh rate, the sample space is reduced to 80 households. Of these 80 households, 38 also purchased a Blu-ray disc (BD) player. Therefore, the probability that a household purchased a BD player, given that the household purchased a television with a faster refresh rate, is

$$P\begin{pmatrix}\text{Purchased BD player} \mid \text{ Purchased} \\ \text{television with faster refresh rate}\end{pmatrix} = \frac{\substack{\text{Number purchasing television with} \\ \text{faster refresh rate } and \text{ BD player}}}{\substack{\text{Number purchasing television} \\ \text{with faster refresh rate}}}$$

$$= \frac{38}{80} = 0.475$$

If you use Equation (5.4b) on page 213:

A = purchased a television with a faster refresh rate

B = purchased a BD player

then

$$P(B|A) = \frac{P(A \text{ and } B)}{P(A)} = \frac{38/300}{80/300} = 0.475$$

Therefore, given that the household purchased a television with a faster refresh rate, there is a 47.5% chance that the household also purchased a Blu-ray disc player. You can compare this conditional probability to the marginal probability of purchasing a Blu-ray disc player, which is 108/300 = 0.36, or 36%. These results tell you that households that purchased televisions with a faster refresh rate are more likely to purchase a Blu-ray disc player than are households that purchased big-screen televisions that have a standard refresh rate.

Decision Trees

In Table 5.1 on page 206, households are classified according to whether they planned to purchase and whether they actually purchased big-screen televisions. A **decision tree** is an alternative to the contingency table. Figure 5.3 represents the decision tree for this example.

FIGURE 5.3

Decision tree for M&R
Electronics World
example

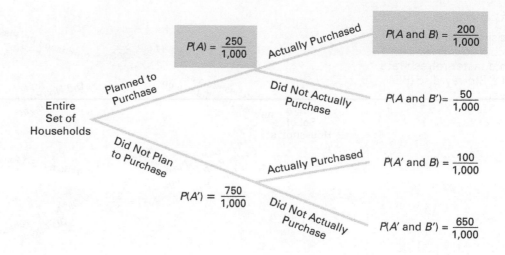

In Figure 5.3, beginning at the left with the entire set of households, there are two "branches" for whether or not the household planned to purchase a big-screen television. Each of these branches has two subbranches, corresponding to whether the household actually purchased or did not actually purchase the big-screen television. The probabilities at the end of the initial branches represent the marginal probabilities of A and A'. The probabilities at the end of each of the four subbranches represent the joint probability for each combination of events A and B. You compute the conditional probability by dividing the joint probability by the appropriate marginal probability.

For example, to compute the probability that the household actually purchased, given that the household planned to purchase the big-screen television, you take P(Planned to purchase *and* actually purchased) and divide by P(Planned to purchase). From Figure 5.3,

$$P(\text{Actually purchased} \mid \text{Planned to purchase}) = \frac{200/1{,}000}{250/1{,}000}$$

$$= \frac{200}{250} = 0.80$$

Example 5.7 illustrates how to construct a decision tree.

EXAMPLE 5.7

Constructing the
Decision Tree for
the Households
That Purchased
Big-Screen
Televisions

Using the cross-classified data in Table 5.2 on page 207, construct the decision tree. Use the decision tree to find the probability that a household purchased a Blu-ray disc player, given that the household purchased a television with a faster refresh rate.

SOLUTION The decision tree for purchased a Blu-ray disc player and a television with a faster refresh rate is displayed in Figure 5.4 on page 216. Using Equation (5.4b) on page 213 and the following definitions,

$$A = \text{purchased a television with a faster refresh rate}$$
$$B = \text{purchased a Blu-ray disc player}$$

$$P(B \mid A) = \frac{P(A \text{ and } B)}{P(A)} = \frac{38/300}{80/300} = 0.475$$

FIGURE 5.4

Decision tree for
purchased a television
with a faster refresh rate
and a Blu-ray disc (BD)
player

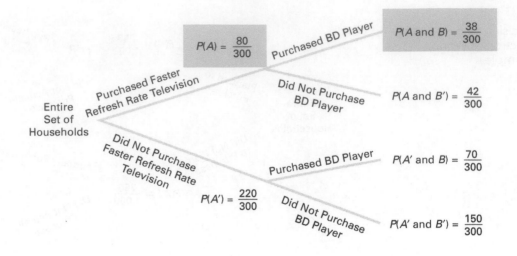

Independence

In the example concerning the purchase of big-screen televisions, the conditional probability is $200/250 = 0.80$ that the selected household actually purchased the big-screen television, given that the household planned to purchase. The simple probability of selecting a household that actually purchased is $300/1{,}000 = 0.30$. This result shows that the prior knowledge that the household planned to purchase affected the probability that the household actually purchased the television. In other words, the outcome of one event is *dependent* on the outcome of a second event.

When the outcome of one event does *not* affect the probability of occurrence of another event, the events are said to be independent. **Independence** can be determined by using Equation (5.5).

INDEPENDENCE
Two events, A and B, are independent if and only if

$$P(A \mid B) = P(A) \qquad \qquad \textbf{(5.5)}$$

where

$$P(A \mid B) = \text{conditional probability of } A \text{ given } B$$

$$P(A) = \text{marginal probability of } A$$

Example 5.8 demonstrates the use of Equation (5.5).

EXAMPLE 5.8

Determining
Independence

In the follow-up survey of the 300 households that actually purchased big-screen televisions, the households were asked if they were satisfied with their purchases. Table 5.3 cross-classifies the responses to the satisfaction question with the responses to whether the television had a faster refresh rate.

TABLE 5.3

Satisfaction with
Purchase of Big-Screen
Televisions

TELEVISION REFRESH RATE	SATISFIED WITH PURCHASE?		
	Yes	No	Total
Faster	64	16	80
Standard	176	44	220
Total	240	60	300

Determine whether being satisfied with the purchase and the refresh rate of the television purchased are independent.

SOLUTION For these data,

$$P(\text{Satisfied}|\text{faster refresh rate}) = \frac{64/300}{80/300} = \frac{64}{80} = 0.80$$

which is equal to

$$P(\text{Satisfied}) = \frac{240}{300} = 0.80$$

Thus, being satisfied with the purchase and the refresh rate of the television purchased are independent. Knowledge of one event does not affect the probability of the other event.

Multiplication Rules

The **general multiplication rule** is derived using Equation (5.4a) on page 213:

$$P(A|B) = \frac{P(A \text{ and } B)}{P(B)}$$

and solving for the joint probability $P(A \text{ and } B)$.

> GENERAL MULTIPLICATION RULE
>
> The probability of A and B is equal to the probability of A given B times the probability of B.
>
> $$P(A \text{ and } B) = P(A|B)P(B) \qquad \textbf{(5.6)}$$

Example 5.9 demonstrates the use of the general multiplication rule.

EXAMPLE 5.9

Using the General Multiplication Rule

Consider the 80 households that purchased televisions that had a faster refresh rate. In Table 5.3 on page 216 you see that 64 households are satisfied with their purchase, and 16 households are dissatisfied. Suppose 2 households are randomly selected from the 80 households. Find the probability that both households are satisfied with their purchase.

SOLUTION Here you can use the multiplication rule in the following way. If

$$A = \text{second household selected is satisfied}$$
$$B = \text{first household selected is satisfied}$$

then, using Equation (5.6),

$$P(A \text{ and } B) = P(A|B)P(B)$$

The probability that the first household is satisfied with the purchase is 64/80. However, the probability that the second household is also satisfied with the purchase depends on the result of the first selection. If the first household is not returned to the sample after the satisfaction level is determined (i.e., sampling without replacement), the number of households remaining is 79. If the first household is satisfied, the probability that the second is also satisfied is 63/79 because 63 satisfied households remain in the sample. Therefore,

$$P(A \text{ and } B) = \left(\frac{63}{79}\right)\left(\frac{64}{80}\right) = 0.6380$$

There is a 63.80% chance that both of the households sampled will be satisfied with their purchase.

The **multiplication rule for independent events** is derived by substituting $P(A)$ for $P(A|B)$ in Equation (5.6).

MULTIPLICATION RULE FOR INDEPENDENT EVENTS

If A and B are independent, the probability of A *and* B is equal to the probability of A times the probability of B.

$$P(A \text{ and } B) = P(A)P(B) \tag{5.7}$$

If this rule holds for two events, A and B, then A and B are independent. Therefore, there are two ways to determine independence:

1. Events A and B are independent if, and only if, $P(A|B) = P(A)$.
2. Events A and B are independent if, and only if, $P(A \text{ and } B) = P(A)P(B)$.

Marginal Probability Using the General Multiplication Rule

In Section 5.1, marginal probability was defined using Equation (5.2) on page 209. You can state the equation for marginal probability by using the general multiplication rule. If

$$P(A) = P(A \text{ and } B_1) + P(A \text{ and } B_2) + \cdots + P(A \text{ and } B_k)$$

then, using the general multiplication rule, Equation (5.8) defines the marginal probability.

MARGINAL PROBABILITY USING THE GENERAL MULTIPLICATION RULE

$$P(A) = P(A|B_1)P(B_1) + P(A|B_2)P(B_2) + \cdots + P(A|B_k)P(B_k) \tag{5.8}$$

where $B_1, B_2, \ldots, B_k$ are k mutually exclusive and collectively exhaustive events.

To illustrate Equation (5.8), refer to Table 5.1 on page 206. Let

$$P(A) = \text{probability of "planned to purchase"}$$
$$P(B_1) = \text{probability of "actually purchased"}$$
$$P(B_2) = \text{probability of "did not actually purchase"}$$

Then, using Equation (5.8), the probability of planned to purchase is

$$P(A) = P(A|B_1)P(B_1) + P(A|B_2)P(B_2)$$
$$= \left(\frac{200}{300}\right)\left(\frac{300}{1,000}\right) + \left(\frac{50}{700}\right)\left(\frac{700}{1,000}\right)$$
$$= \frac{200}{1,000} + \frac{50}{1,000} = \frac{250}{1,000} = 0.25$$

Problems for Section 5.2

LEARNING THE BASICS

5.16 Consider the following contingency table:

	B	B'
A	10	20
A'	20	40

What is the probability of
a. $A|B$?
b. $A|B'$?
c. $A'|B'$?
d. Are events A and B independent?

5.17 Consider the following contingency table:

	B	B'
A	10	30
A'	25	35

What is the probability of
a. $A|B$?
b. $A'|B'$?
c. $A|B'$?
d. Are events A and B independent?

5.18 If $P(A \text{ and } B) = 0.4$ and $P(B) = 0.8$, find $P(A|B)$.

5.19 If $P(A) = 0.7, P(B) = 0.6$, and A and B are independent, find $P(A \text{ and } B)$.

5.20 If $P(A) = 0.3, P(B) = 0.4$, and $P(A \text{ and } B) = 0.2$, are A and B independent?

APPLYING THE CONCEPTS

5.21 Does it take more time to be removed from an email list than it used to take? A study of 100 large online retailers revealed the following:

YEAR	NEED THREE OR MORE CLICKS TO BE REMOVED	
	Yes	No
2009	39	61
2008	7	93

Source: Data extracted from "More Clicks to Escape an Email List," *The New York Times*, March 29, 2010, p. B2.

a. Given that three or more clicks are needed to be removed from an email list, what is the probability that this occurred in 2009?

b. Given that the year 2009 is involved, what is the probability that three or more clicks are needed to be removed from an email list?
c. Explain the difference in the results in (a) and (b).
d. Are needing three or more clicks to be removed from an email list and the year independent?

5.22 Do people of different age groups differ in their response to email messages? A survey by the Center for the Digital Future of the University of Southern California (data extracted from A. Mindlin, "Older E-mail Users Favor Fast Replies," *The New York Times*, July 14, 2008, p. B3) reported that 70.7% of users over 70 years of age believe that email messages should be answered quickly, as compared to 53.6% of users 12 to 50 years old. Suppose that the survey was based on 1,000 users over 70 years of age and 1,000 users 12 to 50 years old. The following table summarizes the results:

AGE OF RESPONDENTS	ANSWERS QUICKLY		
	12–50	Over 70	Total
Yes	536	707	1,243
No	464	293	757
Total	1,000	1,000	2,000

a. Suppose you know that the respondent is between 12 and 50 years old. What is the probability that he or she answers quickly?
b. Suppose you know that the respondent is over 70 years old. What is the probability that he or she answers quickly?
c. Are the two events, answers quickly and age of respondents, independent? Explain.

5.23 What is the preferred way for people to order fast food? A survey was conducted in 2009, but the sample sizes were not reported. Suppose the results, based on a sample of 100 males and 100 females, were as follows:

DINING PREFERENCE	GENDER		
	Male	Female	Total
Dine inside	21	12	33
Order inside to go	19	10	29
Order at the drive-through	60	78	138
Total	100	100	200

Source: Data extracted from **www.qsrmagazine.com/reports/drive-thru_time_study/2009/2009_charts/whats_your_preferred_way_to_order_fast_food.html**.

a. Given that a respondent is a male, what is the probability that he prefers to order at the drive-through?
b. Given that a respondent is a female, what is the probability that she prefers to order at the drive-through?

c. Is dining preference independent of gender? Explain.

5.24 According to a Gallup Poll, the extent to which employees are engaged with their workplace varies from country to country. Gallup reports that the percentage of U.S. workers engaged with their workplace is more than twice as high as the percentage of German workers. The study also shows that having more engaged workers leads to increased innovation, productivity, and profitability, as well as reduced employee turnover. The results of the poll are summarized in the following table:

ENGAGEMENT	COUNTRY		
	United States	**Germany**	**Total**
Engaged	550	246	796
Not engaged	1,345	1,649	2,994
Total	1,895	1,895	3,790

Source: Data extracted from M. Nink, "Employee Disengagement Plagues Germany," *Gallup Management Journal*, **gmj.gallup.com**, April 9, 2009.

a. Given that a worker is from the United States, what is the probability that the worker is engaged?
b. Given that a worker is from the United States, what is the probability that the worker is not engaged?
c. Given that a worker is from Germany, what is the probability that the worker is engaged?
d. Given that a worker is from Germany, what is the probability that the worker is not engaged?

5.25 A survey of 1,085 adults asked "Do you enjoy shopping for clothing for yourself." The results (data extracted from "Split decision on clothes shopping," *USA Today*, January 28, 2011, p. 1B) indicated that 51% of the females enjoyed shopping for clothing for themselves as compared to 44% of the males. The sample sizes of males and females were not provided. Suppose that the results were as shown in the following table:

ENJOYS SHOPPING FOR CLOTHING	GENDER		
	Male	**Female**	**Total**
Yes	238	276	514
No	304	267	571
Total	542	543	1,085

a. Suppose that the respondent chosen is a female. What is the probability that she does not enjoy shopping for clothing?
b. Suppose that the respondent chosen enjoys shopping for clothing. What is the probability that the individual is a male?
c. Are enjoying shopping for clothing and the gender of the individual independent? Explain.

5.26 Each year, ratings are compiled concerning the performance of new cars during the first 90 days of use. Suppose that the cars have been categorized according to whether a car needs warranty-related repair (yes or no) and the country in which the company manufacturing a car is based (United States or not United States). Based on the data collected, the probability that the new car needs a warranty repair is 0.04, the probability that the car is manufactured by a U.S.-based company is 0.60, and the probability that the new car needs a warranty repair *and* was manufactured by a U.S.-based company is 0.025.

a. Suppose you know that a company based in the United States manufactured a particular car. What is the probability that the car needs warranty repair?
b. Suppose you know that a company based in the United States did not manufacture a particular car. What is the probability that the car needs warranty repair?
c. Are need for warranty repair and location of the company manufacturing the car independent?

5.27 In 39 of the 61 years from 1950 through 2010, the S&P 500 finished higher after the first five days of trading. In 34 of those 39 years, the S&P 500 finished higher for the year. Is a good first week a good omen for the upcoming year? The following table gives the first-week and annual performance over this 61-year period:

FIRST WEEK	S&P 500'S ANNUAL PERFORMANCE	
	Higher	**Lower**
Higher	34	5
Lower	11	11

a. If a year is selected at random, what is the probability that the S&P 500 finished higher for the year?
b. Given that the S&P 500 finished higher after the first five days of trading, what is the probability that it finished higher for the year?
c. Are the two events "first-week performance" and "annual performance" independent? Explain.
d. Look up the performance after the first five days of 2011 and the 2011 annual performance of the S&P 500 at **finance.yahoo.com**. Comment on the results.

5.28 A standard deck of cards is being used to play a game. There are four suits (hearts, diamonds, clubs, and spades), each having 13 faces (ace, 2, 3, 4, 5, 6, 7, 8, 9, 10, jack, queen, and king), making a total of 52 cards. This complete deck is thoroughly mixed, and you will receive the first 2 cards from the deck, without replacement (the first card is not returned to the deck after it is selected).

a. What is the probability that both cards are queens?
b. What is the probability that the first card is a 10 and the second card is a 5 or 6?

c. If you were sampling with replacement (the first card is returned to the deck after it is selected), what would be the answer in (a)?

d. In the game of blackjack, the face cards (jack, queen, king) count as 10 points, and the ace counts as either 1 or 11 points. All other cards are counted at their face value. Blackjack is achieved if 2 cards total 21 points. What is the probability of getting blackjack in this problem?

5.29 A box of nine gloves contains two left-handed gloves and seven right-handed gloves.

a. If two gloves are randomly selected from the box, without replacement (the first glove is not returned to the box after it is selected), what is the probability that both gloves selected will be right-handed?

b. If two gloves are randomly selected from the box, without replacement (the first glove is not returned to the box after it is selected), what is the probability that there will be one right-handed glove and one left-handed glove selected?

c. If three gloves are selected, with replacement (the gloves are returned to the box after they are selected), what is the probability that all three will be left-handed?

d. If you were sampling with replacement (the first glove is returned to the box after it is selected), what would be the answers to (a) and (b)?

5.3 Bayes' Theorem

Bayes' theorem is used to revise previously calculated probabilities based on new information. Developed by Thomas Bayes in the eighteenth century (see references 1, 2, and 7), Bayes' theorem is an extension of what you previously learned about conditional probability.

You can apply Bayes' theorem to the situation in which M&R Electronics World is considering marketing a new model of televisions. In the past, 40% of the new-model televisions have been successful, and 60% have been unsuccessful. Before introducing the new model television, the marketing research department conducts an extensive study and releases a report, either favorable or unfavorable. In the past, 80% of the successful new-model television(s) had received favorable market research reports, and 30% of the unsuccessful new-model television(s) had received favorable reports. For the new model of television under consideration, the marketing research department has issued a favorable report. What is the probability that the television will be successful?

Bayes' theorem is developed from the definition of conditional probability. To find the conditional probability of B given A, consider Equation (5.4b) (originally presented on page 213 and shown below):

$$P(B|A) = \frac{P(A \, and \, B)}{P(A)} = \frac{P(A|B)P(B)}{P(A)}$$

Bayes' theorem is derived by substituting Equation (5.8) on page 218 for $P(A)$ in the denominator of Equation (5.4b).

BAYES' THEOREM

$$P(B_i|A) = \frac{P(A|B_i)P(B_i)}{P(A|B_1)P(B_1) + P(A|B_2)P(B_2) + \cdots + P(A|B_k)P(B_k)} \tag{5.9}$$

where B_i is the ith event out of k mutually exclusive and collectively exhaustive events.

To use Equation (5.9) for the television-marketing example, let

event S = successful television   event F = favorable report

event S' = unsuccessful television   event F' = unfavorable report

and

$$P(S) = 0.40 \quad P(F|S) = 0.80$$
$$P(S') = 0.60 \quad P(F|S') = 0.30$$

Then, using Equation (5.9),

$$P(S \mid F) = \frac{P(F \mid S)P(S)}{P(F \mid S)P(S) + P(F \mid S')P(S')}$$

$$= \frac{(0.80)(0.40)}{(0.80)(0.40) + (0.30)(0.60)}$$

$$= \frac{0.32}{0.32 + 0.18} = \frac{0.32}{0.50}$$

$$= 0.64$$

The probability of a successful television, given that a favorable report was received, is 0.64. Thus, the probability of an unsuccessful television, given that a favorable report was received, is $1 - 0.64 = 0.36$.

Table 5.4 summarizes the computation of the probabilities, and Figure 5.5 presents the decision tree.

TABLE 5.4

Bayes' Theorem Calculations for the Television-Marketing Example

Event S_i	Prior Probability $P(S_i)$	Conditional Probability $P(F \mid S_i)$	Joint Probability $P(F \mid S_i)P(S_i)$	Revised Probability $P(S_i \mid F)$
S = successful television	0.40	0.80	0.32	$P(S \mid F) = 0.32/0.50$ $= 0.64$
S' = unsuccessful television	0.60	0.30	0.18 _____ 0.50	$P(S' \mid F) = 0.18/0.50$ $= 0.36$

FIGURE 5.5

Decision tree for marketing a new television

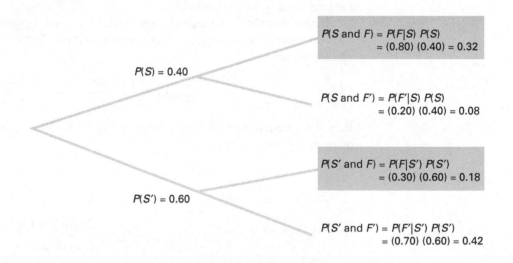

Example 5.10 applies Bayes' theorem to a medical diagnosis problem.

EXAMPLE 5.10

Using Bayes' Theorem in a Medical Diagnosis Problem

The probability that a person has a certain disease is 0.03. Medical diagnostic tests are available to determine whether the person actually has the disease. If the disease is actually present, the probability that the medical diagnostic test will give a positive result (indicating that the disease is present) is 0.90. If the disease is not actually present, the probability of a positive test result (indicating that the disease is present) is 0.02. Suppose that the medical diagnostic test has given a positive result (indicating that the disease is present). What is the probability that the disease is actually present? What is the probability of a positive test result?

SOLUTION Let

event D = has disease $\qquad$ event T = test is positive

event D' = does not have disease $\quad$ event T' = test is negative

and

$$P(D) = 0.03 \quad P(T|\,D) = 0.90$$
$$P(D') = 0.97 \quad P(T|\,D') = 0.02$$

Using Equation (5.9) on page 221,

$$
\begin{aligned}
P(D|\,T) &= \frac{P(T|\,D)P(D)}{P(T|\,D)P(D) + P(T|\,D')P(D')} \\[6pt]
&= \frac{(0.90)(0.03)}{(0.90)(0.03) + (0.02)(0.97)} \\[6pt]
&= \frac{0.0270}{0.0270 + 0.0194} = \frac{0.0270}{0.0464} \\[6pt]
&= 0.582
\end{aligned}
$$

The probability that the disease is actually present, given that a positive result has occurred (indicating that the disease is present), is 0.582. Table 5.5 summarizes the computation of the probabilities, and Figure 5.6 presents the decision tree.

TABLE 5.5

Bayes' Theorem Calculations for the Medical Diagnosis Problem

Event D_i	Prior Probability $P(D_i)$	Conditional Probability $P(T\|D_i)$	Joint Probability $P(T\|D_i)P(D_i)$	Revised Probability $P(D_i\|T)$
D = has disease	0.03	0.90	0.0270	$P(D\|T) = 0.0270/0.0464$ $= 0.582$
D' = does not have disease	0.97	0.02	0.0194 0.0464	$P(D'\|T) = 0.0194/0.0464$ $= 0.418$

FIGURE 5.6

Decision tree for the medical diagnosis problem

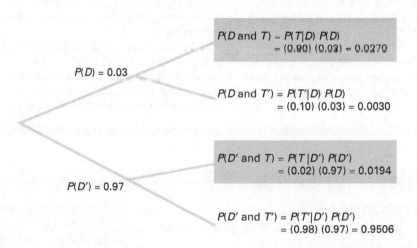

$$P(D \text{ and } T) = P(T|D)\ P(D)$$
$$= (0.90)\ (0.03) = 0.0270$$

$$P(D \text{ and } T') = P(T'|D)\ P(D)$$
$$= (0.10)\ (0.03) = 0.0030$$

$$P(D' \text{ and } T) = P(T|D')\ P(D')$$
$$= (0.02)\ (0.97) = 0.0194$$

$$P(D' \text{ and } T') = P(T'|D')\ P(D')$$
$$= (0.98)\ (0.97) = 0.9506$$

$P(D) = 0.03$

$P(D') = 0.97$

The denominator in Bayes' theorem represents $P(T)$, the probability of a positive test result, which in this case is 0.0464, or 4.64%.

THINK ABOUT THIS   Divine Providence and Spam

Would you ever guess that the essays *Divine Benevolence: Or, An Attempt to Prove That the Principal End of the Divine Providence and Government Is the Happiness of His Creatures* and *An Essay Towards Solving a Problem in the Doctrine of Chances* were written by the same person? Probably not, and in doing so, you illustrate a modern-day application of Bayesian statistics: spam, or junk mail filters.

In not guessing correctly, you probably looked at the words in the titles of the essays and concluded that they were talking about two different things. An implicit rule you used was that word frequencies vary by subject matter. A statistics essay would very likely contain the word *statistics* as well as words such as *chance*, *problem*, and *solving*. An eighteenth-century essay about theology and religion would be more likely to contain the uppercase forms of *Divine* and *Providence*.

Likewise, there are words you would guess to be very unlikely to appear in either book, such as technical terms from finance, and words that are most likely to appear in both—common words such as *a*, *and*, and *the*. That words would either be likely or unlikely suggests an application of probability theory. Of course, likely and unlikely are fuzzy concepts, and we might occasionally misclassify an essay if we kept things too simple, such as relying solely on the occurrence of the words *Divine* and *Providence*.

For example, a profile of the late Harris Milstead, better known as *Divine*, the star of *Hairspray* and other films, visiting Providence (Rhode Island), would most certainly not be an essay about theology. But if we widened the number of words we examined and found such words as *movie* or the name John Waters (Divine's director in many films), we probably would quickly realize the essay had something to do with twentieth-century cinema and little to do with theology and religion.

We can use a similar process to try to classify a new email message in your in-box as either spam or a legitimate message (called "ham," in this context). We would first need to add to your email program a "spam filter" that has the ability to track word frequencies associated with spam and ham messages as you identify them on a day-to-day basis. This would allow the filter to constantly update the prior probabilities necessary to use Bayes' theorem. With these probabilities, the filter can ask, "What is the probability that an email is spam, given the presence of a certain word?"

Applying the terms of Equation (5.9) on page 221, such a Bayesian spam filter would multiply the probability of finding the word in a spam email, $P(A|B)$, by the probability that the email is spam, $P(B)$, and then divide by the probability of finding the word in an email, the denominator in Equation (5.9). Bayesian spam filters also use shortcuts by focusing on a small set of words that have a high probability of being found in a spam message as well as on a small set of other words that have a low probability of being found in a spam message.

As spammers (people who send junk email) learned of such new filters, they tried to outfox them. Having learned that Bayesian filters might be assigning a high $P(A|B)$ value to words commonly found in spam, such as Viagra, spammers thought they could fool the filter by misspelling the word as Vi@gr@ or V1agra. What they overlooked was that the misspelled variants were even *more likely* to be found in a spam message than the original word. Thus, the misspelled variants made the job of spotting spam *easier* for the Bayesian filters.

Other spammers tried to fool the filters by adding "good" words, words that would have a low probability of being found in a spam message, or "rare" words, words not frequently encountered in any message. But these spammers overlooked the fact that the conditional probabilities are constantly updated and that words once considered "good" would be soon discarded from the good list by the filter as their $P(A|B)$ value increased. Likewise, as "rare" words grew more common in spam and yet stayed rare in ham, such words acted like the misspelled variants that others had tried earlier.

Even then, and perhaps after reading about Bayesian statistics, spammers thought that they could "break" Bayesian filters by inserting random words in their messages. Those random words would affect the filter by causing it to see many words whose $P(A|B)$ value would be low. The Bayesian filter would begin to label many spam messages as ham and end up being of no practical use. Spammers again overlooked that conditional probabilities are constantly updated.

Other spammers decided to eliminate all or most of the words in their messages and replace them with graphics so that Bayesian filters would have very few words with which to form conditional probabilities. But this approach failed, too, as Bayesian filters were rewritten to consider things other than words in a message. After all, Bayes' theorem concerns *events*, and "graphics present with no text" is as valid an event as "some word, *X*, present in a message." Other future tricks will ultimately fail for the same reason. (By the way, spam filters use non-Bayesian techniques as well, which makes spammers' lives even more difficult.)

Bayesian spam filters are an example of the unexpected way that applications of statistics can show up in your daily life. You will discover more examples as you read the rest of this book. *By the way, the author of the two essays mentioned earlier was Thomas Bayes, who is a lot more famous for the second essay than the first essay, a failed attempt to use mathematics and logic to prove the existence of God.*

Problems for Section 5.3

LEARNING THE BASICS

5.30 If $P(B) = 0.05, P(A|B) = 0.80, P(B') = 0.95$, and $P(A|B') = 0.40$, find $P(B|A)$.

5.31 If $P(B) = 0.30, P(A|B) = 0.60, P(B') = 0.70$, and $P(A|B') = 0.50$, find $P(B|A)$.

APPLYING THE CONCEPTS

5.32 In Example 5.10 on page 222, suppose that the probability that a medical diagnostic test will give a positive

result if the disease is not present is reduced from 0.02 to 0.01.

a. If the medical diagnostic test has given a positive result (indicating that the disease is present), what is the probability that the disease is actually present?

b. If the medical diagnostic test has given a negative result (indicating that the disease is not present), what is the probability that the disease is not present?

5.33 An advertising executive is studying television viewing habits of married men and women during prime-time hours.

Based on past viewing records, the executive has determined that during prime time, husbands are watching television 60% of the time. When the husband is watching television, 40% of the time the wife is also watching. When the husband is not watching television, 30% of the time the wife is watching television.

a. Find the probability that if the wife is watching television, the husband is also watching television.

b. Find the probability that the wife is watching television during prime time.

5.34 Olive Construction Company is determining whether it should submit a bid for a new shopping center. In the past, Olive's main competitor, Base Construction Company, has submitted bids 70% of the time. If Base Construction Company does not bid on a job, the probability that Olive Construction Company will get the job is 0.50. If Base Construction Company bids on a job, the probability that Olive Construction Company will get the job is 0.25.

a. If Olive Construction Company gets the job, what is the probability that Base Construction Company did not bid?

b. What is the probability that Olive Construction Company will get the job?

5.35 Laid-off workers who become entrepreneurs because they cannot find meaningful employment with another company are known as *entrepreneurs by necessity*. *The Wall Street Journal* reports that these entrepreneurs by necessity are less likely to grow into large businesses than are *entrepreneurs by choice* (J. Bailey, "Desire—More Than Need—Builds a Business," *The Wall Street Journal*, May 21, 2001, p. B4). This article states that 89% of the entrepreneurs in the United States are entrepreneurs by choice and 11% are entrepreneurs by necessity. Only 2% of entrepreneurs by necessity expect their new business to employ 20 or more people within five years, whereas 14% of entrepreneurs by choice expect to employ at least 20 people within five years.

a. If an entrepreneur is selected at random and that individual expects that his or her new business will employ 20 or more people within five years, what is the probability that this individual is an entrepreneur by choice?

b. Discuss several possible reasons why entrepreneurs by choice are more likely than entrepreneurs by necessity to believe that they will grow their businesses.

5.36 The editor of a textbook publishing company is trying to decide whether to publish a proposed business statistics textbook. Information on previous textbooks published indicates that 10% are huge successes, 20% are modest successes, 40% break even, and 30% are losers. However, before a publishing decision is made, the book will be reviewed. In the past, 99% of the huge successes received favorable reviews, 70% of the moderate successes received favorable reviews, 40% of the break-even books received favorable reviews, and 20% of the losers received favorable reviews.

a. If the proposed textbook receives a favorable review, how should the editor revise the probabilities of the various outcomes to take this information into account?

b. What proportion of textbooks receives favorable reviews?

5.37 A municipal bond service has three rating categories (*A*, *B*, and *C*). Suppose that in the past year, of the municipal bonds issued throughout the United States, 70% were rated *A*, 20% were rated *B*, and 10% were rated *C*. Of the municipal bonds rated *A*, 50% were issued by cities, 40% by suburbs, and 10% by rural areas. Of the municipal bonds rated *B*, 60% were issued by cities, 20% by suburbs, and 20% by rural areas. Of the municipal bonds rated *C*, 90% were issued by cities, 5% by suburbs, and 5% by rural areas.

a. If a new municipal bond is to be issued by a city, what is the probability that it will receive an *A* rating?

b. What proportion of municipal bonds are issued by cities?

c. What proportion of municipal bonds are issued by suburbs?

5.4 Counting Rules

In Equation (5.1) on page 204, the probability of occurrence of an outcome was defined as the number of ways the outcome occurs, divided by the total number of possible outcomes. Often, there are a large number of possible outcomes, and determining the exact number can be difficult. In such circumstances, rules have been developed for counting the number of possible outcomes. This section presents five different counting rules.

Counting Rule 1

Counting rule 1 determines the number of possible outcomes for a set of mutually exclusive and collectively exhaustive events.

COUNTING RULE 1

If any one of k different mutually exclusive and collectively exhaustive events can occur on each of n trials, the number of possible outcomes is equal to

$$k^n \qquad\qquad (5.10)$$

For example, using Equation (5.10), the number of different possible outcomes from tossing a two-sided coin five times is $2^5 = 2 \times 2 \times 2 \times 2 \times 2 = 32$.

EXAMPLE 5.11

Rolling a Die Twice

Suppose you roll a die twice. How many different possible outcomes can occur?

SOLUTION If a six-sided die is rolled twice, using Equation (5.10), the number of different outcomes is $6^2 = 36$.

Counting Rule 2

The second counting rule is a more general version of the first and allows the number of possible events to differ from trial to trial.

COUNTING RULE 2

If there are k_1 events on the first trial, k_2 events on the second trial, ... , and k_n events on the nth trial, then the number of possible outcomes is

$$(k_1)(k_2)\ldots(k_n) \qquad\qquad (5.11)$$

For example, a state motor vehicle department would like to know how many license plate numbers are available if a license plate number consists of three letters followed by three numbers (0 through 9). Using Equation (5.11), if a license plate number consists of three letters followed by three numbers, the total number of possible outcomes is $(26)(26)(26)(10)(10)(10) = 17,576,000$.

EXAMPLE 5.12

Determining the Number of Different Dinners

A restaurant menu has a price-fixed complete dinner that consists of an appetizer, an entrée, a beverage, and a dessert. You have a choice of 5 appetizers, 10 entrées, 3 beverages, and 6 desserts. Determine the total number of possible dinners.

SOLUTION Using Equation (5.11), the total number of possible dinners is $(5)(10)(3)(6) = 900$.

Counting Rule 3

The third counting rule involves computing the number of ways that a set of items can be arranged in order.

COUNTING RULE 3

The number of ways that all n items can be arranged in order is

$$n! = (n)(n-1)\ldots(1) \qquad \textbf{(5.12)}$$

where $n!$ is called n factorial, and $0!$ is defined as 1.

EXAMPLE 5.13

Using Counting Rule 3

If a set of six books is to be placed on a shelf, in how many ways can the six books be arranged?

SOLUTION To begin, you must realize that any of the six books could occupy the first position on the shelf. Once the first position is filled, there are five books to choose from in filling the second position. You continue this assignment procedure until all the positions are occupied. The number of ways that you can arrange six books is

$$n! = 6! = (6)(5)(4)(3)(2)(1) = 720$$

Counting Rule 4

In many instances you need to know the number of ways in which a subset of an entire group of items can be arranged in *order*. Each possible arrangement is called a **permutation**.

COUNTING RULE 4: PERMUTATIONS

The number of ways of arranging x objects selected from n objects in order is

$$_nP_x = \frac{n!}{(n-x)!} \qquad \textbf{(5.13)}$$

where

$$n = \text{total number of objects}$$
$$x = \text{number of objects to be arranged}$$
$$n! = n \text{ factorial} = n(n-1)\ldots(1)$$
$$P = \text{symbol for permutations}[1]$$

[1] On many scientific calculators, there is a button labeled nPr that allows you to compute permutations. The symbol r is used instead of x.

EXAMPLE 5.14

Using Counting Rule 4

Modifying Example 5.13, if you have six books, but there is room for only four books on the shelf, in how many ways can you arrange these books on the shelf?

SOLUTION Using Equation (5.13), the number of ordered arrangements of four books selected from six books is equal to

$$_nP_x = \frac{n!}{(n-x)!} = \frac{6!}{(6-4)!} = \frac{(6)(5)(4)(3)(2)(1)}{(2)(1)} = 360$$

Counting Rule 5

In many situations, you are not interested in the *order* of the outcomes but only in the number of ways that x items can be selected from n items, *irrespective of order*. Each possible selection is called a **combination**.

COUNTING RULE 5: COMBINATIONS

The number of ways of selecting x objects from n objects, irrespective of order, is equal to

$$_nC_x = \frac{n!}{x!(n-x)!} \qquad (5.14)$$

where

$$n = \text{total number of objects}$$

$$x = \text{number of objects to be arranged}$$

$$n! = n \text{ factorial} = n(n-1)\ldots(1)$$

$$C = \text{symbol for combinations}[2]$$

[2]On many scientific calculators, there is a button labeled nCr that allows you to compute combinations. The symbol r is used instead of x.

If you compare this rule to counting rule 4, you see that it differs only in the inclusion of a term $x!$ in the denominator. When permutations were used, all of the arrangements of the x objects are distinguishable. With combinations, the $x!$ possible arrangements of objects are irrelevant.

EXAMPLE 5.15

Using Counting Rule 5

Modifying Example 5.14, if the order of the books on the shelf is irrelevant, in how many ways can you arrange these books on the shelf?

SOLUTION Using Equation (5.14), the number of combinations of four books selected from six books is equal to

$$_nC_x = \frac{n!}{x!(n-x)!} = \frac{6!}{4!(6-4)!} = \frac{(6)(5)(4)(3)(2)(1)}{(4)(3)(2)(1)(2)(1)} = 15$$

Problems for Section 5.4

APPLYING THE CONCEPTS

5.38 If there are 10 multiple-choice questions on an exam, each having three possible answers, how many different sequences of answers are there?

5.39 A lock on a bank vault consists of three dials, each with 30 positions. In order for the vault to open, each of the three dials must be in the correct position.
a. How many different possible dial combinations are there for this lock?
b. What is the probability that if you randomly select a position on each dial, you will be able to open the bank vault?
c. Explain why "dial combinations" are not mathematical combinations expressed by Equation (5.14).

5.40 a. If a coin is tossed seven times, how many different outcomes are possible?
b. If a die is tossed seven times, how many different outcomes are possible?
c. Discuss the differences in your answers to (a) and (b).

5.41 A particular brand of women's jeans is available in seven different sizes, three different colors, and three different styles. How many different women's jeans does the store manager need to order to have one pair of each type?

5.42 You would like to make a salad that consists of lettuce, tomato, cucumber, and peppers. You go to the supermarket, intending to purchase one variety of each of these ingredients. You discover that there are eight varieties of lettuce, four varieties of tomatoes, three varieties of cucumbers, and three varieties of peppers for sale at the supermarket. If you buy them all, how many different salads can you make?

5.43 A team is being formed that includes four different people. There are four different positions on the teams. How many different ways are there to assign the four people to the four positions?

5.44 In Major League Baseball, there are five teams in the Eastern Division of the National League: Atlanta, Florida,

New York, Philadelphia, and Washington. How many different orders of finish are there for these five teams? (Assume that there are no ties in the standings.) Do you believe that all these orders are equally likely? Discuss.

5.45 Referring to Problem 5.44, how many different orders of finish are possible for the first four positions?

5.46 A gardener has six rows available in his vegetable garden to place tomatoes, eggplant, peppers, cucumbers, beans, and lettuce. Each vegetable will be allowed one and only one row. How many ways are there to position these vegetables in this garden?

5.47 There are eight members of a team. How many ways are there to select a team leader, assistant team leader, and team coordinator?

5.48 Four members of a group of 10 people are to be selected to a team. How many ways are there to select these four members?

5.49 A student has seven books that she would like to place in her backpack. However, there is room for only four books. Regardless of the arrangement, how many ways are there of placing four books into the backpack?

5.50 A daily lottery is conducted in which 2 winning numbers are selected out of 100 numbers. How many different combinations of winning numbers are possible?

5.51 A reading list for a course contains 20 articles. How many ways are there to choose 3 articles from this list?

5.5 Ethical Issues and Probability

Ethical issues can arise when any statements related to probability are presented to the public, particularly when these statements are part of an advertising campaign for a product or service. Unfortunately, many people are not comfortable with numerical concepts (see reference 5) and tend to misinterpret the meaning of the probability. In some instances, the misinterpretation is not intentional, but in other cases, advertisements may unethically try to mislead potential customers.

One example of a potentially unethical application of probability relates to advertisements for state lotteries. When purchasing a lottery ticket, the customer selects a set of numbers (such as 6) from a larger list of numbers (such as 54). Although virtually all participants know that they are unlikely to win the lottery, they also have very little idea of how unlikely it is for them to select all 6 winning numbers from the list of 54 numbers. They have even less of an idea of the probability of winning a consolation prize by selecting either 4 or 5 winning numbers.

Given this background, you might consider a recent commercial for a state lottery that stated, "We won't stop until we have made everyone a millionaire" to be deceptive and possibly unethical. Do you think the state has any intention of ever stopping the lottery, given the fact that the state relies on it to bring millions of dollars into its treasury? Is it possible that the lottery can make everyone a millionaire? Is it ethical to suggest that the purpose of the lottery is to make everyone a millionaire?

Another example of a potentially unethical application of probability relates to an investment newsletter promising a 90% probability of a 20% annual return on investment. To make the claim in the newsletter an ethical one, the investment service needs to (a) explain the basis on which this probability estimate rests, (b) provide the probability statement in another format, such as 9 chances in 10, and (c) explain what happens to the investment in the 10% of the cases in which a 20% return is not achieved (e.g., is the entire investment lost?).

These are serious ethical issues. If you were going to write an advertisement for the state lottery that ethically describes the probability of winning a certain prize, what would you say? If you were going to write an advertisement for the investment newsletter that ethically states the probability of a 20% return on an investment, what would you say?

USING STATISTICS

© Alan Levenson / Corbis

@ M&R Electronics World Revisited

A s the marketing manager for M&R Electronics World, you analyzed the survey results of an intent-to-purchase study. This study asked the heads of 1,000 households about their intentions to purchase a big-screen television sometime during the next 12 months, and as a follow-up, M&R surveyed the same people 12 months later to see whether such a television was purchased. In addition, for households purchasing big-screen televisions, the survey asked whether the television they purchased had a faster refresh rate, whether they also purchased a Blu-ray disc (BD) player in the past 12 months, and whether they were satisfied with their purchase of the big-screen television.

By analyzing the results of these surveys, you were able to uncover many pieces of valuable information that will help you plan a marketing strategy to enhance sales and better target those households likely to purchase multiple or more expensive products. Whereas only 30% of the households actually purchased a big-screen television, if a household indicated that it planned to purchase a big-screen television in the next 12 months, there was an 80% chance that the household actually made the purchase. Thus the marketing strategy should target those households that have indicated an intention to purchase.

You determined that for households that purchased a television that had a faster refresh rate, there was a 47.5% chance that the household also purchased a Blu-ray disc player. You then compared this conditional probability to the marginal probability of purchasing a Blu-ray disc player, which was 36%. Thus, households that purchased televisions that had a faster refresh rate are more likely to purchase a Blu-ray disc player than are households that purchased big-screen televisions that have a standard refresh rate.

You were also able to apply Bayes' theorem to M&R Electronics World's market research reports. The reports investigate a potential new television model prior to its scheduled release. If a favorable report was received, then there was a 64% chance that the new television model would be successful. However, if an unfavorable report was received, there is only a 16% chance that the model would be successful. Therefore, the marketing strategy of M&R needs to pay close attention to whether a report's conclusion is favorable or unfavorable.

SUMMARY

This chapter began by developing the basic concepts of probability. You learned that probability is a numeric value from 0 to 1 that represents the chance, likelihood, or possibility that a particular event will occur. In addition to simple probability, you learned about conditional probabilities and independent events. Bayes' theorem was used to revise previously calculated probabilities based on new information. You also learned about several counting rules. Throughout the chapter, contingency tables and decision trees were used to display information. In the next chapter, important discrete probability distributions such as the binomial and Poisson distributions are developed.

KEY EQUATIONS

Probability of Occurrence

$$\text{Probability of occurrence} = \frac{X}{T}$$

Marginal Probability

$$P(A) = P(A \text{ and } B_1) + P(A \text{ and } B_2)$$
$$+ \cdots + P(A \text{ and } B_k)$$

General Addition Rule

$$P(A \text{ or } B) = P(A) + P(B) - P(A \text{ and } B)$$

Conditional Probability

$$P(A|B) = \frac{P(A \text{ and } B)}{P(B)}$$

$$P(B|A) = \frac{P(A \text{ and } B)}{P(A)}$$

Independence

$$P(A|B) = P(A)$$

General Multiplication Rule

$$P(A \text{ and } B) = P(A|B)P(B)$$

Multiplication Rule for Independent Events

$$P(A \text{ and } B) = P(A)P(B)$$

Marginal Probability Using the General Multiplication Rule

$$P(A) = P(A|B_1)P(B_1) + P(A|B_2)P(B_2) \\ + \cdots + P(A|B_k)P(B_k)$$

Bayes' Theorem

$$P(B_i|A) = $$

$$\frac{P(A|B_i)P(B_i)}{P(A|B_1)P(B_1) + P(A|B_2)P(B_2) + \cdots + P(A|B_k)P(B_k)}$$

Counting Rule 1

$$k^n$$

Counting Rule 2

$$(k_1)(k_2)\ldots(k_n)$$

Counting Rule 3

$$n! = (n)(n-1)\ldots(1)$$

Counting Rule 4: Permutations

$$_nP_x = \frac{n!}{(n-x)!}$$

Counting Rule 5: Combinations

$$_nC_x = \frac{n!}{x!(n-x)!}$$

KEY TERMS

PROBLEMS

CHECKING YOUR UNDERSTANDING

5.52 What are the differences between *a priori* probability, empirical probability, and subjective probability?

5.53 What is the difference between a simple event and a joint event?

5.54 How can you use the general addition rule to find the probability of occurrence of event *A* or *B*?

5.55 What is the difference between mutually exclusive events and collectively exhaustive events?

5.56 How does conditional probability relate to the concept of independence?

5.57 How does the multiplication rule differ for events that are and are not independent?

5.58 How can you use Bayes' theorem to revise probabilities in light of new information?

5.59 In Bayes' theorem, how does the prior probability differ from the revised probability?

APPLYING THE CONCEPTS

5.60 A survey by the Pew Research Center ("Snapshots: Goals of 'Gen Next' vs. 'Gen X,'" *USA Today*, March 27, 2007, p. 1A) indicated that 81% of 18- to 25-year-olds had getting rich as a goal, as compared to 62% of 26- to 40-year-olds. Suppose that the survey was based on 500 respondents from each of the two groups.
a. Construct a contingency table.
b. Give an example of a simple event and a joint event.
c. What is the probability that a randomly selected respondent has a goal of getting rich?
d. What is the probability that a randomly selected respondent has a goal of getting rich *and* is in the 26- to 40-year-old group?
e. Are the events "age group" and "has getting rich as a goal" independent? Explain.

5.61 The owner of a restaurant serving Continental-style entrées was interested in studying ordering patterns of patrons for the Friday-to-Sunday weekend time period.

Records were maintained that indicated the demand for dessert during the same time period. The owner decided to study two other variables, along with whether a dessert was ordered: the gender of the individual and whether a beef entrée was ordered. The results are as follows:

	GENDER		
DESSERT ORDERED	Male	Female	Total
Yes	96	40	136
No	224	240	464
Total	320	280	600

	BEEF ENTRÉE		
DESSERT ORDERED	Yes	No	Total
Yes	71	65	136
No	116	348	464
Total	187	413	600

A waiter approaches a table to take an order for dessert. What is the probability that the first customer to order at the table

a. orders a dessert?
b. orders a dessert *or* has ordered a beef entrée?
c. is a female *and* does not order a dessert?
d. is a female *or* does not order a dessert?
e. Suppose the first person from whom the waiter takes the dessert order is a female. What is the probability that she does not order dessert?
f. Are gender and ordering dessert independent?
g. Is ordering a beef entrée independent of whether the person orders dessert?

5.62 Which meal are people most likely to order at a drive-through? A survey was conducted in 2009, but the sample sizes were not reported. Suppose the results, based on a sample of 100 males and 100 females, were as follows:

	GENDER		
MEAL	Male	Female	Total
Breakfast	18	10	28
Lunch	47	52	99
Dinner	29	29	58
Snack/beverage	6	9	15
Total	100	100	200

Source: Data extracted from **www.qsrmagazine.com/reports/drive-thru_time_study/2009/2009_charts/whats_your_preferred_way_to_order_fast_food.html**.

If a respondent is selected at random, what is the probability that he or she

a. prefers ordering lunch at the drive-through?
b. prefers ordering breakfast or lunch at the drive-through?
c. is a male *or* prefers ordering dinner at the drive-through?

d. is a male *and* prefers ordering dinner at the drive-through?
e. Given that the person selected is a female, what is the probability that she prefers ordering breakfast at the drive-through?

5.63 According to a Gallup Poll, companies with employees who are engaged with their workplace have greater innovation, productivity, and profitability, as well as less employee turnover. A survey of 1,895 workers in Germany found that 13% of the workers were engaged, 67% were not engaged, and 20% were actively disengaged. The survey also noted that 48% of engaged workers strongly agreed with the statement "My current job brings out my most creative ideas." Only 20% of the not engaged workers and 3% of the actively disengaged workers agreed with this statement (data extracted from M. Nink, "Employee Disengagement Plagues Germany," *Gallup Management Journal*, **gmj.gallup.com**, April 9, 2009). If a worker is known to strongly agree with the statement "My current job brings out my most creative ideas," what is the probability that the worker is engaged?

5.64 Sport utility vehicles (SUVs), vans, and pickups are generally considered to be more prone to roll over than cars. In 1997, 24.0% of all highway fatalities involved rollovers; 15.8% of all fatalities in 1997 involved SUVs, vans, and pickups, given that the fatality involved a rollover. Given that a rollover was not involved, 5.6% of all fatalities involved SUVs, vans, and pickups (data extracted from A. Wilde Mathews, "Ford Ranger, Chevy Tracker Tilt in Test," *The Wall Street Journal*, July 14, 1999, p. A2). Consider the following definitions:

A = fatality involved an SUV, van, or pickup
B = fatality involved a rollover

a. Use Bayes' theorem to find the probability that a fatality involved a rollover, given that the fatality involved an SUV, a van, or a pickup.
b. Compare the result in (a) to the probability that a fatality involved a rollover and comment on whether SUVs, vans, and pickups are generally more prone to rollover accidents than other vehicles.

5.65 Enzyme-linked immunosorbent assay (ELISA) is the most common type of screening test for detecting the HIV virus. A positive result from an ELISA indicates that the HIV virus is present. For most populations, ELISA has a high degree of sensitivity (to detect infection) and specificity (to detect noninfection). (See "HIV InSite Gateway to HIV and AIDS Knowledge" at **HIVInsite.ucsf.edu**.) Suppose the probability that a person is infected with the HIV virus for a certain population is 0.015. If the HIV virus is actually present, the probability that the ELISA test will give a positive result is 0.995. If the HIV virus is not actually present, the probability of a positive result from an ELISA is 0.01. If the ELISA has given a positive result, use

Bayes' theorem to find the probability that the HIV virus is actually present.

TEAM PROJECT

The file `Bond Funds` contains information regarding three categorical variables from a sample of 184 bond funds. The variables include

Type—Bond fund type (intermediate government or short-term corporate)
Fees—Sales charges (no or yes)
Risk—Risk-of-loss factor of the bond fund (below average, average, or above average)

5.66 Construct contingency tables of type and fees, type and risk, and fees and risk.
a. For each of these contingency tables, compute all the conditional and marginal probabilities.
b. Based on (a), what conclusions can you reach about whether these variables are independent?

STUDENT SURVEY DATABASE

5.67 Problem 1.21 on page 20 describes a survey of 62 undergraduate students (see the file `UndergradSurvey`). For these data, construct contingency tables of gender and major, gender and graduate school intention, gender and employment status, gender and computer preference, class and graduate school intention, class and employment status, major and graduate school intention, major and employment status, and major and computer preference.
a. For each of these contingency tables, compute all the conditional and marginal probabilities.
b. Based on (a), what conclusions can you reach about whether these variables are independent?

5.68 Problem 1.21 on page 20 describes a survey of 62 undergraduate students (stored in `UndergradSurvey`).

a. Select a sample of undergraduate students at your school and conduct a similar survey for those students.
b. For your data, construct contingency tables of gender and major, gender and graduate school intention, gender and employment status, gender and computer preference, class and graduate school intention, class and employment status, major and graduate school intention, major and employment status, and major and computer preference.
c. Based on (b), what conclusions can you reach about whether these variables are independent?
d. Compare the results of (c) to those of Problem 5.67 (b).

5.69 Problem 1.22 on page 21 describes a survey of 44 MBA students (stored in `GradSurvey`). For these data, construct contingency tables of gender and graduate major, gender and undergraduate major, gender and employment status, gender and computer preference, graduate major and undergraduate major, graduate major and employment status, and graduate major and computer preference.
a. For each of these contingency tables, compute all the conditional and marginal probabilities.
b. Based on (b), what conclusions can you reach about whether these variables are independent?

5.70 Problem 1.22 on page 21 describes a survey of 44 MBA students (stored in `GradSurvey`).
a. Select a sample of MBA students from your MBA program and conduct a similar survey for those students.
b. For your data, construct contingency tables of gender and graduate major, gender and undergraduate major, gender and employment status, gender and computer preference, graduate major and undergraduate major, graduate major and employment status, and graduate major and computer preference.
c. Based on (b), what conclusions can you reach about whether these variables are independent?
d. Compare the results of (c) to those of Problem 5.69 (b).

DIGITAL CASE

Apply your knowledge about contingency tables and the proper application of simple and joint probabilities in this continuing Digital Case from Chapter 4.

Open **EndRunGuide.pdf**, the EndRun Financial Services "Guide to Investing," and read the information about the Guaranteed Investment Package (GIP). Read the claims and examine the supporting data. Then answer the following questions:

1. How accurate is the claim of the probability of success for EndRun's GIP? In what ways is the claim misleading? How would you calculate and state the probability of having an annual rate of return not less than 15%?

2. Using the table found under the "Show Me The Winning Probabilities" subhead, compute the proper probabilities for the group of investors. What mistake was made in reporting the 7% probability claim?

3. Are there any probability calculations that would be appropriate for rating an investment service? Why or why not?

REFERENCES

1. Bellhouse, D. R., "The Reverend Thomas Bayes, FRS: A Biography to Celebrate the Tercentenary of His Birth," *Statistical Science*, 19 (2004), 3–43.

2. Lowd, D., and C. Meek, "Good Word Attacks on Statistical Spam Filters," presented at the Second Conference on Email and Anti-Spam, CEAS 2005.

3. *Microsoft Excel 2010* (Redmond, WA: Microsoft Corp., 2010).

4. *Minitab Release 16* (State College, PA.: Minitab, Inc., 2010).

5. Paulos, J. A., *Innumeracy* (New York: Hill and Wang, 1988).

6. Silberman, S., "The Quest for Meaning," *Wired 8.02*, February 2000.

7. Zeller, T., "The Fight Against V1@gra (and Other Spam)," *The New York Times*, May 21, 2006, pp. B1, B6.

CHAPTER 5 EXCEL GUIDE

EG5.1 Basic Probability Concepts

Simple and Joint Probability and the General Addition Rule

PHStat2 Use **Simple & Joint Probabilities** to compute basic probabilities. Select **PHStat → Probability & Prob. Distributions → Simple & Joint Probabilities**. The procedure inserts a worksheet similar to Figure EG5.1 into the current workbook. (Unlike with other procedures, no dialog box is first displayed.) To use the worksheet, fill in the **Sample Space** area with your data.

In-Depth Excel Use the **COMPUTE worksheet** of the **Probabilities workbook** as a template for computing basic probabilities (see Figure EG5.1, below). The worksheet contains the Table 5.1 purchase behavior data shown on page 206. Overwrite these values when you enter data for other problems.

Open to the **COMPUTE_FORMULAS worksheet** to examine the formulas used in the worksheet, many of which are shown in the inset to Figure EG5.1.

FIGURE EG5.1 COMPUTE worksheet of the Probabilities workbook

	A	B	C	D	E
1	**Probabilities**				
2					
3	**Sample Space**		**ACTUALLY PURCHASED**		
4			Yes	No	Totals
5	**PLANNED TO PURCHASE**	Yes	200	50	250
6		No	100	650	750
7		Totals	300	700	1000
8					
9	**Simple Probabilities**		**Simple Probabilities**		
10	P(Yes)	0.25	="P(" & B5 & ")"		=E5/E7
11	P(No)	0.75	="P(" & B6 & ")"		=E6/E7
12	P(Yes)	0.30	="P(" & C4 & ")"		=C7/E7
13	P(No)	0.70	="P(" & D4 & ")"		=D7/E7
14					
15	**Joint Probabilities**		**Joint Probabilities**		
16	P(Yes and Yes)	0.20	="P(" & B5 & " and " & C4 & ")"		=C5/E7
17	P(Yes and No)	0.05	="P(" & B5 & " and " & D4 & ")"		=D5/E7
18	P(No and Yes)	0.10	="P(" & B6 & " and " & C4 & ")"		=C6/E7
19	P(No and No)	0.65	="P(" & B6 & " and " & D4 & ")"		=D6/E7
20					
21	**Addition Rule**		**Addition Rule**		
22	P(Yes or Yes)	0.35	="P(" & B5 & " or " & C4 & ")"		=B10 + B12 - B16
23	P(Yes or No)	0.90	="P(" & B5 & " or " & D4 & ")"		=B10 + B13 - B17
24	P(No or Yes)	0.95	="P(" & B6 & " or " & C4 & ")"		=B11 + B12 - B18
25	P(No or No)	0.80	="P(" & B6 & " or " & D4 & ")"		=B11 + B13 - B19

EG5.2 Conditional Probability

There is no Excel material for this section.

EG5.3 Bayes' Theorem

In-Depth Excel Use the **COMPUTE worksheet** of the **Bayes workbook** as a template for computing basic probabilities (see Figure EG5.2, at right). The worksheet contains the television-marketing example of Table 5.4 on page 222. Overwrite these values when you enter data for other problems.

Open to the **COMPUTE_FORMULAS worksheet** to examine the simple arithmetic formulas that compute the probabilities which are also shown in the inset to Figure EG5.2.

	A	B	C	D	E
1	**Bayes Theorem Calculations**				
2					
3			**Probabilities**		
4	**Event**	Prior	Conditional	Joint	Revised
5	S	0.4	0.8	0.32	0.64
6	S'	0.6	0.3	0.18	0.36
7			Total:	0.5	

Joint	Revised
=B5 * C5	=D5/$D$7
=B6 * C6	=D6/$D$7
=D5 + D6	

FIGURE EG5.2 COMPUTE worksheet of the Bayes workbook

EG5.4 Counting Rules

Counting Rule 1

In-Depth Excel Use the **POWER(*k*, *n*)** worksheet function in a cell formula to compute the number of outcomes given k events and n trials. For example, the formula **=POWER(6, 2)** computes the answer for Example 5.11 on page 226.

Counting Rule 2

In-Depth Excel Use a formula that takes the product of successive **POWER(*k*, *n*)** functions to solve problems related to counting rule 2. For example, the formula **=POWER(26, 3) * POWER(10, 3)** computes the answer for the state motor vehicle department example on page 226.

Counting Rule 3

In-Depth Excel Use the **FACT(*n*)** worksheet function in a cell formula to compute how many ways n items can be arranged. For example, the formula **=FACT(6)** computes 6!.

Counting Rule 4

In-Depth Excel Use the **PERMUT(*n*, *x*)** worksheet function in a cell formula to compute the number of ways of arranging x objects selected from n objects in order. For example, the formula **=PERMUT(6, 4)** computes the answer for Example 5.14 on page 227.

Counting Rule 5

In-Depth Excel Use the **COMBIN(*n*, *x*)** worksheet function in a cell formula to compute the number of ways of arranging x objects selected from n objects, irrespective of order. For example, the formula **=COMBIN(6, 4)** computes the answer for Example 5.15 on page 228.

6 Discrete Probability Distributions

Learning Objectives

In this chapter, you learn:

- The properties of a probability distribution
- To compute the expected value and variance of a probability distribution
- To compute probabilities from the binomial and Poisson distributions
- How to use the binomial and Poisson distributions to solve business problems

USING STATISTICS

@ Saxon Home Improvement, Part I

Y ou are an accountant for the Saxon Home Improvement Company, which uses a state-of-the-art accounting information system to manage its accounting and financial operations.

Accounting information systems collect, process, store, transform, and distribute financial information to decision makers both internal and external to a business organization. These systems continuously audit accounting information, looking for errors or incomplete or improbable information. For example, when customers of the Saxon Home Improvement Company submit online orders, the company's accounting information system reviews the order forms for possible mistakes. Any questionable invoices are *tagged* and included in a daily *exceptions report*. Recent data collected by the company show that the likelihood is 0.10 that an order form will be tagged. Saxon would like to determine the likelihood of finding a certain number of tagged forms in a sample of a specific size. For example, what would be the likelihood that none of the order forms is tagged in a sample of four forms? That one of the order forms is tagged?

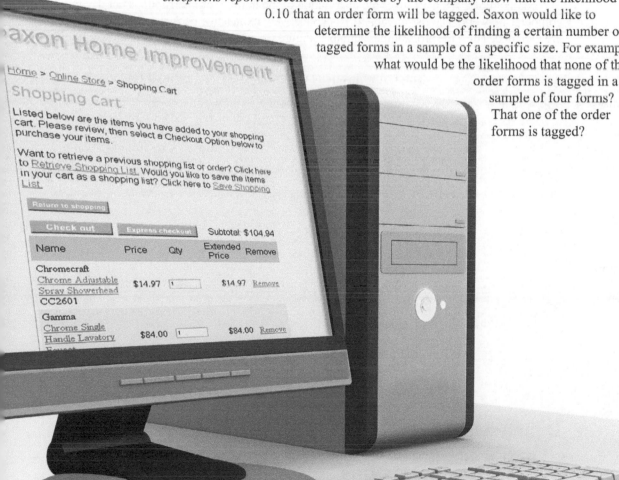

H ow could the Saxon Home Improvement Company determine the solution to this type of probability problem? One way is to use a model, or small-scale representation, that approximates the process. By using such an approximation, Saxon managers could make inferences about the actual order process. In this case, the Saxon managers can use *probability distributions*, mathematical models suited for solving the type of probability problems the managers are facing.

This chapter introduces you to the concept and characteristics of probability distributions. You will also learn how the binomial and Poisson distributions can be applied to help solve business problems.

6.1 The Probability Distribution for a Discrete Random Variable

In Section 1.3, a *numerical variable* was defined as a variable that yields numerical responses, such as the number of magazines you subscribe to or your height. Numerical variables are either *discrete* or *continuous*. Continuous numerical variables produce outcomes that come from a measuring process (e.g., your height). Discrete numerical variables produce outcomes that come from a counting process (e.g., the number of magazines you subscribe to). This chapter deals with probability distributions that represent discrete numerical variables.

> PROBABILITY DISTRIBUTION FOR A DISCRETE RANDOM VARIABLE
>
> A **probability distribution for a discrete random variable** is a mutually exclusive list of all the possible numerical outcomes along with the probability of occurrence of each outcome.

For example, Table 6.1 gives the distribution of the number of interruptions per day in a large computer network. The list in Table 6.1 is collectively exhaustive because all possible outcomes are included. Thus, the probabilities sum to 1. Figure 6.1 is a graphical representation of Table 6.1.

TABLE 6.1

Probability Distribution of the Number of Interruptions per Day

Interruptions per Day	Probability
0	0.35
1	0.25
2	0.20
3	0.10
4	0.05
5	0.05

FIGURE 6.1

Probability distribution of the number of interruptions per day

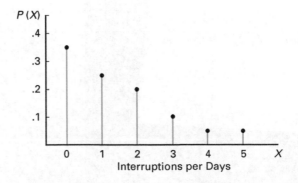

Definitions

Random Variable: A variable whose value is determined by the outcome of a random experiment. The symbol used is usually X.

Discrete Random Variable: A random variable whose possible values are discrete, that is, clearly separated individual values.

Discrete Probability Distribution: A table or formula that shows the probability associated with each possible value of a discrete random variable.

EXAMPLE 6.1

A study of the number of cars sold on Sunday at a particular dealership shows that the following probability distribution exists:

let X = # cars sold on Sunday

The probability distribution of X is

TABLE 6.2

X	P(X)
0	0.1
1	0.1
2	0.4
3	0.3
4	0.1
Total	1.0

EXAMPLE 6.2

A company is in the process of trying to decide whether or not to market a particular new product that it is considering. A market analysis has determined that the probabilities of various acceptance levels are as follows: high with a probability of 0.2, medium with a probability of 0.5, and low with a probability of 0.3. If the company decides to build a local manufacturing facility, the estimated profits over the life of the product if there is high acceptance is $10 million, if there is medium acceptance the profit should be around $3 million, and if there is low acceptance there will be a loss of $2 million.

let X = estimated profit over life of product ($ million)

The probability distribution of X is

TABLE 6.3

Product Acceptance	X	P(X)
High	10	0.2
Medium	3	0.5
Low	-2	0.3
Total		1.0

EXAMPLE 6.3

Toss a fair coin three times. The sample space is composed of eight equally likely outcomes, namely

S = {HHH, HHT, HTH, THH, TTH, THT, HTT, TTT}

let X = # tails

The probability distribution of X is

TABLE 6.4

X	P(X)
0	1/8 = 0.125
1	3/8 = 0.375
2	3/8 = 0.375
3	1/8 = 0.125
Total	1.000

EXAMPLE 6.4

Roll a fair die. The sample space is composed of six equally likely outcomes, namely:

S = {1, 2, 3, 4, 5, 6}

let X = # rolled

The probability distribution of X is

TABLE 6.5

X	P(X)
1	1/6 = 0.167
2	1/6 = 0.167
3	1/6 = 0.167
4	1/6 = 0.167
5	1/6 = 0.167
6	1/6 = 0.167
Total	6/6 = 1

EXAMPLE 6.5

Roll two fair dice. The sample space, as seen previously, is composed of 36 equally likely outcomes.

let X = total of the two dice

The probability distribution of X is

TABLE 6.6

X	P(X)
2	1/36 = 0.028
3	2/36 = 0.056
4	3/36 = 0.083
5	4/36 = 0.111
6	5/36 = 0.139
7	6/36 = 0.167
8	5/36 = 0.139
9	4/36 = 0.111
10	3/36 = 0.083
11	2/36 = 0.056
12	1/36 = 0.028
Total	36/36 = 1

Expected Value of a Discrete Random Variable

The mean, μ, of a probability distribution is the **expected value** of its random variable. To calculate the expected value, multiply each possible outcome, X, by its corresponding probability, $P(X)$, and then sum these products.

EXPECTED VALUE, μ, OF A DISCRETE RANDOM VARIABLE

$$\mu = E(X) = \sum_{i=1}^{N} X_i P(X_i) \qquad \textbf{(6.1)}$$

where

X_i = the ith outcome of the discrete random variable X

$P(X_i)$ = probability of occurrence of the ith outcome of X

For the probability distribution of the number of home mortgages approved per week (Table 6.2), the expected value is computed using Equation (6.1) and is also shown in Table 6.7.

$$\mu = E(X) = \sum_{i=1}^{N} X_i P(X_i)$$

$$= (0)(0.1) + (1)(0.1) + (2)(0.2) + (3)(0.3) + (4)(0.15) + (5)(0.1) + (6)(0.05)$$

$$= 0 + 0.1 + 0.4 + 0.9 + 0.6 + 0.5 + 0.3$$

$$= 2.8$$

SOLUTION

TABLE 6.7

Computing the Expected Value of the Number of Home Mortgages Approved per Week

By Formula			By Casio Calculator

Home Mortgages Approved per Week (X_i)	$P(X_i)$	**Formula:** $X_i P(X_i)$	Calculator instructions:
			 1. Enter the data in List 1 and List 2 where
			     List 1: 0, 1, 2, 3, 4, 5, 6
			     List 2: 0.10, 0.10, 0.20, 0.30, 0.15, 0.10, 0.05
			 2. Press **F2**(CALC)

0	0.10	$(0)(0.10) = 0.0$	3. Press **F6** (SET)
1	0.10	$(1)(0.10) = 0.1$	1Var XList : List 1
2	0.20	$(2)(0.20) = 0.4$	1Var Freq : List 2
3	0.30	$(3)(0.30) = 0.9$	EXE
4	0.15	$(4)(0.15) = 0.6$	4. To obtain results, press **F1**(1Var)
5	0.10	$(5)(0.10) = 0.5$	$\bar{x} = 2.8$
6	0.05	$(6)(0.05) = 0.3$	*Note: the calculator symbol is $\bar{x}$ but it*
	1.00	$\mu = E(X) = 2.8$	*should be μ*

The expected value is 2.8. The expected value of 2.8 for the number of mortgages approved is not a possible outcome because the actual number of mortgages approved in a given week must be an integer value. The expected value represents the *mean* number of mortgages approved per week.

Mean, Variance, and Standard Deviation

A discrete probability distribution is equivalent to a population of data. We can calculate any parameters that can be calculated for a population. However, the formulas will look a little different.

I. MEAN OR EXPECTED VALUE:

Formula: $\mu = E(X) = \sum XP(X)$

EXAMPLE 6.1

(Revisit)

A study of the number of cars sold on Sunday at a particular dealership shows that the following probability distribution exists:

let X = # cars sold on Sunday

The mean or expected number of cars that will be sold on Sunday can be calculated as follows:

SOLUTION

TABLE 6.8

By Formula			By Casio Calculator
X	*P(X)*	**Formula:** *XP(X)*	Calculator instructions: 1. Enter the data in List 1 and List 2 where
0	0.1	(0)(0.1) = 0.0	List 1: 0, 1, 2, 3, 4
1	0.1	(1)(0.1) = 0.1	List 2: 0.1, 0.1, 0.4, 0.3, 0.1
2	0.4	(2)(0.4) = 0.8	2. Press **F2**(CALC)
3	0.3	(3)(0.3) = 0.9	3. Press **F6** (SET)
4	0.1	(4)(0.1) = 0.4	1Var XList : List 1
Total	1.0	$\mu = E(X) = 2.2$	1Var Freq : List 2 EXE

4. To obtain results, press **F1**(1Var)

$$\bar{x} = 2.2$$

Note: the calculator symbol is $\bar{x}$ but it should be μ

Therefore, the *average* number of cars sold on *infinite* Sundays is 2.2. Also, we can say that the number of cars the dealer expects to sell on Sunday is 2.2.

Notes: 1. Calculating a mean for a discrete probability distribution is essentially the same as calculating a *weighted mean,* where the probabilities are the weights.

$$\bar{x}_w = \frac{\sum xw}{\sum w} = \frac{\sum xP(x)}{\sum P(x)} = \sum xP(x) \quad \text{since} \quad \sum P(x) = 1$$

2. To calculate the mean on the Casio calculator, enter the data as follows and set up as if calculating a weighted mean of the X data.

Example 6.1:		**Example 6.4:**	
List 1	**List 2**	**List 1**	**List 2**
0	.1	1	1÷6
1	.1	2	1÷6
2	.4	3	1÷6
3	.3	4	1÷6
4	.1	5	1÷6
		6	1÷6

1 Var Xlist: List 1   **1 Var Xlist: List 1**
1 Var Freq: List 2   yields E(X) = 2.2   **1 Var Freq: List 2**   yields E(X) = 3.5

EXAMPLE 6.2
(Revisit)

Referring to the product marketing decision Example 6.2,

let X = estimated profit over the life of product ($ million)

SOLUTION

TABLE 6.9

By Formula				By Casio Calculator
Product Acceptance	**X**	**P(X)**	**Formula: XP(X)**	Calculator instructions:
High	10	0.2	(10)(0.2) = 2	1. Enter the data in List 1 and List 2 where
Medium	3	0.5	(3)(0.5) = 1.5	List 1: 10, 3, –2
Low	–2	0.3	(–2)(0.3) = –0.6	List 2: 0.2, 0.5, 0.3
Total		1.0	$\mu = E(X) = 2.9$	2. Press **F2**(CALC)

3. Press **F6** (SET)
   1Var XList : List 1
   1Var Freq : List 2
   EXE
4. To obtain results, press **F1**(1Var)
          $\bar{x} = 2.9$
Note: the calculator symbol is $\bar{x}$ but it should be μ

Therefore, the expected profit is $2.9 million.

EXAMPLE 6.3
(Revisit)

Toss a fair coin three times.

let X = # tails

SOLUTION

TABLE 6.10

By Formula			By Casio Calculator
X = Number of Tails	**P(X)**	**Formula: XP(X)**	Calculator instructions:
0	0.125	(0)(0.125) = 0.000	1. Enter the data in List 1 and List 2 where
1	0.375	(1)(0.375) = 0.375	List 1: 0, 1, 2, 3
2	0.375	(2)(0.375) = 0.750	List 2: 0.125, 0.375, 0.375, 0.125
3	0.125	(3)(0.125) = 0.375	2. Press **F2**(CALC)
	1.000	$\mu = E(X) = 1.5$	3. Press **F6** (SET)

   1Var XList : List 1
   1Var Freq : List 2
   EXE
4. To obtain results, press **F1**(1Var)
          $\bar{x} = 1.5$
Note: the calculator symbol is $\bar{x}$ but it should be μ

The average number of tails when a coin is tossed three times, an *infinite* number of times, is 1.5. Also, the expected number of tails if you toss a coin three times is 1.5.

EXAMPLE 6.4
(Revisit)

Roll a fair die.   let X = # rolled

SOLUTION

TABLE 6.11

By Formula			By Casio Calculator

X = **Number of rolled**	**P(X)**	**Formula:** **XP(X)**	Calculator instructions:
			1. Enter the data in List 1 and List 2 where
			   List 1: 1/6, 1/6, 1/6, 1/6, 1/6, 1/6
			   List 2: 1/6, 2/6, 3/6, 4/6, 5/6, 6/6

1	1/6 = 0.167	(1)(1/6) = 1/6	2. Press **F2**(CALC)
2	1/6 = 0.167	(2)(1/6) = 2/6	3. Press **F6** (SET)
3	1/6 = 0.167	(3)(1/6) = 3/6	1Var XList : List 1
4	1/6 = 0.167	(4)(1/6) = 4/6	1Var Freq : List 2
5	1/6 = 0.167	(5)(1/6) = 5/6	EXE
6	1/6 = 0.167	(6)(1/6) = 6/6	4. To obtain results, press **F1**(1Var)
	6/6 = 1	$\mu = E(X) = 21/6 = 3.5$	$\bar{x} = 3.5$ *Note: the calculator symbol is $\bar{x}$ but it should be μ*

If you roll one die infinite times, the average number rolled will be 3.5. Therefore, if you roll a die once, the expected value is 3.5.

EXAMPLE 6.5
(Revisit)

Roll two fair dice.

let X = total of the two dice

SOLUTION

TABLE 6.12

By Formula			By Casio Calculator

X = **Total of the two dice**	**P(X)**	**Formula:** **XP(X)**	Calculator instructions:
			1. Enter the data in List 1 and List 2 where
			   List 1: 0.028, 0.056, 0.083, . . . etc.
			   List 2: 2/36, 6/36, 12/36, . . . etc.

2	1/36 = 0.028	(2)(1/36) = 2/36	2. Press **F2**(CALC)
3	2/36 = 0.056	(3)(2/36) = 6/36	3. Press **F6** (SET)
4	3/36 = 0.083	(4)(3/36) = 12/36	1Var XList : List 1
5	4/36 = 0.111	(5)(4/36) = 20/36	1Var Freq : List 2
6	5/36 = 0.139	(6)(5/36) = 30/36	EXE
7	6/36 = 0.167	(7)(6/36) = 42/36	4. To obtain results, press **F1**(1Var)
8	5/36 = 0.139	(8)(5/36) = 40/36	$\bar{x} - 7$
9	4/36 = 0.111	(9)(4/36) = 36/36	*Note: the calculator symbol is $\bar{x}$*
10	3/36 = 0.083	(10)(3/36) = 30/36	*but it should be μ*
11	2/36 = 0.056	(11)(2/36) = 22/36	
12	1/36 = 0.028	(12)(1/36) = 12/36	
Total	36/36 = 1	$\mu = E(X) = 252/36 = 7$	

Therefore, if we roll two dice we can expect to get a total of 7.

II. VARIANCE

Formula: $\sigma^2 = \sum (X - \mu)^2 \, P(X)$ (6.2)

III. STANDARD DEVIATION

Formula: $\sigma = \sqrt{\left(\sum (X - \mu)^2 \, P(X) \right)}$ (6.3)

Note: We are not interested in showing the use of this formula manually, since if you need to calculate the standard deviation of a random variable you will use your calculator as illustrated earlier.

Expected Value Decision Making

EXAMPLE 6.6

A fast-food company plans to install a new ice-cream dispensing unit in one of two store locations. The company figures that the probability of a unit being successful in location A is 3/4, and the annual profit in this case is $150,000. If it is not successful there will be losses of $80,000. At location B the probability of succeeding is 1/2, but the potential profit and loss are $240,000 and $48,000, respectively.

a) Where should the company locate to maximize expected profit?

SOLUTION X = **Profit**

Location A		Location B	
Profit	Prob.	Profit	Prob.
$150,000	0.75	$240,000	0.5
−$80,000	0.25	−$48,000	0.5

Location A: E(X) = $92,500   Location B: E(X) = $96,000

b) Which location is less risky, that is, has the lowest relative variability?

$$\text{Location A: } CV = \frac{\sigma}{\mu} \times 100\% = \frac{\$99,593}{\$92,500} \times 100\% = 108\%$$

$$\text{Location B: } CV = \frac{\sigma}{\mu} \times 100\% = \frac{\$144,000}{\$96,000} \times 100\% = 150\%$$

Since CV_{Location} = 150% is greater than $CV_{\text{Location A}}$ = 108%, Location A is less risky than Location B.

*CASIO Calculator Instruction to Obtain μ and σ

Location A	Location B
Instructions:	Instructions:
1. Enter data in List 1 and List 2.	1. Enter data in List 1 and List 2.
List 1: 150,000; –80,000	List 1: 240,000; –48,000
List 2: 0.75; 0.25	List 2: 0.5; 0.5
2. Press F2 (CALC).	2. Press F2 (CALC).
3. Press F6 (SET).	3. Press F6 (SET).
1Var XList: List 1	1Var XList: List 1
1Var Freq: List 2	1Var Freq: List 2
4. To obtain result, press F1(1Var).	4. To obtain result, press F1(1Var).
$\bar{x}$ = 92,500 *and* σx = 99,592.9214	$\bar{x}$ = 96,000 *and* σx = 144,000

EXAMPLE 6.7

An investment advisor sends information to various clients via express delivery companies. In all cases it is important that the client receive the information on the day it is sent. Three companies are capable of providing the delivery service. The following information is available:

TABLE 6.13

Company	Cost	Probability of same day arrival
Can-Express	$22.00	0.99
Can-Parcel	14.00	0.97
Canada Mail	6.00	0.89

The average payoff is $200 when the information arrives on time, but there is no payoff if the delivery is late. Based on maximizing expected profit, which delivery service should be used?

SOLUTION let X = profit

TABLE 6.14

Can-Express		Can-Parcel		Canada Mail	
X	P(X)	X	P(X)	X	P(X)
178	0.99	186	0.97	194	0.89
−22	0.01	−14	0.03	−6	0.11

The expected values are as follows:

Can-Express: $E(X) = \$176$

Can-Parcel: $E(X) = \$180$

Canada Mail: $E(X) = \$172$

Therefore, the company should choose **Can-Parcel** since it has the highest expected profit (value).

*CASIO Calculator Instruction to Obtain μ and σ

Can-Express
Instructions:
1. Enter data in List 1 and List 2.
   List 1: 178; −22
   List 2: 0.99; 0.01
2. Press F2 (CALC).
3. Press F6 (SET).
   1Var XList: List 1
   1Var Freq: List 2
4. To obtain result, press F1(1Var).
   $\bar{x} = 176$

Can-Parcel
Instructions:
1. Enter data in List 1 and List 2.
   List 1: 186; −14
   List 2: 0.97; 0.03
2. Press F2 (CALC).
3. Press F6 (SET).
   1Var XList: List 1
   1Var Freq: List 2
4. To obtain result, press F1(1Var).
   $\bar{x} = 180$

Canada Mail
Instructions:
1. Enter data in List 1 and List 2.
   List 1: 194; −6
   List 2: 0.89; 0.11
2. Press F2 (CALC).
3. Press F6 (SET).
   1Var XList: List 1
   1Var Freq: List 2
4. To obtain result, press F1(1Var).
   $\bar{x} = 172$

Variance and Standard Deviation of a Discrete Random Variable

You compute the variance of a probability distribution by multiplying each possible squared difference $[X_i - E(X)]^2$ by its corresponding probability, $P(X = x_i)$, and then summing the resulting products. Equation (6.4) defines the **variance of a discrete random variable**.

VARIANCE OF A DISCRETE RANDOM VARIABLE

$$\sigma^2 = \sum_{i=1}^{N} [X_i - E(X)]^2 P(X = x_i) \tag{6.4}$$

where

$$X_i = \text{the } i\text{th outcome of the discrete random variable } X$$
$$P(X = X_i) = \text{probability of occurrence of the } i\text{th outcome of } X$$

Equation (6.5) defines the **standard deviation of a discrete random variable**.

STANDARD DEVIATION OF A DISCRETE RANDOM VARIABLE

$$\sigma = \sqrt{\sigma^2} = \sqrt{\sum_{i=1}^{N} [X_i - E(X)]^2 P(X - x_i)} \tag{6.5}$$

The variance and the standard deviation of the number of interruptions per day are computed as follows and in Table 6.15, using Equations (6.4) and (6.5):

$$\sigma^2 = \sum_{i=1}^{N} [X_i - E(X)]^2 P(X = x_i)$$

$$= (0 - 1.4)^2(0.35) + (1 - 1.4)^2(0.25) + (2 - 1.4)^2(0.20) + (3 - 1.4)^2(0.10)$$
$$+ (4 - 1.4)^2(0.05) + (5 - 1.4)^2(0.05)$$

$$= 0.686 + 0.040 + 0.072 + 0.256 + 0.338 + 0.648$$

$$= 2.04$$

TABLE 6.15

Computing the Variance and Standard Deviation of the Number of Interruptions per Day

Interruptions per Day (x_i)	$P(X = x_i)$	$x_i P(X = x_i)$	$[x_i - E(X)]^2 P(X = x_i)$
0	0.35	$(0)(0.35) = 0.00$	$(0 - 1.4)^2(0.35) = 0.686$
1	0.25	$(1)(0.25) = 0.25$	$(1 - 1.4)^2(0.25) = 0.040$
2	0.20	$(2)(0.20) = 0.40$	$(2 - 1.4)^2(0.20) = 0.072$
3	0.10	$(3)(0.10) = 0.30$	$(3 - 1.4)^2(0.10) = 0.256$
4	0.05	$(4)(0.05) = 0.20$	$(4 - 1.4)^2(0.05) = 0.338$
5	$\underline{0.05}$	$\underline{(5)(0.05) = 0.25}$	$\underline{(5 - 1.4)^2(0.05) = 0.648}$
	1.00	$\mu = E(X) = 1.40$	$\sigma^2 = 2.04$

and

$$\sigma = \sqrt{\sigma^2} = \sqrt{2.04} = 1.4283$$

Thus, the mean number of interruptions per day is 1.4, the variance is 2.04, and the standard deviation is approximately 1.43 interruptions per day.

Problems for Section 6.1

LEARNING THE BASICS

6.1 Given the following probability distributions:

Distribution A		Distribution B	
X	$P(X = x_i)$	X	$P(X = x_i)$
0	0.50	0	0.05
1	0.20	1	0.10
2	0.15	2	0.15
3	0.10	3	0.20
4	0.05	4	0.50

a. Compute the expected value for each distribution.
b. Compute the standard deviation for each distribution.
c. Compare the results of distributions A and B.

APPLYING THE CONCEPTS

✓SELF **6.2** The following table contains the probability
Test distribution for the number of traffic accidents
daily in a small city:

Number of Accidents Daily (X)	$P(X = x_i)$
0	0.10
1	0.20
2	0.45
3	0.15
4	0.05
5	0.05

a. Compute the mean number of accidents per day.
b. Compute the standard deviation.

6.3 Recently, a regional automobile dealership sent out fliers
to perspective customers, indicating that they had already won
one of three different prizes: a Kia Optima valued at $15,000,
a $500 gas card, or a $5 Walmart shopping card. To claim his
or her prize, a prospective customer needed to present the
flier at the dealership's showroom. The fine print on the back
of the flier listed the probabilities of winning. The chance of
winning the car was 1 out of 31,478, the chance of winning
the gas card was 1 out of 31,478, and the chance of winning
the shopping card was 31,476 out 31,478.
a. How many fliers do you think the automobile dealership
sent out?
b. Using your answer to (a) and the probabilities listed on
the flier, what is the expected value of the prize won by a
prospective customer receiving a flier?
c. Using your answer to (a) and the probabilities listed on
the flier, what is the standard deviation of the value of the
prize won by a prospective customer receiving a flier?
d. Do you think this is an effective promotion? Why or why
not?

6.4 In the carnival game Under-or-Over-Seven, a pair of fair
dice is rolled once, and the resulting sum determines whether
the player wins or loses his or her bet. For example, the player
can bet $1 that the sum will be under 7—that is, 2, 3, 4, 5, or
6. For this bet, the player wins $1 if the result is under 7 and
loses $1 if the outcome equals or is greater than 7. Similarly,
the player can bet $1 that the sum will be over 7—that is, 8, 9,
10, 11, or 12. Here, the player wins $1 if the result is over 7
but loses $1 if the result is 7 or under. A third method of play
is to bet $1 on the outcome 7. For this bet, the player wins $4
if the result of the roll is 7 and loses $1 otherwise.
a. Construct the probability distribution representing the different outcomes that are possible for a $1 bet on under 7.
b. Construct the probability distribution representing the different outcomes that are possible for a $1 bet on over 7.
c. Construct the probability distribution representing the
different outcomes that are possible for a $1 bet on 7.
d. Show that the expected long-run profit (or loss) to the
player is the same, no matter which method of play is used.

6.5 The number of arrivals per minute at a bank located in
the central business district of a large city was recorded over
a period of 200 minutes, with the following results:

Arrivals	Frequency
0	14
1	31
2	47
3	41
4	29
5	21
6	10
7	5
8	2

a. Compute the expected number of arrivals per minute.
b. Compute the standard deviation.

6.6 The manager of a commercial mortgage department
of a large bank has collected data during the past two years
concerning the number of commercial mortgages approved
per week. The results from these two years (104 weeks)
indicated the following:

Number of Commercial Mortgages Approved	Frequency
0	13
1	25
2	32
3	17
4	9
5	6
6	1
7	1

a. Compute the expected number of mortgages approved per week.

b. Compute the standard deviation.

6.7 You are trying to develop a strategy for investing in two different stocks. The anticipated annual return for a $1,000 investment in each stock under four different economic conditions has the following probability distribution:

		Returns	
Probability	**Economic Condition**	**Stock X**	**Stock Y**
0.1	Recession	−50	−100
0.3	Slow growth	20	50
0.4	Moderate growth	100	130
0.2	Fast growth	150	200

Compute the

a. expected return for stock X and for stock Y.

b. standard deviation for stock X and for stock Y.

c. Would you invest in stock X or stock Y? Explain.

6.8 You plan to invest $1,000 in a corporate bond fund or in a common stock fund. The following information about the annual return (per $1,000) of each of these investments under different economic conditions is available, along with the probability that each of these economic conditions will occur:

	Economic	**Corporate**	**Common**
Probability	**Condition**	**Bond Fund**	**Stock Fund**
0.01	Extreme recession	−200	−999
0.09	Recession	−70	−300
0.15	Stagnation	30	−100
0.35	Slow growth	80	100
0.30	Moderate growth	100	150
0.10	High growth	120	350

Compute the

a. expected return for the corporate bond fund and for the common stock fund.

b. standard deviation for the corporate bond fund and for the common stock fund.

c. Would you invest in the corporate bond fund or the common stock fund? Explain.

d. If you chose to invest in the common stock fund in (c), what do you think about the possibility of losing $999 of every $1,000 invested if there is an extreme recession?

6.9 After consulting the sales reps, a marketing manager has decided that the following table represents the potential profits they might make next year for one of the company's products.

Profit	Prob.
$50,000	0.02
35,000	0.12
20,000	0.50
10,000	0.25
0	0.08
−10,000	0.03

What is the expected profit?

6.10 The Chancit Marketing Company is considering the distribution of a new item. It thinks there is a 20% chance that the item will be successful, in which case the company will make $1,000,000 in revenue. There is a 40% chance that the company will break even, and the other possibility is that there will be virtually no revenues. The distribution expenses in all cases will be $200,000. What is the expected net profit from the distribution of this item?

6.11 A mail order magazine service has the exclusive subscription rights to a certain magazine. Subscriptions can be reserved for one, two, three, or five years. A study of the subscriber list for other similar magazines reveals that the following information regarding the probabilities of subscription length would be appropriate: there are five time as many one-year subscriptions as five-year subscriptions, and the number of two-year and three-year subscriptions are each one-fifth of the total.

The mail order service company receives a fee of $2.00 for a one-year subscription, $3.50 for each two-year subscriptions and an additional dollar for every year over two years.

a. What is the probability distribution of subscription fees?

b. What is the expected total fee revenue from 125 new subscriptions?

6.12 A financial analyst for Petrified Paper Products has submitted the following probability distributions of profit for three investment proposals. The company has sufficient funds to consider only one of the proposals.

Project 1		Project 2		Project 3	
Profit	Prob.	Profit	Prob.	Profit	Prob.
−5,000	0.1	−2,000	0.10	−3,000	0.10
0	0.1	0	0.15	2,000	0.20
2,000	0.2	2,000	0.30	4,000	0.40
4,000	0.3	4,000	0.30	6,000	0.25
6,000	0.3	7,000	0.15	8,000	0.05

a. Based on expected profit, which proposal should be selected?

b. Which proposal has the lowest relative variability (i.e., risk)?

6.13 An export company may ship goods to country A at a cost of $2,000; country B at a cost of $3,000; or country C at a cost of $5,000. The revenues earned by selling the goods in these countries are $5,000; $7,000; and $10,000, respectively. Currently the countries are all involved in wars, and only 70% of shipments have been arriving at the destination country. The remainder are being lost at sea.

Based on expected values, to which country would you ship the next shipment of goods?

6.14 B. F. Retread, a tire manufacturer, wants to select one of the feasible designs for a new longer-wearing radial tire. The manufacturing cost of each type of tire is shown next.

Tire Design	Fixed Cost/year	Variable Cost per Tire
A	$60,000	$30
B	90,000	20
C	120,000	15

There are 3 possible levels of annual demand: 4,000 tires; 7,000; tires and 10,000 tires. The respective probabilities are 0.3, 0.5, and 0.2. The selling price will be $80 for A, $75 for B, and $75 for C. Based on expected profit, which design should be produced?

6.15 The normal weekly demand of a certain perishable product sold by QMS Inc. is given by the following distribution:

Demand	Probability
8	0.1
9	0.2
10	0.3
11	0.3
12	0.1

The product costs QMS $3 each. The product sells for $10 each. If not sold by the end of the week, the leftover units must be scrapped.

The supplier only has 10 or 11 units available for QMS to purchase. How many would you recommend QMS purchase based on expected profit?

6.2 Binomial Distribution

The next two sections use mathematical models to solve business problems.

> **MATHEMATICAL MODEL**
>
> A **mathematical model** is a mathematical expression that represents a variable of interest.

When a mathematical expression is available, you can compute the exact probability of occurrence of any particular outcome of the variable.

The **binomial distribution** is one of the most useful mathematical models. You use the binomial distribution when the discrete random variable is the number of events of interest in a sample of *n* observations.

Characteristics of a Binomial Experiment

1. The experiment consists of *n* repetitions (trials) of some action.
   or
   A sample of *n* items are selected from a large population.
2. Each trial will result in one of two possible outcomes called *success* or *failure,* where success is when the outcome of interest occurs.
   or
   Each item in the sample will either possess a certain characteristic (success) or it will not (failure).

3. The probability of success on each trial or selection is constant and is given the symbol π. The probability of failure is therefore $(1 - \pi)$. Note that this condition implies that the trials are *independent*.

The random variable associated with a binomial experiment is

$$X = \text{Number of successes}$$

To calculate the probability that X takes on a specific value we use the

Binomial Probability Distribution Function:

$$P(X = x) = \frac{n!}{x!(n - x)!} \pi^x (1 - \pi)^{n-x}$$

where
$$n = \text{\# of trials or sample size}$$
$$\pi = \text{probability of success in each trial}$$
$$n! = n \text{ factorial}$$
$$= n(n-1)(n-2)(n-3) \ldots 3 \cdot 2 \cdot 1$$

Example: $6! = 6 \cdot 5 \cdot 4 \cdot 3 \cdot 2 \cdot 1 = 720$

EXAMPLE 6.8

Toss a coin six times. Find the probability of getting two tails.

SOLUTION X = # of tails

$$n = 6$$
$$\pi = 0.5$$

$$P(X = 2) = \frac{6!}{2!(6 - 2)!}(0.5)^2(1 - 0.5)^{6-2} = 0.2344$$

Note: The part of the binomial formula $\dfrac{n!}{x!(n - x)!}$ calculates the number of outcomes where there are x successes in n trials. For example, if a coin is tossed 6 times, there will be $\dfrac{6!}{(2!(6 - 2)!}} = 15$ possible outcomes that have exactly 2 tails. These outcomes are the following:

TTHHHH	THTHHH	THHTHH	THHHTH	THHHHT
HTTHHH	HTHTHH	HTHHTH	HTHHHT	
HHTTHH	HHTHTH	HHTHHT		
HHHTTH	HHHTHT			
HHHHTT				

The factor $\dfrac{n!}{x!(n - x)!}$ is often given the shorthand symbol $_nC_x$.

CASIO CALCULATOR INSTRUCTION

Use the CASIO calculator to obtain the probability value (refer to Calculator Lesson 4).

Select **STAT F5**(DIST) **F5**(BINM) **F1**(Bpd), and then select the following options.

Data   : **F2**(Var)
x   : **2 EXE**
Numtrial : **6 EXE**
p   : **0.5**

Now key **EXE** or **F1**(Calc).

Results: Binomial P.D.

$$p(x = 2) = 0.23437$$

EXAMPLE 6.9   Roll a die 10 times. Find the probability of getting three 5s?

SOLUTION X = # of 5s

$$n = 10$$

$$\pi = 1/6$$

$$P(X = 3) = \frac{10!}{3!(10 - 3)!}\left(\frac{1}{6}\right)^3\left(1 - \frac{1}{6}\right)^{10-3} = 0.1550$$

CASIO CALCULATOR INSTRUCTION

Use the CASIO calculator to obtain the probability value.

Select **STAT F5**(DIST)   **F5**(BINM)   **F1**(Bpd), and then select the following options.

Data   : **F2**(Var)
x   : **3**
Numtrial : **10**
p   : **1 ÷ 6**

Results: Binomial P.D.

p(x = 3) = 0.15504

EXAMPLE 6.10   A survey of people in the 30–40 age bracket shows that 43 percent of them have investments in mutual funds. In a particular condominium there are 18 adults in this age bracket. What is the probability that

a. 5 of them will have investments in mutual funds?

SOLUTION X = # of people in their 30s with investments in mutual funds

$$n = 18$$

$$\pi = 0.43$$

$$P(X = 5) = \frac{18!}{5!(18 - 5)!}(0.43)^5(1 - 0.43)^{18-5} = 0.0845$$

CASIO CALCULATOR INSTRUCTION

Use the CASIO calculator to obtain the probability value.

Select **STAT F5**(DIST)   **F5**(BINM)   **F1**(Bpd), and then select the following options.

Data   : **F2**(Var)
x   : **5**
Numtrial : **18**
p   : **0.43**

Results: Binomial P.D.

p(x = 5) = 0.084449

b. at most 2 of these people will have investments in mutual funds?

SOLUTION $P(X \le 2) = P(X = 0) + P(X = 1) + P(X = 2)$
$$= 0.00004 + 0.00055 + 0.00351 = 0.0041$$

CASIO CALCULATOR INSTRUCTION

Use the CASIO calculator to obtain the probability value.

Select **STAT F5**(DIST)   **F5**(BINM)   **F1**(Bcd), and then select the following options.

Data   : **F2**(Var)
x   : **2**
Numtrial : **18**
p   : **0.43**

Results: Binomial C.D.

p(x ≤ 2) = 4.1007E.03

which is 0.0041007

c. more than 10 of these people will have investments in mutual funds?

SOLUTION $P(X > 10) = 1 - P(X \leq 10)$
$$= 1 - 0.9049 = 0.0951$$

Explanation:

Variable X	Probability $P(X = x)$	Calculator Input	Probability Value	
0	$P(X = 0)$	Bpd(0, 18, 0.43)	0.0000403411	
1	$P(X = 1)$	Bpd(1, 18, 0.43)	0.000547789	
2	$P(X = 2)$	Bpd(2, 18, 0.43)	0.003512578	
3	$P(X = 3)$	Bpd(3, 18, 0.43)	0.014132479	Add probabilities from $P(X = 0)$ to $p(X = 10)$ and you will obtain $p(X \leq 10)$.
4	$P(X = 4)$	Bpd(4, 18, 0.43)	0.03998004	
5	$P(X = 5)$	Bpd(5, 18, 0.43)	0.084449068	
6	$P(X = 6)$	Bpd(6, 18, 0.43)	0.138032248	
7	$P(X = 7)$	Bpd(7, 18, 0.43)	0.17850787	
8	$P(X = 8)$	Bpd(8, 18, 0.43)	0.185162768	
9	$P(X = 9)$	Bpd(9, 18, 0.43)	0.15520466	
10	$P(X = 10)$	Bpd(10, 18, 0.43)	0.105375795	
11	$P(X = 11)$	Bpd(11, 18, 0.43)	0.057813833	
12	$P(X = 12)$	Bpd(12, 18, 0.43)	0.025441468	Add probabilities from $P(X = 11)$ to $p(X = 18)$ and you will obtain $p(X > 10)$ or $p(X \geq 11)$.
13	$P(X = 13)$	Bpd(13, 18, 0.43)	0.008858163	
14	$P(X = 14)$	Bpd(14, 18, 0.43)	0.002386598	
15	$P(X = 15)$	Bpd(15, 18, 0.43)	0.000480111	
16	$P(X = 16)$	Bpd(16, 18, 0.43)	0.0000679104	
17	$P(X = 17)$	Bpd(17, 18, 0.43)	0.00000602714	
18	$P(X = 18)$	Bpd(18, 18, 0.43)	0.000000252599	
		Total	1	

Note : $p(X \leq 10) + p(X > 10) = 1$
$p(X > 10) = 1 - p(X \leq 10)$

d. from 3 to 9 of these people will have investments in mutual funds?

SOLUTION $P(3 \leq X \leq 9) = p(X = 3) + p(X = 4) + p(X = 5) + p(X = 6) +$
$p(X = 7) + p(X = 8) + p(X = 9)$

$P(X = 3)$	Bpd(3, 18, 0.43)	0.014132479
$P(X = 4)$	Bpd(4, 18, 0.43)	0.03998004
$P(X = 5)$	Bpd(5, 18, 0.43)	0.084449068
$P(X = 6)$	Bpd(6, 18, 0.43)	0.138032248
$P(X = 7)$	Bpd(7, 18, 0.43)	0.17850787
$P(X = 8)$	Bpd(8, 18, 0.43)	0.185162768
$P(X = 9)$	Bpd(9, 18, 0.43)	0.15520466
	TOTAL	**0.795469**

OR alternatively you may solve $P(3 \leq X \leq 9)$ in the following way.

$$P(3 \leq X \leq 9) = p(X \leq 9) - p(X \leq 2)$$
$$= \text{Bcd}(9, 18, 0.43) - \text{Bcd}(2, 18, 0.43)$$
$$= 0.7996 - 0.0041$$
$$= \mathbf{0.7955}$$

Binomial Template

You will notice that a similar style is used to present all the answers to the sample examples above. You are *not* to follow this style exactly, however, since you will be using a calculator or computer to determine the probability value. Your answers should look like the following template:

X = # of _____
                (successes)

n = _____

π = _____
     (dec.)

P(_____) = P(X symbol #) = _____ = 0._ _ _ _
    (words*)   (calculator or SPSS input)   (4 dec.)

* if the question does not directly say what the number is

EXAMPLE 6.11

Determining
$P(X = 3)$, Given
$n = 4$ and $\pi = 0.1$

If the likelihood of a tagged order form is 0.1, what is the probability that there are three tagged order forms in the sample of four?

SOLUTION The probability of three tagged orders from a sample of four is

$$P(X = 3 | n = 4, \pi = 0.1) = \frac{4!}{3!(4-3)!}(0.1)^3(1 - 0.1)^{4-3}$$

$$= \frac{4!}{3!(1)!}(0.1)^3(0.9)^1$$

$$= 4(0.1)(0.1)(0.1)(0.9) = 0.0036$$

Examples 6.12 and 6.13 show the computations for other values of X.

EXAMPLE 6.12

Determining
$P(X \geq 3)$, Given
$n = 4$ and $\pi = 0.1$

If the likelihood of a tagged order form is 0.1, what is the probability that there are three or more (i.e., at least three) tagged order forms in the sample of four?

SOLUTION In Example 6.11, you found that the probability of *exactly* three tagged order forms from a sample of four is 0.0036. To compute the probability of *at least* three tagged order forms, you need to add the probability of three tagged order forms to the probability of four tagged order forms. The probability of four tagged order forms is

$$P(X = 4 | n = 4, \pi = 0.1) = \frac{4!}{4!(4-4)!}(0.1)^4(1 - 0.1)^{4-4}$$

$$= \frac{4!}{4!(0)!}(0.1)^4(0.9)^0$$

$$= 1(0.1)(0.1)(0.1)(0.1)(1) = 0.0001$$

Thus, the probability of at least three tagged order forms is

$$P(X \geq 3) = P(X = 3) + P(X = 4)$$

$$= 0.0036 + 0.0001$$

$$= 0.0037$$

There is a 0.37% chance that there will be at least three tagged order forms in a sample of four.

EXAMPLE 6.13

Determining
$P(X < 3)$, Given
$n = 4$ and $\pi = 0.1$

If the likelihood of a tagged order form is 0.1, what is the probability that there are fewer than three tagged order forms in the sample of four?

SOLUTION The probability that there are fewer than three tagged order forms is

$$P(X < 3) = P(X = 0) + P(X = 1) + P(X = 2)$$

These probabilities are

$$P(X = 0 | n = 4, \pi = 0.1) = \frac{4!}{0!(4-0)!}(0.1)^0(1 - 0.1)^{4-0} = 0.6561$$

$$P(X = 1 | n = 4, \pi = 0.1) = \frac{4!}{1!(4-1)!}(0.1)^1(1 - 0.1)^{4-1} = 0.2916$$

$$P(X = 2 | n = 4, \pi = 0.1) = \frac{4!}{2!(4-2)!}(0.1)^2(1 - 0.1)^{4-2} = 0.0486$$

Therefore, $P(X < 3) = 0.6561 + 0.2916 + 0.0486 = 0.9963$. $P(X < 3)$ could also be calculated from its complement, $P(X \geq 3)$, as follows:

$$P(X < 3) = 1 - P(X \geq 3)$$

$$= 1 - 0.0037 = 0.9963$$

Computing binomial probabilities become tedious as n gets large. Table 6.16 shows how binomial probabilities can be computed by Excel (left) and Minitab (right). Binomial probabilities can also be looked up in a table of probabilities, as discussed in the **Binomial** online topic available on this book's download page.

TABLE 6.16

Finding a Binomial Probability for $n = 4$, $X = 2$, and $\pi = 0.1$

n	X	0.01	0.02	π	0.10
4	0	0.9606	0.9224	....	0.6561
	1	0.0388	0.0753	....	0.2916
	2	0.0006	0.0023	....	0.0486
	3	0.0000	0.0000	....	0.0036
	4	0.0000	0.0000	....	0.0001

Source: *Table E.6.*

You can also compute the binomial probabilities given in Table A.6 by using the Casio calculator as shown in Figures 6.2 and 6.3 (note that the Casio calculator uses the letter p instead of π to denote the probability of an event of interest).

FIGURE 6.2

CASIO calculator for computing binomial probabilities

Compute the binomial probabilities using the **Bpd** function.

Binomial Probabilities with n = 4 and π = 0.1

Variable X	Probability $P(X = x)$	Calculator Input	Probability Value
0	$P(X = 0)$	Bpd(0, 4, 0.1)	0.6561
1	$P(X = 1)$	Bpd(1, 4, 0.1)	0.2916
2	$P(X = 2)$	Bpd(2, 4, 0.1)	0.0486
3	$P(X = 3)$	Bpd(3, 4, 0.1)	0.0036
4	$P(X = 4)$	Bpd(4, 4, 0.1)	0.0001
		TOTAL	1

FIGURE 6.3

Minitab results for computing binomial probabilities

Compute the binomial probabilities using the LIST and **Bpd** function.

Binomial Probabilities with n = 4 and π = 0.1

Input the variable values (X=0,1,2,3,4) in **LIST 1**

Select **STAT F5**(DIST) **F5**(BINM) **F1**(Bpd) **F1**(List), and then select the following options.

Binomial P.D.
Data   : **List 1**
Numtrial : **4**
p   : **0.10**
Save Res : **None**
Execute

Now key **EXE** or **F1**(CALC).

The calculator will show the following result:

Binomial P.D.

0	0.6561
1	0.2916
2	0.0486
3	0.0036
4	0.0001

The shape of a binomial probability distribution depends on the values of n and π. Whenever $\pi = 0.5$, the binomial distribution is symmetrical, regardless of how large or small the value of n. When $\pi \neq 0.5$, the distribution is skewed. The closer π is to 0.5 and the larger the number of observations, n, the less skewed the distribution becomes. For example, the distribution of the number of tagged order forms is highly right skewed because $\pi = 0.1$ and $n = 4$ (see Figure 6.4).

FIGURE 6.4

Histogram of the binomial probability distribution with $n = 4$ and $\pi = 0.1$

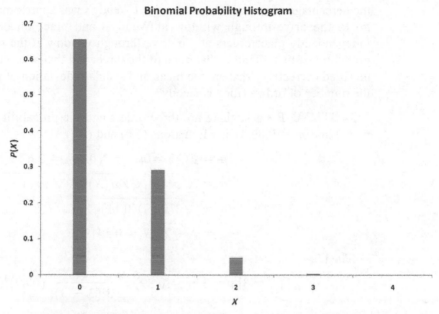

Binomial Probability Histogram

Observe from Figure 6.4 that unlike the histogram for continuous variables in Section 3.10, the bars for the values are very thin, and there is a large gap between each pair of values. That is because the histogram represents a discrete variable. (Theoretically, the bars should have no width. They should be vertical lines.)

The mean (or expected value) of the binomial distribution is equal to the product of n and π. Instead of using Equation (6.1) on page 242 to compute the mean of the probability distribution, you can also use Equation (6.6) to compute the mean for variables that follow the binomial distribution.

MEAN OF THE BINOMIAL DISTRIBUTION

The mean, μ, of the binomial distribution is equal to the sample size, n, multiplied by the probability of an event of interest, π.

$$\mu = E(X) = n\pi \tag{6.6}$$

On the average, over the long run, you theoretically expect $\mu = E(X) = n\pi = (4)(0.1) = 0.4$ tagged order form in a sample of four orders.

The standard deviation of the binomial distribution can be calculated using Equation (6.7).

STANDARD DEVIATION OF THE BINOMIAL DISTRIBUTION

$$\sigma = \sqrt{\sigma^2} = \sqrt{Var(X)} = \sqrt{n\pi(1 - \pi)} \tag{6.7}$$

The standard deviation of the number of tagged order forms is

$$\sigma = \sqrt{4(0.1)(0.9)} = 0.60$$

You get the same result if you use Equation (6.5) on page 249.

Example 6.14 applies the binomial distribution to service at a fast-food restaurant.

EXAMPLE 6.14

Computing
Binomial
Probabilities

Accuracy in taking orders at a drive-through window is important for fast-food chains. Periodically, *QSR Magazine*, (**http://www.qsrmagazine.com/**), publishes the results of its surveys. Accuracy is measured as the percentage of orders that are filled correctly. Recently, the percentage of orders filled correctly at Wendy's was approximately 89%. Suppose that you go to the drive-through window at Wendy's and place an order. Two friends of yours independently place orders at the drive-through window at the same Wendy's. What are the probabilities that all three, that none of the three, and that at least two of the three orders will be filled correctly? What are the mean and standard deviation of the binomial distribution for the number of orders filled correctly?

SOLUTION Because there are three orders and the probability of a correct order is 0.89, $n = 3$ and $\pi = 0.89$. Using Equations (6.6) and (6.7),

$$\mu = E(X) = n\pi = 3(0.89) = 2.67$$
$$\sigma = \sqrt{\sigma^2} = \sqrt{Var(X)} = \sqrt{n\pi(1 - \pi)}$$
$$= \sqrt{3(0.89)(0.11)}$$
$$= \sqrt{0.2937} = 0.5419$$

Then,

$$P(X = 3 \mid n = 3, \pi = 0.89) = \frac{3!}{3!(3 - 3)!}(0.89)^3(1 - 0.89)^{3-3}$$

$$= \frac{3!}{3!(3 - 3)!}(0.89)^3(0.11)^0$$

$$= 1(0.89)(0.89)(0.89)(1) = 0.7050$$

$$P(X = 0 \mid n = 3, \pi = 0.89) = \frac{3!}{0!(3 - 0)!}(0.89)^0(1 - 0.89)^{3-0}$$

$$= \frac{3!}{0!(3 - 0)!}(0.89)^0(0.11)^3$$

$$= 1(1)(0.11)(0.11)(0.11) = 0.0013$$

$$P(X = 2 \mid n = 3, \pi = 0.89) = \frac{3!}{2!(3 - 2)!}(0.89)^2(1 - 0.89)^{3-2}$$

$$= \frac{3!}{2!(3 - 2)!}(0.89)^2(0.11)^1$$

$$= 3(0.89)(0.89)(0.11) = 0.2614$$

$$P(X \geq 2) = P(X = 2) + P(X = 3)$$

$$= 0.2614 + 0.7050$$

$$= 0.9664$$

The mean number of orders filled correctly in a sample of three orders is 2.67, and the standard deviation is 0.5419. The probability that all three orders are filled correctly is 0.7050, or 70.50%. The probability that none of the orders are filled correctly is 0.0013, or 0.13%. The probability that at least two orders are filled correctly is 0.9664, or 96.64%.

In this section, you have been introduced to the binomial distribution. The binomial distribution is an important mathematical model in many business situations.

CALCULATOR LESSON 5

CASIO FX-9750G, CFX-9850GB, OR FX-9750GII CALCULATOR

Lesson 5—Binomial Probabilities

Note: The following instructions refer to examples in the notes on the binomial probability distribution.

The Casio calculator has *two* binomial probability functions programmed into its memory. These are:

i. **Bpd**, which stands for **b**inomial **p**robability **d**istribution. This function calculates a binomial probability of the form

$$P(X = \#)$$

ii. **Bcd**, which stands for **b**inomial **c**umulative **d**istribution. This function calculates a Binomial probability of the form

$$P(X \leq \#)$$

A. Individual values of X—using the built-in **Bpd** distribution function

EXAMPLE 6.8
(Revisit)

$P(X = 2)$ where $n = 6$ and $\pi = 0.5$

Select **STAT F5**(DIST)   **F5**(BINM)   **F1**(Bpd), and then select the following options.

Data	: **F2**(Var) ▼ (Note: Do not key **EXE** now.)
x	: **2 EXE**
Numtrial	: **6 EXE**
p	: **.5 EXE**

Now key **EXE** or **F1**(Calc).

The calculator will show the result 0.23437.

To calculate another binomial probability, key **EXE** and enter new values where necessary.

B. Cumulative values of X—using the built-in **Bcd** distribution function

EXAMPLE 6.10a
(Revisit)

$P(X \leq 2)$ where $n = 18$ and $\pi = 0.43$

Select **STAT F5**(DIST)   **F5**(BINM)   **F2**(Bcd), and then select the following options.

Data	: **F2**(Var) ▼ (Note: Do not key **EXE** now.)
x	: **2 EXE**
Numtrial	: **18 EXE**
p	: **.43 EXE**

Now key **EXE** or **F1**(Calc).

The calculator will show the result 4.1007 E –03, which is scientific notation for the value 0.0041. E –03 means that you should move the decimal point 3 places to the left.

EXAMPLE 6.10c
(Revisit)

$P(X > 10) = 1 - P(X \leq 10)$ where $n = 18$ and $\pi = 0.43$

You must *first* calculate $P(X \leq 10)$.

Select **STAT F5**(DIST)   **F5**(BINM)   **F2**(Bcd), and then select the following options.

Data : **F2**(Var) ▼ (Note: Do not key **EXE** now.)
x : **10 EXE**
Numtrial : **18 EXE**
p : **.43 EXE**

Now key **EXE** or **F1**(Calc)

The calculator will show the result 0.90494.

Therefore, $P(X > 10) = 1 - P(X \le 10) = 1 - 0.9049 = 0.0951$.

EXAMPLE 6.10d
(Revisit)

$P(3 \le X \le 9) = P(X \le 9) - P(X \le 2)$ where $n = 18$ and $\pi = 0.43$

You will have to calculate the two cumulative probabilities separately and then record the results and subtract the appropriate values to get the final result 0.7955.

Problems for Binomial Probabilities

APPLYING THE CONCEPTS

Binomial Template:

X = # of _____
         (successes)

n = _____

π = _____
    (dec.)

P(_____) = P(X symbol #) =
    (words)

_____ = 0._ _ _ _
(calculator or SPSS input)   (4 dec.)

6.16 A new public school is presently being built in your community. The classrooms will include chairs that have a small table attached on the right or left side. The school is trying to determine how many left-handed tables should be included in each classroom. If only 7% of the population is left-handed, what is the probability that in a class of 25 students:

a. two will be left-handed?
b. more than three will be left-handed?
c. What is the expected number of left-handed children in a class of 25?

6.17 The quality inspector for a company that produces heptium computer chips has determined that 3% of the production is defective. The company does not perform final product inspection, but instead agrees to replace any defective chip found by any customer and will give the customer a $5 discount on their next order.

a. If a customer orders 30 heptium chips, what is the probability that 3 or more defective chips will be included in the order?
b. What is the expected number of defective chips in the above order?
c. Another customer assembles computer motherboards, each with 7 heptium chips. If any chip fails, then the motherboard fails. What is the probability that a motherboard will fail?

6.18 According to a well-known accounting firm, the chances of your tax return being audited by Revenue Canada are about 9 in 1000 if your income is less than $50,000. The chances increase to 22 in 1000 if your income is more than $50,000. You are presently employed by an accounting firm and have prepared tax returns for 58 clients with income under $50,000 and for 42 clients with income over $50,000.

a. What is the probability that at most 3 of the clients with incomes under $50,000 will be audited?
b. What is the probability that at least 4 of your clients that have incomes over $50,000 will be audited?

6.19 A salesperson has to sell a minimum of 50 cars in a month in order to get a bonus. One particular salesperson has sold 43 cars so far this month. Today he has appointments with 9 prospective customers. Based on past experience he has a 55% chance of selling a car to any customer. What is the probability that he will earn his bonus today?

6.20 A certain soft drink manufacturer believes that 40% of the people that drink cola prefer their brand. A random sample of 60 cola drinkers was surveyed. If the manufacturer is correct:
a. What is the probability that less than half of those surveyed will prefer the manufacturer's product?
b. What is the probability that at least the expected number of people will prefer the manufacturer's product?

6.21 The increase or decrease in the price of a stock between the beginning and the end of a trading day is assumed to be an equally likely random event. What is the probability that a stock will show an increase in its closing price on five consecutive days?

6.22 The U.S. Department of Transportation reported that in 2009, Southwest led all domestic airlines in on-time arrivals for domestic flights, with a rate of 0.825. Using the binomial distribution, what is the probability that in the next six flights
a. four flights will be on time?
b. all six flights will be on time?
c. at least four flights will be on time?
d. What are the mean and standard deviation of the number of on-time arrivals?
e. What assumptions do you need to make in (a) through (c)?

6.23 A student is taking a multiple-choice exam in which each question has four choices. Assume that the student has no knowledge of the correct answers to any of the questions. She has decided on a strategy in which she will place four balls (marked *A*, *B*, *C*, and *D*) into a box. She randomly selects one ball for each question and replaces the ball in the box. The marking on the ball will determine her answer to the question. There are five multiple-choice questions on the exam. What is the probability that she will get
a. five questions correct?
b. at least four questions correct?
c. no questions correct?
d. no more than two questions correct?

6.24 Investment advisors agree that near-retirees, defined as people aged 55 to 65, should have balanced portfolios. Most advisors suggest that the near-retirees have no more than 50% of their investments in stocks. However, during the huge decline in the stock market in 2008, 22% of near-retirees had 90% or more of their investments in stocks (P. Regnier, "What I Learned from the Crash," *Money*, May

2009, p. 114). Suppose you have a random sample of 10 people who would have been labeled as near-retirees in 2008. What is the probability that during 2008
a. none had 90% or more of their investment in stocks?
b. exactly one had 90% or more of his or her investment in stocks?
c. two or fewer had 90% or more of their investment in stocks?
d. three or more had 90% or more of their investment in stocks?

6.25 When a customer places an order with Rudy's On-Line Office Supplies, a computerized accounting information system (AIS) automatically checks to see if the customer has exceeded his or her credit limit. Past records indicate that the probability of customers exceeding their credit limit is 0.05. Suppose that, on a given day, 20 customers place orders. Assume that the number of customers that the AIS detects as having exceeded their credit limit is distributed as a binomial random variable.
a. What are the mean and standard deviation of the number of customers exceeding their credit limits?
b. What is the probability that zero customers will exceed their limits?
c. What is the probability that one customer will exceed his or her limit?
d. What is the probability that two or more customers will exceed their limits?

✓SELF Test **6.26** In Example 6.14 on page 260, you and two friends decided to go to Wendy's. Now, suppose that instead you go to Popeye's, which last month filled approximately 84.8% of orders correctly. What is the probability that
a. all three orders will be filled correctly?
b. none of the three will be filled correctly?
c. at least two of the three will be filled correctly?
d. What are the mean and standard deviation of the binomial distribution used in (a) through (c)? Interpret these values.

6.27 In Example 6.14 on page 260, you and two friends decided to go to Wendy's. Now, suppose that instead you go to McDonald's, which last month filled approximately 90.1% of the orders correctly. What is the probability that
a. all three orders will be filled correctly?
b. none of the three will be filled correctly?
c. at least two of the three will be filled correctly?
d. What are the mean and standard deviation of the binomial distribution used in (a) through (c)? Interpret these values.
e. Compare the result of (a) through (d) with those of Popeye's in Problem 6.21 and Wendy's in Example 6.14 on page 260.

6.3 Poisson Probability Distribution

Many studies are based on counts of the times a particular event occurs in a given *area of opportunity*. An **area of opportunity** is a continuous unit or interval of time, volume, or any physical area in which there can be more than one occurrence of an event. Examples are the surface defects on a new refrigerator, the number of network failures in a day, the number of people arriving at a bank, and the number of fleas on the body of a dog.

Characteristics of a Poisson Experiment

1. The experiment consists of observing some situation for a period of *time*.
   or
   An *amount of space* is inspected or analyzed. Space may be length, area, volume or weight.
2. In each infinitesimally small amount of time or space there will either be one success or no successes, where success is when the outcome of interest occurs. The successes must occur *randomly*. Note that this condition implies that the successes are *independent* of each other.
3. The average rate of success for the amount of time or space we are interested in is given the symbol λ (lambda).

The **random variable** associated with a Poisson experiment is

   X = # of successes in a certain amount of time or space.

To calculate the probability that X takes on a specific value we use the

Poisson Probability Distribution Function:

$$P(X = x) = \frac{e^{-\lambda}\lambda^{x}}{x!} \qquad\qquad (6.8)$$

   where $e = 2.718281828459\ldots$ (a mathematical constant)

Note: On your calculator there is an e^x key. Try calculating e^1.

EXAMPLE 6.15

Records have been kept for the past several months, and they show that customers arrive to use a certain banking machine at an average rate of 15 per hour.

a. What is the probability that 12 customers will use the machine in the next hour?

SOLUTION X = # of customers at the bank machine in 1 hour
   $\lambda = 15 /$ hour
   $P(X = 12) =$ Ppd $(12, 15) = 0.0829$

b. What is the probability that there will be fewer than 3 customers in the next 10 minutes?

SOLUTION X = # of customers at the bank machine in 10 minutes
   $\lambda = 15 /$ hour $= 2.5 / 10$ minutes
   $P(X < 3) = P(X \le 2)$
   $\qquad = $ Pcd $(2, 2.5) = 0.5438$

a. What is the probability that there will be more than 40 customers in the next 2 hours?

SOLUTION X = # of customers at the bank machine in 2 hours
   $\lambda = 15 /$ hour $= 30 / 2$ hours
   $P(X > 40) = 1 - P(X \le 40) = 1 - $ Pcd $(40, 30)$
   $\qquad\qquad\qquad = 1 - 0.9677 = 0.0323$

EXAMPLE 6.16

It has been noted that potholes on the 401 highway occur randomly. An inspection of a 200 km stretch of the 401 indicated that there were 450 potholes. Today the pothole repair work crew will repair 3 km of the highway. What is the probability that the crew will repair at least 6 potholes?

SOLUTION $X = \#$ of potholes in 3 km

$$\lambda = 450 \, / \, 200 \text{ km} = 2.25 \, / \text{ km} = 6.75 \, / \, 3 \text{ km}$$

$$P(X \geq 6) = 1 - P(X \leq 5) = 1 - \text{Pcd}(5, 6.75)$$
$$= 1 - 0.3338 = 0.6662$$

Consider the number of customers arriving during the lunch hour at a bank located in the central business district in a large city. You are interested in the number of customers who arrive each minute. Does this situation match the four properties of the Poisson distribution given earlier? First, the *event* of interest is a customer arriving, and the *given area of opportunity* is defined as a one-minute interval. Will zero customers arrive, one customer arrive, two customers arrive, and so on? Second, it is reasonable to assume that the probability that a customer arrives during a particular one-minute interval is the same as the probability for all the other one-minute intervals. Third, the arrival of one customer in any one-minute interval has no effect on (i.e., is independent of) the arrival of any other customer in any other one-minute interval. Finally, the probability that two or more customers will arrive in a given time period approaches zero as the time interval becomes small. For example, the probability is virtually zero that two customers will arrive in a time interval of 0.01 second. Thus, you can use the Poisson distribution to determine probabilities involving the number of customers arriving at the bank in a one-minute time interval during the lunch hour.

The Poisson distribution has one characteristic, called λ (the Greek lowercase letter *lambda*), which is the mean or expected number of events per unit. The variance of a Poisson distribution is also equal to λ, and the standard deviation is equal to $\sqrt{\lambda}$. The number of events, X, of the Poisson random variable ranges from 0 to infinity (∞).

Equation (6.9) is the mathematical expression for the Poisson distribution for computing the probability of $X = x$ events, given that λ events are expected.

POISSON DISTRIBUTION

$$P(X = x|\lambda) = \frac{e^{-\lambda}\lambda^x}{x!} \qquad (6.9)$$

where

$P(X = x|\lambda) = $ the probability that $X = x$ events in an area of opportunity given λ

$\lambda = $ expected number of events

$e - $ mathematical constant approximated by 2.71828

$x = $ number of events ($x = 0, 1, 2, \ldots, \infty$)

To illustrate an application of the Poisson distribution, suppose that the mean number of customers who arrive per minute at the bank during the noon-to-1 P.M. hour is equal to 3.0. What is the probability that in a given minute, exactly two customers will arrive? And what is the probability that more than two customers will arrive in a given minute?

Using Equation (6.9) and $\lambda = 3$, the probability that in a given minute exactly two customers will arrive is

$$P(X = 2|\lambda = 3) = \frac{e^{-3.0}(3.0)^2}{2!} = \frac{9}{(2.71828)^3(2)} = 0.2240$$

To determine the probability that in any given minute more than two customers will arrive,

$$P(X > 2) = P(X = 3) + P(X = 4) + \cdots + P(X = \infty)$$

Because in a probability distribution, all the probabilities must sum to 1, the terms on the right side of the equation $P(X > 2)$ also represent the complement of the probability that X is less than or equal to 2 [i.e., $1 - P(X \le 2)$]. Thus,

$$P(X > 2) = 1 - P(X \le 2) = 1 - [P(X = 0) + P(X = 1) + P(X = 2)]$$

Now, using Equation (6.9),

$$P(X > 2) = 1 - \left[\frac{e^{-3.0}(3.0)^0}{0!} + \frac{e^{-3.0}(3.0)^1}{1!} + \frac{e^{-3.0}(3.0)^2}{2!} \right]$$

$$= 1 - [0.0498 + 0.1494 + 0.2240]$$

$$= 1 - 0.4232 = 0.5768$$

You can also use the Bcd function to solve the above question, for example

$$P(X > 2) = 1 - P(X \le 2)$$

$$= 1 - \text{Bcd}(2, 3)$$

$$= 1 - 0.4232 = 0.5768$$

Thus, there is a 57.68% chance that more than two customers will arrive in the same minute.

To avoid the drudgery involved in these computations, you can find Poisson probabilities directly from Table A.7 (in Appendix A), a portion of which is reproduced in Table 6.17. Table A.7 provides the probabilities that the Poisson random variable takes on values of $X = 0, 1, 2, \ldots$, for selected values of the parameter λ. To find the probability that exactly two customers will arrive in a given minute when the mean number of customers arriving is 3.0 per minute, you can read the probability corresponding to the row $X = 2$ and column $\lambda = 3.0$ from the table. The result is 0.2240, as demonstrated in Table 6.17.

TABLE 6.17

Finding a Poisson Probability for $\lambda = 3$

X	2.1	2.2	λ	3.0
0	.1225	.1108	....	.0498
1	.2572	.2438	....	.1494
2	.2700	.2681	....	.2240
3	.1890	.1966	....	.2240
4	.0992	.1082	....	.1680
5	.0417	.0476	....	.1008
6	.0146	.0174	....	.0504
7	.0044	.0055	....	.0216
8	.0011	.0015	....	.0081
9	.0003	.0004	....	.0027
10	.0001	.0001	....	.0008
11	.0000	.0000	....	.0002
12	.0000	.0000	....	.0001

Source: *Table A.7.*

You can also compute the Poisson probabilities given in Table A.7 by using the CASIO calculator, as illustrated in Figures 6.5 and 6.6.

FIGURE 6.5

CASIO calculator for computing Poisson probabilities with $\lambda = 3$

Compute the Poisson probabilities using the **Ppd** function.

Poisson Probabilities with $\lambda = 3$

Variable X	Probability $P(X = x)$	Calculator Input	Probability Value
0	$P(X = 0)$	Ppd(0, 3)	0.049787068
1	$P(X = 1)$	Ppd (1, 3)	0.149361205
2	$P(X = 2)$	Ppd (2, 3)	0.224041808
3	$P(X = 3)$	Ppd (3, 3)	0.224041808
4	$P(X = 4)$	Ppd (4, 3)	0.168031356
5	$P(X = 5)$	Ppd (5, 3)	0.100818813
6	$P(X = 6)$	Ppd (6, 3)	0.050409407
7	$P(X = 7)$	Ppd (7, 3)	0.021604031
8	$P(X = 8)$	Ppd (8, 3)	0.008101512
9	$P(X = 9)$	Ppd (9, 3)	0.002700504
10	$P(X = 10)$	Ppd (10, 3)	0.000810151
11	$P(X = 11)$	Ppd (11, 3)	0.00022095
12	$P(X = 12)$	Ppd (12, 3)	0.0000552376
13	$P(X = 13)$	Ppd (13, 3)	0.0000127471
14	$P(X = 14)$	Ppd (14, 3)	0.00000273153
15	$P(X = 15)$	Ppd (15, 3)	0.000000546306
16	$P(X = 16)$	Ppd (16, 3)	0.000000102432
17	$P(X = 17)$	Ppd (17, 3)	0.0000000180763
18	$P(X = 18)$	Ppd (18, 3)	0.00000000301272
19	$P(X = 19)$	Ppd (17, 3)	0.000000000475692
20	$P(X = 20)$	Ppd (18, 3)	0.0000000000713538
		Total	1

FIGURE 6.6

CASIO calculator results for computing Poisson probabilities with $\lambda = 3$

Compute the Poisson probabilities using the LIST and **Ppd** function.

Poisson Probabilities with $\lambda = 3$

Input the variable values ($X = 0,1,2, ..., 20$) in **LIST 1**.

Select **STAT F5**(DIST) **F1**(POISN) **F1**(Ppd) **F1**(List), and then select the following options.

Binomial P.D.
Data   : **List**
List   : **List 1**
μ : **3**
Save Res : **None**
Execute
Now key **EXE** or **F1**(CALC).

NOTE: The CASIO calculator uses the symbol μ instead of λ to denote the average rate of success.

The calculator will show the following result:

Poisson P.D.

0	0.049787068	7	0.021604031	14	0.00000273153
1	0.149361205	8	0.008101512	15	0.000000546306
2	0.224041808	9	0.002700504	16	0.000000102432
3	0.224041808	10	0.000810151	17	0.0000000180763
4	0.168031356	11	0.00022095	18	0.00000000301272
5	0.100818813	12	0.0000552376	19	0.000000000475692
6	0.050409407	13	0.0000127471	20	0.0000000000713538

EXAMPLE 6.17

Computing Poisson Probabilities

The number of work-related injuries per month in a manufacturing plant is known to follow a Poisson distribution with a mean of 2.5 work-related injuries a month. What is the probability that in a given month, no work-related injuries occur? That at least one work-related injury occurs?

SOLUTION Using Equation (6.9) on page 265 with $\lambda = 2.5$ (or Excel, Minitab, or a Poisson table lookup), the probability that in a given month no work-related injuries occur is

$$P(X = 0 | \lambda = 2.5) = \frac{e^{-2.5}(2.5)^0}{0!} = \frac{1}{(2.71828)^{2.5}(1)} = 0.0821$$

The probability that there will be no work-related injuries in a given month is 0.0821 or 8.21%. Thus,

$$P(X \geq 1) = 1 - P(X = 0)$$
$$= 1 - 0.0821$$
$$= 0.9179$$

The probability that there will be at least one work-related injury is 0.9179 or 91.79%.

CALCULATOR LESSON 6

CASIO FX-9750G, CFX-9850GB, OR FX-9750GII CALCULATOR

Lesson 6—Poisson Probabilities

Note: The following instructions refer to examples in the notes on the Poisson probability distribution.

The Casio calculator has *two* Poisson probability functions programmed into its memory. These are

i. **Ppd**, which stands for **P**oisson **p**robability **d**istribution. This function calculates a Poisson probability of the form

$$P(X = \#)$$

ii. **Pcd**, which stands for **P**oisson **c**umulative **d**istribution. This function calculates a Poisson probability of the form

$$P(X \leq \#)$$

A. Individual values of X—using the built-in **Ppd** distribution function

$P(X = 12)$ where $\lambda = 15$

Select **STAT F5**(DIST) **F6**(×) **F1**(POISN) **F1**(Ppd), and then select the following options.

Data   : **F2**(Var) ▼ (Note: Do not key **EXE** now.)
x   : **12 EXE**
μ   : **15 EXE**   (Note: the calculator uses the μ symbol instead of λ.)

Now key **EXE** or **F1**(Calc).

The calculator will show the result 0.082859.

To calculate another Poisson probability, key **EXE** and enter new values where necessary.

B. Cumulative values of X—using the built-in **Pcd** distribution function

$P(X < 3) = P(X \leq 2)$ where $\lambda = 2.5$

Select **STAT F5**(DIST) **F6**(×) **F1**(POISN) **F2**(Pcd), and then select the following options.

Data   : **F2**(Var) ▼ (Note: Do not key **EXE** now.)
x   : **2 EXE**
μ   : **2.5 EXE**

Now key **EXE** or **F1**(Calc).

The calculator will show the result 0.54381.

$P(X > 40) = 1 - P(X \leq 40)$ where $\lambda = 30$

You must *first* calculate $P(X \leq 40)$.

Select **STAT F5**(DIST)   **F5**(BINM)   **F2**(Bcd), and then select the following options.

Data   : **F2**(Var) ▼ (Note: Do not key **EXE** now.)
x   : **40 EXE**
μ   : **30 EXE**

Now key **EXE** or **F1**(Calc).

The calculator will show the result 0.96769.k

Therefore, $P(X > 40) = 1 - P(X \leq 40) = 1 - 0.9677 = 0.0323$.

Problems for Poisson Probabilities

APPLYING THE CONCEPTS

Poisson Template:

X = # of _____ IN _____
        (successes)   (time or space)

λ = _____ = _____
     (given)   (new—if needed)

P(_____) = P(X symbol #) =
   (words)

_____ = 0._ _ _ _
  (calculator or SPSS input)   (4 dec.)

6.28 A taxicab company has found that, on the average, two accidents occur in a month. The accidents appear to occur randomly. Find the probability of there being 5 or more accidents during a given month.

6.29 Customers arrive randomly at a service desk at an average rate of 2 every five minutes. Find the probability that:
a. None arrive in a five minute period.
b. More than four arrive in a ten minute period.

6.30 Bankruptcies of convenience stores in Toronto occur randomly at an average rate of 4.5 per year. Find the probability that:
a. there will be no corner store bankruptcies in the next four months.
b. there will be at most 3 corner store bankruptcies this year.

6.31 Flaws in plate glass used for large office buildings occur randomly at an average of 1 per 10 square feet. What is the probability that a 6 ft. by 10 ft. sheet of this type of glass will contain:
a. less than 2 flaws?
b. at least 1 flaw?

6.32 A data entry typist makes an average of 2 errors per page. If the errors occur randomly, what is the probability that:
a. there will be one error on the next page?
b. there will be more than 5 errors on the next 2 pages?

6.33 Two students have started a business to seal driveways during the summer months. They rent a pickup truck and a power sprayer. With this they will use a tar based spray to seal asphalt driveways. Past experience has shown that the best time to sign up customers is to ring their doorbells between 5:00 and 8:00 p.m. on any weekday evening. Any jobs that they obtain will be completed the next day. In the months of June, July and August they find that they get an average 2 customers per hour ringing doorbells.

a. What is the probability that they will get from 5 to 9 jobs in an evening of soliciting?

b. They charge $25 per driveway. If the truck costs $50 per day, and the spraying equipment costs $20 per day and the material to seal one driveway costs $5, what is the probability that they will make a profit on any given day.

6.34 Assume that the number of network errors experienced in a day on a local area network (LAN) is distributed as a Poisson random variable. The mean number of network errors experienced in a day is 2.4. What is the probability that in any given day

a. zero network errors will occur?

b. exactly one network error will occur?

c. two or more network errors will occur?

d. fewer than three network errors will occur?

✓SELF 6.35 The quality control manager of Marilyn's **Test** Cookies is inspecting a batch of chocolate-chip cookies that has just been baked. If the production process is in control, the mean number of chip parts per cookie is 6.0. What is the probability that in any particular cookie being inspected

a. fewer than five chip parts will be found?

b. exactly five chip parts will be found?

c. five or more chip parts will be found?

d. either four or five chip parts will be found?

6.36 Refer to Problem 6.35. How many cookies in a batch of 100 should the manager expect to discard if company policy requires that all chocolate-chip cookies sold have at least four chocolate-chip parts?

6.37 The U.S. Department of Transportation maintains statistics for mishandled bags per 1,000 airline passengers. In the first nine months of 2010, Delta had mishandled 3.52 bags per 1,000 passengers. What is the probability that in the next 1,000 passengers, Delta will have

a. no mishandled bags?

b. at least one mishandled bag?

c. at least two mishandled bags?

6.38 The U.S. Department of Transportation maintains statistics for consumer complaints per 100,000 airline passengers. In the first nine months of 2009, consumer complaints were 0.99 per 100,000 passengers. What is the probability that in the next 100,000 passengers, there will be

a. no complaints?

b. at least one complaint?

c. at least two complaints?

6.39 Based on past experience, it is assumed that the number of flaws per foot in rolls of grade 2 paper follows a Poisson distribution with a mean of 1 flaw per 5 feet of paper (0.2 flaw per foot). What is the probability that in a

a. 1-foot roll, there will be at least 2 flaws?

b. 12-foot roll, there will be at least 1 flaw?

c. 50-foot roll, there will be more than or equal to 5 flaws and fewer than or equal to 15 flaws?

6.40 J.D. Power and Associates calculates and publishes various statistics concerning car quality. The initial quality score measures the number of problems per new car sold. For 2009 model cars, Ford had 1.02 problems per car and Dodge had 1.34 problems per car (data extracted from S. Carty, "U.S. Autos Power Forward with Gains in Quality Survey," *USA Today*, June 23, 2009, p. 3B). Let the random variable X be equal to the number of problems with a newly purchased 2009 Ford.

a. What assumptions must be made in order for X to be distributed as a Poisson random variable? Are these assumptions reasonable?

Making the assumptions as in (a), if you purchased a 2009 Ford, what is the probability that the new car will have

b. zero problems?

c. two or fewer problems?

d. Give an operational definition for *problem*. Why is the operational definition important in interpreting the initial quality score?

6.41 Refer to Problem 6.40. If you purchased a 2009 Dodge, what is the probability that the new car will have

a. zero problems?

b. two or fewer problems?

c. Compare your answers in (a) and (b) to those for the Ford in Problem 6.40 (b) and (c).

6.42 Refer to Problem 6.40. Another article reported that in 2008, Ford had 1.12 problems per car and Dodge had 1.41 problems per car (data extracted from S. Carty, "Ford Moves Up in Quality Survey," *USA Today*, June 5, 2008, p. 3B). If you purchased a 2008 Ford, what is the probability that the new car will have

a. zero problems?

b. two or fewer problems?

c. Compare your answers in (a) and (b) to those for the 2009 Ford in Problem 6.40 (b) and (c).

6.43 Refer to Problem 6.42. If you purchased a 2008 Dodge, what is the probability that the new car will have

a. zero problems?

b. two or fewer problems?

c. Compare your answers in (a) and (b) to those for the 2009 Dodge in Problem 6.41 (a) and (b).

6.44 A toll-free phone number is available from 9 A.M. to 9 P.M. for your customers to register complaints about a product purchased from your company. Past history indicates that an average of 0.8 calls is received per minute.

a. What properties must be true about the situation described here in order to use the Poisson distribution to calculate probabilities concerning the number of phone calls received in a one-minute period?

Assuming that this situation matches the properties discussed in (a), what is the probability that during a one-minute period

b. zero phone calls will be received?

c. three or more phone calls will be received?

d. What is the maximum number of phone calls that will be received in a one-minute period 99.99% of the time?

USING STATISTICS @ Saxon Home Improvement, Part I Revisited

Monkey Business Images / Shutterstock.com

In the Saxon Home Improvement scenario at the beginning of this chapter, you were an accountant for the Saxon Home Improvement Company. The company's accounting information system automatically reviews order forms from online customers for possible mistakes. Any questionable invoices are tagged and included in a daily exceptions report. Knowing that the probability that an order will be tagged is 0.10, you were able to use the binomial distribution to determine the chance of finding a certain number of tagged forms in a sample of size four. There was a 65.6% chance that none of the forms would be tagged, a 29.2% chance that one would be tagged, and a 5.2% chance that two or more would be tagged. You were also able to determine that, on average, you would expect 0.4 forms to be tagged, and the standard deviation of the number of tagged order forms would be 0.6. Now that you have learned the mechanics of using the binomial distribution for a known probability of 0.10 and a sample size of four, you will be able to apply the same approach to any given probability and sample size. Thus, you will be able to make inferences about the online ordering process and, more importantly, evaluate any changes or proposed changes to the process.

SUMMARY

In this chapter, you have studied mathematical expectation and two important discrete probability distributions: the binomial and Poisson distributions. In the next chapter, you will study the most important continuous distribution, the normal distribution.

To help decide what probability distribution to use for a particular situation, you need to ask the following question:

- Is there a fixed number of observations, n, each of which is classified as an event of interest or not an event of interest? Or is there an area of opportunity?

- If there is a fixed number of observations, n, each of which is classified as an event of interest or not an event of interest, you use the binomial distribution. If there is an area of opportunity, you use the Poisson distribution.

KEY EQUATIONS

Expected Value, μ, of a Discrete Random Variable

$$\mu = E(X) = \sum_{i=1}^{N} x_i P(X = x_i)$$

Variance

$$\sigma^2 = \sum (X - \mu)^2 P(X)$$

Standard Deviation

$$\sigma = \sqrt{\left(\sum (X - \mu)^2 P(X) \right)}$$

Variance of a Discrete Random Variable

$$\sigma^2 = \sum_{i=1}^{N} [x_i - E(X)]^2 P(X = x_i)$$

Standard Deviation of a Discrete Random Variable

$$\sigma = \sqrt{\sigma^2} = \sqrt{\sum_{i=1}^{N} [x_i - E(X)]^2 P(X = x_i)}$$

Mean of the Binomial Distribution

$$\mu = E(X) = n\pi$$

Standard Deviation of the Binomial Distribution

$$\sigma = \sqrt{\sigma^2} = \sqrt{Var(X)} = \sqrt{n\pi(1 - \pi)}$$

Poisson Probability Distribution Function

$$P(X = x) = \frac{e^{-\lambda}\lambda^x}{x!}$$

Poisson Distribution

$$P(X = x|\lambda) = \frac{e^{-\lambda}\lambda^x}{x!}$$

KEY TERMS

area of opportunity   262
binomial distribution   250
expected value   240
mathematical model   250

probability distribution for a discrete
   random variable   238
random variable   238

standard deviation of a discrete
   random variable   247
variance of a discrete random
   variable   247

PROBLEMS

CHECKING YOUR UNDERSTANDING

6.45 What is the meaning of the expected value of a probability distribution?

6.46 What are the four properties that must be present in order to use the binomial distribution?

6.47 What are the four properties that must be present in order to use the Poisson distribution?

APPLYING THE CONCEPTS

6.48 Darwin Head, a 35-year-old sawmill worker, won $1 million and a Chevrolet Malibu Hybrid by scoring 15 goals within 24 seconds at the Vancouver Canucks National Hockey League game (B. Ziemer, "Darwin Evolves into an Instant Millionaire," *Vancouver Sun*, February 28, 2008, p. 1). Head said he would use the money to pay off his mortgage and provide for his children, and he had no plans to quit his job. The contest was part of the Chevrolet Malibu Million Dollar Shootout, sponsored by General Motors Canadian Division. Did GM-Canada risk the $1 million? No! GM-Canada purchased event insurance from a company specializing in promotions at sporting events such as a half-court basketball shot or a hole-in-one giveaway at the local charity golf outing. The event insurance company estimates the probability of a contestant winning the contest, and for a modest charge, insures the event. The promoters pay the insurance premium but take on no added risk as the insurance company will make the large payout in the unlikely event that a contestant wins. To see how it works, suppose that the insurance company estimates that the probability a contestant would win a Million Dollar Shootout is 0.001, and that the insurance company charges $4,000.
a. Calculate the expected value of the profit made by the insurance company.

b. Many call this kind of situation a win–win opportunity for the insurance company and the promoter. Do you agree? Explain.

6.49 Between 1896 when the Dow Jones Index was created and 2009, the index rose in 64% of the years (data extracted from M. Hulbert, "What the Past Can't Tell Investors," *The New York Times*, January 3, 2010, p. BU2). Based on this information, and assuming a binomial distribution, what do you think is the probability that the stock market will rise
a. next year?
b. the year after next?
c. in four of the next five years?
d. in none of the next five years?
e. For this situation, what assumption of the binomial distribution might not be valid?

6.50 In late 2007, it was reported that 79% of U.S. adults owned a cell phone (data extracted from E. C. Baig, "Tips Help Navigate Tech-Buying Maze," *USA Today*, November 28, 2007, p. 5B). Suppose that by the end of 2010, that percentage was 85%. If a sample of 10 U.S. adults is selected, what is the probability that
a. 8 own a cell phone?
b. at least 8 own a cell phone?
c. all 10 own a cell phone?
d. If you selected the sample in a particular geographical area and found that none of the 10 respondents owned a cell phone, what conclusion might you reach about whether the percentage of cell phone owners in this area was 85%?

6.51 One theory concerning the Dow Jones Industrial Average is that it is likely to increase during U.S. presidential election years. From 1964 through 2008, the Dow Jones Industrial Average increased in 9 of the 12 U.S. presidential election years. Assuming that this indicator is a random event with no predictive value, you would expect that the indicator would be correct 50% of the time.

a. What is the probability of the Dow Jones Industrial Average increasing in 9 or more of the 12 U.S. presidential election years if the probability of an increase in the Dow Jones Industrial Average is 0.50?

b. What is the probability that the Dow Jones Industrial Average will increase in 9 or more of the 12 U.S. presidential election years if the probability of an increase in the Dow Jones Industrial Average in any year is 0.75?

6.52 Errors in a billing process often lead to customer dissatisfaction and ultimately hurt bottom-line profits. An article in *Quality Progress* (L. Tatikonda, "A Less Costly Billing Process," *Quality Progress*, January 2008, pp. 30–38) discussed a company where 40% of the bills prepared contained errors. If 10 bills are processed, what is the probability that

a. 0 bills will contain errors?

b. exactly 1 bill will contain an error?

c. 2 or more bills will contain errors?

d. What are the mean and the standard deviation of the probability distribution?

6.53 Refer to Problem 6.52. Suppose that a quality improvement initiative has reduced the percentage of bills containing errors to 20%. If 10 bills are processed, what is the probability that

a. 0 bills will contain errors?

b. exactly 1 bill will contain an error?

c. 2 or more bills will contain errors?

d. What are the mean and the standard deviation of the probability distribution?

e. Compare the results of (a) through (c) to those of Problem 6.41 (a) through (c).

6.54 Social log-ins involve recommending or sharing an article that you read online. According to Janrain ("T. Wayne, One Log-In Catches on for Many Sites," *Drilling Down, The New York Times*, May 2, 2011, p. B2) in the first quarter of 2011, 35% signed in via Facebook compared with 31% for Google.

If a sample of 10 social log-ins is selected, what is the probability that

a. more than 4 signed in using Facebook?

b. more than 4 signed in using Google?

c. none signed in using Facebook?

d. What assumptions did you have to make to answer (a) through (c)?

6.55 One of the biggest frustrations for the consumer electronics industry is that customers are accustomed to returning goods for any reason (C. Lawton, "The War on Returns," *The Wall Street Journal*, May 8, 2008, pp. D1, D6). Recently, it was reported that returns for "no trouble found" were 68% of all the returns. Consider a sample of 20 customers who returned consumer electronics purchases. Use the binomial model to answer the following questions:

a. What is the expected value, or mean, of the binomial distribution?

b. What is the standard deviation of the binomial distribution?

c. What is the probability that 15 of the 20 customers made a return for "no trouble found"?

d. What is the probability that no more than 10 of the customers made a return for "no trouble found"?

e. What is the probability that 10 or more of the customers made a return for "no trouble found"?

6.56 Refer to Problem 6.55. In the same time period, 27% of the returns were for "buyer's remorse."

a. What is the expected value, or mean, of the binomial distribution?

b. What is the standard deviation of the binomial distribution?

c. What is the probability that none of the 20 customers made a return for "buyer's remorse"?

d. What is the probability that no more than 2 of the customers made a return for "buyer's remorse"?

e. What is the probability that 3 or more of the customers made a return for "buyer's remorse"?

6.57 One theory concerning the S&P 500 Index is that if it increases during the first five trading days of the year, it is likely to increase during the entire year. From 1950 through 2010, the S&P 500 Index had these early gains in 39 years. In 34 of these 39 years, the S&P 500 Index increased for the entire year. Assuming that this indicator is a random event with no predictive value, you would expect that the indicator would be correct 50% of the time. What is the probability of the S&P 500 Index increasing in 34 or more years if the true probability of an increase in the S&P 500 Index is

a. 0.50?

b. 0.70?

c. 0.90?

d. Based on the results of (a) through (c), what do you think is the probability that the S&P 500 Index will increase if there is an early gain in the first five trading days of the year? Explain.

6.58 *Spurious correlation* refers to the apparent relationship between variables that either have no true relationship or are related to other variables that have not been measured. One widely publicized stock market indicator in the United States that is an example of spurious correlation is the relationship between the winner of the National Football League Super Bowl and the performance of the Dow Jones Industrial Average in that year. The "indicator" states that when a team that existed before the National Football League merged with the American Football League wins the Super Bowl, the Dow Jones Industrial Average will increase in that year. (Of course, any correlation between these is spurious as one thing has absolutely nothing to do with the other!) Since the first Super Bowl was held in 1967 through 2010, the indicator has been correct 35 out of 44 times (data extracted from W. Power, "The Bulls Want Jets Grounded," *The Wall Street Journal*, January 22, 2011, p. B2). Assuming that this indicator is a random event with no predictive value, you would expect that the indicator would be correct 50% of the time.

a. What is the probability that the indicator would be correct 35 or more times in 44 years?

b. What does this tell you about the usefulness of this indicator?

6.59 Approximately 300 million golf balls were lost in the United States in 2009. Assume that the number of golf balls lost in an 18-hole round is distributed as a Poisson random variable with a mean of 5 balls.

a. What assumptions need to be made so that the number of golf balls lost in an 18-hole round is distributed as a Poisson random variable?

Making the assumptions given in (a), what is the probability that

b. 0 balls will be lost in an 18-hole round?

c. 5 or fewer balls will be lost in an 18-hole round?

d. 6 or more balls will be lost in an 18-hole round?

6.60 According to a Virginia Tech survey, college students make an average of 11 cell phone calls per day. Moreover,

80% of the students surveyed indicated that their parents pay their cell phone expenses (J. Elliot, "Professor Researches Cell Phone Usage Among Students," **www .physorg.com**, February 26, 2007).

a. What distribution can you use to model the number of calls a student makes in a day?

b. If you select a student at random, what is the probability that he or she makes more than 10 calls in a day? More than 15? More than 20?

c. If you select a random sample of 10 students, what distribution can you use to model the proportion of students who have parents who pay their cell phone expenses?

d. Using the distribution selected in (c), what is the probability that all 10 have parents who pay their cell phone expenses? At least 9? At least 8?

MANAGING ASHLAND MULTICOMM SERVICES

The Ashland MultiComm Services (AMS) marketing department wants to increase subscriptions for its *3-For-All* telephone, cable, and Internet combined service. AMS marketing has been conducting an aggressive direct-marketing campaign that includes postal and electronic mailings and telephone solicitations. Feedback from these efforts indicates that including premium channels in this combined service is a very important factor for both current and prospective subscribers. After several brainstorming sessions, the marketing department has decided to add premium cable channels as a no-cost benefit of subscribing to the *3-For-All* service.

The research director, Mona Fields, is planning to conduct a survey among prospective customers to determine how many premium channels need to be added to the *3-For-All* service in order to generate a subscription to the service. Based on past campaigns and on industry-wide data, she estimates the following:

Number of Free Premium Channels	Probability of Subscriptions
0	0.02
1	0.04
2	0.06
3	0.07
4	0.08
5	0.085

1. If a sample of 50 prospective customers is selected and no free premium channels are included in the *3-For-All* service offer, given past results, what is the probability that

a. fewer than 3 customers will subscribe to the *3-For-All* service offer?

b. 0 customers or 1 customers will subscribe to the *3-For- All* service offer?

c. more than 4 customers will subscribe to the *3-For-All* service offer?

Suppose that in the actual survey of 50 prospective customers, 4 customers subscribe to the *3-For-All* service offer.

d. What does this tell you about the previous estimate of the proportion of customers who would subscribe to the *3-For-All* service offer?

2. Instead of offering no premium free channels as in Problem 1, suppose that two free premium channels are included in the *3-For-All* service offer, Given past results, what is the probability that

a. fewer than 3 customers will subscribe to the *3-For-All* service offer?

b. 0 customers or 1 customer will subscribe to the *3-For-All* service offer?

c. more than 4 customers will subscribe to the *3-For-All* service offer?

d. Compare the results of (a) through (c) to those of 1.

Suppose that in the actual survey of 50 prospective customers, 6 customers subscribe to the *3-For-All* service offer.

e. What does this tell you about the previous estimate of the proportion of customers who would subscribe to the *3-For-All* service offer?

f. What do the results in (e) tell you about the effect of offering free premium channels on the likelihood of obtaining subscriptions to the *3-For-All* service?

3. Suppose that additional surveys of 50 prospective customers were conducted in which the number of free premium channels was varied. The results were as follows:

Number of Free Premium Channels	Number of Subscriptions
1	5
3	6
4	6
5	7

How many free premium channels should the research director recommend for inclusion in the *3-For-All* service? Explain.

REFERENCES

1. Levine, D. M., P. Ramsey, and R. Smidt, *Applied Statistics for Engineers and Scientists Using Microsoft Excel and Minitab* (Upper Saddle River, NJ: Prentice Hall, 2001).
2. *Microsoft Excel 2010* (Redmond, WA: Microsoft Corp., 2010).
3. *Minitab Release* 16 (State College, PA.: Minitab, Inc., 2010).
4. Moscove, S. A., M. G. Simkin, and N. A. Bagranoff, *Core Concepts of Accounting Information Systems*, 11th ed. (New York: Wiley, 2010).

EG6.1 The Probability Distribution for a Discrete Random Variable

In-Depth Excel Use the **COMPUTE worksheet** of the **Discrete Random Variable workbook** (shown below) as a template for computing the expected value, variance, and standard deviation of a discrete random variable. The worksheet contains the data for the Section 6.1 example on page 240 involving the number of interruptions per day in a large computer network. For other problems, overwrite the X and $P(X)$ values in columns A and B, respectively. If a problem has more or fewer than six outcomes, select the cell range **A5:E5**. If the problem has more than six outcomes:

1. Right-click and click **Insert** from the shortcut menu.

2. If a dialog box appears, click **Shift cells down** and then click **OK**.

3. Repeat steps 1 and 2 as many times as necessary.

4. Select the formulas in cell range **C4:E4** and copy them down through the new table rows.

5. Enter the new X and $P(X)$ values in columns **A** and **B**.

If the problem has fewer than six outcomes, right-click and click **Delete** from the shortcut menu. If a dialog box appears, click **Shift cells up** and then click **OK**. Repeat as many times as necessary and then enter the new X and $P(X)$ values in columns A and B.

	A	B	C	D	E	F	G	H
1	Discrete Random Variable Probability Distribution							
2							Statistics	
3	X	P(X)	X*P(X)	[X-E(X)]^2	[X-E(X)]^2*P(X)		Expected value	1.4 =SUM(C:C)
4	0	0.35	0	1.96	0.686		Variance	2.04 =SUM(E:E)
5	1	0.25	0.25	0.16	0.04		Standard deviation	1.43 =SQRT(H4)
6	2	0.20	0.4	0.36	0.072			
7	3	0.10	0.3	2.56	0.256	X*P(X)	[X-E(X)]^2	[X-E(X)]^2*P(X)
8	4	0.05	0.2	6.76	0.338	=A4 * B4	=(A4 - $H$3)^2	=D4 * B4
9	5	0.05	0.25	12.96	0.648	=A5 * B5	=(A5 - $H$3)^2	=D5 * B5
						=A6 * B6	=(A6 - $H$3)^2	=D6 * B6
						=A7 * B7	=(A7 - $H$3)^2	=D7 * B7
						=A8 * B8	=(A8 - $H$3)^2	=D8 * B8
						=A9 * B9	=(A9 - $H$3)^2	=D9 * B9

EG6.2 Binomial Distribution

PHStat2 Use **Binomial** to compute binomial probabilities. For example, to create a binomial probabilities table and histogram for Example 6.13 on page 257, similar to those in Table 6.16 and Figure 6.4, select **PHStat → Probability & Prob. Distributions → Binomial**. In the procedure's dialog box (shown in next column):

1. Enter **4** as the **Sample Size**.

2. Enter **0.1** as the **Prob. of an Event of Interest**.

3. Enter **0** as the **Outcomes From** value and enter **4** as the (Outcomes) **To** value.

4. Enter a **Title**, check **Histogram**, and click **OK**.

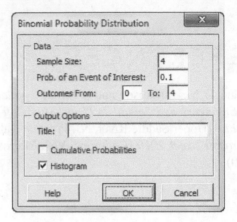

To add columns to the binomial probabilities table for $P(<=X), P(<X), P(>X)$, and $P(\geq X)$, check **Cumulative Probabilities** before clicking **OK** in step 4.

In-Depth Excel Use the **BINOMDIST** worksheet function to compute binomial probabilities. Enter the function as **BINOMDIST** (*X, sample size, π, cumulative*), where X is the number of events of interest, π is the probability of an event of interest, and *cumulative* is a **True** or **False** value. (When *cumulative* is **True**, the function computes the probability of X or fewer events of interest; when *cumulative* is **False**, the function computes the probability of exactly X events of interest.)

Use the **COMPUTE worksheet** of the **Binomial workbook**, shown in Table 6.16 on page 258, as a template for computing binomial probabilities. The worksheet contains the data for the Section 6.2 tagged orders example. Overwrite these values and adjust the table of probabilities for other problems. To create a histogram of the probability distribution, use the instructions in Appendix Section F.5.

EG6.3 Poisson Distribution

PHStat2 Use **Poisson** to compute Poisson probabilities. For example, to create a Poisson probabilities table similar to Table 6.17 on page 266, select **PHStat → Probability &**

Prob. Distributions → Poisson. In this procedure's dialog box (shown below):

1. Enter **3** as the **Mean/Expected No. of Events of Interest**.
2. Enter a **Title** and click **OK**.

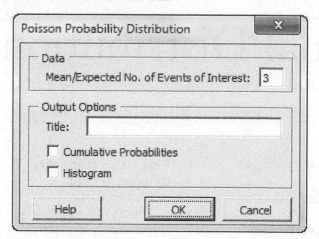

To add columns to the Poisson probabilities table for $P(<=X), P(<X), P(>X)$, and $P(\geq X)$, check **Cumulative**

Probabilities before clicking **OK** in step 2. To create a histogram of the probability distribution on a separate chart sheet, check **Histogram** before clicking **OK** in step 2.

In-Depth Excel Use the **POISSON** worksheet function to compute Poisson probabilities. Enter the function as **POISSON(X, lambda, cumulative)**, where X is the number of events of interest, *lambda* is the average or expected number of events of interest, and *cumulative* is a **True** or **False** value. (When *cumulative* is **True**, the function computes the probability of X or fewer events of interest; when *cumulative* is **False**, the function computes the probability of exactly X events of interest.)

Use the **COMPUTE worksheet** of the **Poisson workbook**, shown in Table 6.17 on page 266, as a template for computing Poisson probabilities. The worksheet contains the entries for the bank customer arrivals problem of Section 6.3. To adapt this worksheet to other problems, change the **Mean/Expected number of events of interest value** in cell **E4**. To create a histogram of the probability distribution, use the instructions in Appendix Section F.5.

7

The Normal Distribution

Learning Objectives
In this chapter, you learn:

- To compute probabilities from the normal distribution
- How to use the normal distribution to solve business problems
- To use the normal probability plot to determine whether a set of data is approximately normally distributed

USING STATISTICS

@ OurCampus!

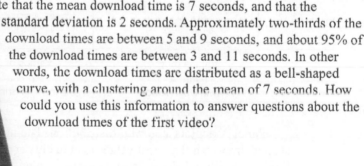

Y ou are a designer for the OurCampus! website, a social networking site that targets college students. To attract and retain visitors to the site, you need to make sure that the exclusive-content daily videos can be quickly downloaded and played in a user's browser. Download time, the amount of time, in seconds, that passes from first linking to the website home page until the first video is ready to play, is both a function of the streaming media technology used and the number of simultaneous users of the website.

To check how fast a video downloads, you open a web browser on a PC at the corporate offices of OurCampus! and measure the download time. Past data indicate that the mean download time is 7 seconds, and that the standard deviation is 2 seconds. Approximately two-thirds of the download times are between 5 and 9 seconds, and about 95% of the download times are between 3 and 11 seconds. In other words, the download times are distributed as a bell-shaped curve, with a clustering around the mean of 7 seconds. How could you use this information to answer questions about the download times of the first video?

I n Chapter 6, Saxon Home Improvement Company managers wanted to be able to answer questions about the number of tagged items in a given sample size. As an OurCampus! web designer, you face a different task, one that involves a continuous measurement because a download time could be any value and not just a whole number. How can you answer questions, such as the following, about this *continuous numerical variable*:

- What proportion of the video downloads take more than 9 seconds?
- How many seconds elapse before 10% of the downloads are complete?
- How many seconds elapse before 99% of the downloads are complete?
- How would enhancing the streaming media technology used affect the answers to these questions?

As in Chapter 6, you can use a probability distribution as a model. Reading this chapter will help you learn about characteristics of continuous probability distributions and how to use the normal distribution to solve business problems.

7.1 Continuous Probability Distributions

A **probability density function** is a mathematical expression that defines the distribution of the values for a continuous random variable. Figure 7.1 graphically displays three probability density functions.

FIGURE 7.1

Three continuous probability distributions

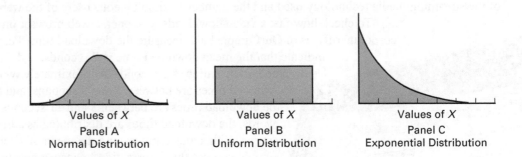

Panel A depicts a *normal* distribution. The normal distribution is symmetrical and bell-shaped, implying that most values tend to cluster around the mean, which, due to the distribution's symmetrical shape, is equal to the median. Although the values in a normal distribution can range from negative infinity to positive infinity, the shape of the distribution makes it very unlikely that extremely large or extremely small values will occur.

Panel B shows a *uniform distribution* where each value has an equal probability of occurrence anywhere in the range between the smallest value and the largest value. Sometimes referred to as the *rectangular distribution*, the uniform distribution is symmetrical, and therefore the mean equals the median.

Panel C illustrates an *exponential distribution*. This distribution is skewed to the right, making the mean larger than the median. The range for an exponential distribution is zero to positive infinity, but the distribution's shape makes the occurrence of extremely large values unlikely.

7.2 The Normal Distribution

The **normal distribution** (sometimes referred to as the *Gaussian distribution*) is the most common continuous distribution used in statistics. The normal distribution is vitally important in statistics for three main reasons:

- Numerous continuous variables common in business have distributions that closely resemble the normal distribution.
- The normal distribution can be used to approximate various discrete probability distributions.
- The normal distribution provides the basis for *classical statistical inference* because of its relationship to the *central limit theorem* (which is discussed in Section 8.4).

The normal distribution is represented by the classic bell shape shown in Panel A of Figure 7.1. In the normal distribution, you can calculate the probability that values occur within certain ranges or intervals. However, because probability for continuous variables is measured as an area under the curve, the *exact* probability of a *particular value* from a continuous distribution such as the normal distribution is zero. As an example, time (in seconds) is measured and not counted. Therefore, you can determine the probability that the download time for a video on a web browser is between 7 and 10 seconds, or the probability that the download time is between 8 and 9 seconds, or the probability that the download time is between 7.99 and 8.01 seconds. However, the probability that the download time is *exactly* 8 seconds is zero.

The normal distribution has several important theoretical properties:

- It is symmetrical, and its mean and median are therefore equal.
- It is bell-shaped in appearance.
- Its interquartile range is equal to 1.33 standard deviations. Thus, the middle 50% of the values are contained within an interval of two-thirds of a standard deviation below the mean and two-thirds of a standard deviation above the mean.
- It has an infinite range $(-\infty < X < \infty)$.

In practice, many variables have distributions that closely resemble the theoretical properties of the normal distribution. The data in Table 7.1 represent the amount of soft drink in 10,000 1-liter bottles filled on a recent day. The continuous variable of interest, the amount of soft drink filled, can be approximated by the normal distribution. The measurements of the amount of soft drink in the 10,000 bottles cluster in the interval 1.05 to 1.055 liters and distribute symmetrically around that grouping, forming a bell-shaped pattern.

TABLE 7.1

Amount of Fill in 10,000 Bottles of a Soft Drink

Amount of Fill (liters)	Relative Frequency
< 1.025	48/10,000 = 0.0048
1.025 < 1.030	122/10,000 = 0.0122
1.030 < 1.035	325/10,000 = 0.0325
1.035 < 1.040	695/10,000 = 0.0695
1.040 < 1.045	1,198/10,000 = 0.1198
1.045 < 1.050	1,664/10,000 = 0.1664
1.050 < 1.055	1,896/10,000 = 0.1896
1.055 < 1.060	1,664/10,000 = 0.1664
1.060 < 1.065	1,198/10,000 = 0.1198
1.065 < 1.070	695/10,000 = 0.0695
1.070 < 1.075	325/10,000 = 0.0325
1.075 < 1.080	122/10,000 = 0.0122
1.080 or above	48/10,000 = 0.0048
Total	1.0000

Figure 7.2 shows the relative frequency histogram and polygon for the distribution of the amount filled in 10,000 bottles.

FIGURE 7.2

Relative frequency histogram and polygon of the amount filled in 10,000 bottles of a soft drink

Source: Data are taken from Table 7.1.

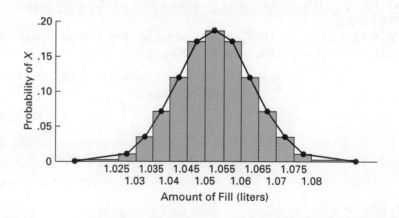

For these data, the first three theoretical properties of the normal distribution are approximately satisfied. However, the fourth one, having an infinite range, is not. The amount filled in a bottle cannot possibly be zero or below, nor can a bottle be filled beyond its capacity. From Table 7.1, you see that only 48 out of every 10,000 bottles filled are expected to contain 1.08 liters or more, and an equal number are expected to contain less than 1.025 liters.

The symbol $f(X)$ is used to represent a probability density function. The **probability density function for the normal distribution** is given in Equation (7.1).

NORMAL PROBABILITY DENSITY FUNCTION

$$f(X) = \frac{1}{\sqrt{2\pi}\sigma} e^{-(1/2)[(X-\mu)/\sigma]^2} \qquad (7.1)$$

where

e = mathematical constant approximated by 2.71828

π = mathematical constant approximated by 3.14159

μ = mean

σ = standard deviation

X = any value of the continuous variable, where $-\infty < X < \infty$

Although Equation (7.1) may look complicated, because e and π are mathematical constants, the probabilities of the random variable X are dependent only on the two parameters of the normal distribution—the mean, μ, and the standard deviation, σ. Every time you specify particular values of μ and σ, a *different* normal probability distribution is generated. Figure 7.3 illustrates this principle. The distributions labeled A and B have the same mean (μ) but have different standard deviations. Distributions A and C have the same standard deviation (σ) but have different means. Distributions B and C have different values for both μ and σ.

FIGURE 7.3
Three normal distributions

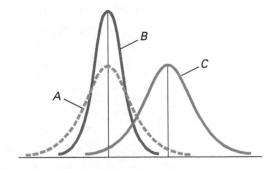

CALCULATOR LESSON 7

CASIO FX-9750G, CFX-9850GB, OR FX-9750GII CALCULATOR

Lesson 7—Normal Distribution

The Casio calculator has *two* normal probability functions programmed into its memory. These are the following:

i. **Ncd**, which stands for **n**ormal **c**umulative **d**istribution. This function calculates a normal probability of the form

$$P(X \leq \#)$$

ii. **InvN**, which stands for **i**nverse **n**ormal. This function calculates an "x" value (i.e., ?) for a known normal probability of the form

$$P(X \leq ?) = \text{given probability}$$

Suppose that the weights of adults are normally distributed with a mean of 170.0 lbs. and a standard deviation of 25.0 lbs.

a. What is the probability that a person weighs from 150 to 190 lbs.?

> **Solution:**   X = a person's weight
> μ = 170.0 lbs.
> σ = 25.0 lbs.

Select **STAT   F5**(DIST)   **F1**(NORM)   **F2**(Ncd), and then select the following options:

Lower   : **150 EXE**
Upper   : **190 EXE**
σ : **25 EXE**
μ : **170 EXE**

Now key **EXE** or **F1**(Calc).

The calculator will now show the result 0.5762892.

(i.e., P(150 ≤ X ≤ 190) = 0.5763)

b. What is the probability that a person weighs less than 140 lbs.?

Lower   : **−100 EXE**
Upper   : **140 EXE**
σ : **25 EXE**
μ : **170 EXE**

Now key **EXE** or **F1**(Calc).

The calculator will now show the result 0.11506967.

(i.e., P(X < 140) = 0.1151)

Note: To represent ∞ use any value less than μ 6σ.
To represent ∞ use any value more than μ + 6σ.

c. What is the probability that a person weighs at least 160 lbs.?

Lower   : **160 EXE**
Upper   : **1000 EXE**
σ : **25 EXE**
μ : **170 EXE**

P(X ≥ 160) = 0.6554

d. What is the maximum weight of the lightest 15% of the adult population?

P(X ≤ ?) = 0.15

Select **STAT   F5**(DIST)   **F1**(NORM)   **F3**(InvN), and then select the following options.

Area   : **.15 EXE**
σ : **25 EXE**
μ : **170 EXE**

Now key **EXE** or **F1**(Calc).   The calculator will now show the result 144.089165.

(i.e., The lightest 15% of adults weigh at most 144.1 lbs.)

e. What is the minimum weight to be in the heaviest 30% of the adult population?

P(X ≥ ?) = 0.3

Select **STAT F5**(DIST) **F1**(NORM) **F3**(InvN), and then select the following options:

Area	: .7	**EXE**
σ	: **25**	**EXE**
μ	: **170 EXE**	

Now key **EXE** or **F1**(Calc).   The calculator will now show the result 183.110013.

(i.e., The heaviest 30% weigh at least 183.1 lbs.)

Note: When using the InvN function, the *Area* value that is required is the area to the *left* of the desired X value.

Problems for Section 7.2

NORMAL PROBABILITY EXERCISES

Normal Template:

X = _____

μ =
          } Normal
σ =

P(_____) = P(X symbol #) =
   (words*)

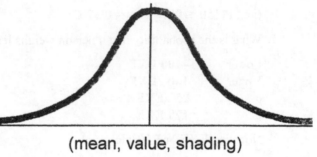

(mean, value, shading)

_____ = 0._ _ _ _
   (calculator or SPSS input)   (4 dec.)

Inverse Normal Template:

X = _____

μ =
          } Normal
σ =

P(_____) = P(X symbol ?) = 0._____
   (words*)   (given)

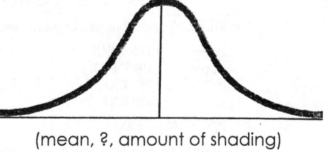

(mean, ?, amount of shading)

? = _____ = _____
      (calculator or SPSS input)   (same dec. as μ)

Concluding statement.

7.1 The lifetime of a certain brand of tire is normally distributed with a mean of 90,000 km. and standard deviation of 8,000 km. The tire carries a warranty for 80,000 km.
a. What is the probability that the tire you recently purchased will last more than 100,000 km.?
b. What percent of this brand of tire will fail before the warranty expires?
c. What should the mileage warranty be so that only 4% of the tires need to be replaced under warranty?

7.2 A firm's marketing manager believes that total sales for next year can be represented by a normal distribution, with a mean of $2.5 million and a standard deviation of $300,000. The firm has fixed costs of $1.8 million.
a. What is the probability that the firm's sales will be less than $3.0 million?
b. What is the probability that the firm will have sufficient sales to cover fixed costs?

c. What is the probability that the firm's sales will be within $150,000 of the expected (i.e., mean) sales?

d. Determine the sales level that has only a 9% chance of being exceeded.

7.3 The owner of a convenience store has copies of the local newspaper delivered early each morning. The demand for papers is normally distributed with a mean of 75 and a standard deviation of 16.

a. What is the probability that the newspapers will be sold out if the owner orders 65 copies?

b. How many copies should be ordered so that the probability of selling out is at most 15%?

7.4 In the movie *Forest Gump*, the public school required an IQ of at least 80 for admittance.

a. If IQ test scores are normally distributed with a mean of 100 and a standard deviation of 16, what percent of children would qualify for admittance to the school?

b. If the public school wished to have only 5% of all children not qualify for admittance, what minimum IQ test score should be required for admittance?

7.5 An investment broker reports that the annual returns on common stock and municipal bonds are both normally distributed. The stocks have a mean return of 12.4% with a standard deviation of 20.6%. On the other hand, the bonds have a mean return of 5.2% with a standard deviation of 8.6%.

a. If you are a conservative investor and just don't like to lose money, which type of investment should you choose?

b. If you are a more ambitious investor and would like to have the best chance of making more than 15%, which investment should you choose?

c. What minimum return would a stock have to earn to be rated in the top 20% of stocks in terms of return?

7.6 At a certain university the cumulative grade point average (CGPA) of first year students usually averages 2.73 with a standard deviation of 0.37. It has been found that the marks are usually approximately normally distributed.

a. What is the probability that a student will have a CGPA that is between 2.00 and 3.00?

b. What percent of students will be on probation (i.e., their CGPA is less than 2.00)?

c. Academic scholarships are awarded to the top 1% of first year students. What minimum CGPA is needed to receive a scholarship?

APPLYING THE CONCEPTS

7.7 In 2008, the per capita consumption of coffee in the United States was reported to be 4.2 kg, or 9.24 pounds (data extracted from **en.wikipedia.org/wiki/List_of_countries_by_coffee_consumption_per_capita**). Assume that the per capita consumption of coffee in the United States is approxi-

mately distributed as a normal random variable, with a mean of 9.24 pounds and a standard deviation of 3 pounds.

a. What is the probability that someone in the United States consumed more than 10 pounds of coffee in 2008?

b. What is the probability that someone in the United States consumed between 3 and 5 pounds of coffee in 2008?

c. What is the probability that someone in the United States consumed less than 5 pounds of coffee in 2008?

d. 99% of the people in the United States consumed less than how many pounds of coffee?

✓ SELF Test 7.8 Toby's Trucking Company determined that the distance traveled per truck per year is normally distributed, with a mean of 50 thousand miles and a standard deviation of 12 thousand miles.

a. What proportion of trucks can be expected to travel between 34 and 50 thousand miles in a year?

b. What percentage of trucks can be expected to travel either below 30 or above 60 thousand miles in a year?

c. How many miles will be traveled by at least 80% of the trucks?

d. What are your answers to (a) through (c) if the standard deviation is 10 thousand miles?

7.9 Consumers spend an average of $21 per week in cash without being aware of where it goes (data extracted from "Snapshots: A Hole in Our Pockets," *USA Today*, January 18, 2010, p. 1A). Assume that the amount of cash spent without being aware of where it goes is normally distributed and that the standard deviation is $5.

a. What is the probability that a randomly selected person will spend more than $25?

b. What is the probability that a randomly selected person will spend between $10 and $20?

c. Between what two values will the middle 95% of the amounts of cash spent fall?

7.10 A set of final examination grades in an introductory statistics course is normally distributed, with a mean of 73 and a standard deviation of 8.

a. What is the probability that a student scored below 91 on this exam?

b. What is the probability that a student scored between 65 and 89?

c. The probability is 5% that a student taking the test scores higher than what grade?

d. If the professor grades on a curve (i.e., gives A's to the top 10% of the class, regardless of the score), are you better off with a grade of 81 on this exam or a grade of 68 on a different exam, where the mean is 62 and the standard deviation is 3? Show your answer statistically and explain.

7.11 A statistical analysis of 1,000 long-distance telephone calls made from the headquarters of the Bricks and Clicks Computer Corporation indicates that the length of these calls is normally distributed, with $\mu = 240$ seconds and $\sigma = 40$ seconds.

a. What is the probability that a call lasted less than 180 seconds?

b. What is the probability that a call lasted between 180 and 300 seconds?

c. What is the probability that a call lasted between 110 and 180 seconds?

d. 1% of all calls will last less than how many seconds?

7.12 In 2008, the per capita consumption of coffee in Sweden was reported to be 8.2 kg, or 18.04 pounds (data extracted from **en.wikipedia.org/wiki/List_of_countries_by_coffee_consumption_per_capita**). Assume that the per capita consumption of coffee in Sweden is approximately distributed as a normal random variable, with a mean of 18.04 pounds and a standard deviation of 5 pounds.

a. What is the probability that someone in Sweden consumed more than 10 pounds of coffee in 2008?

b. What is the probability that someone in Sweden consumed between 3 and 5 pounds of coffee in 2008?

c. What is the probability that someone in Sweden consumed less than 5 pounds of coffee in 2008?

d. 99% of the people in Sweden consumed less than how many pounds of coffee?

7.13 Many manufacturing problems involve the matching of machine parts, such as shafts that fit into a valve hole. A particular design requires a shaft with a diameter of 22.000 mm, but shafts with diameters between 21.990 mm and 22.010 mm are acceptable. Suppose that the manufacturing process yields shafts with diameters normally distributed, with a mean of 22.002 mm and a standard deviation of 0.005 mm. For this process, what is

a. the proportion of shafts with a diameter between 21.99 mm and 22.00 mm?

b. the probability that a shaft is acceptable?

c. the diameter that will be exceeded by only 2% of the shafts?

d. What would be your answers in (a) through (c) if the standard deviation of the shaft diameters were 0.004 mm?

7.3 Computing Z-Scores and Normal Probability

To compute normal probabilities, you first convert a normally distributed random variable, X, to a **standardized normal random variable**, Z, using the **transformation formula**, shown in Equation (7.2). Applying this formula allows you to look up values in a normal probability table and avoid the tedious and complex computations that Equation (7.1) would otherwise require.

THE TRANSFORMATION FORMULA

The Z value is equal to the difference between X and the mean, μ, divided by the standard deviation, σ.

$$Z = \frac{X - \mu}{\sigma} \tag{7.2}$$

The transformation formula computes a Z value that expresses the difference of the X value from the mean, μ, in units of the standard deviation called *standardized units*. While a random variable, X, has mean, μ, and standard deviation, σ, the standardized random variable, Z, always has mean $\mu = 0$ and standard deviation $\sigma = 1$.

Then you can determine the probabilities by using Table E.2, the **cumulative standardized normal distribution**. For example, recall from the Using Statistics scenario on page 279 that past data indicate that the time to download a video is normally distributed, with a mean $\mu = 7$ seconds and a standard deviation $\sigma = 2$ seconds. From Figure 7.4, you see that every measurement X has a corresponding standardized measurement Z, computed from Equation (7.2), the transformation formula. Therefore, a download time of 9 seconds is equivalent to 1 standardized unit (1 standard deviation) above the mean because

$$Z = \frac{9 - 7}{2} = +1$$

Z Scores

An **extreme value** or **outlier** is a value located far away from the mean. Z scores are useful in identifying outliers. The larger the Z score, the greater the distance from the value to the mean. The **Z score** is the difference between the value and the mean, divided by the standard deviation.

Z SCORES

$$Z = \frac{X - \overline{X}}{S} \tag{7.3}$$

For the time-to-get-ready data, the mean is 39.6 minutes, and the standard deviation is 6.77 minutes. The time to get ready on the first day is 39.0 minutes. You compute the Z score for Day 1 by using Equation (4.7):

$$Z = \frac{X - \overline{X}}{S}$$

$$= \frac{39.0 - 39.6}{6.77}$$

$$= -0.09$$

Table 7.2 shows the Z scores for all 10 days. The largest Z score is 1.83 for Day 4, on which the time to get ready was 52 minutes. The lowest Z score was -1.57 for Day 2, on which the time to get ready was 29 minutes. As a general rule, a Z score is considered an outlier if it is less than -3.0 or greater than $+3.0$. None of the times met that criterion to be considered outliers.

TABLE 7.2

Z Scores for the 10 Getting-Ready Times

	Time (X)	Z Score
	39	−0.09
	29	−1.57
	43	0.50
	52	1.83
	39	−0.09
	44	0.65
	40	0.06
	31	−1.27
	44	0.65
	35	−0.68
Mean	39.6	
Standard deviation	6.77	

EXAMPLE 7.1

Computing the Z Scores of the Number of Calories in Iced Coffee Drinks

The data in the file `CoffeeDrink` represent the calories of 16-ounce iced coffee drinks at Dunkin' Donuts and Starbucks. Compute the Z scores of the calories of 16-ounce iced coffee drinks.

SOLUTION Table 7.3 illustrates the Z scores of the calories of 16-ounce iced coffee drinks. The largest Z score is 1.33, for an iced coffee drink with 530 calories. The lowest Z score is -1.24, for an iced coffee drink with 240 calories. There are no apparent outliers in these data because none of the Z scores is less than -3.0 or greater than $+3.0$.

TABLE 7.3

Z Scores of the Number of Calories in Iced Coffee Drinks

	Calories	Z Scores
	240	−1.24
	260	−1.06
	350	−0.27
	350	−0.27
	420	0.35
	510	1.15
	530	1.33
Mean	380	
Standard Deviation	113.1371	

FIGURE 7.4

Transformation of scales

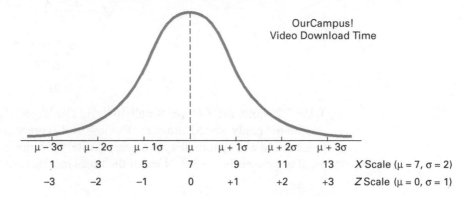

A download time of 1 second is equivalent to –3 standardized units (3 standard deviations) below the mean because

$$Z = \frac{1 - 7}{2} = -3$$

Figure 7.4 illustrates that the standard deviation is the unit of measurement. In other words, a time of 9 seconds is 2 seconds (1 standard deviation) higher, or *slower*, than the mean time of 7 seconds. Similarly, a time of 1 second is 6 seconds (3 standard deviations) lower, or *faster*, than the mean time.

To further illustrate the transformation formula, suppose that another website has a download time for a video that is normally distributed, with a mean $\mu = 4$ seconds and a standard deviation $\sigma = 1$ second. Figure 7.5 shows this distribution.

FIGURE 7.5

A different transformation of scales

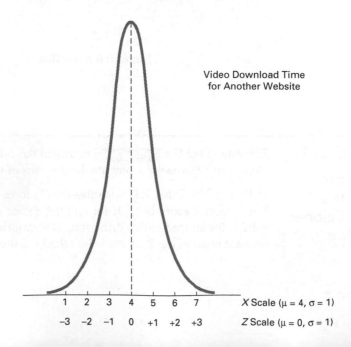

Comparing these results with those of the OurCampus! website, you see that a download time of 5 seconds is 1 standard deviation above the mean download time because

$$Z = \frac{5 - 4}{1} = +1$$

A time of 1 second is 3 standard deviations below the mean download time because

$$Z = \frac{1 - 4}{1} = -3$$

With the Z value computed, you look up the normal probability using a table of values from the cumulative standardized normal distribution, such as Table E.2 in Appendix E. Suppose you wanted to find the probability that the download time for the OurCampus! site is less than 9 seconds. Recall from page 288 that transforming $X = 9$ to standardized Z units, given a mean $\mu = 7$ seconds and a standard deviation $\sigma = 2$ seconds, leads to a Z value of +1.00.

With this value, you use Table E.2 to find the cumulative area under the normal curve less than (to the left of) $Z = +1.00$. To read the probability or area under the curve less than $Z = +1.00$, you scan down the Z column in Table E.2 until you locate the Z value of interest (in 10ths) in the Z row for 1.0. Next, you read across this row until you intersect the column that contains the 100ths place of the Z value. Therefore, in the body of the table, the probability for $Z = 1.00$ corresponds to the intersection of the row $Z = 1.0$ with the column $Z = .00$. Table 7.2, which reproduces a portion of Table E.2, shows this intersection. The probability listed at the intersection is 0.8413, which means that there is an 84.13% chance that the download time will be less than 9 seconds. Figure 7.6 graphically shows this probability.

TABLE 7.4

Finding a Cumulative Area Under the Normal Curve

Cumulative Probabilities									
Z	.00	.01	.02	.03	.04	.05	.06	.07	.08	.09
0.0	.5000	.5040	.5080	.5120	.5160	.5199	.5239	.5279	.5319	.5359
0.1	.5398	.5438	.5478	.5517	.5557	.5596	.5636	.5675	.5714	.5753
0.2	.5793	.5832	.5871	.5910	.5948	.5987	.6026	.6064	.6103	.6141
0.3	.6179	.6217	.6255	.6293	.6331	.6368	.6406	.6443	.6480	.6517
0.4	.6554	.6591	.6628	.6664	.6700	.6736	.6772	.6808	.6844	.6879
0.5	.6915	.6950	.6985	.7019	.7054	.7088	.7123	.7157	.7190	.7224
0.6	.7257	.7291	.7324	.7357	.7389	.7422	.7454	.7486	.7518	.7549
0.7	.7580	.7612	.7642	.7673	.7704	.7734	.7764	.7794	.7823	.7852
0.8	.7881	.7910	.7939	.7967	.7995	.8023	.8051	.8078	.8106	.8133
0.9	.8159	.8186	.8212	.8238	.8264	.8289	.8315	.8340	.8365	.8389
1.0	.8413	.8438	.8461	.8485	.8508	.8531	.8554	.8577	.8599	.8621

Source: Extracted from Table E.2.

Finding Z Value Using the CASIO Calculator

To find a particular value, Z, associated with a known probability, mean and standard deviation, follow these calculator steps.

Select **STAT F5**(DIST) **F1**(NORM) **F3**(InvN) **F2**(Var), and then select the following options:

Inverse Normal
Data   : **Variable**
Tail   : **Left (F1)** OR **Right (F2)** OR **CNTR (F3)**
Area   :
σ :
μ :
Save Res : **None**
Execute
Now key **EXE** or **F1**(CALC).

FIGURE 7.6

Determining the area
less than Z from
a cumulative
standardized normal
distribution

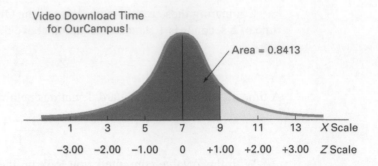

However, for the other website, you see that a time of 5 seconds is 1 standardized unit above the mean time of 4 seconds. Thus, the probability that the download time will be less than 5 seconds is also 0.8413. Figure 7.7 shows that regardless of the value of the mean, μ, and standard deviation, σ, of a normally distributed variable, Equation (7.2) can transform the X value to a Z value.

FIGURE 7.7

Demonstrating a
transformation of scales
for corresponding
cumulative portions
under two normal curves

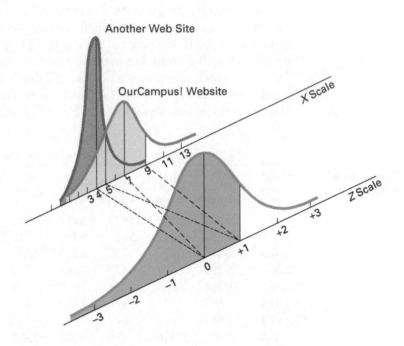

Now that you have learned to use Table E.2 with Equation (7.2), you can answer many questions related to the OurCampus! video download, using the normal distribution.

The Empirical Rule

In most data sets, a large portion of the values tend to cluster somewhere near the median. In right-skewed data sets, this clustering occurs to the left of the mean—that is, at a value less than the mean. In left-skewed data sets, the values tend to cluster to the right of the mean—that is, greater than the mean. In symmetrical data sets, where the median and mean are the same, the values often tend to cluster around the median and mean, producing a bell-shaped distribution. You can use the **empirical rule** to examine the variability in such distributions:

- Approximately 68% of the values are within a distance of ± 1 standard deviation from the mean.
- Approximately 95% of the values are within a distance of ± 2 standard deviations from the mean.
- Approximately 99.7% of the values are within a distance of ± 3 standard deviations from the mean.

The empirical rule helps you measure how the values distribute above and below the mean and can help you identify outliers. The empirical rule implies that for bell-shaped distributions, only about 1 out of 20 values will be beyond two standard deviations from the mean in either direction. As a general rule, you can consider values not found in the interval $\mu \pm 2\sigma$ as potential outliers. The rule also implies that only about 3 in 1,000 will be beyond three standard deviations from the mean. Therefore, values not found in the interval $\mu \pm 3\sigma$ are almost always considered outliers.

EXAMPLE 7.2

Using the Empirical Rule

A population of 12-ounce cans of cola is known to have a mean fill-weight of 12.06 ounces and a standard deviation of 0.02. The population is known to be bell-shaped. Describe the distribution of fill-weights. Is it very likely that a can will contain less than 12 ounces of cola?

SOLUTION

$$\mu \pm \sigma = 12.06 \pm 0.02 = (12.04, 12.08)$$

$$\mu \pm 2\sigma = 12.06 \pm 2(0.02) = (12.02, 12.10)$$

$$\mu \pm 3\sigma = 12.06 \pm 3(0.02) = (12.00, 12.12)$$

Using the empirical rule, approximately 68% of the cans will contain between 12.04 and 12.08 ounces, approximately 95% will contain between 12.02 and 12.10 ounces, and approximately 99.7% will contain between 12.00 and 12.12 ounces. Therefore, it is highly unlikely that a can will contain less than 12 ounces.

For heavily skewed data sets, or those not appearing bell-shaped for any other reason, the Chebyshev rule discussed next should be applied instead of the empirical rule.

The Chebyshev Rule

The **Chebyshev rule** states that for any data set, regardless of shape, the percentage of values that are found within distances of k standard deviations from the mean must be at least

$$(1 - 1/k^2) \times 100\%$$

You can use this rule for any value of k greater than 1. Consider $k = 2$. The Chebyshev rule states that at least $[1 - (1/2)^2] \times 100\% = 75\%$ of the values must be found within ± 2 standard deviations of the mean.

The Chebyshev rule is very general and applies to any type of distribution. The rule indicates *at least* what percentage of the values fall within a given distance from the mean. However, if the data set is approximately bell-shaped, the empirical rule will more accurately reflect the greater concentration of data close to the mean. Table 7.5 compares the Chebyshev and empirical rules.

TABLE 7.5

How Data Vary Around the Mean

	% of Values Found in Intervals Around the Mean	
Interval	**Chebyshev (any distribution)**	**Empirical Rule (bell-shaped distribution)**
$(\mu - \sigma, \mu + \sigma)$	At least 0%	Approximately 68%
$(\mu - 2\sigma, \mu + 2\sigma)$	At least 75%	Approximately 95%
$(\mu - 3\sigma, \mu + 3\sigma)$	At least 88.89%	Approximately 99.7%

EXAMPLE 7.3

Using the Chebyshev Rule

A population of 12-ounce cans of cola is known to have a mean fill-weight of 12.06 ounces and a standard deviation of 0.02. However, the shape of the population is unknown, and you cannot assume that it is bell-shaped. Describe the distribution of fill-weights. Is it very likely that a can will contain less than 12 ounces of cola?

SOLUTION

$$\mu \pm \sigma = 12.06 \pm 0.02 = (12.04, 12.08)$$

$$\mu \pm 2\sigma = 12.06 \pm 2(0.02) = (12.02, 12.10)$$

$$\mu \pm 3\sigma = 12.06 \pm 3(0.02) = (12.00, 12.12)$$

Because the distribution may be skewed, you cannot use the empirical rule. Using the Chebyshev rule, you cannot say anything about the percentage of cans containing between 12.04 and 12.08 ounces. You can state that at least 75% of the cans will contain between 12.02 and 12.10 ounces and at least 88.89% will contain between 12.00 and 12.12 ounces. Therefore, between 0 and 11.11% of the cans will contain less than 12 ounces.

You can use these two rules for understanding how data are distributed around the mean when you have sample data. In each case, you use the value you calculated for $\overline{X}$ in place of μ and the value you calculated for S in place of σ. The results you compute using the sample statistics are *approximations* because you used sample statistics $(\overline{X}, S)$ and not population parameters (μ, σ).

EXAMPLE 7.4

Finding $P(X > 9)$

What is the probability that the video download time for the OurCampus! website will be at least 9 seconds?

SOLUTION The probability that the download time will be less than 9 seconds is 0.8413 (see Figure 7.6 on page 290). Thus, the probability that the download time will be at least 9 seconds is the *complement* of less than 9 seconds, $1 - 0.8413 = 0.1587$. Figure 7.8 illustrates this result.

FIGURE 7.8

Finding $P(X > 9)$

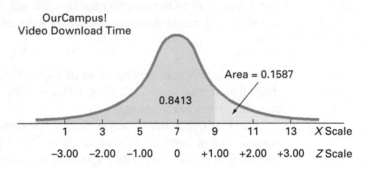

CASIO Calculator Instruction

Use the Casio calculator to find $P(X > 9)$.

Select **STAT F5**(DIST) **F1**(NORM) **F2**(Ncd) **F2**(Var), and then select the following options:

Normal C.D.
Data   : **Variable**
Lower   : **9**
Upper   : **10000** (Note: The calculator will not accept "+ ∞." Therefore, you input a large positive number relative to its mean value.)
σ : **2**
μ : **7**
Save Res : **None**
Execute
Now key **EXE** or **F1**(CALC).

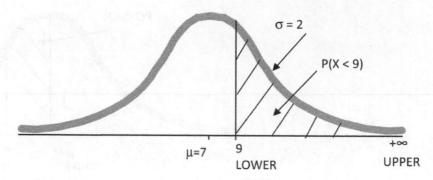

The calculator will now show the following result:

Normal C.D.
$p\ \ = 0.15865525$
z: Low $= 1$
z : Up $\ = 4996.5$

Answer: The probability that the download time will be more than 9 seconds is 0.1587.

EXAMPLE 7.5
Finding
$P(X < 7 \text{ or } X > 9)$

What is the probability that the video download time for the OurCampus! website will be under 7 seconds or over 9 seconds?

SOLUTION To find this probability, you separately calculate the probability of a download time less than 7 seconds and the probability of a download time greater than 9 seconds and then add these two probabilities together. Figure 7.9 illustrates this result. Because the mean is 7 seconds, 50% of download times are under 7 seconds. From Example 7.4, you know that the probability that the download time is greater than 9 seconds is 0.1587. Therefore, the probability that a download time is under 7 or over 9 seconds, $P(X < 7 \text{ or } X > 9)$, is $0.5000 + 0.1587 = 0.6587$.

FIGURE 7.9
Finding
$P(X < 7 \text{ or } X > 9)$

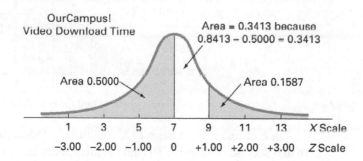

CASIO Calculator Instruction

Use the Casio calculator to find $P(7 < X < 9)$.

Select **STAT F5**(DIST) **F1**(NORM) **F2**(Ncd) **F2**(Var), and then select the following options:

Normal C.D.
Data   : **Variable**
Lower   : 7
Upper   : **9**
σ : 2
μ : **7**
Save Res   : **None**
Execute
Now key **EXE** or **F1**(CALC).

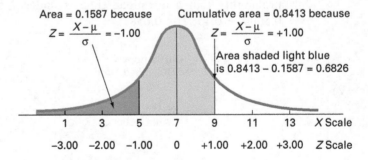

The calculator will now show the following result:

Normal C.D.
p = 0.34134474
z: Low = 0
z : Up = 1

Answer: The probability that the download time will be between 7 and 9 seconds is 0.3413.

EXAMPLE 7.6

Finding
$P(5 < X < 9)$

FIGURE 7.10
Finding $P(5 < X < 9)$

What is the probability that video download time for the OurCampus! website will be between 5 and 9 seconds—that is, $P(5 < X < 9)$?

SOLUTION In Figure 7.10, you can see that the area of interest is located between two values, 5 and 9.

Area = 0.1587 because   Cumulative area = 0.8413 because
$Z = \dfrac{X-\mu}{\sigma} = -1.00$ $Z = \dfrac{X-\mu}{\sigma} = +1.00$

Area shaded light blue
is 0.8413 − 0.1587 = 0.6826

	1	3	5	7	9	11	13	X Scale
	−3.00	−2.00	−1.00	0	+1.00	+2.00	+3.00	Z Scale

In Example 7.4 on page 292, you already found that the area under the normal curve less than 9 seconds is 0.8413. To find the area under the normal curve less than 5 seconds,

$$Z = \frac{5 - 7}{2} = -1.00$$

Using Table E.2, you look up $Z = -1.00$ and find 0.1587. Therefore, the probability that the download time will be between 5 and 9 seconds is $0.8413 - 0.1587 = 0.6826$, as displayed in Figure 7.10.

CASIO Calculator Instruction

Use the Casio calculator to find $P(X < 7)$ or $P(X > 9)$. You have to solve this problem in two stages. In stage 1 you solve for $P(X < 7)$, and in stage 2 you solve for $P(X > 9)$.

Stage 1: Solve for $P(X < 7)$.

Select **STAT F5**(DIST) **F1**(NORM) **F2**(Ncd) **F2**(Var), and then select the following options:

Normal C.D.
Data   : **Variable**
Lower   : **−10000** (Note: The calculator will not accept "- ∞." Therefore, you input a large negative number relative to its mean value.)
Upper   : **7**
σ   : 2
μ   : **7**
Save Res   : **None**
Execute
Now key **EXE** or **F1**(CALC).

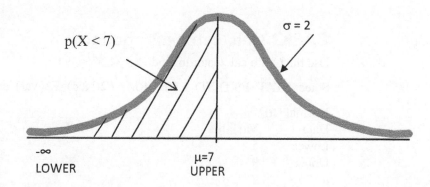

The calculator will now show the following result:

Normal C.D.
p = 0.5
z: Low = −5003.5
z : Up = 0

Answer: The probability that the download time is under 7 seconds is 0.5.

Stage 2: Solve for $P(X > 9)$.

Select **STAT F5**(DIST) **F1**(NORM) **F2**(Ncd) **F2**(Var), and then select the following options:

Normal C.D.
Data   : **Variable**
Lower   : 9
Upper   : **10000** (Note: The calculator will not accept "+ ∞." Therefore, you input a large positive number relative to its mean value.)
σ   : 2
μ   : **7**
Save Res   : **None**
Execute
Now key **EXE** or **F1**(CALC).

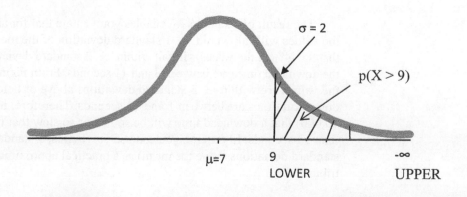

The calculator will now show the following result:

Normal C.D.
p = 0.15865525
z: Low = 1
z: Up   = 4996.5

Answer: The probability that the download time is over 9 seconds is 0.1587.

Hence, the probability that a download time is under 7 or over 9 seconds is $0.5 + 0.1587 = 0.6587$.

CASIO Calculator Instruction

Use the Casio calculator to find $P(5 < X < 9)$.

Select **STAT** **F5**(DIST) **F1**(NORM) **F2**(Ncd) **F2**(Var), and then select the following options:

Normal C.D.
Data   : **Variable**
Lower   : 5
Upper   : **9**
σ : 2
μ : 7
Save Res : **None**
Execute
Now key **EXE** or **F1**(CALC).

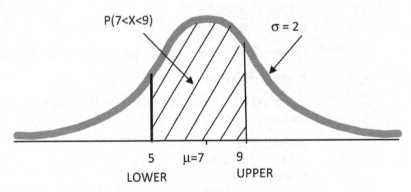

The calculator will now show the following result:

Normal C.D.
p = 0.68268949
z: Low = −1
z : Up = 1

Answer: The probability that the download time will be between 5 and 9 seconds is 0.6827.

The result of Example 7.6 enables you to state that for any normal distribution, 68.26% of the values will fall within ± 1 standard deviation of the mean. From Figure 7.11, you can see that 95.44% of the values will fall within ± 2 standard deviations of the mean. Thus, 95.44% of the download times are between 3 and 11 seconds. From Figure 7.12, you can see that 99.73% of the values are within ± 3 standard deviations above or below the mean. Thus, 99.73% of the download times are between 1 and 13 seconds. Therefore, it is unlikely (0.0027, or only 27 in 10,000) that a download time will be so fast or so slow that it will take under 1 second or more than 13 seconds. In general, you can use 6σ (that is, 3 standard deviations below the mean to 3 standard deviations above the mean) as a practical approximation of the range for normally distributed data.

FIGURE 7.11

Finding $P(3 < X < 11)$

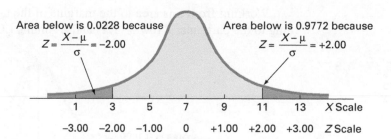

FIGURE 7.12

Finding $P(1 < X < 13)$

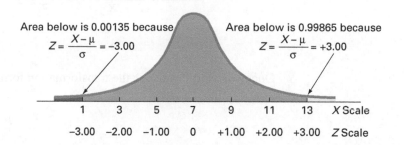

Figures 7.10, 7.11, and 7.12 illustrate that for any normal distribution,

- Approximately 68.26% of the values fall within ± 1 standard deviation of the mean.
- Approximately 95.44% of the values fall within ± 2 standard deviations of the mean.
- Approximately 99.73% of the values fall within ± 3 standard deviations of the mean.

This result is the justification for the empirical rule. The accuracy of the empirical rule improves as a data set follows the normal distribution more closely.

Examples 7.4 through 7.6 require you to use the normal distribution Table E.2 to find an area under the normal curve that corresponds to a specific X value. There are many circumstances in which you want to find the X value that corresponds to a specific area. Examples 7.7 and 7.8 illustrate such situations.

Inverse Normal

Find x given the probability.

EXAMPLE 7.7

Finding the X Value for a Cumulative Probability of 0.10

How much time (in seconds) will elapse before the fastest 10% of the downloads of an Our-Campus! video are complete?

SOLUTION Because 10% of the videos are expected to download in under X seconds, the area under the normal curve less than this value is 0.1000. Using the body of Table E.2, you search for the area or probability of 0.1000. The closest result is 0.1003, as shown in Table 7.6 (which is extracted from Table E.2).

TABLE 7.6

Finding a Z Value Corresponding to a Particular Cumulative Area (0.10) Under the Normal Curve

					Cumulative Probabilities				
Z	**.00**	**.01**	**.02**	**.03**	**.04**	**.05**	**.06**	**.07**	**.08**	**.09**
.	.	.	.	.	.	.	.	.	.
.	.	.	.	.	.	.	.	.	.
.	.	.	.	.	.	.	.	.	.
−1.5	.0668	.0655	.0643	.0630	.0618	.0606	.0594	.0582	.0571	.0559
−1.4	.0808	.0793	.0778	.0764	.0749	.0735	.0721	.0708	.0694	.0681
−1.3	.0968	.0951	.0934	.0918	.0901	.0885	.0869	.0853	.0838	.0823
−1.2	.1151	.1131	.1112	.1093	.1075	.1056	.1038	.1020	.1003	.0985

Source: Extracted from Table E.2.

Working from this area to the margins of the table, you find that the Z value corresponding to the particular Z row (-1.2) and Z column ($.08$) is -1.28 (see Figure 7.13).

FIGURE 7.13
Finding Z to
determine X

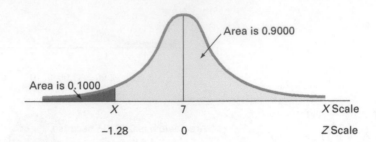

Once you find Z, you use the transformation formula Equation (7.2) on page 290 to determine the X value. Because

$$Z = \frac{X - \mu}{\sigma}$$

then

$$X = \mu + Z\sigma$$

Substituting $\mu = 7, \sigma = 2$, and $Z = -1.28$,

$$X = 7 + (-1.28)(2) = 4.44 \text{ seconds}$$

Thus, 10% of the download times are 4.44 seconds or less.

CASIO Calculator Instruction

Use the Casio calculator to obtain the inverse normal probability (i.e., find X given the probability).

Select **STAT F5**(DIST) **F1**(NORM) **F3**(InvN) **F2**(Var), and then select the following options:

Inverse Normal
Data   : **Variable**
Tail   : **Left (F1)** (Note: Left (F1), Right (F2), CNTR (F3))
Area   : **0.1**
σ : 2
μ : **7**
Save Res : **None**
Execute
Now key **EXE** or **F1**(CALC).

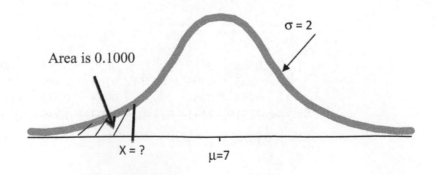

The calculator will now show the following result:

Inverse Normal
XInv= 4.43689687

Answer: 10% of the download times are 4.44 seconds or less.

Finding an X Value Associated with Known Probability Using the CASIO Calculator

To find a particular value, X, associated with a known probability, mean and standard deviation, follow these calculator steps.

Select **STAT** **F5**(DIST) **F1**(NORM) **F3**(InvN) **F2**(Var), and then select the following options:

Inverse Normal
Data   : **Variable**
Tail   : **Left (F1)** OR **Right (F2)** OR **CNTR (F3)**
Area   :
σ :
μ :
Save Res : **None**
Execute
Now key **EXE** or **F1**(CALC).

EXAMPLE 7.8

Finding the X Values That Include 95% of the Download Times

What are the lower and upper values of X, symmetrically distributed around the mean, that include 95% of the download times for a video at the OurCampus! website?

SOLUTION First, you need to find the lower value of X (called X_L). Then, you find the upper value of X (called X_U). Because 95% of the values are between X_L and X_U, and because X_L and X_U are equally distant from the mean, 2.5% of the values are below X_L (see Figure 7.14).

FIGURE 7.14

Finding Z to determine X_L

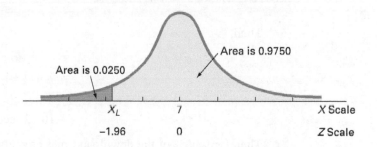

Although X_L is not known, you can find the corresponding Z value because the area under the normal curve less than this Z is 0.0250. Using the body of Table 7.7, you search for the probability 0.0250.

TABLE 7.7

Finding a Z Value Corresponding to a Cumulative Area of 0.025 Under the Normal Curve

	Cumulative Area									
Z	.00	.01	.02	.03	.04	.05	.06	.07	.08	.09
⋮	⋮	⋮	⋮	⋮	⋮	⋮	⋮	⋮	⋮	⋮
−2.0	.0228	.0222	.0217	.0212	.0207	.0202	.0197	.0192	.0188	.0183
−1.9	.0287	.0281	.0274	.0268	.0262	.0256	.0250	.0244	.0239	.0233
−1.8	.0359	.0351	.0344	.0336	.0329	.0232	.0314	.0307	.0301	.0294

Source: Extracted from Table E.2.

Working from the body of the table to the margins of the table, you see that the Z value corresponding to the particular Z row (-1.9) and Z column ($.06$) is -1.96.

Once you find Z, the final step is as follows:

$$X = \mu + Z\sigma$$
$$= 7 + (-1.96)(2)$$
$$= 7 - 3.92$$
$$= 3.08 \text{ seconds}$$

You use a similar process to find X_U. Because only 2.5% of the video downloads take longer than X_U seconds, 97.5% of the video downloads take less than X_U seconds. From the symmetry of the normal distribution, you find that the desired Z value, as shown in Figure 7.15, is $+1.96$ (because Z lies to the right of the standardized mean of 0). You can also extract this Z value from Table 7.8. You can see that 0.975 is the area under the normal curve less than the Z value of $+1.96$.

FIGURE 7.15

Finding Z to determine X_U

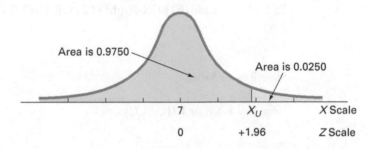

Area is 0.9750

Area is 0.0250

| | 7 | X_U | X Scale |
| | 0 | +1.96 | Z Scale |

TABLE 7.8

Finding a Z Value Corresponding to a Cumulative Area of 0.975 Under the Normal Curve

					Cumulative Area					
Z	.00	.01	.02	.03	.04	.05	.06	.07	.08	.09
$+1.8$	.9641	.9649	.9656	.9664	.9671	.9678	.9686	.9693	.9699	.9706
$+1.9$	.9713	.9719	.9726	.9732	.9738	.9744	.9750	.9756	.9761	.9767
$+2.0$	.9772	.9778	.9783	.9788	.9793	.9798	.9803	.9808	.9812	.9817

Source: Extracted from Table E.2.

Then,

$$X = \mu + Z\sigma$$
$$= 7 + (+1.96)(2)$$
$$= 7 + 3.92$$
$$= 10.92 \text{ seconds}$$

Therefore, 95% of the download times are between 3.08 and 10.92 seconds. Using Example 7.8, illustrate the calculator steps to obtain the lower and upper values of X.

FIGURE 7.16

Calculator steps for computing inverse normal probability

Question: What are the lower and upper values of X, symmetrically distributed around the mean, that include 95% of the download times?

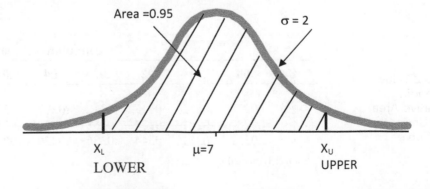

Area =0.95

$\sigma = 2$

| X_L | $\mu=7$ | X_U |
| LOWER | | UPPER |

To find the values X_L and X_U associated with a known probability, $\mu = 7$ and $\sigma = 2$, follow these calculator steps.

Select **STAT F5**(DIST) **F1**(NORM) **F3**(InvN) **F2**(Var), and then select the following options:

Inverse Normal
Data   : **Variable**
Tail   : **CNTR (F3)**
Area   : **0.95**
σ : **2**
μ : **7**
Save Res : **None**
Execute
Now key **EXE** or **F1**(CALC).

The calculator will now show the following result:

Inverse Normal
X1 Inv = 3.08007203
X2 Inv = 10.919928

Answer: 95% of the download times are between 3.08 and 10.92 seconds.

Instead of looking up cumulative probabilities in a table, you can use Excel or Minitab to compute normal probabilities. Figure 7.17 is an Excel worksheet that computes normal probabilities for problems similar to Examples 7.4 through 7.7. Figure 7.18 shows Minitab results for Examples 7.4 and 7.7.

FIGURE 7.17
Excel worksheet for computing normal probabilities

	A	B			D	E	
1	**Normal Probabilities**			1			
2				2			
3	**Common Data**			3			
4	Mean	7		4			
5	Standard Deviation	2		5			
6				6	**Probability for a Range**		
7	**Probability for X <=**			7	From X Value	5	
8	X Value	7		8	To X Value	9	
9	Z Value	0	=STANDARDIZE(B8,B4,B5)	9	Z Value for 5	-1	=STANDARDIZE(E7,B4,B5)
10	P(X<=7)	0.5000	=NORMDIST(B8,B4,B5,TRUE)	10	Z Value for 9	1	=STANDARDIZE(E8,B4,B5)
11				11	P(X<=5)	0.1587	=NORMDIST(E7,B4,B5,TRUE)
12	**Probability for X >**			12	P(X<=9)	0.8413	=NORMDIST(E8,B4,B5,TRUE)
13	X Value	9		13	P(5<=X<=9)	0.6827	=ABS(E12-E11)
14	Z Value	1	=STANDARDIZE(B13,B4,B5)	14			
15	P(X>9)	0.1587	=1-NORMDIST(B13,B4,B5,TRUE)	15	**Find X and Z Given Cum. Pctage.**		
16				16	Cumulative Percentage	10.00%	
17	**Probability for X<7 or X >9**			17	Z Value	-1.2816	=NORMSINV(E16)
18	P(X<7 or X >9)	0.6587	=B10+B15	18	X Value	4.4369	=NORMINV(E16,B4,B5)

FIGURE 7.18
Minitab results for Examples 7.4 and 7.7

Cumulative Distribution Function
Normal with mean = 7 and standard deviation = 2
```
x    P( X <= x )
9    0.841345
```

Inverse Cumulative Distribution Function
Normal with mean = 7 and standard deviation = 2
```
P( X <= x )       x
0.1         4.43690
```

THINK ABOUT THIS   What Is Normal?

Ironically, the statistician who popularized the use of "normal" to describe the distribution discussed in Section 7.2 was someone who saw the distribution as anything but the everyday, anticipated occurrence that the adjective *normal* usually suggests.

Starting with an 1894 paper, Karl Pearson argued that measurements of phenomena do not naturally, or "normally," conform to the classic bell shape. While this principle underlies statistics today, Pearson's point of view was radical to contemporaries who saw the world as standardized and normal. Pearson changed minds by showing that some populations are naturally *skewed* (coining that term in passing), and he helped put to rest the notion that the normal distribution underlies all phenomena.

Today, unfortunately, people still make the type of mistake that Pearson refuted. As a student, you are probably familiar with discussions about grade inflation, a real phenomenon at many schools. But, have you ever realized that a "proof" of this inflation—that there are "too few" low grades because grades are skewed toward A's and B's—wrongly implies that grades should be "normally" distributed. By the time you finish reading this book, you may realize that because college students represent small nonrandom samples, there are plenty of reasons to suspect that the distribution of grades would not be "normal."

Misunderstandings about the normal distribution have occurred both in business and in the public sector through the years. These misunderstandings have caused a number of business blunders and have sparked several public policy debates, including the causes of the collapse of large financial institutions in 2008. According to one theory, the investment banking industry's application of the normal distribution to assess risk may have contributed to the global collapse (see "A Finer Formula for Assessing Risks," *The New York Times*, May 11, 2010, p. B2). Using the normal distribution led these banks to overestimate the probability of having stable market conditions and underestimate the chance of unusually large market losses. According to this theory, the use of other distributions that have less area in the middle of their curves, and, therefore, more in the "tails" that represent unusual market outcomes, may have led to less serious losses.

As you study this chapter, make sure you understand the assumptions that must hold for the proper use of the "normal" distribution, assumptions that were not explicitly verified by the investment bankers. And, most importantly, always remember that the name *normal* distribution does not mean normal in the everyday sense of the word.

VISUAL EXPLORATIONS   Exploring the Normal Distribution

Use the Visual Explorations Normal Distribution procedure to see the effects of changes in the mean and standard deviation on the area under a normal distribution curve. Open the **Visual Explorations add-in workbook** (see Appendix Section D.4). Select **Add-ins → VisualExplorations → Normal Distribution.**

The add-in displays a normal curve for the OurCampus! download example and a floating control panel (see illustration at right). Use the control panel spinner buttons to change the values for the mean, standard deviation, and X value and note the effects of these changes on the probability of $X <$ value and the corresponding shaded area under the curve (see illustration at right). If you prefer to see the normal curve labeled with Z values, click **Z Values.**

Click the **Reset** button to reset the control panel values or click **Help** for additional information about the problem. Click **Finish** when you are done exploring.

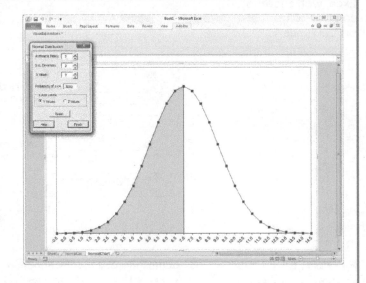

Problems for Section 7.3

LEARNING THE BASICS

7.14 Given a standardized normal distribution (with a mean of 0 and a standard deviation of 1, as in Table E.2), what is the probability that
a. Z is less than 1.57?
b. Z is greater than 1.84?
c. Z is between 1.57 and 1.84?
d. Z is less than 1.57 or greater than 1.84?

7.15 Given a standardized normal distribution (with a mean of 0 and a standard deviation of 1, as in Table E.2), what is the probability that
a. Z is between −1.57 and 1.84?
b. Z is less than −1.57 or greater than 1.84?
c. What is the value of Z if only 2.5% of all possible Z values are larger?
d. Between what two values of Z (symmetrically distributed around the mean) will 68.26% of all possible Z values be contained?

7.16 Given a standardized normal distribution (with a mean of 0 and a standard deviation of 1, as in Table E.2), what is the probability that
a. Z is less than 1.08?
b. Z is greater than −0.21?
c. Z is less than −0.21 or greater than the mean?
d. Z is less than −0.21 or greater than 1.08?

7.17 Given a standardized normal distribution (with a mean of 0 and a standard deviation of 1, as in Table E.2), determine the following probabilities:
a. $P(Z > 1.08)$
b. $P(Z < -0.21)$
c. $P(-1.96 < Z < -0.21)$
d. What is the value of Z if only 15.87% of all possible Z values are larger?

7.18 Given a normal distribution with $\mu = 100$ and $\sigma = 10$, what is the probability that
a. $X > 75$?
b. $X < 70$?
c. $X < 80$ or $X > 110$?
d. Between what two X values (symmetrically distributed around the mean) are 80% of the values?

7.19 Given a normal distribution with $\mu = 50$ and $\sigma = 4$, what is the probability that
a. $X > 43$?
b. $X < 42$?
c. 5% of the values are less than what X value?
d. Between what two X values (symmetrically distributed around the mean) are 60% of the values?

APPLYING THE CONCEPTS

7.20 In 2008, the per capita consumption of coffee in the United States was reported to be 4.2 kg, or 9.24 pounds (data extracted from **en.wikipedia.org/wiki/List_of_countries_by_coffee_consumption_per_capita**). Assume that the per capita consumption of coffee in the United States is approximately distributed as a normal random variable, with a mean of 9.24 pounds and a standard deviation of 3 pounds.
a. What is the probability that someone in the United States consumed more than 10 pounds of coffee in 2008?
b. What is the probability that someone in the United States consumed between 3 and 5 pounds of coffee in 2008?
c. What is the probability that someone in the United States consumed less than 5 pounds of coffee in 2008?
d. 99% of the people in the United States consumed less than how many pounds of coffee?

SELF Test **7.21** Toby's Trucking Company determined that the distance traveled per truck per year is normally distributed, with a mean of 50 thousand miles and a standard deviation of 12 thousand miles.
a. What proportion of trucks can be expected to travel between 34 and 50 thousand miles in a year?
b. What percentage of trucks can be expected to travel either below 30 or above 60 thousand miles in a year?
c. How many miles will be traveled by at least 80% of the trucks?
d. What are your answers to (a) through (c) if the standard deviation is 10 thousand miles?

7.22 Consumers spend an average of $21 per week in cash without being aware of where it goes (data extracted from "Snapshots: A Hole in Our Pockets," *USA Today*, January 18, 2010, p. 1A). Assume that the amount of cash spent without being aware of where it goes is normally distributed and that the standard deviation is $5.
a. What is the probability that a randomly selected person will spend more than $25?
b. What is the probability that a randomly selected person will spend between $10 and $20?
c. Between what two values will the middle 95% of the amounts of cash spent fall?

7.23 A set of final examination grades in an introductory statistics course is normally distributed, with a mean of 73 and a standard deviation of 8.
a. What is the probability that a student scored below 91 on this exam?
b. What is the probability that a student scored between 65 and 89?
c. The probability is 5% that a student taking the test scores higher than what grade?

d. If the professor grades on a curve (i.e., gives A's to the top 10% of the class, regardless of the score), are you better off with a grade of 81 on this exam or a grade of 68 on a different exam, where the mean is 62 and the standard deviation is 3? Show your answer statistically and explain.

7.24 A statistical analysis of 1,000 long-distance telephone calls made from the headquarters of the Bricks and Clicks Computer Corporation indicates that the length of these calls is normally distributed, with $\mu = 240$ seconds and $\sigma = 40$ seconds.

a. What is the probability that a call lasted less than 180 seconds?

b. What is the probability that a call lasted between 180 and 300 seconds?

c. What is the probability that a call lasted between 110 and 180 seconds?

d. 1% of all calls will last less than how many seconds?

7.25 In 2008, the per capita consumption of coffee in Sweden was reported to be 8.2 kg, or 18.04 pounds (data extracted from **en.wikipedia.org/wiki/List_of_countries_by_coffee_consumption_per_capita**). Assume that the per capita consumption of coffee in Sweden is approximately distributed as a normal random variable, with a mean of 18.04 pounds and a standard deviation of 5 pounds.

a. What is the probability that someone in Sweden consumed more than 10 pounds of coffee in 2008?

b. What is the probability that someone in Sweden consumed between 3 and 5 pounds of coffee in 2008?

c. What is the probability that someone in Sweden consumed less than 5 pounds of coffee in 2008?

d. 99% of the people in Sweden consumed less than how many pounds of coffee?

7.26 Many manufacturing problems involve the matching of machine parts, such as shafts that fit into a valve hole. A particular design requires a shaft with a diameter of 22.000 mm, but shafts with diameters between 21.990 mm and 22.010 mm are acceptable. Suppose that the manufacturing process yields shafts with diameters normally distributed, with a mean of 22.002 mm and a standard deviation of 0.005 mm. For this process, what is

a. the proportion of shafts with a diameter between 21.99 mm and 22.00 mm?

b. the probability that a shaft is acceptable?

c. the diameter that will be exceeded by only 2% of the shafts?

d. What would be your answers in (a) through (c) if the standard deviation of the shaft diameters were 0.004 mm?

7.4 Evaluating Normality

As discussed in Section 7.3, many continuous variables used in business closely follow a normal distribution. To determine whether a set of data can be approximated by the normal distribution, you either compare the characteristics of the data with the theoretical properties of the normal distribution or construct a normal probability plot.

Comparing Data Characteristics to Theoretical Properties

The normal distribution has several important theoretical properties:

- It is symmetrical; thus, the mean and median are equal.
- It is bell-shaped; thus, the empirical rule applies.
- The interquartile range equals 1.33 standard deviations.
- The range is approximately equal to 6 standard deviations.

Many continuous variables have characteristics that approximate these theoretical properties. However, other continuous variables are often neither normally distributed nor approximately normally distributed. For such variables, the descriptive characteristics of the data are inconsistent with the properties of a normal distribution. One approach that you can use to determine whether a variable follows a normal distribution is to compare the observed characteristics of the variable with what would be expected if the variable followed a normal distribution. To do so, you can

- Construct charts and observe their appearance. For small- or moderate-sized data sets, create a stem-and-leaf display or a boxplot. For large data sets, in addition, plot a histogram or polygon.
- Compute descriptive statistics and compare these statistics with the theoretical properties of the normal distribution. Compare the mean and median. Is the interquartile range

approximately 1.33 times the standard deviation? Is the range approximately 6 times the standard deviation?
- Evaluate how the values are distributed. Determine whether approximately two-thirds of the values lie between the mean and ±1 standard deviation. Determine whether approximately four-fifths of the values lie between the mean and ±1.28 standard deviations. Determine whether approximately 19 out of every 20 values lie between the mean and ±2 standard deviations.

For example, you can use these techniques to determine whether the returns in 2009 (stored in **Bond Funds**) follow a normal distribution. Figures 7.19 and 7.20 display relevant Excel results for these data, and Figure 7.21 displays a Minitab boxplot for the same data.

FIGURE 7.19

Descriptive statistics for the 2009 returns

Return 2009	
Mean	7.1641
Standard Error	0.4490
Median	6.4000
Mode	6.0000
Standard Deviation	6.0908
Sample Variance	37.0984
Kurtosis	2.4560
Skewness	0.9085
Range	40.8000
Minimum	-8.8000
Maximum	32.0000
Sum	1318.2000
Count	184

FIGURE 7.20

Five-number summary and boxplot for the 2009 returns

Five-Number Summary	
Minimum	-8.8
First Quartile	3.4
Median	6.4
Third Quartile	10.8
Maximum	32

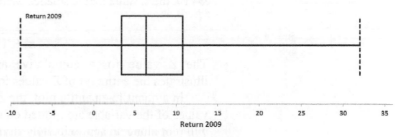

FIGURE 7.21

Minitab boxplot

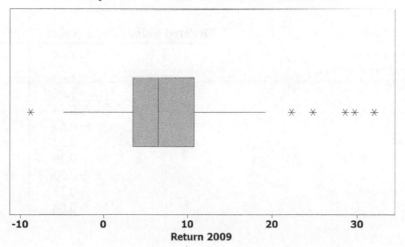

Boxplot for Bond Funds 2009 Returns

From Figures 7.19 through 7.21, and from an ordered array of the returns (not shown here), you can make the following statements:

- The mean of 7.1641 is greater than the median of 6.4. (In a normal distribution, the mean and median are equal.)
- The boxplot is very right-skewed, with a long tail on the right. (The normal distribution is symmetrical.)
- The interquartile range of 7.4 is approximately 1.21 standard deviations. (In a normal distribution, the interquartile range is 1.33 standard deviations.)
- The range of 40.8 is equal to 6.70 standard deviations. (In a normal distribution, the range is approximately 6 standard deviations.)
- 73.91% of the returns are within ±1 standard deviation of the mean. (In a normal distribution, 68.26% of the values lie within ±1 standard deviation of the mean.)
- 85.33% of the returns are within ±1.28 standard deviations of the mean. (In a normal distribution, 80% of the values lie within ±1.28 standard deviations of the mean.)
- 96.20% of the returns are within ±2 standard deviations of the mean. (In a normal distribution, 95.44% of the values lie within ±2 standard deviations of the mean.)
- The skewness statistic is 0.9085 and the kurtosis statistic is 2.456. (In a normal distribution, each of these statistics equals zero.)

Based on these statements and the criteria given on pages 304–305, you can conclude that the 2009 returns are highly right-skewed and have somewhat more values within ±1 standard deviation of the mean than expected. The range is higher than what would be expected in a normal distribution, but this is mostly due to the single outlier at 32. Primarily because of the skewness, you can conclude that the data characteristics of the 2009 returns differ from the theoretical properties of a normal distribution.

Constructing the Normal Probability Plot

A **normal probability plot** is a visual display that helps you evaluate whether the data are normally distributed. One common plot is called the **quantile–quantile plot**. To create this plot, you first transform each ordered value to a Z value. For example, if you have a sample of $n=19$, the Z value for the smallest value corresponds to a cumulative area of

$$\frac{1}{n+1} = \frac{1}{19+1} = \frac{1}{20} = 0.05.$$

The Z value for a cumulative area of 0.05 (from Table E.2) is −1.65. Table 7.9 illustrates the entire set of Z values for a sample of $n=19$.

In a quantile–quantile plot, the Z values are plotted on the X axis, and the corresponding values of the variable are plotted on the Y axis. If the data are normally distributed, the values will plot along an approximately straight line.

TABLE 7.9

Ordered Values and Corresponding Z Values for a Sample of $n = 19$

Ordered Value	Z Value	Ordered Value	Z Value
1	−1.65	11	0.13
2	−1.28	12	0.25
3	−1.04	13	0.39
4	−0.84	14	0.52
5	−0.67	15	0.67
6	−0.52	16	0.84
7	−0.39	17	1.04
8	−0.25	18	1.28
9	−0.13	19	1.65
10	−0.00		

Figure 7.22 illustrates the typical shape of the quantile–quantile normal probability plot for a left-skewed distribution (Panel A), a normal distribution (Panel B), and a right-skewed distribution (Panel C). If the data are left-skewed, the curve will rise more rapidly at first and then level off. If the data are normally distributed, the points will plot along an approximately straight line. If the data are right-skewed, the data will rise more slowly at first and then rise at a faster rate for higher values of the variable being plotted.

FIGURE 7.22

Normal probability plots for a left-skewed distribution, a normal distribution, and a right-skewed distribution

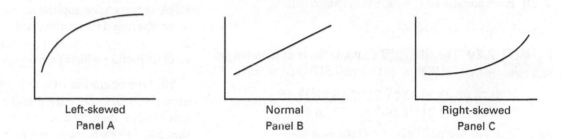

| Left-skewed | Normal | Right-skewed |
| Panel A | Panel B | Panel C |

Figure 7.23 shows a normal probability plot for the 2009 returns as created using Excel (left results, a quantile–quantile plot) and Minitab (right results). The Excel quantile–quantile plot shows that the 2009 returns rise slowly at first and then rise more rapidly. Therefore, you can conclude that the 2009 returns are right-skewed.

The Minitab normal probability plot has the Return 2009 variable on the X axis and the cumulative percentage for a normal distribution on the Y axis. As is the case with the quantile–quantile plot, if the data are normally distributed, the points will plot along an approximately

FIGURE 7.23

Excel (quantile–quantile) and Minitab normal probability plots for 2009 returns

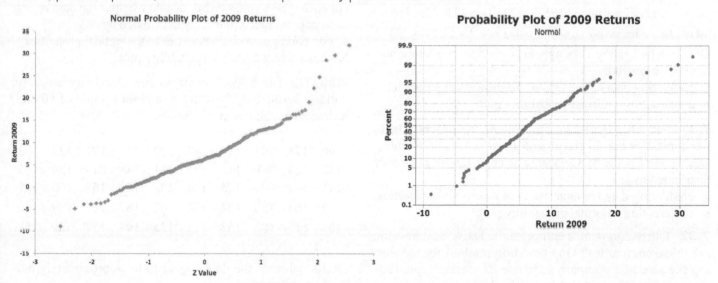

straight line. However, if the data are right-skewed, the curve will rise more rapidly at first and then level off. If the data are left-skewed, the data will rise more slowly at first and then rise at a faster rate for higher values of the variable being plotted. Observe that the values rise more rapidly at first and then level off, indicating a right-skewed distribution.

Problems for Section 7.4

LEARNING THE BASICS

7.27 Show that for a sample of $n = 39$, the smallest and largest Z values are -1.96 and $+1.96$, and the middle (i.e., 20th) Z value is 0.00.

7.28 For a sample of $n = 6$, list the six Z values.

APPLYING THE CONCEPTS

 7.29 The file **SUV** contains the overall miles per gallon (MPG) of 2011 small SUVs ($n = 25$):

    20 24 22 23 20 22 21 22 22 19 22 22 26
    19 19 23 24 21 21 19 21 22 22 16 16

Source: Data extracted from "Ratings," *Consumer Reports,* April 2011, pp. 35–36.

Decide whether the data appear to be approximately normally distributed by
a. comparing data characteristics to theoretical properties.
b. constructing a normal probability plot.

7.30 As player salaries have increased, the cost of attending baseball games has increased dramatically. The file **BBCost 2010** contains the cost of four tickets, two beers, four soft drinks, four hot dogs, two game programs, two baseball caps, and the parking fee for one car for each of the 30 Major League Baseball teams in 2010:

    172, 335, 250, 180, 173, 162, 132, 207, 316, 178,
    184, 141, 168, 208, 115, 158, 330, 151, 161, 170,
    212, 222, 160, 227, 227, 127, 217, 121, 221, 216

Source: Data extracted from **teammarketing.com**, April 1, 2010.

Decide whether the data appear to be approximately normally distributed by
a. comparing data characteristics to theoretical properties.
b. constructing a normal probability plot.

7.31 The file **PropertyTaxes** contains the property taxes per capita for the 50 states and the District of Columbia. Decide whether the data appear to be approximately normally distributed by
a. comparing data characteristics to theoretical properties.
b. constructing a normal probability plot.

7.32 Thirty companies comprise the DJIA. Just how big are these companies? One common method for measuring the size of a company is to use its market capitalization, which is computed by multiplying the number of stock shares by the price of a share of stock. On April 8, 2011, the market capitalization of these companies ranged from Alcoa's $19.2 billion to ExxonMobil's $426.4 billion. The entire population of market capitalization values is stored in **DowMarketCap**.

Source: Data extracted from **money.cnn.com**, April 8, 2011.

Decide whether the market capitalization of companies in the DJIA appears to be approximately normally distributed by
a. comparing data characteristics to theoretical properties.
b. constructing a normal probability plot.
c. constructing a histogram.

7.33 One operation of a mill is to cut pieces of steel into parts that will later be used as the frame for front seats in an automotive plant. The steel is cut with a diamond saw, and the resulting parts must be within ± 0.005 inch of the length specified by the automobile company. The data come from a sample of 100 steel parts and are stored in **Steel**. The measurement reported is the difference, in inches, between the actual length of the steel part, as measured by a laser measurement device, and the specified length of the steel part. Determine whether the data appear to be approximately normally distributed by
a. comparing data characteristics to theoretical properties.
b. constructing a normal probability plot.

7.34 The file **CDRate** contains the yields for a one-year certificate of deposit (CD) and a five-year certificate of deposit (CD) for 23 banks in the United States, as of April 4, 2011.

Source: Data extracted from **www.Bankrate.com**, April 4, 2011.

For each type of investment, decide whether the data appear to be approximately normally distributed by
a. comparing data characteristics to theoretical properties.
b. constructing a normal probability plot.

7.35 The file **Utility** contains the electricity costs, in dollars, during July 2010 for a random sample of 50 one-bedroom apartments in a large city:

96	171	202	178	147	102	153	197	127	82
157	185	90	116	172	111	148	213	130	165
141	149	206	175	123	128	144	168	109	167
95	163	150	154	130	143	187	166	139	149
108	119	183	151	114	135	191	137	129	158

Decide whether the data appear to be approximately normally distributed by
a. comparing data characteristics to theoretical properties.
b. constructing a normal probability plot.

USING STATISTICS @ OurCampus! Revisited

Lee Morris / Shutterstock.com

I n the OurCampus! scenario, you were a designer for a social networking website. You sought to ensure that a video could be downloaded quickly for playback in the web browsers of site visitors. (Quick playback of videos would help attract and retain those visitors.) By running experiments in the corporate offices, you determined that the amount of time, in seconds, that passes from first linking to the website until a video is fully displayed is a bell-shaped distribution with a mean download time of 7 seconds and standard deviation of 2 seconds. Using the normal distribution, you were able to calculate that approximately 84% of the download times are 9 seconds or less, and 95% of the download times are between 3.08 and 10.92 seconds.

Now that you understand how to calculate probabilities from the normal distribution, you can evaluate download times of a video using different web page designs. For example, if the standard deviation remained at 2 seconds, lowering the mean to 6 seconds would shift the entire distribution lower by 1 second. Thus, approximately 84% of the download times would be 8 seconds or less, and 95% of the download times would be between 2.08 and 9.92 seconds. Another change that could reduce long download times would be reducing the variation. For example, consider the case where the mean remained at the original 7 seconds but the standard deviation was reduced to 1 second. Again, approximately 84% of the download times would be 8 seconds or less, and 95% of the download times would be between 5.04 and 8.96 seconds.

SUMMARY

In this and the previous chapter, you have learned about mathematical models called probability distributions and how they can be used to solve business problems. In Chapter 6, you used discrete probability distributions in situations where the outcomes come from a counting process (e.g., the number of courses you are enrolled in, the number of tagged order forms in a report generated by an accounting information system). In this chapter, you learned about continuous probability distributions where the outcomes come from a measuring process (e.g., your height, the download time of a video). Continuous probability distributions come in various shapes, but the most common and most important in business is the normal distribution. The normal distribution is symmetrical; thus, its mean and

median are equal. It is also bell-shaped, and approximately 68.26% of its observations are within 1 standard deviation of the mean, approximately 95.44% of its observations are within 2 standard deviations of the mean, and approximately 99.73% of its observations are within 3 standard deviations of the mean. Although many data sets in business are closely approximated by the normal distribution, do not think that all data can be approximated using the normal distribution. In Section 7.4, you learned about various methods for evaluating normality in order to determine whether the normal distribution is a reasonable mathematical model to use in specific situations.

Chapter 8 uses the normal distribution to develop the subject of statistical inference.

KEY EQUATIONS

Normal Probability Density Function

$$f(X) = \frac{1}{\sqrt{2\pi}\sigma} e^{-(1/2)[(X-\mu)/\sigma]^2}$$

Transformation Formula

$$Z = \frac{X - \mu}{\sigma}$$

Finding an X Value Associated with a Known Probability

$$X = \mu + Z\sigma$$

KEY TERMS

Chebyshev Rule   291
cumulative standardized normal
   distribution   286
empirical rule   290
normal distribution   280

normal probability plot   306
probability density function   280
probability density function for the
   normal distribution   282

quantile–quantile plot   306
standardized normal random
   variable   286
transformation formula   286

PROBLEMS

CHECKING YOUR UNDERSTANDING

7.36 Why is only one normal distribution table such as Table E.2 needed to find any probability under the normal curve?

7.37 How do you find the area between two values under the normal curve?

7.38 How do you find the X value that corresponds to a given percentile of the normal distribution?

7.39 What are some of the distinguishing properties of a normal distribution?

7.40 How does the shape of the normal distribution differ from the shapes of the uniform and exponential distributions?

7.41 How can you use the normal probability plot to evaluate whether a set of data is normally distributed?

APPLYING THE CONCEPTS

7.42 An industrial sewing machine uses ball bearings that are targeted to have a diameter of 0.75 inch. The lower and upper specification limits under which the ball bearings can operate are 0.74 inch and 0.76 inch, respectively. Past experience has indicated that the actual diameter of the ball bearings is approximately normally distributed, with a mean of 0.753 inch and a standard deviation of 0.004 inch. What is the probability that a ball bearing is
a. between the target and the actual mean?
b. between the lower specification limit and the target?
c. above the upper specification limit?
d. below the lower specification limit?
e. Of all the ball bearings, 93% of the diameters are greater than what value?

7.43 The fill amount in 2-liter soft drink bottles is normally distributed, with a mean of 2.0 liters and a standard deviation of 0.05 liter. If bottles contain less than 95% of the listed net content (1.90 liters, in this case), the manufacturer may be subject to penalty by the state office of consumer affairs. Bottles that have a net content above 2.10 liters may cause excess spillage upon opening. What proportion of the bottles will contain
a. between 1.90 and 2.0 liters?
b. between 1.90 and 2.10 liters?
c. below 1.90 liters or above 2.10 liters?
d. At least how much soft drink is contained in 99% of the bottles?
e. 99% of the bottles contain an amount that is between which two values (symmetrically distributed) around the mean?

7.44 In an effort to reduce the number of bottles that contain less than 1.90 liters, the bottler in Problem 6.43 sets the filling machine so that the mean is 2.02 liters. Under these circumstances, what are your answers in Problem 6.43 (a) through (e)?

7.45 An orange juice producer buys all his oranges from a large orange grove. The amount of juice squeezed from each of these oranges is approximately normally distributed, with a mean of 4.70 ounces and a standard deviation of 0.40 ounce.
a. What is the probability that a randomly selected orange will contain between 4.70 and 5.00 ounces of juice?
b. What is the probability that a randomly selected orange will contain between 5.00 and 5.50 ounces of juice?
c. At least how many ounces of juice will 77% of the oranges contain?
d. 80% of the oranges contain between what two values (in ounces of juice), symmetrically distributed around the population mean?

7.46 The file **DomesticBeer** contains the percentage alcohol, number of calories per 12 ounces, and number of carbohydrates (in grams) per 12 ounces for 145 of the best-selling domestic beers in the United States. For each of the three variables, decide whether the data appear to be approximately normally distributed. Support your decision through the use of appropriate statistics and graphs.
Source: Data extracted from **www.Beer100.com**, April 1, 2011.

7.47 The evening manager of a restaurant was very concerned about the length of time some customers were waiting in line to be seated. She also had some concern about the seating times—that is, the length of time between when a customer is seated and the time he or she leaves the restaurant. Over the course of one week, 100 customers (no more than 1 per party) were randomly selected, and their waiting and seating times (in minutes) were recorded in **Wait**.
a. Think about your favorite restaurant. Do you think waiting times more closely resemble a uniform, an exponential, or a normal distribution?
b. Again, think about your favorite restaurant. Do you think seating times more closely resemble a uniform, an exponential, or a normal distribution?
c. Construct a histogram and a normal probability plot of the waiting times. Do you think these waiting times more closely resemble a uniform, an exponential, or a normal distribution?
d. Construct a histogram and a normal probability plot of the seating times. Do you think these seating times more closely resemble a uniform, an exponential, or a normal distribution?

7.48 All the major stock market indexes posted gains in 2010. The mean one-year return for stocks in the S&P 500, a group of 500 very large companies, was 12.8%. The mean one-year return for the NASDAQ, a group of 3,200 small and medium-sized companies, was 16.9%. Historically, the one-year returns are approximately normally distributed, the standard deviation in the S&P 500 is approximately 20%, and the standard deviation in the NASDAQ is approximately 30%.
a. What is the probability that a stock in the S&P 500 gained value in 2010?
b. What is the probability that a stock in the S&P 500 gained 10% or more in 2010?
c. What is the probability that a stock in the S&P 500 lost 20% or more in 2010?
d. What is the probability that a stock in the S&P 500 lost 40% or more in 2010?
e. Repeat (a) through (d) for a stock in the NASDAQ.
f. Write a short summary on your findings. Be sure to include a discussion of the risks associated with a large standard deviation.

7.49 The speed in which the home page of a website is downloaded is an important quality characteristic of that website. Suppose that the mean time to download the home page for the Internal Revenue Service is 1.2 seconds. Suppose that the download time is normally distributed, with a standard deviation of 0.2 second. What is the probability that a download time is
a. less than 2 seconds?
b. between 1.5 and 2.5 seconds?
c. above 1.8 seconds?
d. 99% of the download times are slower (higher) than how many seconds?
e. 95% of the download times are between what two values, symmetrically distributed around the mean?

7.50 Suppose that the mean download time for a commercial tax preparation site is 2.0 seconds. Suppose that the download time is normally distributed, with a standard deviation of 0.5 second. What is the probability that a download time is
a. less than 2 seconds?
b. between 1.5 and 2.5 seconds?
c. above 1.8 seconds?
d. 99% of the download times are slower (higher) than how many seconds ?
e. Compare the results for the IRS site computed in Problem 7.49 to those of the commercial site.

7.51 (Class Project) One theory about the daily changes in the closing price of stock is that these changes follow a *random walk*—that is, these daily events are independent of each other and move upward or downward in a random manner—and can be approximated by a normal distribution. To test this theory, use either a newspaper or the Internet to select one company traded on the NYSE, one company traded on the American Stock Exchange, and one company traded on the NASDAQ and then do the following:
1. Record the daily closing stock price of each of these companies for six consecutive weeks (so that you have 30 values per company).

2. Compute the daily changes in the closing stock price of each of these companies for six consecutive weeks (so that you have 30 values per company).

For each of your six data sets, decide whether the data are approximately normally distributed by
a. constructing the stem-and-leaf display, histogram or polygon, and boxplot.
b. comparing data characteristics to theoretical properties.
c. constructing a normal probability plot.
d. Discuss the results of (a) through (c). What can you say about your three stocks with respect to daily closing prices and daily changes in closing prices? Which, if any, of the data sets are approximately normally distributed?

Note: *The random-walk theory pertains to the daily changes in the closing stock price, not the daily closing stock price.*

TEAM PROJECT

The file `Bond Funds` contains information regarding eight variables from a sample of 184 bond mutual funds:

Type—Type of bonds comprising the bond mutual fund (intermediate government or short-term corporate)
Assets—In millions of dollars
Fees—Sales charges (no or yes)
Expense ratio—Ratio of expenses to net assets in percentage
Return 2009—Twelve-month return in 2009
Three-year return—Annualized return, 2007–2009
Five-year return—Annualized return, 2005–2009
Risk—Risk-of-loss factor of the mutual fund (below average, average, or above average)

7.52 For the expense ratio, three-year return, and five-year return, decide whether the data are approximately normally distributed by
a. comparing data characteristics to theoretical properties.
b. constructing a normal probability plot.

STUDENT SURVEY DATABASE

7.53 Problem 1.21 on page 20 describes a survey of 62 undergraduate students (stored in `UndergradSurvey`). For these data, for each numerical variable, decide whether the data are approximately normally distributed by
a. comparing data characteristics to theoretical properties.
b. constructing a normal probability plot.

7.54 Problem 1.21 on page 20 describes a survey of 62 undergraduate students (stored in `UndergradSurvey`).
a. Select a sample of undergraduate students and conduct a similar survey for those students.
b. For the data collected in (a), repeat (a) and (b) of Problem 7.53.
c. Compare the results of (b) to those of Problem 7.53.

7.55 Problem 1.22 on page 21 describes a survey of 44 MBA students (stored in `GradSurvey`). For these data, for each numerical variable, decide whether the data are approximately normally distributed by

a. comparing data characteristics to theoretical properties.
b. constructing a normal probability plot.

7.56 Problem 1.22 on page 21 describes a survey of 44 MBA students (stored in GradSurvey).

a. Select a sample of graduate students and conduct a similar survey for those students.
b. For the data collected in (a), repeat (a) and (b) of Problem 7.55.
c. Compare the results of (b) to those of Problem 7.55.

MANAGING ASHLAND MULTICOMM SERVICES

The AMS technical services department has embarked on a quality improvement effort. Its first project relates to maintaining the target upload speed for its Internet service subscribers. Upload speeds are measured on a standard scale in which the target value is 1.0. Data collected over the past year indicate that the upload speed is approximately normally distributed, with a mean of 1.005 and a standard deviation of 0.10. Each day, one upload speed is measured. The upload speed is considered acceptable if the measurement on the standard scale is between 0.95 and 1.05.

Exercises

1. Assuming that the distribution has not changed from what it was in the past year, what is the probability that the upload speed is
   a. less than 1.0?
   b. between 0.95 and 1.0?
   c. between 1.0 and 1.05?
   d. less than 0.95 or greater than 1.05?

2. The objective of the operations team is to reduce the probability that the upload speed is below 1.0. Should the team focus on process improvement that increases the mean upload speed to 1.05 or on process improvement that reduces the standard deviation of the upload speed to 0.075? Explain.

DIGITAL CASE

Apply your knowledge about the normal distribution in this Digital Case, which extends the Using Statistics scenario from this chapter.

To satisfy concerns of potential customers, the management of OurCampus! has undertaken a research project to learn the amount of time it takes users to load a complex video features page. The research team has collected data and has made some claims based on the assertion that the data follow a normal distribution.

Open **OC_QRTStudy.pdf**, which documents the work of a quality response team at OurCampus! Read the internal report that documents the work of the team and their conclusions. Then answer the following:

1. Can the collected data be approximated by the normal distribution?

2. Review and evaluate the conclusions made by the OurCampus! research team. Which conclusions are correct? Which ones are incorrect?

3. If OurCampus! could improve the mean time by five seconds, how would the probabilities change?

REFERENCES

1. Gunter, B., "Q-Q Plots," *Quality Progress* (February 1994), 81–86.
2. Levine, D. M., P. Ramsey, and R. Smidt, *Applied Statistics for Engineers and Scientists Using Microsoft Excel and Minitab* (Upper Saddle River, NJ: Prentice Hall, 2001).
3. *Microsoft Excel 2010* (Redmond, WA: Microsoft Corp., 2010).
4. Miller, J., "Earliest Known Uses of Some of the Words of Mathematics," **http://jeff560.tripod.com/mathword.html**.
5. *Minitab Release 16* (State College, PA: Minitab Inc., 2010).
6. Pearl, R., "Karl Pearson, 1857–1936," *Journal of the American Statistical Association*, 31 (1936), 653–664.
7. Pearson, E. S., "Some Incidents in the Early History of Biometry and Statistics, 1890–94," *Biometrika*, 52 (1965), 3–18.
8. Walker, H., "The Contributions of Karl Pearson," *Journal of the American Statistical Association*, 53 (1958), 11–22.

CHAPTER 7 EXCEL GUIDE

EG7.1 Continuous Probability Distributions

There are no Excel Guide instructions for this section.

EG7.2 The Normal Distribution

PHStat2 Use **Normal** to compute normal probabilities. For example, to create the Figure 7.17 worksheet (see page 301) that computes probabilities for several Chapter 7 examples, select **PHStat → Probability & Prob. Distributions → Normal**. In this procedure's dialog box (shown below):

1. Enter **7** as the **Mean** and **2** as the **Standard Deviation**.
2. Check **Probability for:** X< = and enter **7** in its box.
3. Check **Probability for:** X > and enter **9** in its box.
4. Check **X for Cumulative Percentage** and enter **10** in its box.
5. Enter a **Title** and click **OK**.

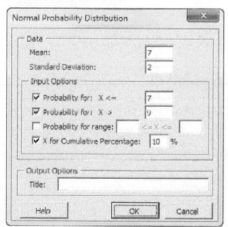

In-Depth Excel Use the **NORMDIST** worksheet function to compute normal probabilities. Enter the function as **NORMDIST(***X value, mean, standard deviation***, True)** to return the cumulative probability for less than or equal to the specified *X* value.

Use the **COMPUTE worksheet** of the **Normal workbook**, shown in Figure 7.17 on page 301, as a template for computing normal probabilities. The worksheet contains the data for solving the problems in Examples 7.4 through 7.7. Change the values for the **Mean**, **Standard Deviation**, **X Value, From X Value, To X Value**, and/or **Cumulative Percentage** to solve similar problems. To solve a problem that is similar to Example 7.8 on page 299, change the **Cumulative Percentage** cell twice, once to determine the lower value of *X* and the other time to determine the upper value of *X*.

The COMPUTE worksheet also uses the **STANDARD-IZE** worksheet function to compute *Z* values, **NORMDIST** to

compute the probability of less than or equal to the *X* value given, **NORMSINV** to compute the *Z* value for the cumulative percentage, and **NORMINV** to compute the *X* value for the given cumulative probability, mean, and standard deviation.

The worksheet also includes formulas that update probability labels when an *X* value is changed. Open to the **COMPUTE_FORMULAS worksheet** to examine all formulas.

EG7.3 Evaluating Normality

Comparing Data Characteristics to Theoretical Properties

Use instructions in Sections EG3.1 through EG3.3 in the Chapter 3 Excel Guide to compare data characteristics to theoretical properties.

Constructing the Normal Probability Plot

PHStat2 Use **Normal Probability Plot** to create a normal probability plot. For example, to create the Figure 7.23 normal probability plot for the 2009 returns on page 307, open to the **DATA worksheet** of the **Bond Funds workbook**. Select **PHStat → Probability & Prob. Distributions → Normal Probability Plot**. In the procedure's dialog box (shown below):

1. Enter **F1:F185** as the **Variable Cell Range**.
2. Check **First cell contains label**.
3. Enter a **Title** and click **OK**.

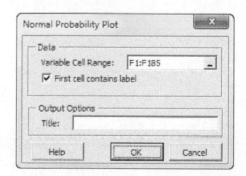

In addition to the chart sheet containing the normal probability plot, the procedure creates a worksheet of plot data that uses the **NORMSINV** function to compute the *Z* values used in the plot.

In-Depth Excel Create a normal probability plot in a two-step process. First create a worksheet that computes *Z* values for the data to be plotted. Then create a chart from that worksheet. Use the **PLOT_DATA worksheet** of the **NPP workbook** as a model for computing Z values. This worksheet contains columns for the rank, proportion, Z value, and the **Return 2009** variable and is the source of the data for the **NORMAL_PLOT chart sheet** that contains the Figure 7.23 normal probability plot (see page 307). For other problems, paste sorted variable data in column D, update the number of ranks in column A, and adjust the formulas in columns B and C. Column B formulas divide the column A cell by the quantity $n + 1$ (185 for the 2009 returns data) to compute cumulative percentages and column C formulas use the NORMSINV function to compute the Z values for those cumulative percentages. (Open to the **PLOT_FORMULAS worksheet** in the same workbook to examine these formulas.)

If you have fewer than 184 values, delete rows from the bottom up. If you have more than 184 values, insert rows from somewhere inside the body of the table to ensure that the normal probability plot is properly updated. To create your own normal probability plot for the Return 2009 variable, select the cell range **C1:D185**. Then select **Insert → Scatter** and select the first **Scatter** gallery choice (**Scatter with only Markers**). Relocate the chart to a chart sheet and adjust the chart formatting by using the instructions in Appendix F.

8 Sampling and Sampling Distributions

Learning Objectives
In this chapter, you learn:

- About different sampling methods
- The concept of the sampling distribution
- To compute probabilities related to the sample mean and the sample proportion
- The importance of the Central Limit Theorem

© Corbis

@ Oxford Cereals, Part I

Oxford Cereals fills thousands of boxes of cereal during an eight-hour shift. As the plant operations manager, you are responsible for monitoring the amount of cereal placed in each box. To be consistent with package labeling, boxes should contain a mean of 368 grams of cereal. Because of the speed of the process, the cereal weight varies from box to box, causing some boxes to be underfilled and others overfilled. If the process is not working properly, the mean weight in the boxes could vary too much from the label weight of 368 grams to be acceptable.

Because weighing every single box is too time-consuming, costly, and inefficient, you must take a sample of boxes. For each sample you select, you plan to weigh the individual boxes and calculate a sample mean. You need to determine the probability that such a sample mean could have been randomly selected from a population whose mean is 368 grams. Based on your analysis, you will have to decide whether to maintain, alter, or shut down the cereal-filling process.

R. MACKAY PHOTOGRAPHY / Shutterstock.com

In Chapter 7, you used the normal distribution to study the distribution of video download times from the OurCampus! website. In this chapter, you need to make a decision about the cereal-filling process, based on the weights of a sample of cereal boxes packaged at Oxford cereals. You will learn different methods of sampling and about sampling distributions and how to use them to solve business problems.

8.1 Types of Sampling Methods

In Section 1.4, a sample is defined as the portion of a population that has been selected for analysis. Rather than selecting every item in the population, statistical sampling procedures focus on collecting a small representative portion of the larger population. The results of the sample are then used to estimate characteristics of the entire population. There are three main reasons for selecting a sample:

- Selecting a sample is less time-consuming than selecting every item in the population.
- Selecting a sample is less costly than selecting every item in the population.
- Analyzing a sample is less cumbersome and more practical than analyzing the entire population.

The sampling process begins by defining the **frame**, a listing of items that make up the population. Frames are data sources such as population lists, directories, or maps. Samples are drawn from frames. Inaccurate or biased results can occur if a frame excludes certain portions of the population. Using different frames to generate data can lead to different conclusions.

After you select a frame, you draw a sample from the frame. As illustrated in Figure 8.1, there are two types of samples: nonprobability samples and probability samples.

FIGURE 8.1
Types of samples

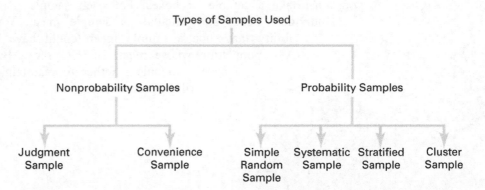

In a **nonprobability sample**, you select the items or individuals without knowing their probabilities of selection. Because of this, the theory of statistical inference that has been developed for probability sampling cannot be applied to nonprobability samples. A common type of nonprobability sampling is **convenience sampling**. In convenience sampling, items selected are easy, inexpensive, or convenient to sample. For example, if you were sampling tires stacked in a warehouse, it would be much more convenient to sample tires at the top of a stack than tires at the bottom of a stack. In many cases, participants in the sample select themselves. For example, many companies conduct surveys by giving visitors to their website the opportunity to complete survey forms and submit them electronically. The responses to these surveys can provide large amounts of data quickly and inexpensively, but the sample consists of self-selected web users. For many studies, only a nonprobability sample such as a judgment sample is available. In a **judgment sample**, you get the opinions of preselected experts in the subject matter. Although the experts may be well informed, you cannot generalize their results to the population.

Nonprobability samples can have certain advantages, such as convenience, speed, and low cost. However, their lack of accuracy due to selection bias and the fact that the results cannot be used for statistical inference more than offset these advantages.

In a **probability sample**, you select items based on known probabilities. Whenever possible, you should use probability sampling methods. Probability samples allow you to make inferences about the population of interest. The four types of probability samples most commonly used are simple random, systematic, stratified, and cluster samples. These sampling methods vary in their cost, accuracy, and complexity.

Simple Random Samples

In a **simple random sample**, every item from a frame has the same chance of selection as every other item. In addition, every sample of a fixed size has the same chance of selection as every other sample of that size. Simple random sampling is the most elementary random sampling technique. It forms the basis for the other random sampling techniques.

With simple random sampling, you use n to represent the sample size and N to represent the frame size. You number every item in the frame from 1 to N. The chance that you will select any particular member of the frame on the first selection is $1/N$.

You select samples with replacement or without replacement. **Sampling with replacement** means that after you select an item, you return it to the frame, where it has the same probability of being selected again. Imagine that you have a fishbowl containing N business cards, one card for each person. On the first selection, you select the card for Judy Craven. You record pertinent information and replace the business card in the bowl. You then mix up the cards in the bowl and select a second card. On the second selection, Judy Craven has the same probability of being selected again, $1/N$. You repeat this process until you have selected the desired sample size, n.

However, usually you do not want the same item to be selected again. **Sampling without replacement** means that once you select an item, you cannot select it again. The chance that you will select any particular item in the frame—for example, the business card for Judy Craven—on the first selection is $1/N$. The chance that you will select any card not previously chosen on the second selection is now 1 out of $N - 1$. This process continues until you have selected the desired sample of size n.

Regardless of whether you have sampled with or without replacement, "fishbowl" methods of sample selection have a major drawback—the ability to thoroughly mix the cards and randomly select the sample. As a result, fishbowl methods are not very useful. You need to use less cumbersome and more scientific methods of selection.

One such method uses a **table of random numbers** (see Table E.1 in Appendix E) for selecting the sample. A table of random numbers consists of a series of digits listed in a randomly generated sequence (see reference 8). Because the numeric system uses 10 digits (0, 1, 2, ..., 9), the chance that you will randomly generate any particular digit is equal to the probability of generating any other digit. This probability is 1 out of 10. Hence, if you generate a sequence of 800 digits, you would expect about 80 to be the digit 0, 80 to be the digit 1, and so on. Because every digit or sequence of digits in the table is random, the table can be read either horizontally or vertically. The margins of the table designate row numbers and column numbers. The digits themselves are grouped into sequences of five in order to make reading the table easier.

To use Table E.1 instead of a fishbowl for selecting the sample, you first need to assign code numbers to the individual items of the frame. Then you generate the random sample by reading the table of random numbers and selecting those individuals from the frame whose assigned code numbers match the digits found in the table. You can better understand the process of sample selection by studying Example 8.1.

EXAMPLE 8.1

Selecting a Simple Random Sample by Using a Table of Random Numbers

A company wants to select a sample of 32 full-time workers from a population of 800 full-time employees in order to collect information on expenditures concerning a company-sponsored dental plan. How do you select a simple random sample?

SOLUTION The company decides to conduct an e-mail survey. Assuming that not everyone will respond to the survey, you need to send more than 32 surveys to get the necessary 32 responses. Assuming that 8 out of 10 full-time workers will respond to such a survey (i.e., a response rate of 80%), you decide to send 40 surveys. Because you want to send the 40 surveys to 40 different individuals, you should sample without replacement.

The frame consists of a listing of the names and e-mail addresses of all $N = 800$ full-time employees taken from the company personnel files. Thus, the frame is a complete listing of the population. To select the random sample of 40 employees from this frame, you use a table of random numbers. Because the frame size (800) is a three-digit number, each assigned code number must also be three digits so that every full-time worker has an equal chance of selection. You assign a code of 001 to the first full-time employee in the population listing, a code of 002 to the second full-time employee in the population listing, and so on, until a code of 800 is assigned to the Nth full-time worker in the listing. Because $N = 800$ is the largest possible coded value, you discard all three-digit code sequences greater than 800 (i.e., 801 through 999 and 000).

To select the simple random sample, you choose an arbitrary starting point from the table of random numbers. One method you can use is to close your eyes and strike the table of random numbers with a pencil. Suppose you used this procedure and you selected row 06, column 05 of Table 8.1 (which is extracted from Table E.1) as the starting point. Although you can go in any direction, in this example you read the table from left to right, in sequences of three digits, without skipping.

TABLE 8.1

Using a Table of Random Numbers

		Column							
Row		**00000** **12345**	**00001** **67890**	**11111** **12345**	**11112** **67890**	**22222** **12345**	**22223** **67890**	**33333** **12345**	**33334** **67890**
	01	49280	88924	35779	00283	81163	07275	89863	02348
	02	61870	41657	07468	08612	98083	97349	20775	45091
	03	43898	65923	25078	86129	78496	97653	91550	08078
	04	62993	93912	30454	84598	56095	20664	12872	64647
	05	33850	58555	51438	85507	71865	79488	76783	31708
Begin	06	97340	03364	88472	04334	63919	36394	11095	92470
selection	07	70543	29776	10087	10072	55980	64688	68239	20461
(row 06,	08	89382	93809	00796	95945	34101	81277	66090	88872
column 05)	09	37818	72142	67140	50785	22380	16703	53362	44940
	10	60430	22834	14130	96593	23298	56203	92671	15925
	11	82975	66158	84731	19436	55790	69229	28661	13675
	12	39087	71938	40355	54324	08401	26299	49420	59208
	13	55700	24586	93247	32596	11865	63397	44251	43189
	14	14756	23997	78643	75912	83832	32768	18928	57070
	15	32166	53251	70654	92827	63491	04233	33825	69662
	16	23236	73751	31888	81718	06546	83246	47651	04877
	17	45794	26926	15130	82455	78305	55058	52551	47182
	18	09893	20505	14225	68514	46427	56788	96297	78822
	19	54382	74598	91499	14523	68479	27686	46162	83554
	20	94750	89923	37089	20048	80336	94598	26940	36858
	21	70297	34135	53140	33340	42050	82341	44104	82949
	22	85157	47954	32979	26575	57600	40881	12250	73742
	23	11100	02340	12860	74697	96644	89439	28707	25815
	24	36871	50775	30592	57143	17381	68856	25853	35041
	25	23913	48357	63308	16090	51690	54607	72407	55538

Source: Data extracted from Rand Corporation, *A Million Random Digits with 100,000 Normal Deviates* (Glencoe, IL: The Free Press, 1955) and contained in Table E.1.

The individual with code number 003 is the first full-time employee in the sample (row 06 and columns 05–07), the second individual has code number 364 (row 06 and columns 08–10), and the third individual has code number 884. Because the highest code for any employee is 800, you discard the number 884. Individuals with code numbers 720, 433, 463, 363, 109, 592, 470, and 705 are selected third through tenth, respectively.

You continue the selection process until you get the required sample size of 40 full-time employees. If any three-digit sequence repeats during the selection process, you discard the repeating sequence because you are sampling without replacement.

Systematic Samples

In a **systematic sample**, you partition the N items in the frame into n groups of k items, where

$$k = \frac{N}{n}$$

You round k to the nearest integer. To select a systematic sample, you choose the first item to be selected at random from the first k items in the frame. Then, you select the remaining $n - 1$ items by taking every kth item thereafter from the entire frame.

If the frame consists of a listing of prenumbered checks, sales receipts, or invoices, taking a systematic sample is faster and easier than taking a simple random sample. A systematic sample is also a convenient mechanism for collecting data from telephone books, class rosters, and consecutive items coming off an assembly line.

To take a systematic sample of $n = 40$ from the population of $N = 800$ full-time employees, you partition the frame of 800 into 40 groups, each of which contains 20 employees. You then select a random number from the first 20 individuals and include every twentieth individual after the first selection in the sample. For example, if the first random number you select is 008, your subsequent selections are 028, 048, 068, 088, 108, ..., 768, and 788.

Simple random sampling and systematic sampling are simpler than other, more sophisticated, probability sampling methods, but they generally require a larger sample size. In addition, systematic sampling is prone to selection bias. When using systematic sampling, if there is a pattern in the frame, you could have severe selection biases. To overcome the inefficiency of simple random sampling and the potential selection bias involved with systematic sampling, you can use either stratified sampling methods or cluster sampling methods.

Stratified Samples

In a **stratified sample**, you first subdivide the N items in the frame into separate subpopulations, or **strata**. A stratum is defined by some common characteristic, such as gender or year in school. You select a simple random sample within each of the strata and combine the results from the separate simple random samples. Stratified sampling is more efficient than either simple random sampling or systematic sampling because you are ensured of the representation of items across the entire population. The homogeneity of items within each stratum provides greater precision in the estimates of underlying population parameters.

EXAMPLE 8.2

Selecting a
Stratified Sample

A company wants to select a sample of 32 full-time workers from a population of 800 full-time employees in order to estimate expenditures from a company-sponsored dental plan. Of the full-time employees, 25% are managers and 75% are nonmanagerial workers. How do you select the stratified sample in order for the sample to represent the correct percentage of managers and nonmanagerial workers?

SOLUTION If you assume an 80% response rate, you need to send 40 surveys to get the necessary 32 responses. The frame consists of a listing of the names and e-mail addresses of all $N = 800$ full-time employees included in the company personnel files. Because 25% of the full-time employees are managers, you first separate the frame into two strata: a subpopulation listing of all 200 managerial-level personnel and a separate subpopulation listing of all 600 full-time nonmanagerial workers. Because the first stratum consists of a listing of 200 managers, you assign three-digit code numbers from 001 to 200. Because the second stratum contains a listing of 600 nonmanagerial workers, you assign three-digit code numbers from 001 to 600.

To collect a stratified sample proportional to the sizes of the strata, you select 25% of the overall sample from the first stratum and 75% of the overall sample from the second stratum. You take two separate simple random samples, each of which is based on a distinct random starting point from a table of random numbers (Table E.1). In the first sample, you select 10 managers from the listing of 200 in the first stratum, and in the second sample, you select 30 nonmanagerial workers from the listing of 600 in the second stratum. You then combine the results to reflect the composition of the entire company.

Cluster Samples

In a **cluster sample**, you divide the N items in the frame into clusters that contain several items. **Clusters** are often naturally occurring designations, such as counties, election districts, city blocks, households, or sales territories. You then take a random sample of one or more clusters and study all items in each selected cluster.

Cluster sampling is often more cost-effective than simple random sampling, particularly if the population is spread over a wide geographic region. However, cluster sampling often requires a larger sample size to produce results as precise as those from simple random sampling or stratified sampling. A detailed discussion of systematic sampling, stratified sampling, and cluster sampling procedures can be found in reference 1.

Problems for Section 8.1

LEARNING THE BASICS

8.1 For a population containing $N = 902$ individuals, what code number would you assign for
a. the first person on the list?
b. the fortieth person on the list?
c. the last person on the list?

8.2 For a population of $N = 902$, verify that by starting in row 05, column 01 of the table of random numbers (Table E.1), you need only six rows to select a sample of $N = 60$ *without* replacement.

8.3 Given a population of $N = 93$, starting in row 29, column 01 of the table of random numbers (Table E.1), and reading across the row, select a sample of $N = 15$
a. *without* replacement.
b. *with* replacement.

APPLYING THE CONCEPTS

8.4 For a study that consists of personal interviews with participants (rather than mail or phone surveys), explain why simple random sampling might be less practical than some other sampling methods.

8.5 You want to select a random sample of $n = 1$ from a population of three items (which are called A, B, and C). The rule for selecting the sample is as follows: Flip a coin; if it is heads, pick item A; if it is tails, flip the coin again; this time, if it is heads, choose B; if it is tails, choose C. Explain why this is a probability sample but not a simple random sample.

8.6 A population has four members (called A, B, C, and D). You would like to select a random sample of $n = 2$, which you decide to do in the following way: Flip a coin; if it is heads, the sample will be items A and B; if it is tails, the sample will be items C and D. Although this is a random sample, it is not a simple random sample. Explain why. (Compare the procedure described in Problem 8.5 with the procedure described in this problem.)

8.7 The registrar of a college with a population of $N = 4,000$ full-time students is asked by the president to conduct a survey to measure satisfaction with the quality of life on campus.

The following table contains a breakdown of the 4,000 registered full-time students, by gender and class designation:

| Gender | Class Designation | | | | |
	Fr.	So.	Jr.	Sr.	Total
Female	700	520	500	480	2,200
Male	560	460	400	380	1,800
Total	1,260	980	900	860	4,000

The registrar intends to take a probability sample of $n = 200$ students and project the results from the sample to the entire population of full-time students.
a. If the frame available from the registrar's files is an alphabetical listing of the names of all $N = 4,000$ registered full-time students, what type of sample could you take? Discuss.
b. What is the advantage of selecting a simple random sample in (a)?
c. What is the advantage of selecting a systematic sample in (a)?
d. If the frame available from the registrar's files is a listing of the names of all $N = 4,000$ registered full-time students compiled from eight separate alphabetical lists, based on the gender and class designation breakdowns shown in the class designation table, what type of sample should you take? Discuss.
e. Suppose that each of the $N = 4,000$ registered full-time students lived in one of the 10 campus dormitories. Each dormitory accommodates 400 students. It is college policy to fully integrate students by gender and class designation in each dormitory. If the registrar is able to compile a listing of all students by dormitory, explain how you could take a cluster sample.

✓**SELF** **8.8** Prenumbered sales invoices are kept in a
Test sales journal. The invoices are numbered from 0001 to 5000.
a. Beginning in row 16, column 01, and proceeding horizontally in Table E.1, select a simple random sample of 50 invoice numbers.
b. Select a systematic sample of 50 invoice numbers. Use the random numbers in row 20, columns 05–07, as the starting point for your selection.

c. Are the invoices selected in (a) the same as those selected in (b)? Why or why not?

8.9 Suppose that 5,000 sales invoices are separated into four strata. Stratum 1 contains 50 invoices, stratum 2 contains 500

invoices, stratum 3 contains 1,000 invoices, and stratum 4 contains 3,450 invoices. A sample of 500 sales invoices is needed.
a. What type of sampling should you do? Why?
b. Explain how you would carry out the sampling according to the method stated in (a).
c. Why is the sampling in (a) not simple random sampling?

8.2 Evaluating Survey Worthiness

Surveys are used to collect data. Nearly every day, you read or hear about survey or opinion poll results in newspapers, on the Internet, or on radio or television. To identify surveys that lack objectivity or credibility, you must critically evaluate what you read and hear by examining the worthiness of the survey. First, you must evaluate the purpose of the survey, why it was conducted, and for whom it was conducted.

The second step in evaluating the worthiness of a survey is to determine whether it was based on a probability or nonprobability sample (as discussed in Section 8.1). You need to remember that the only way to make valid statistical inferences from a sample to a population is through the use of a probability sample. Surveys that use nonprobability sampling methods are subject to serious, perhaps unintentional, biases that may make the results meaningless.

Survey Error

Even when surveys use random probability sampling methods, they are subject to potential errors. There are four types of survey errors:

- Coverage error
- Nonresponse error
- Sampling error
- Measurement error

Well-designed surveys reduce or minimize these four types of errors, often at considerable cost.

Coverage Error The key to proper sample selection is having an adequate frame. Remember that a frame is an up-to-date list of all the items from which you will select the sample. **Coverage error** occurs if certain groups of items are excluded from the frame so that they have no chance of being selected in the sample. Coverage error results in a **selection bias**. If the frame is inadequate because certain groups of items in the population were not properly included, any random probability sample selected will provide only an estimate of the characteristics of the frame, not the *actual* population.

Nonresponse Error Not everyone is willing to respond to a survey. In fact, research has shown that individuals in the upper and lower economic classes tend to respond less frequently to surveys than do people in the middle class. **Nonresponse error** arises from failure to collect data on all items in the sample and results in a **nonresponse bias**. Because you cannot always assume that persons who do not respond to surveys are similar to those who do, you need to follow up on the nonresponses after a specified period of time. You should make several attempts to convince such individuals to complete the survey. The follow-up responses are then compared to the initial responses in order to make valid inferences from the survey (see reference 1). The mode of response you use affects the rate of response. Personal interviews and telephone interviews usually produce a higher response rate than do mail surveys—but at a higher cost.

Sampling Error As discussed earlier, a sample is selected because it is simpler, less costly, and more efficient to examine than an entire population. However, chance dictates which individuals or items will or will not be included in the sample. **Sampling error** reflects the variation, or "chance differences," from sample to sample, based on the probability of particular individuals or items being selected in the particular samples.

When you read about the results of surveys or polls in newspapers or magazines, there is often a statement regarding a margin of error, such as "the results of this poll are expected to be within ±4 percentage points of the actual value." This **margin of error** is the sampling error. You can reduce sampling error by using larger sample sizes, although doing so increases the cost of conducting the survey.

Measurement Error In the practice of good survey research, you design a questionnaire with the intention of gathering meaningful information. But you have a dilemma here: Getting meaningful measurements is often easier said than done. Consider the following proverb:

> A person with one watch always knows what time it is;
>
> A person with two watches always searches to identify the correct one;
>
> A person with ten watches is always reminded of the difficulty in measuring time.

Unfortunately, the process of measurement is often governed by what is convenient, not what is needed. The measurements you get are often only a proxy for the ones you really desire. Much attention has been given to measurement error that occurs because of a weakness in question wording (see reference 2). A question should be clear, not ambiguous. Furthermore, in order to avoid *leading questions*, you need to present questions in a neutral manner.

Three sources of **measurement error** are ambiguous wording of questions, the Hawthorne effect, and respondent error. As an example of ambiguous wording, several years ago, the U.S. Department of Labor reported that the unemployment rate in the United States had been underestimated for more than a decade because of poor questionnaire wording in the Current Population Survey. In particular, the wording had led to a significant undercount of women in the labor force. Because unemployment rates are tied to benefit programs such as state unemployment compensation, survey researchers had to rectify the situation by adjusting the questionnaire wording.

The *Hawthorne effect* occurs when a respondent feels obligated to please the interviewer. Proper interviewer training can minimize the Hawthorne effect.

Respondent error occurs as a result of an overzealous or underzealous effort by the respondent. You can minimize this error in two ways: (1) by carefully scrutinizing the data and then recontacting those individuals whose responses seem unusual and (2) by establishing a program of recontacting a small number of randomly chosen individuals in order to determine the reliability of the responses.

Ethical Issues

Ethical considerations arise with respect to coverage error, nonresponse error, sampling error, and measurement error. Coverage error can result in selection bias and becomes an ethical issue if particular groups or individuals are *purposely* excluded from the frame so that the survey results are more favorable to the survey's sponsor. Nonresponse error can lead to nonresponse bias and becomes an ethical issue if the sponsor knowingly designs the survey so that particular groups or individuals are less likely than others to respond. Sampling error becomes an ethical issue if the findings are purposely presented without reference to sample size and margin of error so that the sponsor can promote a viewpoint that might otherwise be inappropriate. Measurement error becomes an ethical issue in one of three ways: (1) a survey sponsor chooses leading questions that guide the responses in a particular direction; (2) an interviewer, through mannerisms and tone, purposely creates a Hawthorne effect or otherwise guides the responses in a particular direction; or (3) a respondent willfully provides false information.

Ethical issues also arise when the results of nonprobability samples are used to form conclusions about the entire population. When you use a nonprobability sampling method, you need to explain the sampling procedures and state that the results cannot be generalized beyond the sample.

THINK ABOUT THIS New Media Surveys/Old Sampling Problems

Imagine that you are a software distributor and you decide to create a "customer experience improvement program" that records how your customers are using your products, with the goal of using the collected data to improve your products. Or say that you're the moderator of an opinion blog who decides to create an instant poll to ask your readers about important political issues. Or you're a marketer of products aimed at a specific demographic and decide to create a page in a social networking site through which you plan to collect consumer feedback. What might you have in common with a *dead-tree* publication that went out of business over 70 years ago?

By 1932, before there was ever an Internet—or even commercial television—a "straw poll" conducted by the magazine *Literary Digest* had successfully predicted five U.S. presidential elections in a row. For the 1936 election, the magazine promised its largest poll ever and sent about 10 million ballots to people all across the country. After receiving and tabulating more than 2.3 million ballots, the *Digest* confidently proclaimed that Alf Landon would be an easy winner over Franklin D. Roosevelt. As things turned out, FDR won in a landslide, with Landon receiving the fewest electoral votes in U.S. history. The reputation of the *Literary Digest* was ruined; the magazine would cease publication less than two years later.

The failure of the *Literary Digest* poll was a watershed event in the history of sample surveys and polls. This failure refuted the notion that the larger the sample is, the better. (Remember this the next time someone complains about a political survey's "small" sample size.) The failure opened the door to new and more modern methods of sampling—the theory and concepts this book discusses in Sections 8.1 and 8.2. Today's Gallup polls of political opinion (**www.gallup.com**) or Roper (now GfK Roper) Reports about consumer behavior (**www.gfkamerica.com/practice_areas/roper_consulting/roper_reports**) arose,

in part, due to this failure. George Gallup, the "Gallup" of the poll, and Elmo Roper, of the eponymous reports, both first gained widespread public notice for their correct "scientific" predictions of the 1936 election.

The failed *Literary Digest* poll became fodder for several postmortems, and the reason for the failure became almost an urban legend. Typically, the explanation is coverage error: The ballots were sent mostly to "rich people," and this created a frame that excluded poorer citizens (presumably more inclined to vote for the Democrat Roosevelt than the Republican Landon). However, later analyses suggest that this was not true; instead, low rates of response (2.3 million ballots represented less than 25% of the ballots distributed) and/or nonresponse error (Roosevelt voters were less likely to mail in a ballot than Landon voters) were significant reasons for the failure (see reference 9).

When Microsoft introduced its new Office Ribbon interface with Office 2007, a program manager explained how Microsoft had applied data collected from its "Customer Experience Improvement Program" to the redesign of the user interface. This led others to speculate that the data were biased toward beginners—who might be less likely to *decline* participation in the

program—and that, in turn, had led Microsoft to make decisions that ended up perplexing more experienced users. This was another case of nonresponse error!

The blog moderator's instant poll mentioned earlier is targeted to the moderator's community, and the social network–based survey is aimed at "friends" of a product; such polls can also suffer from nonresponse error, and this fact is often overlooked by users of these new media. Often, marketers extol how much they "know" about survey respondents, thanks to information that can be "mined" from a social network community. But no amount of information about the respondents can tell marketers who the nonresponders are. Therefore, new media surveys fall prey to the same old type of error that may have been fatal to *Literary Digest* way back when.

Today, companies establish formal surveys based on probability sampling and go to great lengths—and spend large sums—to deal with coverage error, nonresponse error, sampling error, and measurement error. Instant polling and tell-a-friend surveys can be interesting and fun, but they are not replacements for the methods discussed in this chapter.

Problems for Section 8.2

APPLYING THE CONCEPTS

8.10 A survey indicates that the vast majority of college students own their own personal computers. What information would you want to know before you accepted the results of this survey?

8.11 A simple random sample of $n = 300$ full-time employees is selected from a company list containing the names of all $N = 5,000$ full-time employees in order to evaluate job satisfaction.
a. Give an example of possible coverage error.
b. Give an example of possible nonresponse error.
c. Give an example of possible sampling error.
d. Give an example of possible measurement error.

✓SELF Test 8.12 Business Professor Thomas Callarman traveled to China more than a dozen times from 2000 to 2005. He warns people about believing everything they read about surveys conducted in China and gives two specific reasons: "First, things are changing so rapidly that what you hear today may not be true tomorrow. Second, the people who answer the surveys may tell you what they think you want to hear, rather than what they really believe" (T. E. Callarman, "Some Thoughts on China," *Decision Line*, March 2006, pp. 1, 43–44).
a. List the four types of survey error discussed in the paragraph above.

b. Which of the types of survey error in (a) are the basis for Professor Callarman's two reasons to question the surveys being conducted in China?

8.13 A recent survey of college freshmen investigated the amount of involvement their parents have with decisions concerning their education. When asked about the decision to go to college, 84% said their parents' involvement was about right, 10.3% said it was too much, and 5.7% said it was too little. When it came to selecting individual courses, 72.5% said their parents' involvement was about right, 3.5% said it was too much, and 24.0% said it was too little (M. B. Marklein, "Study: Colleges Shouldn't Fret Over Hands-on Parents," **www.usatoday.com**, January 23, 2008). What additional information would you want to know about the survey before you accepted the results of the study?

8.14 Recruiters are finding a wealth of unfiltered information about candidates on social-networking websites. A recent survey found that 83% of recruiters use search engines to learn more about candidates, and 43% eliminated candidates based on information they found (I. Phaneuf, "Who's Googling You?" *Job Postings*, Spring 2009, pp. 12–13). What additional information would you want to know about a survey before you accepted the results of the study?

8.3 Sampling Distributions

In many applications, you want to make inferences that are based on statistics calculated from samples to estimate the values of population parameters. In the next two sections, you will learn about how the sample mean (a statistic) is used to estimate the population mean (a parameter) and how the sample proportion (a statistic) is used to estimate the population proportion (a parameter). Your main concern when making a statistical inference is reaching conclusions about a population, *not* about a sample. For example, a political pollster is interested in the sample results only as a way of estimating the actual proportion of the votes that each candidate will receive from the population of voters. Likewise, as plant operations manager for Oxford Cereals, you are only interested in using the sample mean weight calculated from a sample of cereal boxes for estimating the mean weight of a population of boxes.

In practice, you select a single random sample of a predetermined size from the population. Hypothetically, to use the sample statistic to estimate the population parameter, you could examine *every* possible sample of a given size that could occur. A **sampling distribution** is the distribution of the results if you actually selected all possible samples. The single result you obtain in practice is just one of the results in the sampling distribution.

8.4 Sampling Distribution of the Mean

In Chapter 4, several measures of central tendency, including the mean, median, and mode, were discussed. Undoubtedly, the mean is the most widely used measure of central tendency. The sample mean is often used to estimate the population mean. The **sampling distribution of the mean** is the distribution of all possible sample means if you select all possible samples of a given size.

The Unbiased Property of the Sample Mean

The sample mean is **unbiased** because the mean of all the possible sample means (of a given sample size, n) is equal to the population mean, μ. A simple example concerning a population of four administrative assistants demonstrates this property. Each assistant is asked to apply the same set of updates to a human resources database. Table 8.2 presents the number of errors made by each of the administrative assistants. This population distribution is shown in Figure 8.2.

TABLE 8.2

Number of Errors Made by Each of Four Administrative Assistants

Administrative Assistant	Number of Errors
Ann	$X_1 = 3$
Bob	$X_2 = 2$
Carla	$X_3 = 1$
Dave	$X_4 = 4$

FIGURE 8.2

Number of errors made by a population of four administrative assistants

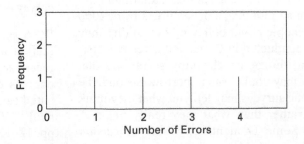

When you have the data from a population, you compute the mean by using Equation (8.1).

POPULATION MEAN

The population mean is the sum of the values in the population divided by the population size, N.

$$\mu = \frac{\sum_{i=1}^{N} X_i}{N} \tag{8.1}$$

You compute the population standard deviation, σ, by using Equation (8.2).

POPULATION STANDARD DEVIATION

$$\sigma = \sqrt{\frac{\sum_{i=1}^{N} (X_i - \mu)^2}{N}} \tag{8.2}$$

Thus, for the data of Table 8.2,

$$\mu = \frac{3 + 2 + 1 + 4}{4} = 2.5 \text{ errors}$$

and

$$\sigma = \sqrt{\frac{(3 - 2.5)^2 + (2 - 2.5)^2 + (1 - 2.5)^2 + (4 - 2.5)^2}{4}} = 1.12 \text{ errors}$$

If you select samples of two administrative assistants *with* replacement from this population, there are 16 possible samples ($N^n = 4^2 = 16$). Table 8.3 lists the 16 possible sample outcomes. If you average all 16 of these sample means, the mean of these values, is equal to 2.5, which is also the mean of the population, μ.

TABLE 8.3

All 16 Samples of $n = 2$ Administrative Assistants from a Population of $N = 4$ Administrative Assistants When Sampling with Replacement

Sample	Administrative Assistants	Sample Outcomes	Sample Mean
1	Ann, Ann	3, 3	$\bar{X}_1 = 3$
2	Ann, Bob	3, 2	$\bar{X}_2 = 2.5$
3	Ann, Carla	3, 1	$\bar{X}_3 = 2$
4	Ann, Dave	3, 4	$\bar{X}_4 = 3.5$
5	Bob, Ann	2, 3	$\bar{X}_5 = 2.5$
6	Bob, Bob	2, 2	$\bar{X}_6 = 2$
7	Bob, Carla	2, 1	$\bar{X}_7 = 1.5$
8	Bob, Dave	2, 4	$\bar{X}_8 = 3$
9	Carla, Ann	1, 3	$\bar{X}_9 = 2$
10	Carla, Bob	1, 2	$\bar{X}_{10} = 1.5$
11	Carla, Carla	1, 1	$\bar{X}_{11} = 1$
12	Carla, Dave	1, 4	$\bar{X}_{12} = 2.5$
13	Dave, Ann	4, 3	$\bar{X}_{13} = 3.5$
14	Dave, Bob	4, 2	$\bar{X}_{14} = 3$
15	Dave, Carla	4, 1	$\bar{X}_{15} = 2.5$
16	Dave, Dave	4, 4	$\bar{X}_{16} = 4$
			$\mu_{\bar{X}} = 2.5$

Because the mean of the 16 sample means is equal to the population mean, the sample mean is an unbiased estimator of the population mean. Therefore, although you do not know how close the sample mean of any particular sample selected comes to the population mean, you are assured that the mean of all the possible sample means that could have been selected is equal to the population mean.

Standard Error of the Mean

Figure 8.3 illustrates the variation in the sample means when selecting all 16 possible samples.

FIGURE 8.3

Sampling distribution of the mean, based on all possible samples containing two administrative assistants

Source: Data are from Table 8.3.

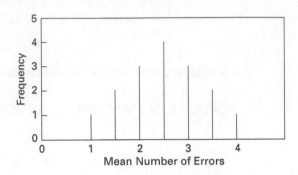

In this small example, although the sample means vary from sample to sample, depending on which two administrative assistants are selected, the sample means do not vary as much as the individual values in the population. That the sample means are less variable than the individual values in the population follows directly from the fact that each sample mean averages together all the values in the sample. A population consists of individual outcomes that can take on a wide range of values, from extremely small to extremely large. However, if a sample contains an extreme value, although this value will have an effect on the sample mean, the effect is reduced because the value is averaged with all the other values in the sample. As the sample size increases, the effect of a single extreme value becomes smaller because it is averaged with more values.

The value of the standard deviation of all possible sample means, called the **standard error of the mean**, expresses how the sample means vary from sample to sample. As the sample size increases, the standard error of the mean decreases by a factor equal to the square root of the sample size.

> **STANDARD ERROR OF THE MEAN**
>
> The standard error of the mean, $\sigma_{\bar{X}}$, is equal to the standard deviation in the population, σ, divided by the square root of the sample size, n.
>
> $$\sigma_{\bar{X}} = \frac{\sigma}{\sqrt{n}} \tag{8.3}$$

Equation (8.3) defines the standard error of the mean when sampling *with* replacement or sampling *without* replacement from large or infinite populations.

Example 8.3 computes the standard error of the mean when the sample selected without replacement contains less than 5% of the entire population.

EXAMPLE 8.3

Computing the Standard Error of the Mean

Returning to the cereal-filling process described in the Using Statistics scenario on page 317, if you randomly select a sample of 25 boxes without replacement from the thousands of boxes filled during a shift, the sample contains much less than 5% of the population. Given that the standard deviation of the cereal-filling process is 15 grams, compute the standard error of the mean.

SOLUTION Using Equation (8.3) with $n = 25$ and $\sigma = 15$, the standard error of the mean is

$$\sigma_{\bar{X}} = \frac{\sigma}{\sqrt{n}} = \frac{15}{\sqrt{25}} = \frac{15}{5} = 3$$

The variation in the sample means for samples of $n = 25$ is much less than the variation in the individual boxes of cereal (i.e., $\sigma_{\bar{X}} = 3$, while $\sigma = 15$).

Sampling from Normally Distributed Populations

Now that the concept of a sampling distribution has been introduced and the standard error of the mean has been defined, what distribution will the sample mean, $\overline{X}$, follow? If you are sampling from a population that is normally distributed with mean, μ, and standard deviation, σ, then regardless of the sample size, n, the sampling distribution of the mean is normally distributed, with mean, $\mu_{\overline{X}} = \mu$, and standard error of the mean, $\sigma_{\overline{X}} = \sigma/\sqrt{n}$.

In the simplest case, if you take samples of size $n = 1$, each possible sample mean is a single value from the population because

$$\overline{X} = \frac{\sum_{i=1}^{n} X_i}{n} = \frac{X_1}{1} = X_1$$

Therefore, if the population is normally distributed, with mean μ and standard deviation σ, the sampling distribution $\overline{X}$ for samples of $n = 1$ must also follow the normal distribution, with mean $\mu_{\overline{X}} = \mu$ and standard error of the mean $\sigma_{\overline{X}} = \sigma/\sqrt{1} = \sigma$. In addition, as the sample size increases, the sampling distribution of the mean still follows a normal distribution, with $\mu_{\overline{X}} = \mu$, but the standard error of the mean decreases, so that a larger proportion of sample means are closer to the population mean. Figure 8.4 illustrates this reduction in variability. Note that 500 samples of size 1, 2, 4, 8, 16, and 32 were randomly selected from a normally distributed population. From the polygons in Figure 8.4, you can see that, although the sampling distribution of the mean is approximately[1] normal for each sample size, the sample means are distributed more tightly around the population mean as the sample size increases.

[1]Remember that "only" 500 samples out of an infinite number of samples have been selected, so that the sampling distributions shown are only approximations of the population distributions.

FIGURE 8.4

Sampling distributions of the mean from 500 samples of sizes $n = 1, 2, 4, 8, 16$, and 32 selected from a normal population

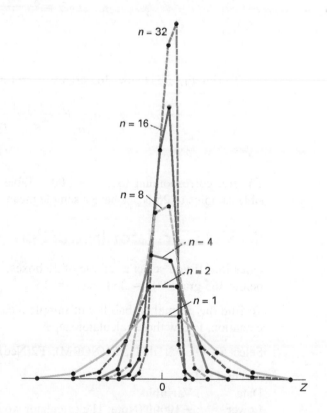

To further examine the concept of the sampling distribution of the mean, consider the Using Statistics scenario described on page 317. The packaging equipment that is filling 368-gram boxes of cereal is set so that the amount of cereal in a box is normally distributed, with a mean of 368 grams. From past experience, you know the population standard deviation for this filling process is 15 grams.

If you randomly select a sample of 25 boxes from the many thousands that are filled in a day and the mean weight is computed for this sample, what type of result could you expect? For example, do you think that the sample mean could be 368 grams? 200 grams? 365 grams?

The sample acts as a miniature representation of the population, so if the values in the population are normally distributed, the values in the sample should be approximately normally distributed. Thus, if the population mean is 368 grams, the sample mean has a good chance of being close to 368 grams.

How can you determine the probability that the sample of 25 boxes will have a mean below 365 grams? From the normal distribution (Section 7.2), you know that you can find the area below any value X by converting to standardized Z values:

$$Z = \frac{X - \mu}{\sigma}$$

In the examples in Section 7.2, you studied how any single value, X, differs from the population mean. Now, in this example, you want to study how a sample mean, $\bar{X}$, differs from the population mean. Substituting $\bar{X}$ for X, $\mu_{\bar{X}}$ for μ, and $\sigma_{\bar{X}}$ for σ in the equation above results in Equation (8.4).

FINDING Z FOR THE SAMPLING DISTRIBUTION OF THE MEAN

The Z value is equal to the difference between the sample mean, $\bar{X}$, and the population mean, μ, divided by the standard error of the mean, $\sigma_{\bar{X}}$.

$$Z = \frac{\bar{X} - \mu_{\bar{X}}}{\sigma_{\bar{X}}} = \frac{\bar{X} - \mu}{\dfrac{\sigma}{\sqrt{n}}} \tag{8.4}$$

To find the area below 365 grams, from Equation (8.4),

$$Z = \frac{\bar{X} - \mu_{\bar{X}}}{\sigma_{\bar{X}}} = \frac{365 - 368}{\dfrac{15}{\sqrt{25}}} = \frac{-3}{3} = -1.00$$

The area corresponding to $Z = -1.00$ in Table E.2 is 0.1587. Therefore, 15.87% of all the possible samples of 25 boxes have a sample mean below 365 grams.

CASIO Calculator Instruction

Question: If you select a sample of 25 boxes, what is the probability that the sample mean is below 365 grams? $\mu = 368$ and $\sigma = 15$

To find the normal probability of sample mean, associated with a known mean and standard deviation, follow these calculator steps:

Select **STAT**, **F5**(DIST), **F1**(NORM), **F2**(Ncd), and **F2**(Var). Then select the following options.

Normal C.D.
Data   : **Variable**
Lower   : **−10000** (Note: The calculator would not accept "- ∞. Therefore, you input a large negative number relative to its mean value.)
Upper   : **365**
σ : $\dfrac{15}{\sqrt{25}}$
μ : **368**
Save Res : **None**
Execute
Now press **EXE** or **F1**(CALC).

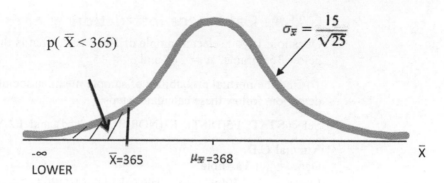

The calculator will now show the result:

Normal C.D.
$p \quad = 0.15865525$
z: Low $= -3456$
z : Up $= -1$

Answer: 15.87% of the samples of 25 boxes have means below 365 grams.

The preceding statement is not the same as saying that a certain percentage of *individual* boxes will contain less than 365 grams of cereal. You compute that percentage as follows:

$$Z = \frac{X - \mu}{\sigma} = \frac{365 - 368}{15} = \frac{-3}{15} = -0.20$$

The area corresponding to $Z = -0.20$ in Table E.2 is 0.4207. Therefore, 42.07% of the *individual* boxes are expected to contain less than 365 grams. Comparing these results, you see that many more *individual boxes* than *sample means* are below 365 grams. This result is explained by the fact that each sample consists of 25 different values, some small and some large. The averaging process dilutes the importance of any individual value, particularly when the sample size is large. Thus, the chance that the sample mean of 25 boxes is far away from the population mean is less than the chance that a *single* box is far away.

Examples 8.4 and 8.5 show how these results are affected by using different sample sizes.

EXAMPLE 8.4

The Effect of Sample Size, n, on the Computation of $\sigma_{\bar{X}}$

How is the standard error of the mean affected by increasing the sample size from 25 to 100 boxes?

SOLUTION If $n = 100$ boxes, then using Equation (8.3) on page 328:

$$\sigma_{\bar{X}} = \frac{\sigma}{\sqrt{n}} = \frac{15}{\sqrt{100}} = \frac{15}{10} = 1.5$$

The fourfold increase in the sample size from 25 to 100 reduces the standard error of the mean by half—from 3 grams to 1.5 grams. This demonstrates that taking a larger sample results in less variability in the sample means from sample to sample.

EXAMPLE 8.5

The Effect of Sample Size, n, on the Clustering of Means in the Sampling Distribution

If you select a sample of 100 boxes, what is the probability that the sample mean is below 365 grams?

SOLUTION Using Equation (8.4) on page 330,

$$Z = \frac{\bar{X} - \mu_{\bar{X}}}{\sigma_{\bar{X}}} = \frac{365 - 368}{\frac{15}{\sqrt{100}}} = \frac{-3}{1.5} = -2.00$$

From Table E.2, the area less than $Z = -2.00$ is 0.0228. Therefore, 2.28% of the samples of 100 boxes have means below 365 grams, as compared with 15.87% for samples of 25 boxes.

CASIO Calculator Instruction

Question: If you select a sample of 100 boxes, what is the probability that the sample mean is below 365 grams? $\mu = 368$ and $\sigma = 15$

To find the normal probability of sample mean, associated with a known mean and standard deviation, follow these calculator steps:

Select **STAT**, **F5**(DIST), **F1**(NORM), **F2**(Ncd), and **F2**(Var). Then select the following options.

Normal C.D.
Data   : **Variable**
Lower   : **−10000** (Note: The calculator would not accept "- ∞. Therefore, you input a large negative number relative to its mean value.)
Upper   : **365**
σ : $\dfrac{15}{\sqrt{100}}$
μ : **368**
Save Res   : **None**
Execute
Now press **EXE** or **F1**(CALC).

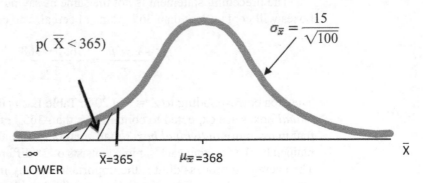

The calculator will now show the result:

Normal C.D.
p $= 0.02275013$
z: Low $= -6912$
z : Up $= -2$

Answer: 2.28% of the samples of 100 boxes have means below 365 grams.

Note: If everything else remains the same, as n increases, the probability decreases.

Sometimes you need to find the interval that contains a fixed proportion of the sample means. To do so, determine a distance below and above the population mean containing a specific area of the normal curve. From Equation (8.4) on page 330,

$$Z = \frac{\overline{X} - \mu}{\dfrac{\sigma}{\sqrt{n}}}$$

Solving for $\overline{X}$ results in Equation (8.5).

FINDING $\overline{X}$ FOR THE SAMPLING DISTRIBUTION OF THE MEAN

$$\overline{X} = \mu + Z\frac{\sigma}{\sqrt{n}} \qquad (8.5)$$

Example 8.6 illustrates the use of Equation (8.5).

Inverse Normal

Find $\bar{x}$ (sample mean) given the probability.

EXAMPLE 8.6

Determining the Interval That Includes a Fixed Proportion of the Sample Means

In the cereal-filling example, find an interval symmetrically distributed around the population mean that will include 95% of the sample means, based on samples of 25 boxes.

SOLUTION If 95% of the sample means are in the interval, then 5% are outside the interval. Divide the 5% into two equal parts of 2.5%. The value of Z in Table E.2 corresponding to an area of 0.0250 in the lower tail of the normal curve is -1.96, and the value of Z corresponding to a cumulative area of 0.9750 (i.e., 0.0250 in the upper tail of the normal curve) is $+1.96$. The lower value of $\bar{X}$ (called $\bar{X}_L$) and the upper value of $\bar{X}$ (called $\bar{X}_U$) are found by using Equation (8.5):

$$\bar{X}_L = 368 + (-1.96)\frac{15}{\sqrt{25}} = 368 - 5.88 = 362.12$$

$$\bar{X}_U = 368 + (1.96)\frac{15}{\sqrt{25}} = 368 + 5.88 = 373.88$$

Therefore, 95% of all sample means, based on samples of 25 boxes, are between 362.12 and 373.88 grams.

CASIO Calculator Instruction

Use the Casio calculator to obtain the inverse normal probability (i.e., find $\bar{X}$ given the probability).

Select **STAT**, **F5**(DIST), **F1**(NORM), **F3**(InvN), and **F2**(Var). Then select the following options.

Inverse Normal
Data	: **Variable**
Tail	: **CNTR (F3)**
Area	: **0.95**
σ	: $\dfrac{15}{\sqrt{25}}$
μ	: **368**
Save Res	: **None**
Execute	

Now press **EXE** or **F1**(CALC).

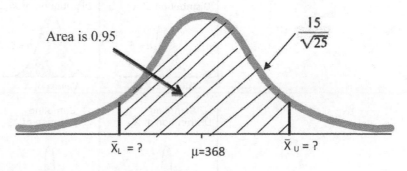

The calculator will now show the result:

Inverse Normal
$X_1\text{Inv} = 362.120108$
$X_2\text{Inv} = 373.879892$

Answer: 95% of all sample means based on samples of 25 boxes are between 362.12 and 373.88 grams.

Sampling from Non-Normally Distributed Populations—The Central Limit Theorem

Thus far in this section, only the sampling distribution of the mean for a normally distributed population has been considered. However, in many instances, either you know that the population is not normally distributed or it is unrealistic to assume that the population is normally distributed. An important theorem in statistics, the Central Limit Theorem, deals with this situation.

THE CENTRAL LIMIT THEOREM

The **Central Limit Theorem** states that as the sample size (i.e., the number of values in each sample) gets *large enough*, the sampling distribution of the mean is approximately normally distributed. This is true regardless of the shape of the distribution of the individual values in the population.

What sample size is large enough? A great deal of statistical research has gone into this issue. As a general rule, statisticians have found that for many population distributions, when the sample size is at least 30, the sampling distribution of the mean is approximately normal. However, you can apply the Central Limit Theorem for even smaller sample sizes if the population distribution is approximately bell-shaped. In the case in which the distribution of a variable is extremely skewed or has more than one mode, you may need sample sizes larger than 30 to ensure normality in the sampling distribution of the mean.

Figure 8.5 illustrates the application of the Central Limit Theorem to different populations. The sampling distributions from three different continuous distributions (normal, uniform, and exponential) for varying sample sizes ($n = 2, 5, 30$) are displayed.

FIGURE 8.5

Sampling distribution of the mean for different populations for samples of $n = 2, 5,$ and 30

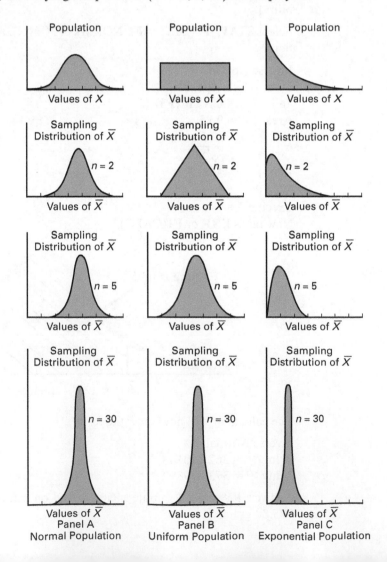

In each of the panels, because the sample mean is an unbiased estimator of the population mean, the mean of any sampling distribution is always equal to the mean of the population.

Panel A of Figure 8.5 shows the sampling distribution of the mean selected from a normal population. As mentioned earlier in this section, when the population is normally distributed, the sampling distribution of the mean is normally distributed for any sample size. [You can measure the variability by using the standard error of the mean, Equation (8.3), on page 328.]

Panel B of Figure 8.5 depicts the sampling distribution from a population with a uniform (or rectangular) distribution (see Section 7.1). When samples of size $n = 2$ are selected, there is a peaking, or *central limiting*, effect already working. For $n = 5$, the sampling distribution is bell-shaped and approximately normal. When $n = 30$, the sampling distribution looks very similar to a normal distribution. In general, the larger the sample size, the more closely the sampling distribution will follow a normal distribution. As with all other cases, the mean of each sampling distribution is equal to the mean of the population, and the variability decreases as the sample size increases.

Panel C of Figure 8.5 presents an exponential distribution (see Section 7.1). This population is extremely right-skewed. When $n = 2$, the sampling distribution is still highly right-skewed but less so than the distribution of the population. For $n = 5$, the sampling distribution is slightly right-skewed. When $n = 30$, the sampling distribution looks approximately normal. Again, the mean of each sampling distribution is equal to the mean of the population, and the variability decreases as the sample size increases.

Using the results from the normal, uniform, and exponential distributions, you can reach the following conclusions regarding the Central Limit Theorem:

- For most population distributions, regardless of shape, the sampling distribution of the mean is approximately normally distributed if samples of at least size 30 are selected.
- If the population distribution is fairly symmetrical, the sampling distribution of the mean is approximately normal for samples as small as size 5.
- If the population is normally distributed, the sampling distribution of the mean is normally distributed, regardless of the sample size.

The Central Limit Theorem is of crucial importance in using statistical inference to reach conclusions about a population. It allows you to make inferences about the population mean without having to know the specific shape of the population distribution.

VISUAL EXPLORATIONS Exploring Sampling Distributions

Use the Visual Explorations **Two Dice Probability** procedure to observe the effects of simulated throws on the frequency distribution of the sum of the two dice. Open the **Visual Explorations add-in workbook** (see Appendix Section D.4) and:

1. Select **Add-Ins → VisualExplorations → Two Dice Probability**.
2. Click the **Tally** button to tally a set of throws in the frequency distribution table and histogram. Optionally, click the spinner buttons to adjust the number of throws per tally (round).
3. Repeat step 2 as many times as necessary.
4. Click **Finish** to end the simulation.

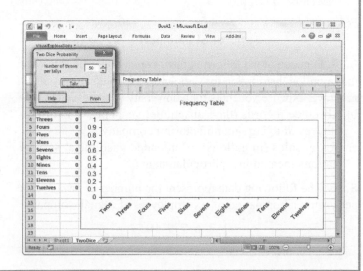

Problems for Section 8.4

LEARNING THE BASICS

8.15 Given a normal distribution with $\mu = 100$ and $\sigma = 10$, if you select a sample of $n = 25$, what is the probability that $\bar{X}$ is
a. less than 95?
b. between 95 and 97.5?
c. above 102.2?
d. There is a 65% chance that $\bar{X}$ is above what value?

8.16 Given a normal distribution with $\mu = 50$ and $\sigma = 5$, if you select a sample of $n = 100$, what is the probability that $\bar{X}$ is
a. less than 47?
b. between 47 and 49.5?
c. above 51.1?
d. There is a 35% chance that $\bar{X}$ is above what value?

APPLYING THE CONCEPTS

Central Limit Theorem Template:

X = _____

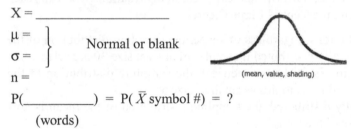

$\left.\begin{array}{c}\mu = \\ \\ \sigma = \end{array}\right\}$ Normal or blank

n =

(mean, value, shading)

P(_____) = P($\bar{X}$ symbol #) = ?
    (words)

Info about $\bar{X}$

1. $\mu_{\bar{x}} = \mu =$

2. $\sigma_{\bar{x}} = \dfrac{\sigma}{\sqrt{n}} =$

3. a) The original population is normal; therefore, $\bar{X}$ is normal.

   OR

   b) The original population is not normal, but $\bar{X}$ is normal because n ≥ 30.

P($\bar{X}$ symbol #) = $\dfrac{\rule{3cm}{0.4pt}}{\text{(calc. or SPSS input)}}$ = 0._ _ _ _
                          (4 dec.)

8.17 For each of the following three populations, indicate what the sampling distribution for samples of 25 would consist of:
a. Travel expense vouchers for a university in an academic year
b. Absentee records (days absent per year) in 2011 for employees of a large manufacturing company.
c. Yearly sales (in gallons) of unleaded gasoline at service stations located in a particular state.

8.18 The following data represent the number of days absent per year in a population of six employees of a small company:

1 3 6 7 9 10

a. Assuming that you sample without replacement, select all possible samples of $n = 2$ and construct the sampling distribution of the mean. Compute the mean of all the sample means and also compute the population mean. Are they equal? What is this property called?
b. Repeat (a) for all possible samples of $n = 3$.
c. Compare the shape of the sampling distribution of the mean in (a) and (b). Which sampling distribution has less variability? Why?
d. Assuming that you sample with replacement, repeat (a) through (c) and compare the results. Which sampling distributions have the least variability—those in (a) or (b)? Why?

8.19 The diameter of a brand of Ping-Pong balls is approximately normally distributed, with a mean of 1.30 inches and a standard deviation of 0.04 inch. If you select a random sample of 16 Ping-Pong balls,
a. what is the sampling distribution of the mean?
b. what is the probability that the sample mean is less than 1.28 inches?
c. what is the probability that the sample mean is between 1.31 and 1.33 inches?
d. The probability is 60% that the sample mean will be between what two values, symmetrically distributed around the population mean?

8.20 The U.S. Census Bureau announced that the median sales price of new houses sold in 2010 was $221,000, and the mean sales price was $272,400 (**www.census.gov/ newhomesales**, April 1, 2011). Assume that the standard deviation of the prices is $90,000.
a. If you select samples of $n = 2$, describe the shape of the sampling distribution of $\bar{X}$.
b. If you select samples of $n = 100$, describe the shape of the sampling distribution of $\bar{X}$.
c. If you select a random sample of $n = 100$, what is the probability that the sample mean will be less than $300,000?
d. If you select a random sample of $n = 100$, what is the probability that the sample mean will be between $275,000 and $290,000?

8.21 Time spent using e-mail per session is normally distributed, with $\mu = 8$ minutes and $\sigma = 2$ minutes. If you select a random sample of 25 sessions,
a. what is the probability that the sample mean is between 7.8 and 8.2 minutes?
b. what is the probability that the sample mean is between 7.5 and 8 minutes?
c. If you select a random sample of 100 sessions, what is the probability that the sample mean is between 7.8 and 8.2 minutes?
d. Explain the difference in the results of (a) and (c).

SELF Test **8.22** The amount of time a bank teller spends with each customer has a population mean $\mu = 3.10$ minutes and a standard deviation $\sigma = 0.40$ minute. If you select a random sample of 16 customers,

a. what is the probability that the mean time spent per customer is at least 3 minutes?

b. there is an 85% chance that the sample mean is less than how many minutes?

c. What assumption must you make in order to solve (a) and (b)?

d. If you select a random sample of 64 customers, there is an 85% chance that the sample mean is less than how many minutes?

PROBABILITY DISTRIBUTIONS—REVIEW EXERCISES

8.23 A manufacturing company anticipates that its daily demand for electric power during the next few months will fluctuate around a mean of 100.0 kilowatts. Based on past results, the daily power usage distribution should be normally distributed, with a standard deviation of 10.0 kilowatts.

a. What is the probability that the demand for electric power on a given day will range from 90.0 to 125.0 kilowatts?

b. What is the level of usage that will be exceeded only 20 percent of the time?

8.24 The defects in an automatic weaving process occur randomly at an average rate of 0.0025 per square metre and a standard deviation of 0.05 per square metre. The process has just been set up to run 1,000 square metres of fabric. What is the probability that there will be at least four defects in this fabric?

8.25 The occurrence of the first breakdown of an automatic washing machine is normally distributed, with a mean of 5.9 years and a standard deviation of 1.5 years. How long (full years) should these washing machines be guaranteed so that no more than 10% would require repairs during the warrantee period?

8.26 A large company is currently evaluating 14 cost-reducing proposals submitted by employees. Past experience has shown that 30 percent of such proposals are implemented by the company.

a. What is the probability that more than five proposals will be implemented?

b. What is the probability that at least half of the proposals will be implemented?

c. What is the expected number of proposals implemented?

8.27 The manufacturer of a quartz travel clock claims that, on average, its clocks deviate from perfect time by an average of 30 seconds in a month, with a standard deviation of 10 seconds. The test group that works for a consumer magazine purchased 40 of these clocks and found that the average deviation from perfect time was 35 seconds after one month.

a. If the manufacturer's claim is correct, what is the probability that the average deviation from perfect time for the 40 clocks would be 35 seconds or more?

b. If the average clock deviates by 33 seconds from perfect in one month, what is the probability that the average deviation from perfect time for the 40 clocks would be 35 seconds or more?

8.28 The Executours Corp. offers tours of the city to visiting businesspersons and uses a 12-passenger luxury bus. From past experience 10% of the people who make advance reservations will cancel at the last minute, therefore, Executours usually takes 13 reservations. For what percent of tours will they have enough seats for the passengers who show up for the tour?

8.29 The number of man-hours required by the Victory Construction Co. to assemble its prefabricated two-bedroom house is normally distributed, with a mean of 400 man-hours and a standard deviation of 40 man-hours.

a. The probability is 0.9 that the assembly of a house will take less than how many hours?

b. What is the probability that assembly of a house will take more than 420 man-hours?

8.30 There are two major steps in the production of solar covers for swimming pools. First, a 1-metre wide continuous strip of plastic air bubble material is produced. Then the material is cut to the required length (in this case 10 metres) and an appropriate number of these strips are sewn together to produce a solar cover.

Records kept by the quality control department indicate that on average:

i. there is one puncture in every 1,000 m^2 of plastic material.

ii. there is one sewing defect for every 1,500 m of sewing.

For a 4 m by 10 m solar cover:

a. What is the probability that the cover will not have a puncture?

b. What is the probability that the cover will not have a sewing defect?

8.31 In an attempt to improve sales, the management of a large chain of fast-food restaurants has decided to implement a reward/reprimand system based on monthly sales figures. The initial standards have been set up as follows:

i. Reward the managers of restaurants that have placed in the top 15% of sales for the month.

ii. Reprimand managers with sales less than $180,000 for the month.

For the month just past, the sales figures for the 4,350 restaurants were normally distributed, with a mean of $230,000 and a standard deviation of $22,000.

a. How many managers will be reprimanded?

b. What will be the minimum sales that will qualify for a reward?

8.32 A checkout counter is considered 'over-occupied' if more than eight customers arrive within a five-minute period. The average number of customers per hour is 78.

a. What is the probability that in one minute at most two customers arrive?

b. What is the probability that the counter is 'over-occupied' in a five-minute period?

8.33A From past experience, an airline has found that the luggage weight for individual air travelers on their trans-Atlantic route averages 40 kg, with a standard deviation of 10 kg. The plane consistently is booked with 100 passengers. The pilot insists on loading an extra 500 litres of fuel whenever the total luggage weight exceeds 4,200 kg. On what percent of the flights will the extra fuel be required?

8.33B The manufacturing process for automobile windshields involves placing a plastic adhesive film between two panes of glass. Then high pressure is applied to bond the three layers. The glass is then cut and bent to the required shape.

Quality standards require that there be no bubbles in order for a windshield to be considered suitable for installation into an automobile. Also, the glass must withstand an impact of 10 kg dropped from a height of 3 metres. The thickness of the finished windshield must be from 3.2 to 3.4 mm.

The High-Lite Glass Company makes rectangular windshield glass in sheets that are 2 metres wide by 1.5 metres high. The process usually averages 0.39 bubbles per sheet. Usually, only 3% of the windshields made from this company's glass fail the impact test.

One particular auto manufacturer just ordered 20 sheets of glass, which will be enough to make 60 windshields that are 2 metres wide by 0.5 metres high.

a. What is the probability that a finished windshield will have no bubbles?

b. What is the probability that at least 57 of the windshields will be able to withstand the impact test?

8.34 The Long-Life Tire Co. claims that its Super-All-Season tire lasts an average of 110,000 km. It is known that the tire life is normally distributed, with a standard deviation of 2800 km. Your company has just purchased all new tires for its fleet of 10 cars. Assuming that the manufacturer's claim is true, answer the following questions

a. What is the probability that a tire will last longer than 112,000 km?

b. What is the probability that the tires for your company car will last an average of at least 112,000 km?

c. What is the probability that the average life of all the tires purchased by your company will be at least 112,000 km?

d. What is the probability that all the tires of your car will last more than 112,000 km?

8.35 A sand and gravel dealer has received an order for five hundred 10.0 kg. bags of sand. Currently, the company has 5,150 kg of sand available.

A specialized sand-bag filling machine will be used to fill the bags. The machine can fill 100 bags per hour. The weight of sand in each bag will be normally distributed, with a standard deviation of 0.3 kg. The sand bags' mean weight can be adjusted by the filling machine operator.

If the mean weight is set at 10.25 kg, how many of the 500 bags are expected to meet the customer's expectations?

8.36 An automobile battery has a mean life of 1,200 days, with a standard deviation of 100 days. If the battery lifetimes are normally distributed, how long should the manufacturer make the guarantee in order to replace at most 10% of the batteries under warranty?

8.37 A hardware store chain has just received a truckload of 5,000 electric drills. Before accepting the shipment, the purchasing manager will test a random selection of 10 drills. The drills will be tested for maximum power consumption and the shipment will be rejected if the mean consumption is more than the 300 watts indicated on the product label. Suppose that the maximum power consumption of the drills in the shipment is normally distributed and averages only 295 watts, with a standard deviation of 12 watts.

a. What is the probability that the shipment will be rejected?

b. How many of the drills in the shipment are expected to exceed the maximum power consumption indicated on the label?

8.38 The quality control manager of Marilyn's Cookies is inspecting a batch of chocolate-chip cookies that has just been baked. If the production process is operating properly, the average number of chocolate chips per cookie is 6.76, with a standard deviation of 2.6 chocolate chips. What percent of the cookies will have fewer than four chocolate chips?

8.39 A student is about to write his marketing final exam that consists of 30 multiple-choice questions, each of which has five possible answers. If he has not studied, has no common sense regarding marketing, and thus has to guess the answer to each question, what is the probability that he will pass the exam?

8.40 The time to get an oil change at a certain car dealership averages 42.3 minutes, with a standard deviation of 8.6 minutes.

a. There are 45 cars booked for oil changes today. What is the probability that the jobs can be done in an average of 38 minutes or less?

b. Suppose 90 oil changes were done in one particular week. There is a 95% chance that the mean time was more than _____ minutes.

8.41 Table A at the bottom of this page appeared in the November 2000 issue of *Quality Progress* magazine. Assume that the salary distributions for all categories of analysts are normal.

a. What is the probability that an analyst with 3.1 to 6 years experience in the quality field will earn more than $60,000?

b. What is the third quartile salary of analysts with 10.1 to 20 years experience in the quality field?

8.42 The following table appeared in the Autumn 2003 issue of *Canadian Social Trends*.

EST — One in four rotating shift employees worry about the risk of accident or injury

	Total '000	Too many demands/ hours	Risk of accident/ injury	Poor interpersonal relations	Threat of layoff/ job loss	Having to learn computer skills	Other
					%		
Work arrangements							
Class of worker							
All workers	16,800	34	13	15	13	11	6
Self-employed	2,800	37	12	10	8	11	10
Employees	14,000	34	13	16	14	11	6
Employees only							
Hours of work							
All employees[1]	14,000	34	13	16	14	11	6
Full-time	11,500	37	14	17	15	12	6
30-35 hours/week	1,900	29	11	15	15	11	6
36-40 hours/week	6,100	33	14	17	16	12	6
41 or more hours/week	3,600	47	16	18	13	13	6
Part-time	2,300	20	9	11	10	7	5
1-15 hours/week	900	16	6	10	8	4E	4E
16-29 hours/week	1,400	22	11	12	11	9	5
Work schedules							
Regular daytime	9,500	35	11	15	14	12	6
Rotating shift	1,800	35	24	20	16	11	5
Regular evening or night	1,400	27	16	16	12	5	4
Irregular/split shift	900	35	17	16	13	11	5E
Other/on call	300	21	11E	15E	13E	F	9E

Full-time and part-time employees.
High sampling variability.
Sample too small to provide reliable estimate.
Source: Statistics Canada, General Social Survey, 2000.

Living in one particular neighbourhood are 183 full-time workers that work 36–40 hours per week.

a. What is the probability that more than 15% of them worry about the risk of accident or injury?

b. In a sample of 120 rotating shift workers, what is the relative variability of the number who worry about the threat of layoff or job loss?

PROBABILITY DISTRIBUTIONS— COMBINATION QUESTIONS

8.43 In the 1840, Lambert Quetelet recorded data on an entire regiment of 5,732 soldiers. According to the records of Monsieur Quetelet,

- soldiers' chest measurements were normal, with a mean of 39.80 inches and a standard deviation of 2.05 inches;
- 12% of soldiers reported that they suffered from skin rash; and
- on average, 25 soldiers reported to Sick Bay each day.

a. What percentage of the soldiers in this regiment could be expected to have had chest measurements less than 38.5 inches?

b. Twenty-five percent of the soldiers had a chest measurement below what size?

c. In a group of 50 soldiers, what is the probability that more than four of them suffered from skin rash?

d. In a group of 40 soldiers, what is the probability that no more than eight of them suffered from skin rash?

e. What is the probability that exactly 30 soldiers reported to Sick Bay on a particular day?

f. What is the probability that a maximum of 200 soldiers reported to Sick Bay in a week?

g. In a sample of 35 randomly selected soldiers, what is the probability that the average chest measurement of the soldiers in this sample was at least 40.5 inches?

8.44 There are 12 agents in one office of a certain real estate firm. Much of the business in this office is conducted by taking a prospective customer out to view a particular property. The time to drive to and view a property is normally distributed and averages 47.3 minutes, with a standard deviation of 11.7 minutes. Past studies have shown that 26 percent of customers who visit properties with an agent will eventually buy a property being shown by that agent. On average, each agent visits 3.6 properties a day, with a standard deviation of 1.9 visits. All these activities are independent of each other.

a. What is the probability that an agent will visit at least seven properties over the next three days?

Table A. Salary by Job Title and Number of Years' Experience in the Quality Field for Respondents Who Work in the United States

	Minimum	Maximum	Standard deviation	Count	Mean	Median
Analyst						
Less than 1 year	$50,000	$64,000	$ 7,095	3	$56,333	$55,000
1 to 3 years	22,000	70,000	13,414	29	43,835	42,300
3.1 to 6 years	28,500	85,000	14,148	34	48,351	45,000
6.1 to 10 years	30,000	98,000	16,221	26	50,438	44,000
10.1 to 20 years	26,800	85,000	14,780	36	50,733	53,000
More than 20 years	21,000	83,000	18,851	9	54,111	55,000
No experience	42,000	77,000	11,404	6	58,731	58,000

b. What is the probability that the average time of the next 50 property viewings will be less than 45 minutes?

c. A particular agent currently has 17 prospective customers that are being shown properties for sale. What is the probability that fewer than four of these customers will eventually buy a property being shown by the agent?

d. Eighty-two (82) percent of property visits will take what range of time, centered at the mean?

8.45 For the Seashell gas station in your neighbourhood, records indicate that the number of customers arriving in any five-minute interval averages 0.94 customers, with a standard deviation of 0.97 customers. Sixty-five (65) percent of the customers use a credit card to pay for their purchase. There are eight pumps at this service station. The time that a car is parked at a pump is normally distributed, with a mean of 6.35 minutes and a standard deviation of 2.10 minutes. All these activities are independent of each other.

a. Ninety-four (94) percent of the customers will be parked for what maximum amount of time?

b. For 12 randomly selected customers, what is the probability that at least 10 of them will pay using a credit card?

c. What is the probability that more than five customers will arrive in a 15-minute period?

d. What is the probability that the average parked time for the next 40 customers will be less than six minutes?

8.46 There are 12 brokers in one office of a certain brokerage firm. Much of the business in this office is conducted by telephone. The duration of a telephone call is normally distributed and averages 7.45 minutes, with a standard deviation of 1.7 minutes. Past studies have shown that 57 percent of telephone calls result in a buy or sell order. On average, each broker receives 1.6 calls every 20 minutes, with a standard deviation of 1.3 calls. All these activities are independent of each other.

a. What is the probability that a broker will receive at least four calls in the next hour?

b. What is the probability that the average duration of the next 40 calls will be less than seven minutes?

c. For nine randomly selected calls, what is the probability that at least seven of them will result in a buy or sell order?

d. Ninety-two (92) percent of the calls will last for what minimum amount of time?

8.47 During the month of December, the average number of customers entering Reader's Bookstore is 7.84 every 20 minutes, with a standard deviation of 2.8 customers. The time to get through the check-out counter is approximately normally distributed, with a mean of 5.6 minutes and a standard deviation of 1.9 minutes. Fifteen percent of customers are first-time shoppers and 25% of all customers use their debit card to pay for their books.

a. Currently, there are 40 customers in the store. What is the probability that more than three-quarters of them will have shopped at Reader's before?

b. What is the probability that a customer will take less than four minutes to check-out?

c. What is the probability that more than 10 customers will enter the store in the next half-hour?

d. Ten percent of the customers will take longer than _____ to check out.

8.48 New houses are being built and sold at record paces in the GTA this year. It was reported on the radio last week that, on average, one new home was sold every six minutes. In February, 3,215 new houses were sold in the GTA region, of which 80% were located in the 905 area code municipalities.

The prices of new homes being built and sold this year are also at record high levels. The average price of a two-bedroom home was $212,000, with a standard deviation of $5,300. The mean and standard deviation of the prices of three-bedroom homes were $276,000 and $10,700, respectively. For four-bedroom homes, the corresponding figures were $328,000 and $24,800. All the price data sets were normally distributed.

The figures also showed that 32% of homes being built this year had two bedrooms, 45% had three bedrooms, 15% had four bedrooms, and the remainder were equal numbers of five- and six-bedroom homes. The time to build a three-bedroom home averaged 205 days, with a standard deviation of 12 days. The sizes of three-bedroom homes were normally distributed, with a mean of 2,540 ft^2 and a standard deviation of 175 ft^2.

In Mississauga, just west of Winston Churchill Blvd., a large new community of 2,400 houses is being built on a 3-square-kilometre (3,000,000 m^2) area. Only 10% of the houses will be bungalows—that is, one-storey. All others will be two-storey houses. The bungalows are to be randomly distributed throughout the community.

(Note: All figures above, except those in the first paragraph, also apply to the Mississauga community.)

a. What is the probability that a two-bedroom home will cost more than $225,000?

b. On one street in the Mississauga development, there are 23 houses. What is the probability that at most five of them have four bedrooms?

c. One developer is building 53 three-bedroom homes in the new Mississauga community. What is the probability that the mean time to construct these homes will be less than 200 days?

d. What is the probability that 12 new homes will be sold in an hour?

e. One developer in the new Mississauga community has a special deal this weekend on three-bedroom houses. There will be a $20,000 price discount on the largest 15% of houses. How big a three-bedroom house do you have to buy to get this discount?

f. What is the expected number of bedrooms in new homes being built this year?

g. What is the probability that there would be at least three bungalows in a 10,000 m² area in the new development in Mississauga?

8.49 The production process used to produce 500-ft spools of electrical cable operates continuously, 24 hours a day, and is capable of producing approximately six spools per day. The time required to produce one spool is normally distributed, with a mean of 4.23 hours and a standard deviation of 0.45 hours. Defects occur in the wire at an average rate of 1 per 1,000 feet. As a result, 61% of all spools have no defects. The machine used to produce the wire, needs to be adjusted an average of four times per day, with a standard deviation of two times per day.

a. What is the probability that in a week's production, i.e. (i.e., 42 spools) there will be at least 35 spools without defects?

b. What is the probability that a spool can be produced in less than four hours?

c. What is the probability that the wire-producing machine will need to be adjusted at most once in an eight-hour shift?

d. What is the probability that the average time to produce the next 15 spools will be more than 4.1 hours?

e. Seventy-eight (78) percent of the spools will be produced within what range of time, centered at the mean?

8.5 Sampling Distribution of the Proportion

Consider a categorical variable that has only two categories, such as the customer prefers your brand or the customer prefers the competitor's brand. You are interested in the proportion of items belonging to one of the categories—for example, the proportion of customers that prefer your brand. The population proportion, represented by π, is the proportion of items in the entire population with the characteristic of interest. The sample proportion, represented by p, is the proportion of items in the sample with the characteristic of interest. The sample proportion, a statistic, is used to estimate the population proportion, a parameter. To calculate the sample proportion, you assign one of two possible values, 1 or 0, to represent the presence or absence of the characteristic. You then sum all the 1 and 0 values and divide by n, the sample size. For example, if, in a sample of five customers, three preferred your brand and two did not, you have three 1s and two 0s. Summing the three 1s and two 0s and dividing by the sample size of 5 results in a sample proportion of 0.60.

SAMPLE PROPORTION

$$p = \frac{X}{n} = \frac{\text{Number of items having the characteristic of interest}}{\text{Sample size}} \tag{8.6}$$

The sample proportion, p, will be between 0 and 1. If all items have the characteristic, you assign each a score of 1, and p is equal to 1. If half the items have the characteristic, you assign half a score of 1 and assign the other half a score of 0, and p is equal to 0.5. If none of the items have the characteristic, you assign each a score of 0, and p is equal to 0.

In Section 8.4, you learned that the sample mean, $\overline{X}$ is an unbiased estimator of the population mean, μ. Similarly, the statistic p is an unbiased estimator of the population proportion, π. By analogy to the sampling distribution of the mean, whose standard error is $\sigma_{\overline{X}} = \dfrac{\sigma}{\sqrt{n}}$, the **standard error of the proportion**, σ_p, is given in Equation (8.7).

STANDARD ERROR OF THE PROPORTION

$$\sigma_p = \sqrt{\frac{\pi(1-\pi)}{n}} \tag{8.7}$$

The **sampling distribution of the proportion** follows the binomial distribution, as discussed in Section 6.2 when sampling with replacement (or without replacement from extremely large populations). However, you can use the normal distribution to approximate the binomial distribution when $n\pi$ and $n(1-\pi)$ are each at least 5. In most cases in which inferences are made about the proportion, the sample size is substantial enough to meet the conditions for using the normal approximation (see reference 1). Therefore, in many instances, you can use the normal distribution to estimate the sampling distribution of the proportion.

Substituting p for $\overline{X}$, π for μ, and $\sqrt{\dfrac{\pi(1-\pi)}{n}}$ for $\dfrac{\sigma}{\sqrt{n}}$ in Equation (8.4) on page 330 results in Equation (8.8).

FINDING Z FOR THE SAMPLING DISTRIBUTION OF THE PROPORTION

$$Z = \frac{p - \pi}{\sqrt{\dfrac{\pi(1 - \pi)}{n}}} \tag{8.8}$$

To illustrate the sampling distribution of the proportion, suppose that the manager of the local branch of a bank determines that 40% of all depositors have multiple accounts at the bank. If you select a random sample of 200 depositors, because $n\pi = 200(0.40) = 80 \geq 5$ and $n(1 - \pi) = 200(0.60) = 120 \geq 5$, the sample size is large enough to assume that the sampling distribution of the proportion is approximately normally distributed. Then, you can calculate the probability that the sample proportion of depositors with multiple accounts is less than 0.30 by using Equation (8.8):

$$Z = \frac{p - \pi}{\sqrt{\dfrac{\pi(1 - \pi)}{n}}}$$

$$= \frac{0.30 - 0.40}{\sqrt{\dfrac{(0.40)(0.60)}{200}}} = \frac{-0.10}{\sqrt{\dfrac{0.24}{200}}} = \frac{-0.10}{0.0346}$$

$$= -2.89$$

Using Table E.2, the area under the normal curve less than -2.89 is 0.0019. Therefore, if the population proportion of items of interest is 0.40, only 0.19% of the samples of $n = 200$ would be expected to have sample proportions less than 0.30.

Problems for Section 8.5

LEARNING THE BASICS

8.50 In a random sample of 64 people, 48 are classified as "successful."
a. Determine the sample proportion, p, of "successful" people.
b. If the population proportion is 0.70, determine the standard error of the proportion.

8.51 A random sample of 50 households was selected for a telephone survey. The key question asked was, "Do you or any member of your household own a cellular telephone that you can use to access the Internet?" Of the 50 respondents, 20 said yes and 30 said no.
a. Determine the sample proportion, p, of households with cellular telephones that can be used to access the Internet.

b. If the population proportion is 0.45, determine the standard error of the proportion.

8.52 The following data represent the responses (Y for yes and N for no) from a sample of 40 college students to the question "Do you currently own shares in any stocks?"

N N Y N N Y N Y N Y N N Y N Y Y N N N Y
N Y N N N N Y N N Y Y N N N Y N N Y N N

a. Determine the sample proportion, p, of college students who own shares of stock.
b. If the population proportion is 0.30, determine the standard error of the proportion.

APPLYING THE CONCEPTS

✓SELF **8.53** A political pollster is conducting an analy-
Test sis of sample results in order to make predictions
on election night. Assuming a two-candidate election, if a
specific candidate receives at least 55% of the vote in the
sample, that candidate will be forecast as the winner of the
election. If you select a random sample of 100 voters, what
is the probability that a candidate will be forecast as the
winner when

a. the population percentage of her vote is 50.1%?
b. the population percentage of her vote is 60%?
c. the population percentage of her vote is 49% (and she
will actually lose the election)?
d. If the sample size is increased to 400, what are your
answers to (a) through (c)? Discuss.

8.54 You plan to conduct a marketing experiment in which
students are to taste one of two different brands of soft
drink. Their task is to correctly identify the brand tasted.
You select a random sample of 200 students and assume that
the students have no ability to distinguish between the two
brands. (Hint: If an individual has no ability to distinguish
between the two soft drinks, then the two brands are equally
likely to be selected.)

a. What is the probability that the sample will have between
50% and 60% of the identifications correct?
b. The probability is 90% that the sample percentage is contained within what symmetrical limits of the population
percentage?
c. What is the probability that the sample percentage of correct identifications is greater than 65%?
d. Which is more likely to occur—more than 60% correct
identifications in the sample of 200 or more than 55%
correct identifications in a sample of 1,000? Explain.

8.55 In a recent survey of full-time female workers ages 22
to 35 years, 46% said that they would rather give up some of
their salary for more personal time. (Data extracted from
"I'd Rather Give Up," *USA Today*, March 4, 2010, p. 1B.)
Suppose you select a sample of 100 full-time female workers 22 to 35 years old.

a. What is the probability that in the sample, fewer than
50% would rather give up some of their salary for more
personal time?
b. What is the probability that in the sample, between 40%
and 50% would rather give up some of their salary for
more personal time?
c. What is the probability that in the sample, more than
40% would rather give up some of their salary for more
personal time?
d. If a sample of 400 is taken, how does this change your
answers to (a) through (c)?

8.56 Companies often make flextime scheduling available
to help recruit and keep female employees who have chil-

dren. Other workers sometimes view these flextime schedules as unfair. An article in *USA Today* indicates that 25% of
male employees state that they have to pick up the slack for
moms working flextime schedules. (Data extracted from
D. Jones, "Poll Finds Resentment of Flextime," **www.usa
today.com**, May 11, 2007.) Suppose you select a random
sample of 100 male employees working for companies offering flextime.

a. What is the probability that 25% or fewer male employees will indicate that they have to pick up the slack for
moms working flextime?
b. What is the probability that 20% or fewer male employees will indicate that they have to pick up the slack for
moms working flextime?
c. If a random sample of 500 is taken, how does this change
your answers to (a) and (b)?

8.57 According to Gallup's poll on consumer behavior,
36% of Americans say they will consider only cars manufactured by an American company when purchasing a new car.
(Data extracted from *The Gallup Poll*, **www.gallup.com**,
March 31, 2010.) If you select a random sample of
200 Americans,

a. what is the probability that the sample will have between
30% and 40% who say they will consider only cars manufactured by an American company when purchasing a
new car?
b. the probability is 90% that the sample percentage will be
contained within what symmetrical limits of the population percentage?
c. the probability is 95% that the sample percentage will be
contained within what symmetrical limits of the population percentage?

8.58 The Agency for Healthcare Research and Quality reports that medical errors are responsible for injury to 1 out
of every 25 hospital patients in the United States. (Data extracted from M. Ozan-Rafferty, "Hospitals: Never Have a
Never Event," *The Gallup Management Journal*, **gmj
.gallup.com**, May 7, 2009.) These errors are tragic and expensive. Preventable health care–related errors cost an estimated $29 billion each year in the United States. Suppose
that you select a sample of 100 U.S. hospital patients.

a. What is the probability that the sample percentage reporting
injury due to medical errors will be between 5% and 10%?
b. The probability is 90% that the sample percentage will be
within what symmetrical limits of the population
percentage?
c. The probability is 95% that the sample percentage will
be within what symmetrical limits of the population
percentage?
d. Suppose you selected a sample of 400 U.S. hospital
patients. How does this change your answers in (a)
through (c)?

8.59 A survey of 2,250 American adults reported that 59% got news both online and offline in a typical day. (Data extracted from "How Americans Get News in a Typical Day," *USA Today*, March 10, 2010, p. 1A.)

a. Suppose that you take a sample of 100 American adults. If the population proportion of American adults who get news both online and offline in a typical day is 0.59, what is the probability that fewer than half in your sample will get news both online and offline in a typical day?

b. Suppose that you take a sample of 500 American adults. If the population proportion of American adults who get news both online and offline in a typical day is 0.59, what is the probability that fewer than half in your sample will get news both online and offline in a typical day?

c. Discuss the effect of sample size on the sampling distribution of the proportion in general and the effect on the probabilities in (a) and (b).

USING STATISTICS @ Oxford Cereals, Part I Revisited

© Corbis

As the plant operations manager for Oxfords Cereals, you were responsible for monitoring the amount of cereal placed in each box. To be consistent with package labeling, boxes should contain a mean of 368 grams of cereal. Thousands of boxes are produced during a shift, and weighing every single box was determined to be too time-consuming, costly, and inefficient. Instead, a sample of boxes was selected. Based on your analysis of the sample, you had to decide whether to maintain, alter, or shut down the process.

Using the concept of the sampling distribution of the mean, you were able to determine probabilities that such a sample mean could have been randomly selected from a population with a mean of 368 grams. Specifically, if a sample of size $n = 25$ is selected from a population with a mean of 368 and standard deviation of 15, you calculated the probability of selecting a sample with a mean of 365 grams or less to be 15.87%. If a larger sample size is selected, the sample mean should be closer to the population mean. This result was illustrated when you calculated the probability if the sample size were increased to $n = 100$. Using the larger sample size, you determined the probability of selecting a sample with a mean of 365 grams or less to be 2.28%.

SUMMARY

You have learned that in many business situations, the population is so large that you cannot gather information on every item. Instead, statistical sampling procedures focus on selecting a small representative group of the larger population. The results of the sample are then used to estimate characteristics of the entire population. Selecting a sample is less time-consuming, less costly, and more practical than analyzing the entire population.

In this chapter, you studied four common probability sampling methods—simple random, systematic, stratified, and cluster sampling. You also studied the sampling distribution of the sample mean and the sampling distribution of the sample proportion and their relationship to the Central Limit Theorem. You learned that the sample mean is an unbiased estimator of the population mean, and the sample proportion is an unbiased estimator of the population proportion. In the next five chapters, the techniques of confidence intervals and tests of hypotheses commonly used for statistical inference are discussed.

KEY EQUATIONS

Population Mean

$$\mu = \frac{\sum_{i=1}^{N} X_i}{N}$$

Population Standard Deviation

$$\sigma = \sqrt{\frac{\sum_{i=1}^{N} (X_i - \mu)^2}{N}}$$

Standard Error of the Mean

$$\sigma_{\overline{X}} = \frac{\sigma}{\sqrt{n}}$$

Finding Z for the Sampling Distribution of the Mean

$$Z = \frac{\overline{X} - \mu_{\overline{X}}}{\sigma_{\overline{X}}} = \frac{\overline{X} - \mu}{\frac{\sigma}{\sqrt{n}}}$$

Finding $\overline{X}$ for the Sampling Distribution of the Mean

$$\overline{X} = \mu + Z\frac{\sigma}{\sqrt{n}}$$

Sample Proportion

$$p = \frac{X}{n}$$

Standard Error of the Proportion

$$\sigma_p = \sqrt{\frac{\pi(1 - \pi)}{n}}$$

Finding Z for the Sampling Distribution of the Proportion

$$Z = \frac{p - \pi}{\sqrt{\frac{\pi(1 - \pi)}{n}}}$$

KEY TERMS

Central Limit Theorem   334
cluster   322
cluster sample   322
convenience sampling   318
coverage error   323
frame   318
judgment sample   318
margin of error   324
measurement error   324
nonprobability sample   318

nonresponse bias   323
nonresponse error   323
probability sample   318
sampling distribution   326
sampling distribution of the mean   326
sampling distribution of the proportion   342
sampling error   323
sampling with replacement   319
sampling without replacement   319

selection bias   323
simple random sample   319
standard error of the mean   328
standard error of the proportion   321
strata   321
stratified sample   321
systematic sample   321
table of random numbers   319
unbiased   326

PROBLEMS

CHECKING YOUR UNDERSTANDING

8.60 Why is the sample mean an unbiased estimator of the population mean?

8.61 Why does the standard error of the mean decrease as the sample size, n, increases?

8.62 Why does the sampling distribution of the mean follow a normal distribution for a large enough sample size, even though the population may not be normally distributed?

8.63 What is the difference between a population distribution and a sampling distribution?

8.64 Under what circumstances does the sampling distribution of the proportion approximately follow the normal distribution?

8.65 What is the difference between probability sampling and nonprobability sampling?

8.66 What are some potential problems with using "fishbowl" methods to select a simple random sample?

8.67 What is the difference between sampling *with* replacement versus sampling *without* replacement?

8.68 What is the difference between a simple random sample and a systematic sample?

8.69 What is the difference between a simple random sample and a stratified sample?

8.70 What is the difference between a stratified sample and a cluster sample?

APPLYING THE CONCEPTS

8.71 An industrial sewing machine uses ball bearings that are targeted to have a diameter of 0.75 inch. The lower and upper specification limits under which the ball bearing can operate are 0.74 inch (lower) and 0.76 inch (upper). Past experience has indicated that the actual diameter of the ball bearings is approximately normally distributed, with a mean of 0.753 inch and a standard deviation of 0.004 inch. If you select a random sample of 25 ball bearings, what is the probability that the sample mean is
a. between the target and the population mean of 0.753?
b. between the lower specification limit and the target?
c. greater than the upper specification limit?
d. less than the lower specification limit?
e. The probability is 93% that the sample mean diameter will be greater than what value?

8.72 The fill amount of bottles of a soft drink is normally distributed, with a mean of 2.0 liters and a standard deviation of 0.05 liter. If you select a random sample of 25 bottles, what is the probability that the sample mean will be
a. between 1.99 and 2.0 liters?
b. below 1.98 liters?
c. greater than 2.01 liters?
d. The probability is 99% that the sample mean amount of soft drink will be at least how much?
e. The probability is 99% that the sample mean amount of soft drink will be between which two values (symmetrically distributed around the mean)?

8.73 An orange juice producer buys oranges from a large orange grove that has one variety of orange. The amount of juice squeezed from these oranges is approximately normally distributed, with a mean of 4.70 ounces and a standard deviation of 0.40 ounce. Suppose that you select a sample of 25 oranges.
a. What is the probability that the sample mean amount of juice will be at least 4.60 ounces?
b. The probability is 70% that the sample mean amount of juice will be contained between what two values symmetrically distributed around the population mean?
c. The probability is 77% that the sample mean amount of juice will be greater than what value?

8.74 In Problem 8.73, suppose that the mean amount of juice squeezed is 5.0 ounces.
a. What is the probability that the sample mean amount of juice will be at least 4.60 ounces?
b. The probability is 70% that the sample mean amount of juice will be contained between what two values symmetrically distributed around the population mean?

c. The probability is 77% that the sample mean amount of juice will be greater than what value?

8.75 The stock market in Chile reported strong returns in 2010. The population of stocks earned a mean return of 49.6% in 2010. (Data extracted from *The Wall Street Journal*, January 3, 2011, p. R7.) Assume that the returns for stocks on the Chilean stock market were distributed as a normal random variable, with a mean of 49.6 and a standard deviation of 20. If you selected a random sample of 16 stocks from this population, what is the probability that the sample would have a mean return
a. less than 50?
b. between 40 and 60?
c. greater than 40?

8.76 The article mentioned in Problem 8.75 reported that the stock market in France had a mean return of −5.7% in 2010. Assume that the returns for stocks on the French stock market were distributed as a normal random variable, with a mean of −5.7 and a standard deviation of 10. If you select an individual stock from this population, what is the probability that it would have a return
a. less than 0 (i.e., a loss)?
b. between −10 and −20?
c. greater than 5?
If you selected a random sample of four stocks from this population, what is the probability that the sample would have a mean return
d. less than 0—that is, a loss?
e. between −10 and −20?
f. greater than 5?
g. Compare your results in parts (d) through (f) to those in (a) through (c).

8.77 (Class Project) The table of random numbers is an example of a uniform distribution because each digit is equally likely to occur. Starting in the row corresponding to the day of the month in which you were born, use the table of random numbers (Table E.1) to take one digit at a time.

Select five different samples each of $n = 2$, $n = 5$, and $n = 10$. Compute the sample mean of each sample. Develop a frequency distribution of the sample means for the results of the entire class, based on samples of sizes $n = 2$, $n = 5$, and $n = 10$.

What can be said about the shape of the sampling distribution for each of these sample sizes?

8.78 (Class Project) Toss a coin 10 times and record the number of heads. If each student performs this experiment five times, a frequency distribution of the number of heads can be developed from the results of the entire class. Does this distribution seem to approximate the normal distribution?

8.79 (Class Project) The number of cars waiting in line at a car wash is distributed as follows:

Number of Cars	Probability
0	0.25
1	0.40
2	0.20
3	0.10
4	0.04
5	0.01

You can use the table of random numbers (Table E.1) to select samples from this distribution by assigning numbers as follows:
1. Start in the row corresponding to the day of the month in which you were born.
2. Select a two-digit random number.
3. If you select a random number from 00 to 24, record a length of 0; if from 25 to 64, record a length of 1; if from 65 to 84, record a length of 2; if from 85 to 94, record a length of 3; if from 95 to 98, record a length of 4; if 99, record a length of 5.

   Select samples of $n = 2, n = 5$, and $n = 10$. Compute the mean for each sample. For example, if a sample of size 2 results in the random numbers 18 and 46, these would correspond to lengths 0 and 1, respectively, producing a sample mean of 0.5. If each student selects five different samples for each sample size, a frequency distribution of the sample means (for each sample size) can be developed from the results of the entire class. What conclusions can you reach concerning the sampling distribution of the mean as the sample size is increased?

8.80 (Class Project) Using Table E.1, simulate the selection of different-colored balls from a bowl, as follows:
1. Start in the row corresponding to the day of the month in which you were born.
2. Select one-digit numbers.
3. If a random digit between 0 and 6 is selected, consider the ball white; if a random digit is a 7, 8, or 9, consider the ball red.

   Select samples of $n = 10, n = 25$, and $n = 50$ digits. In each sample, count the number of white balls and compute the proportion of white balls in the sample. If each student in the class selects five different samples for each sample size, a frequency distribution of the proportion of white balls (for each sample size) can be developed from the results of the entire class. What conclusions can you reach about the sampling distribution of the proportion as the sample size is increased?

8.81 (Class Project) Suppose that step 3 of Problem 8.80 uses the following rule: "If a random digit between 0 and 8 is selected, consider the ball to be white; if a random digit of 9 is selected, consider the ball to be red." Compare and contrast the results in this problem and those in Problem 8.80.

MANAGING ASHLAND MULTICOMM SERVICES

Continuing the quality improvement effort first described in the Chapter 6 Managing Ashland MultiComm Services case, the target upload speed for AMS Internet service subscribers has been monitored. As before, upload speeds are measured on a standard scale in which the target value is 1.0. Data collected over the past year indicate that the upload speeds are approximately normally distributed, with a mean of 1.005 and a standard deviation of 0.10.

Exercise

1. Each day, at 25 random times, the upload speed is measured. Assuming that the distribution has not changed from what it was in the past year, what is the probability that the upload speed is
   a. less than 1.0?
   b. between 0.95 and 1.0?
   c. between 1.0 and 1.05?
   d. less than 0.95 or greater than 1.05?
   e. Suppose that the mean upload speed of today's sample of 25 is 0.952. What conclusion can you reach about the upload speed today based on this result? Explain.
2. Compare the results of AMS1 (a) through (d) to those of AMS1 in Chapter 7 on page 312. What conclusions can you reach concerning the differences?

DIGITAL CASE

Apply your knowledge about sampling distributions in this Digital Case, which reconsiders the Oxford Cereals Using Statistics scenario.

The advocacy group Consumers Concerned About Cereal Cheaters (CCACC) suspects that cereal companies, including Oxford Cereals, are cheating consumers by packaging cereals at less than labeled weights. Recently, the group investigated the package weights of two popular Oxford brand cereals. Open **CCACC.pdf** to examine the group's claims and supporting data, and then answer the following questions:

1. Are the data collection procedures that the CCACC uses to form its conclusions flawed? What procedures could the group follow to make its analysis more rigorous?

2. Assume that the two samples of five cereal boxes (one sample for each of two cereal varieties) listed on the CCACC website were collected randomly by organization members. For each sample, do the following:

a. Calculate the sample mean.

b. Assume that the standard deviation of the process is 15 grams and the population mean is 368 grams. Calculate the percentage of all samples for each process that have a sample mean less than the value you calculated in (a).

c. Again, assuming that the standard deviation is 15 grams, calculate the percentage of individual boxes of cereal that have a weight less than the value you calculated in (a).

3. What, if any, conclusions can you form by using your calculations about the filling processes for the two different cereals?

4. A representative from Oxford Cereals has asked that the CCACC take down its page discussing shortages in Oxford Cereals boxes. Is that request reasonable? Why or why not?

5. Can the techniques discussed in this chapter be used to prove cheating in the manner alleged by the CCACC? Why or why not?

REFERENCES

1. Cochran, W. G., *Sampling Techniques*, 3rd ed. (New York: Wiley, 1977).

2. Gallup, G. H., *The Sophisticated Poll-Watcher's Guide* (Princeton, NJ: Princeton Opinion Press, 1972).

3. Goleman, D., "Pollsters Enlist Psychologists in Quest for Unbiased Results," *The New York Times*, September 7, 1993, pp. C1, C11.

4. Hahn, G., and W. Meeker, *Statistical Intervals: A Guide for Practitioners* (New York: John Wiley and Sons, Inc., 1991).

5. "Landon in a Landslide: The Poll That Changed Polling," *History Matters: The U.S. Survey Course on the Web*, New York: American Social History Productions, 2005, downloaded at **http://historymatters.gmu .edu/d/5168/.**

6. *Microsoft Excel 2010* (Redmond, WA: Microsoft Corp., 2010).

7. *Minitab Release 16* (State College, PA: Minitab, Inc., 2010).

8. Rand Corporation, *A Million Random Digits with 100,000 Normal Deviates* (New York: The Free Press, 1955).

9. Squire, P., "Why the 1936 *Literary Digest* Poll Failed," *Public Opinion Quarterly 52*, 1988, pp.125–133.

CHAPTER 8 EXCEL GUIDE

EG8.1 Types of Sampling Methods

Simple Random Samples

PHStat2 Use **Random Sample Generation** to create a random sample *without replacement*. For example, to select the Example 8.1 sample of 40 workers on page 319, select **PHStat → Sampling → Random Sample Generation**. In the procedure's dialog box (shown below):

1. Enter **40** as the **Sample Size**.
2. Click **Generate list of random numbers** and enter **800** as the **Population Size**.
3. Enter a **Title** and click **OK**.

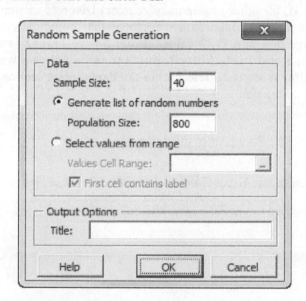

In-Depth Excel Use the **RANDBETWEEN** worksheet function to select a random integer that can be used to select an item from a frame. Enter the function as **RANDBETWEEN(1, *population size*)**.

Use the **COMPUTE worksheet** of the **Random workbook** as a template for creating a random sample. This worksheet contains 40 copies of the formula **=RANDBETWEEN(1, 800)** in column B and provides an alternative way of selecting the sample desired in Example 8.1 on page 319. Because the RANDBETWEEN function samples *with replacement*, add additional copies of the formula in new column B rows until you have the sample size *without replacement* that Example 8.1 needs.

Analysis ToolPak Use **Sampling** to create a random sample *with replacement*. For example, to select a random sample of *n* = 20 from a cell range A1:A201 of 200 values that

contains a column heading in cell A1, select **Data → Data Analysis**. In the Data Analysis dialog box, select **Sampling** from the **Analysis Tools** list and then click **OK**. In the procedure's dialog box (see below):

1. Enter **A1:A201** as the **Input Range** and check **Labels**.
2. Click **Random** and enter **20** as the **Number of Samples**.
3. Click **New Worksheet Ply** and then click **OK**.

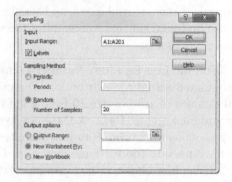

EG8.2 Evaluating Survey Worthiness

There are no Excel Guide instructions for this section.

EG8.3 Sampling Distributions

There are no Excel Guide instructions for this section.

EG8.4 Sampling Distribution of the Mean

PHStat2 Use **Sampling Distributions Simulation** to create a simulated sampling distribution. For example, to create 100 samples of *n* = 30 from a uniformly distributed population, select **PHStat → Sampling → Sampling Distributions Simulation**. In the procedure's dialog box (shown at the top of page 350):

1. Enter **100** as the **Number of Samples**.
2. Enter **30** as the **Sample Size**.
3. Click **Uniform**.
4. Enter a **Title** and click **OK**.

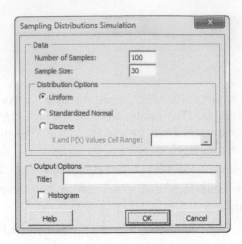

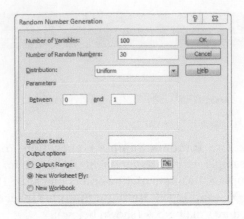

The sample means, overall mean, and standard error of the mean can be found starting in row 34 of the worksheet that the procedure creates.

Analysis ToolPak Use **Random Number Generation** to create a simulated sampling distribution. For example, to create 100 samples of sample size 30 from a uniformly distributed population, select **Data → Data Analysis**. In the Data Analysis dialog box, select **Random Number Generation** from the **Analysis Tools** list and then click **OK**. In the procedure's dialog box (shown at the top of the next column):

1. Enter **100** as the **Number of Variables**
2. Enter **30** as the **Number of Random Numbers**.
3. Select **Uniform** from the **Distribution** drop-down list.
4. Keep the **Parameters** values as is.
5. Click **New Worksheet Ply** and then click **OK**.

Use the formulas that appear in rows 35 through 39 in the **SDS_FORMULAS worksheet** of the **SDS workbook** as models if you want to compute sample means, the overall mean, and the standard error of the mean.

If, for other problems, you select **Discrete** in step 3, you must be open to a worksheet that contains a cell range of X and $P(X)$ values. Enter this cell range as the **Value and Probability Input Range** (not shown when **Uniform** has been selected) in the **Parameters** section of the dialog box.

EG8.5 Sampling Distribution of the Proportion

There are no Excel Guide instructions for this section.

9

Statistical Applications in Quality Management

Learning Objectives

In this chapter, you learn:

- How to construct various control charts
- Which control chart to use for a particular type of data
- The basic themes of total quality management and Deming's 14 points
- The basic aspects of Six Sigma

USING STATISTICS

@ Beachcomber Hotel

Y ou find yourself managing the Beachcomber Hotel, one of the resorts owned by T.C. Resort Properties (see Chapter 14). Your business objective is to continually improve the quality of service that your guests receive so that overall guest satisfaction increases. To help you achieve this improvement, T.C. Resort Properties has provided its managers with training in Six Sigma. In order to meet the business objective of increasing the return rate of guests at your hotel, you have decided to focus on the critical first impressions of the service that your hotel provides. Is the assigned hotel room ready when a guest checks in? Are all expected amenities, such as extra towels and a complimentary guest basket, in the room when the guest first walks in? Are the video-entertainment center and high-speed Internet access working properly? And do guests receive their luggage in a reasonable amount of time?

To study these guest satisfaction issues, you have embarked on an improvement project that focuses on the readiness of the room and the time it takes to deliver luggage. You would like to learn the following:

- Are the proportion of rooms ready and the time required to deliver luggage to the rooms acceptable?
- Are the proportion of rooms ready and the luggage delivery time consistent from day to day, or are they increasing or decreasing?
- On the days when the proportion of rooms that are not ready or the time to deliver luggage is greater than normal, are these fluctuations due to a chance occurrence, or are there fundamental flaws in the processes used to make rooms ready and to deliver luggage?

Ian Logan / Getty Images

ll companies, whether they manufacture products or provide services, as T.C. Resort Properties does in the Beachcomber Hotel scenario, understand that quality is essential for survival in the global economy. Quality has an impact on our everyday work and personal lives in many ways: in the design, production, and reliability of our automobiles; in the services provided by hotels, banks, schools, retailers, and telecommunications companies; in the continuous improvement in integrated circuits that makes for more capable consumer electronics and computers; and in the availability of new technology and equipment that has led to improved diagnosis of illnesses and improved delivery of health care services.

In this chapter you will learn how to develop and analyze control charts, a statistical tool that is widely used for quality improvement. You will then learn how businesses and organizations around the world are using control charts as part of two important quality improvement approaches: total quality management (TQM) and Six Sigma.

9.1 The Theory of Control Charts

A **process** is the value-added transformation of inputs to outputs. The inputs and outputs of a process can involve machines, materials, methods, measurement, people, and the environment. Each of the inputs is a source of variability. Variability in the output can result in poor service and poor product quality, both of which often decrease customer satisfaction.

Control charts, developed by Walter Shewhart in the 1920s (see reference 16), are commonly used statistical tools for monitoring and improving processes. A **control chart** analyzes a process in which data are collected sequentially over time. You use a control chart to study past performance, to evaluate present conditions, or to predict future outcomes. You use control charts at the beginning of quality improvement efforts to study an existing process (such charts are called *Phase 1 control charts*). Information gained from analyzing Phase 1 control charts forms the basis for process improvement. After improvements to the process are implemented, you then use control charts to monitor the process to ensure that the improvements continue (these charts are called *Phase 2 control charts*).

Different types of control charts allow you to analyze different types of **critical-to-quality** (*CTQ* in Six Sigma lingo—see Section 9.4) variables—for categorical variables, such as the proportion of hotel rooms that are nonconforming in terms of the availability of amenities and the working order of all appliances in the room; for discrete variables such as the number of hotel guests registering complaints in a week; and for continuous variables, such as the length of time required for delivering luggage to the room.

In addition to providing a visual display of data representing a process, a principal focus of a control chart is the attempt to separate special causes of variation from common causes of variation.

> THE TWO TYPES OF CAUSES OF VARIATION
>
> **Special causes of variation** represent large fluctuations or patterns in data that are not part of a process. These fluctuations are often caused by unusual events and represent either problems to correct or opportunities to exploit. Some organizations refer to special causes of variation as **assignable causes of variation**.
>
> **Common causes of variation** represent the inherent variability that exists in a process. These fluctuations consist of the numerous small causes of variability that operate randomly or by chance. Some organizations refer to common causes of variation as **chance causes of variation**.

Walter Shewhart (see reference 16) developed an experiment that illustrates the distinction between common and special causes of variation. The experiment asks you to repeatedly write the letter A in a horizontal line across a piece of paper:

AAAAAAAAAAAAAAAA

When you do this, you immediately notice that the A's are all similar but not exactly the same. In addition, you may notice some difference in the size of the A's from letter to letter. This difference is due to common cause variation. Nothing special happened that caused the differences in the size of the A. You probably would have a hard time trying to explain why the largest A is bigger than the smallest A. These types of differences almost certainly represent common cause variation.

However, if you did the experiment over again but wrote half of the A's with your right hand and the other half of the A's with your left hand, you would almost certainly see a very big difference in the A's written with each hand. In this case, the hand that you used to write the A's is the source of the special cause variation.

Common and special cause variation have a crucial difference. Common causes of variation can be reduced only by changing the process. (Such systemic changes are the responsibility of management.) In contrast, because special causes of variation are not part of a process, special causes are correctable or exploitable without changing the process. (In the example, changing the hand to write the A's corrects the special cause variation but does nothing to change the underlying process of handwriting.)

Control charts allow you to monitor a process and identify the presence or absence of special causes. By doing so, control charts help prevent two types of errors. The first type of error involves the belief that an observed value represents special cause variation when it is due to the common cause variation of the process. Treating common cause variation as special cause variation often results in overadjusting a process. This overadjustment, known as **tampering**, increases the variation in the process. The second type of error involves treating special cause variation as common cause variation. This error results in not taking immediate corrective action when necessary. Although both of these types of errors can occur even when using a control chart, they are far less likely.

To construct a control chart, you collect samples from the output of a process over time. The samples used for constructing control charts are known as **subgroups**. For each subgroup (i.e., sample), you calculate a sample statistic. Commonly used statistics include the sample proportion for a categorical variable and the mean and range of a numerical variable. You then plot the values over time and add control limits around the center line of the chart. The most typical form of a control chart sets control limits that are within ±3 standard deviations[1] of the statistical measure of interest. Equation (9.1) defines, in general, the upper and lower control limits for control charts.

[1]Recall from Section 7.2 that in the normal distribution, $\mu \pm 3\sigma$ includes almost all (99.73%) of the values in the population.

CONSTRUCTING CONTROL LIMITS

$$\text{Process mean} \pm 3 \text{ standard deviations} \qquad (9.1)$$

so that

Upper control limit (UCL) = Process mean +3 standard deviations

Lower control limit (LCL) = Process mean −3 standard deviations

---

When these control limits are set, you evaluate the control chart by trying to find whether any pattern exists in the values over time and by determining whether any points fall outside the control limits. Figure 9.1 illustrates three different patterns.

FIGURE 9.1

Three control chart patterns

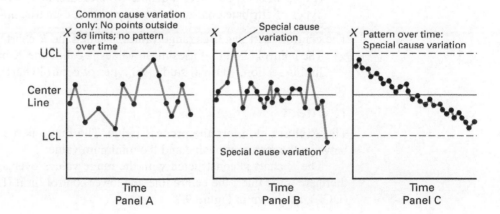

In Panel A of Figure 9.1, there is no apparent pattern in the values over time and there are no points that fall outside the 3 standard deviation control limits. The process appears stable and contains only common cause variation. Panel B, on the contrary, contains two points that fall outside the 3 standard deviation control limits. You should investigate these points to try to determine the special causes that led to their occurrence. Although Panel C does not have any points outside the control limits, it has a series of consecutive points above the mean value (the center line) as well as a series of consecutive points below the mean value. In addition, a long-term overall downward trend is clearly visible. You should investigate the situation to try to determine what may have caused this pattern.

Detecting a pattern is not always so easy. The following simple rule (see references 8, 12, and 18) can help you to detect a trend or a shift in the mean level of a process:

Eight or more *consecutive* points that lie above the center line or eight or more *consecutive* points that lie below the center line.[2]

A process whose control chart indicates an out-of-control condition (i.e., a point outside the control limits or a series of points that exhibits a pattern) is said to be out of control. An **out-of-control process** contains both common causes of variation and special causes of variation. Because special causes of variation are not part of the process design, an out-of-control process is unpredictable. When you determine that a process is out of control, you must identify the special causes of variation that are producing the out-of-control conditions. If the special causes are detrimental to the quality of the product or service, you need to implement plans to eliminate this source of variation. When a special cause increases quality, you should change the process so that the special cause is incorporated into the process design. Thus, this beneficial special cause now becomes a common cause source of variation, and the process is improved.

A process whose control chart does not indicate any out-of-control conditions is said to be in control. An **in-control process** contains only common causes of variation. Because these sources of variation are inherent to the process itself, an in-control process is predictable. In-control processes are sometimes said to be in a **state of statistical control**. When a process is in control, you must determine whether the amount of common cause variation in the process is small enough to satisfy the customers of the products or services. If the common cause variation is small enough to consistently satisfy the customers, you then use control charts to monitor the process on a continuing basis to make sure the process remains in control. If the common cause variation is too large, you need to alter the process itself.

[2]This rule is often referred to as the *runs rule*. A similar rule that some companies use is called the *trend rule*: eight or more consecutive points that increase in value or eight or more consecutive points that decrease in value. Some statisticians (see reference 4) have criticized the trend rule. It should be used only with extreme caution.

9.2 Types of Control Charts

There are two types of control charts:

1. A control chart that uses a quantitative measurement is called a **variable control chart**. Types of variable control charts are R charts, $\overline{X}$ charts (also called X-bar charts), and S charts.
2. A control chart that uses a qualitative measurement is called an **attribute control chart**. Types of attribute control charts are p charts, c-charts, np-charts, and u-charts.

The control chart that uses range values is called the R chart.

The control chart that uses mean values is called the X-bar chart.

In this section, you will study two types of control charts, namely X-bar and R charts.

R Chart

The **R chart** monitors the process range. The range is measured by taking the difference between the maximum value and the minimum value.

The R chart is constructed with the range values over a period of time. On the R chart, there are three lines: the centre line, the lower control limit (LCL), and the upper control limit (UCL), as shown in Figure 9.2.

FIGURE 9.2

R chart

*NOTE: "Std dev" denotes
standard deviation.*

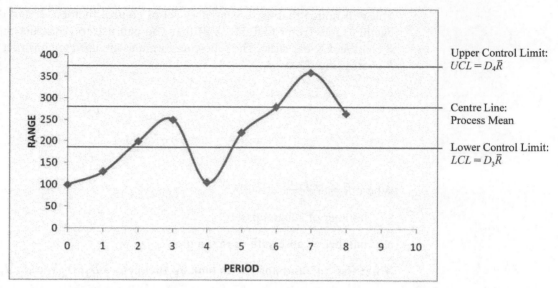

The formulas used to construct the three lines are as follows:

a) The plotted points on the graph (see Figure 9.2) are the range (R) values.
b) Range (R) = Maximum Value − Minimum Value
c) Central Line: Average Range, denoted as $\bar{R} = \dfrac{\sum_{i=1}^{k} R_i}{k}$
d) Upper Control Limit: $UCL = D_4\bar{R}$
e) Lower Control Limit: $LCL = D_3\bar{R}$

Note that

i. the values of D_3 and D_4 are obtained from TABLE E.8 in Appendix E on page 810. The values of D_3 and D_4 depend on the number of observations in the sample.
ii. all the formulas are based on the assumption that the population of measurements follows a normal distribution.

TABLE E.8

Control Chart Factors

Number of Observations in Sample	d_2	d_3	D_3	D_4	A_2
2	1.128	0.853	0	3.267	1.880
3	1.693	0.888	0	2.575	1.023
4	2.059	0.880	0	2.282	0.729
5	2.326	0.864	0	2.114	0.577
6	2.534	0.848	0	2.004	0.483
7	2.704	0.833	0.076	1.924	0.419
8	2.847	0.820	0.136	1.864	0.373
9	2.970	0.808	0.184	1.816	0.337
10	3.078	0.797	0.223	1.777	0.308
11	3.173	0.787	0.256	1.744	0.285
12	3.258	0.778	0.283	1.717	0.266
13	3.336	0.770	0.307	1.693	0.249
14	3.407	0.763	0.328	1.672	0.235
15	3.472	0.756	0.347	1.653	0.223
16	3.532	0.750	0.363	1.637	0.212
17	3.588	0.744	0.378	1.622	0.203
18	3.640	0.739	0.391	1.609	0.194
19	3.689	0.733	0.404	1.596	0.187
20	3.735	0.729	0.415	1.585	0.180
21	3.778	0.724	0.425	1.575	0.173
22	3.819	0.720	0.435	1.565	0.167
23	3.858	0.716	0.443	1.557	0.162
24	3.895	0.712	0.452	1.548	0.157
25	3.931	0.708	0.459	1.541	0.153

You will notice that there is another set of control factors, d_2 and d_3, in the Control Chart Factors table (refer to Table A.9) that you can use to construct the control limits for the R chart and X-bar chart. The following formulas are used to construct the control limits for an R chart using d_2 and d_3.

$$LCL = \overline{R} - \frac{3\overline{R}d_3}{d_2}$$

$$UCL = \overline{R} + \frac{3\overline{R}d_3}{d_2}$$

Where $\overline{R} = \dfrac{\sum_{i=1}^{k}R_i}{k}$

k = number of subgroups

n = number of observations in sample

Note: Use "n" and not "k" to look up the factors D_3, D_4 and d_2, d_3.

X-bar Chart

The **X-bar chart** monitors the process sample means.

The X-bar chart is constructed with the mean values over a period of time. On the X-bar chart, there are three lines: the centre line, the lower control limit (LCL), and the upper control limit (UCL).

FIGURE 9.3
X-bar chart

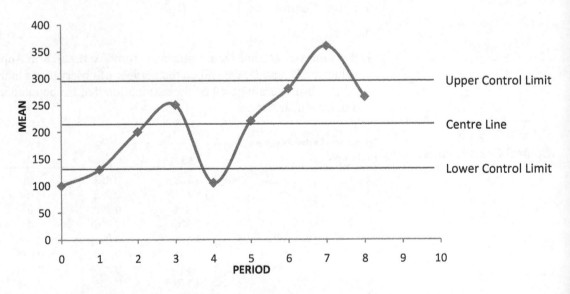

The formulas used to construct the three lines are as follows:

a) The plotted points on the graph (see Figure 9.3) are the sample mean ($\overline{X}$) values.

b) Mean $(\overline{x}) = \dfrac{\sum_{i=1}^{n}x_i}{n}$

c) Central Line: Average of means, denoted as $(\overline{\overline{x}}) = \dfrac{\sum_{i=1}^{k}\overline{X}_i}{k}$ where $\overline{x}_i$ is the sample mean at time i.

d) Upper Control Limit: $UCL = \overline{\overline{x}} + A_2\overline{R}$

e) Lower Control Limit: $LCL = \overline{\overline{x}} - A_2\overline{R}$

Note that

i. the value of A_2 is obtained from Table A.9 in Appendix A. The value of A_2 depends on the number of samples (denoted as k).

ii. all the formulas are based on the assumption that the population of measurements follows a normal distribution.

You will notice that there is another set of control factors, d_2 and d_3, in the Control Chart Factors table (refer to Table A.9) that you can use to construct the control limits for the R chart and X-bar chart. The following formulas are used to construct the control limits for the X-bar chart using d_2 and d_3.

$$UCL = \bar{\bar{X}} + 3\,\frac{\bar{R}}{d_2\sqrt{n}}$$

$$LCL = \bar{\bar{X}} - 3\,\frac{\bar{R}}{d_2\sqrt{n}}$$

Where $\bar{R} = \dfrac{\sum_{i=1}^{k} R_i}{k}$, $\bar{\bar{X}} = \dfrac{\sum_{i=1}^{k} \bar{x}_i}{k}$

k = number of subgroups

n = number of observations in sample

Note: Use "n" and not "k" to look up the factors D_3, D_4 and d_2, d_3.

TABLE 9.1

Summary of Equations for Control Chart Limits for Mean and Range using factors D_3, D_4 and d_2, d_3

| | Control Limits for | | Control Limits for | |
| | Range | Mean | Range | Mean |
	Using the D_3, D_4 factors		Using the d_2, d_3 factors	
Upper Control Limit	$D_4\bar{R}$	$\bar{\bar{x}} + A_2\bar{R}$	$\bar{R} + \dfrac{3\bar{R}d_3}{d_2}$	$\bar{\bar{X}} + 3\dfrac{\bar{R}}{d_2\sqrt{n}}$
Centre Line (Process mean)	$\bar{R} = \dfrac{\sum_{i=1}^{k} R_i}{k}$	$\bar{\bar{X}} = \dfrac{\sum_{i=1}^{k} \bar{x}_i}{k}$	$\bar{R} = \dfrac{\sum_{i=1}^{k} R_i}{k}$	$\bar{\bar{X}} = \dfrac{\sum_{i=1}^{k} \bar{x}_i}{k}$
Lower Control Limit	$D_3\bar{R}$	$\bar{\bar{x}} - A_2\bar{R}$	$\bar{R} - \dfrac{3\bar{R}d_3}{d_2}$	$\bar{\bar{X}} - 3\dfrac{\bar{R}}{d_2\sqrt{n}}$

Quality Control Charts

We will only be studying two charts, X-bars and R charts. Also, the only out-of-control indications that we will be concerned with are the following:

a. A point above the UCL on the range chart

b. A point above the UCL or a point below the LCL on the X-bar chart

In a real-life setting, if there is an indication that the process is out of control, the people monitoring the process will find a "special cause" for the situation. They will then take appropriate steps to make changes in the process so that this instability does not occur again in the future. It is these changes that will result in the improvement of quality.

In order to establish the centre-lines and the upper and lower control limits for the X-bar charts and R charts we need some initial sample data. Usually the results from 10 to 30 samples are used. The following two examples will illustrate the formulas and techniques for setting up X-bar chart and R chart limits. It should be noted that all the formulas shown are based on the assumption that the population of measurements would fit a *normal* distribution.

EXAMPLE 9.1

A chocolate company monitors the weights of its chocolate bars. One particular bar will have a label indicating that it is a 60-gram bar. In order to monitor the bar weights, every hour a sample of 4 bars is taken and the bars are weighed. The results of the first 15 samples are shown in Table 9.2.

TABLE 9.2

Weight of a bar (grams)						
Sample	Bar 1	Bar 2	Bar 3	Bar 4	Mean	Range
1	60.2	60.4	60.1	60.5	60.300	0.4
2	60.6	60.2	60.7	60.6	60.525	0.5
3	60.2	60.2	60.5	60.7	60.400	0.5
4	60.1	60.1	60.6	60.4	60.300	0.5
5	60.3	60.6	60.3	60.1	60.325	0.5
6	60.5	60.4	60.3	60.1	60.325	0.4
7	60.5	60.4	60.5	60.2	60.400	0.3
8	60.3	60.5	60.2	60.3	60.325	0.3
9	60.5	60.1	60.0	60.5	60.275	0.5
10	60.7	60.4	60.4	60.5	60.500	0.3
11	60.0	60.3	60.7	60.3	60.325	0.7
12	60.2	60.7	60.3	60.6	60.450	0.5
13	60.6	60.0	60.6	60.2	60.350	0.6
14	59.9	60.1	60.3	60.6	60.225	0.7
15	60.5	60.2	60.5	60.5	60.425	0.3

First you calculate the R chart values using the control factors as follows:

$$\bar{R} = 0.47$$
$$UCL_R = D_4\bar{R} = 2.282(0.47) = 1.064933333333333 = 1.07$$
$$LCL_R = D_3\bar{R} = 0(0.47) = 0$$

Then you check the sample ranges to see if any range values are higher than 1.07. There are none. You can now proceed to calculate the X-bar chart values.

$$\bar{\bar{X}} = 60.36333333$$
$$UCL_{\bar{X}} = \bar{\bar{X}} + A_2\bar{R} = 60.36333333 + (0.729)(0.47) = 60.7059$$
$$LCL_{\bar{X}} = \bar{\bar{X}} - A_2\bar{R} = 60.36333333 - (0.729)(0.47) = 60.0207$$

Now you check the sample means to see if any values are higher than 60.7059 or lower than 60.0207. There are none. This process is in control (i.e., stable), and you have established the control chart limits for future samples of this product.

If in the initial samples used to set up the control charts points are found to be out of control, then you will assume that a special cause can be found to account for this problem. In the meantime, the sample data for any point that is out of control is removed from the calculations, and the control chart values are recalculated. The following example will illustrate the appropriate procedure to follow.

EXAMPLE 9.2

A company is concerned about a particular measurement. The results of 24 samples of 5 items are shown in Table 9.3.

TABLE 9.3

Sample results							
Sample	**Item 1**	**Item 2**	**Item 3**	**Item 4**	**Item 5**	**Mean**	**Range**
1	10.65	10.70	10.65	10.65	10.85	10.70	0.20
2	10.75	10.85	10.75	10.85	10.65	10.77	0.20
3	10.75	10.80	10.80	10.70	10.75	10.76	0.10
4	10.60	10.70	10.70	10.75	10.65	10.68	0.15
5	10.70	10.75	10.65	10.85	10.80	10.75	0.20
6	10.60	10.75	10.75	10.85	10.70	10.73	0.25
7	10.60	10.80	10.70	10.75	10.75	10.72	0.20
8	10.75	10.80	10.65	10.75	10.70	10.73	0.15
9	10.65	10.80	10.85	10.85	10.75	10.78	0.20
10	10.60	10.70	10.60	10.80	10.65	10.67	0.20
11	10.80	10.75	10.90	10.50	10.85	10.76	0.40
12	10.85	10.75	10.85	10.65	10.70	10.76	0.20
13	10.70	10.70	10.75	10.75	10.70	10.72	0.05
14	10.65	10.70	10.85	10.75	10.60	10.71	0.25
15	10.75	10.80	10.75	10.80	10.65	10.75	0.15
16	10.90	10.80	10.80	10.75	10.85	10.82	0.15
17	10.75	10.70	10.85	10.70	10.80	10.76	0.15
18	10.75	10.70	10.60	10.70	10.60	10.67	0.15
19	10.65	10.65	10.85	10.65	10.70	10.70	0.20
20	10.55	10.55	10.60	10.50	10.60	10.56	0.10
21	10.50	10.55	10.65	10.80	10.80	10.66	0.30
22	10.80	10.65	10.75	10.65	10.65	10.70	0.15
23	10.65	10.60	10.65	10.60	10.70	10.64	0.10
24	10.65	10.70	10.70	10.60	10.65	10.66	0.10

First you calculate the R chart values:

$$\overline{R} = 0.179$$
$$UCL_R = D_4\overline{R} = 2.114(0.179) = 0.378$$
$$LCL_R - D_3\overline{R} - 0(0.179) - 0$$

Then you look at the sample ranges and find that sample 11 with R = 0.40 is out of control. You can assume that a special cause can be found, and proceed to **remove** sample 11 and recalculate the R chart values.

$$\overline{R} = 0.170$$

You now get:
$$UCL_R = D_4\overline{R} = 2.114(0.170) = 0.359$$
$$LCL_R = D_3\overline{R} = 0(0.170) = 0$$

Once again you check the sample ranges, and this time there are no range values that are out of control.

Now you calculate the $\overline{X}$ bar chart values (with sample 11 having been removed from the data).

$$\bar{\bar{X}} = 10.713$$

You get
$$UCL_{\bar{X}} = \bar{\bar{X}} + A_2\bar{R} = 10.713 + (0.577)(0.170) = 10.811$$
$$LCL_{\bar{X}} = \bar{\bar{X}} - A_2\bar{R} = 10.713 - (0.577)(0.170) = 10.615$$

You now check the sample means and find that sample 16 with $\bar{X} = 10.82$ and sample 20 with $\bar{X} = 10.56$ are out of control. Once again you assume that special causes can be found to account for these out of control results, and proceed to **remove** samples 16 and 20.

Since the R chart values have been calculated including samples 16 and 20, these results are no longer valid. We must calculate new R chart values before calculating new X-bar chart values.

$$\bar{R} = 0.174$$

You now get
$$UCL_R = D_4\bar{R} = 2.114(0.174) = 0.368$$
$$LCL_R = D_3\bar{R} = 0(0.174) = 0$$

Now check again the sample ranges for any out-of-control points. There are none. You therefore proceed to calculate the X-bar chart values.

$$\bar{\bar{X}} = 10.715$$

You get
$$UCL_{\bar{X}} = \bar{\bar{X}} + A_2\bar{R} = 10.715 + (0.577)(0.174) = 10.815$$
$$LCL_{\bar{X}} = \bar{\bar{X}} - A_2\bar{R} = 10.715 - (0.577)(0.174) = 10.615$$

Once again you check the sample means and find that none of the remaining samples is out of control. You now have determined the appropriate X-bar chart and R chart control limits.

Problems for Section 9.2

(Note: Some of these exercises may not be indicative of real world processes, but are intended to demonstrate the correct procedures for establishing control chart limits.)

9.1 The following results came from samples of size 4. Determine the X-bar and R chart control limits. If any sample results are out-of-control assume an assignable cause can be found and make the necessary adjustments to the control chart values.

Sample	Mean	Range	Sample	Mean	Range
1	75.72	1.0	11	75.80	0.6
2	75.24	0.9	12	75.22	0.2
3	75.18	0.8	13	75.56	1.5
4	75.44	0.4	14	75.22	0.5
5	75.46	0.5	15	75.04	0.8
6	75.32	1.2	16	75.62	1.1
7	75.40	0.9	17	75.92	0.6
8	75.44	0.3	18	75.46	0.5
9	75.08	0.2	19	75.60	0.4
10	75.50	0.6	20	75.74	0.3

9.2 The following results came from samples of size 6. Determine the X-bar and R chart control limits. If any sample results are out-of-control assume an assignable cause can be found and make the necessary adjustments to the control chart values.

Sample	Mean	Range	Sample	Mean	Range
1	35.35	0.34	14	35.41	0.36
2	35.40	0.36	15	35.45	0.24
3	35.36	0.32	16	35.34	0.36
4	35.65	0.26	17	35.42	0.37
5	35.20	0.46	18	35.50	0.58
6	35.40	0.35	19	35.36	0.35
7	35.43	0.31	20	35.31	0.18
8	35.37	0.34	21	35.39	0.73
9	35.48	0.30	22	35.39	0.33
10	35.42	0.37	23	35.40	0.32
11	35.39	0.19	24	35.41	0.34
12	35.38	0.50	25	35.40	0.30
13	35.40	0.33			

9.3 The following results came from samples of size 5. Use the first 20 samples to determine the X-bar and R chart control limits. If any sample results are out-of-control assume an assignable cause can be found and make the necessary adjustments to the control chart values. Are any of the samples 21 to 30 out of control? Explain.

Sample	Mean	Range	Sample	Mean	Range
1	101	22	16	109	12
2	104	17	17	111	38
3	109	36	18	100	30
4	98	19	19	97	19
5	105	23	20	89	31
6	107	16	21	103	27
7	109	16	22	97	36
8	115	30	23	92	25
9	99	20	24	89	23
10	119	29	25	98	18
11	91	14	26	108	24
12	99	20	27	114	19
13	115	39	28	117	51
14	100	30	29	110	21
15	103	26	30	99	30

9.4 The following results came from samples of size 4. Determine the X-bar and R chart control limits. If any sample results are out-of-control assume an assignable cause can be found and make the necessary adjustments to the control chart values.

Sample	Mean	Range	Sample	Mean	Range
1	376.2	32	14	382.7	22
2	366.7	24	15	406.3	23
3	384.3	32	16	396.4	23
4	366.7	26	17	378.7	25
5	370.1	24	18	384.2	24
6	394.2	24	19	406.9	23
7	386.9	28	20	376.4	25
8	396.4	23	21	385.8	29
9	388.0	24	22	390.2	25
10	382.3	26	23	363.5	22
11	398.8	25	24	363.1	27
12	364.6	24	25	374.8	22
13	384.5	24			

9.5 Motel Inn plans to improve service by reducing the mean and variation in time it takes to clean and prepare rooms. In order to study the situation 5 rooms are randomly selected each day and the time required to clean and prepare each room is recorded. The data for the first 10 days is given below.

	Cleaning and Preparation time (minutes)				
Day	Room 1	Room 2	Room 3	Room 4	Room 5
1	14.0	17.7	16.9	14.0	14.9
2	17.6	16.5	15.3	14.5	15.1
3	14.6	14.0	14.7	16.9	14.2
4	14.0	15.5	16.5	15.4	14.7
5	15.3	15.3	15.9	15.0	17.8
6	21.4	14.9	17.7	16.6	13.8
7	18.9	19.9	18.6	17.2	17.9
8	14.8	15.1	16.6	16.3	14.5
9	16.1	14.6	17.5	16.9	17.7
10	14.2	14.7	15.3	15.7	14.3

Determine the X-bar and R chart control limits, assuming that any out-of-control results have assignable causes.

9.6 A chemical company has collected 15 daily samples of measurements of an important chemical property called 'acid value' for one of its products. Each sample consists of six acid value readings, where a single reading is taken every 4 hours during the day. The measurements are shown in the table below.

	Acid Value measurements					
Day	1	2	3	4	5	6
1	202.1	201.2	196.2	201.6	201.6	201.6
2	202.4	201.9	202.0	201.8	201.9	201.8
3	200.4	200.0	200.8	200.1	198.7	200.4
4	200.4	200.4	200.4	200.8	200.4	201.2
5	203.4	201.6	203.9	201.6	201.4	202.0
6	200.0	200.4	200.8	200.8	199.5	200.4
7	200.4	200.0	200.4	200.4	200.4	200.4
8	200.0	200.8	200.0	200.4	200.0	200.0
9	199.1	200.1	200.4	200.4	200.4	200.0
10	201.2	195.3	197.4	201.2	200.0	201.6
11	201.6	200.8	200.4	201.2	200.4	199.5
12	200.0	199.5	200.4	200.8	200.4	200.8
13	201.2	201.6	200.8	201.2	200.8	200.8
14	200.4	200.0	202.5	200.4	201.2	201.2
15	200.0	200.0	201.6	200.8	200.4	200.0

Determine the X-bar and R chart control limits, assuming that any out-of-control results have assignable causes.

LEARNING THE BASICS

9.7 The following data were collected on nonconformances for a period of 10 days:

Day	Sample Size	Nonconformances
1	100	12
2	100	14
3	100	10
4	100	18
5	100	22
6	100	14
7	100	15
8	100	13
9	100	14
10	100	16

a. On what day is the proportion of nonconformances largest? Smallest?
b. What are the LCL and UCL?
c. Are there any special causes of variation?

9.8 The following data were collected on nonconformances for a period of 10 days:

Day	Sample Size	Nonconformances
1	111	12
2	93	14
3	105	10
4	92	18
5	117	22
6	88	14
7	117	15
8	87	13
9	119	14
10	107	16

a. On what day is the proportion of nonconformances largest? Smallest?
b. What are the LCL and UCL?
c. Are there any special causes of variation?

APPLYING THE CONCEPTS

9.9 A medical transcription service enters medical data on patient files for hospitals. The service has the business objective of improving the turnaround time (defined as the time between sending data and the time the client receives completed files). After studying the process, it was determined that turnaround time was increased by transmission errors. A transmission error was defined as data transmitted that did not go through as planned and needed to be retrans-

mitted. Data were collected for a period of 31 days from a daily random sample of 125 transmissions and stored in Transmit . The following table presents the number and proportion of transmissions with errors:

Day (i)	Number of Errors (X_i)	Proportion of Errors (p_i)	Day (i)	Number of Errors (X_i)	Proportion of Errors (p_i)
1	6	0.048	17	4	0.032
2	3	0.024	18	6	0.048
3	4	0.032	19	3	0.024
4	4	0.032	20	5	0.040
5	9	0.072	21	1	0.008
6	0	0.000	22	3	0.024
7	0	0.000	23	14	0.112
8	8	0.064	24	6	0.048
9	4	0.032	25	7	0.056
10	3	0.024	26	3	0.024
11	4	0.032	27	10	0.080
12	1	0.008	28	7	0.056
13	10	0.080	29	5	0.040
14	9	0.072	30	0	0.000
15	3	0.024	31	3	0.024
16	1	0.008			

a. Construct an R-chart and X-bar chart.
b. Is the process in a state of statistical control? Why?

SELF Test **9.10** A manufacturer of film canisters has the business objective of reducing the number of nonconforming film canisters. During each day of a 32-day study, 500 film canisters were sampled and inspected. The following table (stored in Canister) lists the number of defective film canisters (the nonconforming items) for each day (the subgroup):

Day	Number Nonconforming	Day	Number Nonconforming
1	26	17	23
2	25	18	19
3	23	19	18
4	24	20	27
5	26	21	28
6	20	22	24
7	21	23	26
8	27	24	23
9	23	25	27
10	25	26	28
11	22	27	24
12	26	28	22
13	25	29	20
14	29	30	25
15	20	31	27
16	19	32	19

a. Construct an R-chart and X-bar chart.

b. Is the process in a state of statistical control? Why?

9.11 A hospital administrator has the business objective of reducing the time to process patients' medical records after discharge. She determined that all records should be processed within 5 days of discharge. Thus, any record not processed within 5 days of a patient's discharge is nonconforming. The administrator recorded the number of patients discharged and the number of records not processed within the 5-day standard for a 30-day period and stored in `MedRec`.

a. Construct an R-chart and X-bar chart for these data.

b. Does the process give an out-of-control signal? Explain.

c. If the process is out of control, assume that special causes were subsequently identified and corrective action was taken to keep them from happening again. Then eliminate the data causing the out-of-control signals and recalculate the control limits.

9.12 The bottling division of Sweet Suzy's Sugarless Cola has the business objective of reducing the occurrence of unacceptable cans flowing from the filling and sealing machine. Data are collected and stored in `Colaspc` from a sample of cans filled for one month (based on a five-day workweek).

a. Construct an R-chart and X-bar chart for the proportion of unacceptable cans for the month. Does the process give an out-of-control signal?

b. If you want to develop a process for reducing the proportion of unacceptable cans, how should you proceed?

9.13 The manager of the accounting office of a large hospital has the business objective of reducing the number of incorrect account numbers entered into the computer system. Data are collected from a subgroup of 200 account numbers selected from each day's output, and each account number is inspected to determine whether it is nonconforing. The results for a period of 39 days are stored in `Errorspc`.

a. Construct an R-chart and X-bar chart for the proportion of nonconforming items. Does the process give an out-of-control signal?

b. Based on your answer in (a), if you were the manager of the accounting office, what would you do to improve the process of account number entry?

9.14 A regional manager of a telephone company is responsible for processing requests concerning additions, changes, and deletions of telephone service. She has the business objective of reducing the number of orders that need correction. Data are collected over a period of 30 days and are stored in `Telespc`.

a. Construct an R-chart and X-bar chart for the proportion of corrections. Does the process give an out-of-control signal?

b. What should the regional manager do to improve the processing of requests for changes in telephone service?

9.3 Total Quality Management

An increased interest in improving the quality of products and services in the United States occurred as a reaction to improvements of Japanese industry that began as early as 1950. Individuals such as W. Edwards Deming, Joseph Juran, and Kaoru Ishikawa developed an approach that focuses on continuous improvement of products and services through an increased emphasis on statistics, process improvement, and optimization of the total system. This approach, widely known as **total quality management (TQM)**, is characterized by these themes:

- The primary focus is on process improvement.
- Most of the variation in a process is due to the system and not the individual.
- Teamwork is an integral part of a quality management organization.
- Customer satisfaction is a primary organizational goal.
- Organizational transformation must occur in order to implement quality management.
- Fear must be removed from organizations.
- Higher quality costs less, not more, but requires an investment in training.

In the 1980s, the federal government of the United States increased its efforts to encourage the improvement of quality in American business. Congress passed the Malcolm Baldrige National Improvement Act of 1987 and began awarding the Malcolm Baldrige Award to companies making the greatest strides in improving quality and customer satisfaction. Deming became a prominent consultant to many Fortune 500 companies, including Ford Motor Company, and Procter & Gamble. Many companies adopted some or all the basic themes of TQM.

Today, quality improvement systems have been implemented in many organizations worldwide. Although most organizations no longer use the name TQM, the underlying philosophy and statistical methods used in today's quality improvement systems are consistent with TQM, as reflected by **Deming's 14 points for management**:

1. Create constancy of purpose for improvement of product and service.
2. Adopt the new philosophy.
3. Cease dependence on inspection to achieve quality.
4. End the practice of awarding business on the basis of price tag alone. Instead, minimize total cost by working with a single supplier.
5. Improve constantly and forever every process for planning, production, and service.
6. Institute training on the job.
7. Adopt and institute leadership.
8. Drive out fear.
9. Break down barriers between staff areas.
10. Eliminate slogans, exhortations, and targets for the workforce.
11. Eliminate numerical quotas for the workforce and numerical goals for management.
12. Remove barriers that rob people of pride of workmanship. Eliminate the annual rating or merit system.
13. Institute a vigorous program of education and self-improvement for everyone.
14. Put everyone in the company to work to accomplish the transformation.

Points 1, 2, 5, 7, and 14 focus on the need for organizational transformation and the responsibility of top management to assert leadership in committing to the transformation. Without this commitment, any improvements obtained will be limited.

One aspect of the improvement process is illustrated by the **Shewhart–Deming cycle**, shown in Figure 9.4. The Shewhart–Deming cycle represents a continuous cycle of "plan, do, study, and act." The first step, planning, represents the initial design phase for planning a change in a manufacturing or service process. This step involves teamwork among individuals from different areas within an organization. The second step, doing, involves implementing the change, preferably on a small scale. The third step, studying, involves analyzing the results, using statistical methods to determine what was learned. The fourth step, acting, involves the acceptance of the change, its abandonment, or further study of the change under different conditions.

FIGURE 9.4
Shewhart–Deming cycle

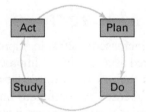

Point 3, cease dependence on inspection to achieve quality, implies that any inspection whose purpose is to improve quality is too late because the quality is already built into the product. It is better to focus on making it right the first time. Among the difficulties involved in inspection (besides high costs) are the failure of inspectors to agree on the operational definitions for nonconforming items and the problem of separating good and bad items. The following example illustrates the difficulties inspectors face.

Suppose your job involves proofreading the sentence in Figure 9.5, with the objective of counting the number of occurrences of the letter F. Perform this task and record the number of occurrences of the letter F that you discover.

FIGURE 9.5

An example of a proofreading process

Source: Adapted from W. W. Scherkenbach, *The Deming Route to Quality and Productivity: Road Maps and Roadblocks* (Washington, DC: CEEP Press, 1987).

FINISHED FILES ARE THE RESULT OF YEARS OF SCIENTIFIC STUDY COMBINED WITH THE EXPERIENCE OF MANY YEARS

People usually see either three *F*s or six *F*s. The correct number is six *F*s. The number you see depends on the method you use to examine the sentence. You are likely to find three *F*s if you read the sentence phonetically and six *F*s if you count the number of *F*s carefully. If such a simple process as counting *F*s leads to inconsistency of inspectors' results, what will happen when a much more complicated process fails to provide clear operational definitions?

Point 4, end the practice of awarding business on the basis of price tag alone, focuses on the idea that there is no real long-term meaning to price without knowledge of the quality of the product. In addition, minimizing the number of entities in the supply chain will reduce the variation involved.

Points 6 and 13 refer to training and reflect the needs of all employees. Continuous learning is critical for quality improvement within an organization. In particular, management needs to understand the differences between special causes and common causes of variation so that proper action is taken in each circumstance.

Points 8 through 12 relate to the evaluation of employee performance. Deming believed that an emphasis on targets and exhortations places an improper burden on the workforce. Workers cannot produce beyond what the system allows. It is management's job to *improve* the system, not to raise the expectations on workers beyond the system's capability.

Although Deming's points are thought provoking, some have criticized his approach for lacking a formal, objective accountability (see reference 11). Many managers of large organizations, used to seeing financial analyses of policy changes, need a more prescriptive approach.

9.4 Six Sigma

Six Sigma is a quality improvement system originally developed by Motorola in the mid-1980s. After seeing the huge financial successes at Motorola, GE, and other early adopters of Six Sigma, many companies worldwide have now instituted Six Sigma to improve efficiency, cut costs, eliminate defects, and reduce product variation (see references 1, 3, 10, and 17). Six Sigma offers a more prescriptive and systematic approach to process improvement than TQM. It is also distinguished from other quality improvement systems by its clear focus on achieving bottom-line results in a relatively short three- to six-month period of time.

The name *Six Sigma* comes from the fact that it is a managerial approach designed to create processes that result in no more than 3.4 defects per million. The Six Sigma approach assumes that processes are designed so that the upper and lower specification limits are each six standard deviations away from the mean. Then, if the processes are monitored correctly with control charts, the worst possible scenario is for the mean to shift to within 4.5 standard deviations from the nearest specification limit. The area under the normal curve less than 4.5 standard deviations below the mean is approximately 3.4 out of 1 million. (Table E.2 reports this probability as 0.000003398.)

The DMAIC Model

To guide managers in their task of improving short-term and long-term results, Six Sigma uses a five-step process known as the **DMAIC model**—named for the five steps in the process:

- **Define**   The problem is defined, along with the costs, the benefits, and the impact on the customer.
- **Measure**   Important characteristics related to the quality of the service or product are identified and discussed. Variables measuring these characteristics are defined and called *critical-to-quality (CTQ)* variables. Operational definitions for all the CTQ variables are then developed. In addition, the measurement procedure is verified so that it is consistent over repeated measurements.
- **Analyze**   The root causes of *why* defects occur are determined, and variables in the process causing the defects are identified. Data are collected to determine benchmark values for each process variable. This analysis often uses control charts.
- **Improve**   The importance of each process variable on the CTQ variable is studied using designed experiments (see Chapter 12 and references 8, 9, and 12). The objective is to determine the best level for each variable.
- **Control**   The objective is to maintain the benefits for the long term by avoiding potential problems that can occur when a process is changed.

The *Define* phase of a Six Sigma project consists of the development of a project charter, performing a SIPOC analysis, and identifying the customers for the output of the process. The development of a project charter involves forming a table of business objectives and indicators for all potential Six Sigma projects. Importance ratings are assigned by top management, projects are prioritized, and the most important project is selected. A **SIPOC analysis** is used to identify the **S**uppliers to the process, list the **I**nputs provided by the suppliers, flowchart the **P**rocess, list the process **O**utputs, and identify the **C**ustomers of the process. This is followed by a Voice of the Customer analysis that involves market segmentation in which different types of users of the process are identified and the circumstances of their use of the process are identified. Statistical methods used in the *Define* phase include tables and charts, descriptive statistics, and control charts.

In the *Measure* phase of a Six Sigma project, members of a team identify the CTQ variables that measure important quality characteristics. Next, operational definitions (see Section 1.3) of each CTQ variable are developed so that everyone will have a firm understanding of the CTQ. Then studies are undertaken to ensure that there is a valid measurement system for the CTQ that is consistent across measurements. Finally, baseline data are collected to determine the capability and stability of the current process. Statistical methods used in the *Measure* phase include tables and charts, descriptive statistics, the normal distribution, the Analysis of Variance, and control charts.

The *Analyze* phase of a Six Sigma project focuses on the factors that affect the central tendency, variation, and shape of each CTQ variable. Factors are identified, and the relationships between the factors and the CTQs are analyzed. Statistical methods used in the *Analyze* phase include tables and charts, descriptive statistics, the Analysis of Variance, regression analysis, and control charts.

In the *Improve* phase of a Six Sigma project, team members carry out designed experiments to actively intervene in a process. The objective of the experiments is to determine the settings of the factors that will optimize the central tendency, variation, and shape of each CTQ variable. Statistical methods used in the *Improve* phase include tables and charts, descriptive statistics, regression analysis, hypothesis testing, the Analysis of Variance, and designed experiments.

The *Control* phase of a Six Sigma project focuses on the maintenance of improvements that have been made in the *Improve* phase. A risk abatement plan is developed to identify elements that can cause damage to a process. Statistical methods used in the *Control* phase include tables and charts, descriptive statistics, and control charts.

Roles in a Six Sigma Organization

Six Sigma requires that the employees of an organization have well-defined roles. The roles senior executive (CEO or president), executive committee, champion, process owner, master black belt, black belt, and green belt are critical to Six Sigma. More importantly, everyone must be properly trained in order to successfully fulfill their roles' tasks and responsibilities.

The role of the **senior executive** is critical for Six Sigma's ultimate success. The most successful, highly publicized Six Sigma efforts have all had unwavering, clear, and committed leadership from top management. Although Six Sigma concepts and processes can be initiated at lower levels, high-level success cannot be achieved without the leadership of the senior executive.

The members of the **executive committee** consist of the top management of an organization. They need to operate at the same level of commitment to Six Sigma as the senior executive.

Champions take a strong sponsorship and leadership role in conducting and implementing Six Sigma projects. They work closely with the executive committee, the black belt assigned to their project, and the master black belt overseeing their project. A champion should be a member of the executive committee, or at least someone who reports directly to a member of the executive committee. He or she should have enough influence to remove obstacles or provide resources without having to go higher in the organization.

A **process owner** is the manager of a process. He or she has responsibility for the process and has the authority to change the process on her or his signature. The process owner should be identified and involved immediately in all Six Sigma projects related to his or her own area.

A **master black belt** takes on a leadership role in the implementation of the Six Sigma process and as an advisor to senior executives. The master black belt must use his or her skills while working on projects that are led by black belts and green belts. A master black belt has successfully led many teams through complex Six Sigma projects. He or she is a proven change agent, leader, facilitator, and technical expert in Six Sigma.

A **black belt** works full time on Six Sigma projects. A black belt is mentored by a master black belt but may report to a manager for his or her tour of duty as a black belt. Ideally, a black belt works well in a team format, can manage meetings, is familiar with statistics and systems theory, and has a focus on the customer.

A **green belt** is an individual who works on Six Sigma projects part time (approximately 25%), either as a team member for complex projects or as a project leader for simpler projects. Most managers in a mature Six Sigma organization are green belts. Green belt certification is a critical prerequisite for advancement into upper management in a Six Sigma organization.

Recent research (see reference 3) indicates that more than 80% of the top 100 publicly traded companies in the United States use Six Sigma. So, you do need to be aware of the distinction between master black belt, black belt, and green belt if you are to function effectively in a Six Sigma organization.

In a Six Sigma organization, 25% to 50% of the organization will be green belts, only 6% to 12% of the organization will be black belts, and only 1% of the organization will be master black belts (reference 8). Individual companies, professional organizations such as the American Society for Quality, and universities such as the University of Miami offer certification programs for green belt, black belt, and master black belt. For more information on certification and other aspects of Six Sigma, see references 8, 9, and 12.

USING STATISTICS @ Beachcomber Hotel Revisited

I n the Using Statistics scenario, you were the manager of the Beachcomber Hotel. After being trained in Six Sigma, you decided to focus on two critical first impressions: Is the room ready when a guest checks in? And, do guests receive their luggage in a reasonable amount of time?

You constructed a p chart of the proportion of rooms not ready at check-in. The p chart indicated that the check-in process was in control and that, on average, the proportion of rooms not ready was approximately 0.08 (i.e., 8%). You then constructed $\overline{X}$ and R charts for the amount of time required to deliver luggage. Although there was a considerable amount of variability around the overall mean of approximately 9.5 minutes, you determined that the luggage delivery process was also in control.

You have learned that an in-control process contains common causes of variation but no special causes of variation. Improvements in the outcomes of in-control processes must come from changes in the actual processes. Thus, if you want to reduce the proportion of rooms not ready at check-in and/or lower the mean luggage delivery time, you will need to change the check-in process and/or the luggage delivery process. From your knowledge of Six Sigma and statistics, you know that during the *Improve* phase of the DMAIC model, you will be able to perform and analyze experiments using different process designs. Hopefully you will discover better process designs that will lead to a higher percentage of rooms being ready on time and/or quicker luggage delivery times. These improvements should ultimately lead to greater guest satisfaction.

SUMMARY

In this chapter you have learned how to use control charts to distinguish between common causes and special causes of variation. For categorical variables, you learned how to construct and analyze p charts. For numerically measured variables, you learned how to construct and analyze $\overline{X}$ and R charts. The chapter also discussed managerial approaches such as TQM and Six Sigma that improve the quality of products and services.

KEY EQUATIONS

Constructing Control Limits

Process mean ± 3 standard deviations

Upper control limit $(\mathbf{UCL})$ = process mean
$\quad\quad\quad\quad\quad\quad\quad\quad +3$ standard deviations

Lower control limit $(\mathbf{LCL})$ = process mean
$\quad\quad\quad\quad\quad\quad\quad\quad -3$ standard deviations

KEY TERMS

PROBLEMS

CHECKING YOUR UNDERSTANDING

9.15 What is the difference between common cause variation and special cause variation?

9.16 What should you do to improve a process when special causes of variation are present?

9.17 What should you do to improve a process when only common causes of variation are present?

9.18 Under what circumstances do you use a p chart?

9.19 What is the difference between attribute control charts and variables control charts?

9.20 Why are $\overline{X}$ and R charts used together?

APPLYING THE CONCEPTS

9.21 According to the American Society for Quality, customers in the United States consistently rate service quality lower than product quality (American Society for Quality, *The Quarterly Quality Report*, **www.asq.org**, May 16, 2006). For example, products in the beverage, personal care, and cleaning industries, as well as the major appliance sector all received very high customer satisfaction ratings. At the other extreme, services provided by airlines, banks, and insurance companies all received low customer satisfaction ratings.
a. Why do you think service quality consistently rates lower than product quality?
b. What are the similarities and differences between measuring service quality and product quality?
c. Do Deming's 14 points apply to both products and services?
d. Can Six Sigma be used for both products and services?

9.22 Suppose that you have been hired as a summer intern at a large amusement park. Every day, your task is to conduct 200 exit interviews in the parking lot when customers leave. You need to construct questions to address the cleanliness of the park and the customers' intent to return. When you begin to construct a short questionnaire, you remember the control charts you learned in a statistics course, and you decide to write questions that will provide you with data to graph on control charts. After collecting data for 30 days, you plan to construct the control charts.
a. Write a question that will allow you to develop a control chart of customers' perceptions of cleanliness of the park.
b. Give examples of common cause variation and special cause variation for the control chart.
c. If the control chart is in control, what does that indicate and what do you do next?
d. If the control chart is out of control, what does this indicate and what do you do next?
e. Repeat (a) through (d), this time addressing the customers' intent to return to the park.
f. After the initial 30 days, assuming that the charts indicate in-control processes or that the root sources of special cause variation have been corrected, explain how the charts can be used on a daily basis to monitor and improve the quality in the park.

9.23 Researchers at Miami University in Oxford, Ohio, investigated the use of p charts to monitor the market share of a product and to document the effectiveness of marketing promotions. Market share is defined as the company's proportion of the total number of products sold in a category. If a *p* chart based on a company's market share indicates an in-control process, then the company's share in the marketplace is deemed to be stable and consistent over time. In the example given in the article, the RudyBird Disk Company collected daily sales data from a nationwide retail audit service. The first 30 days of data in the accompanying table (stored in RudyBird) indicate the total number of cases of computer disks sold and the number of RudyBird disks sold. The final 7 days of data were taken after Rudy-Bird launched a major in-store promotion. A control chart was used to see if the in-store promotion would result in special cause variation in the marketplace.

Cases Sold Before the Promotion

Day	Total	RudyBird	Day	Total	RudyBird
1	154	35	16	177	56
2	153	43	17	143	43
3	200	44	18	200	69
4	197	56	19	134	38
5	194	54	20	192	47
6	172	38	21	155	45
7	190	43	22	135	36
8	209	62	23	189	55
9	173	53	24	184	44
10	171	39	25	170	47
11	173	44	26	178	48
12	168	37	27	167	42
13	184	45	28	204	71
14	211	58	29	183	64
15	179	35	30	169	43

Cases Sold After the Promotion

Day	Total	RudyBird
31	201	92
32	177	76
33	205	85
34	199	90
35	187	77
36	168	79
37	198	97

Source: Data extracted from C. T. Crespy, T. C. Krehbiel, and J. M. Stearns, "Integrating Analytic Methods into Marketing Research Education: Statistical Control Charts as an Example," *Marketing Education Review*, 5 (Spring 1995), 11–23.

a. Construct a *p* chart, using data from the first 30 days (prior to the promotion) to monitor the market share for RudyBird disks.
b. Is the market share for RudyBird in control before the start of the in-store promotion?
c. On your control chart, extend the control limits generated in (b) and plot the proportions for days 31 through 37.

What effect, if any, did the in-store promotion have on RudyBird's market share?

9.24 The manufacturer of Boston and Vermont asphalt shingles constructed control charts and analyzed several quality characteristics. One characteristic of interest is the strength of the sealant on the shingle. During each day of production, three shingles are tested for their sealant strength. (Thus, a subgroup is operationally defined as one day of production, and the sample size for each subgroup is 3.) Separate pieces are cut from the upper and lower portions of a shingle and then reassembled to simulate shingles on a roof. A timed heating process is used to simulate the sealing process. The sealed shingle pieces are pulled apart, and the amount of force (in pounds) required to break the sealant bond is measured and recorded. This variable is called the *sealant strength*. The file Sealant contains sealant strength measurements on 25 days of production for Boston shingles and 19 days for Vermont shingles.

For the 25 days of production for Boston shingles,
a. construct a control chart for the range.
b. construct a control chart for the mean.
c. is the process in control?
d. Repeat (a) through (c), using the 19 production days for Vermont shingles.

9.25 A professional basketball player has embarked on a program to study his ability to shoot foul shots. On each day in which a game is not scheduled, he intends to shoot 100 foul shots. He maintains records over a period of 40 days of practice, with the results stored in Foulspc :
a. Construct a *p* chart for the proportion of successful foul shots. Do you think that the player's foul-shooting process is in statistical control? If not, why not?
b. What if you were told that the player used a different method of shooting foul shots for the last 20 days? How might this information change your conclusions in (a)?
c. If you knew the information in (b) prior to doing (a), how might you do the analysis differently?

9.26 The funds-transfer department of a bank has the business objective of reducing the turnaround time for investigations of funds-transfer payments. A payment may involve the bank as a remitter of funds, a beneficiary of funds, or an intermediary in the payment. An investigation is initiated by a payment inquiry or a query by a party involved in the payment or any department affected by the flow of funds. When a query is received, an investigator reconstructs the transaction trail of the payment and verifies that the information is correct and that the proper payment is transmitted. The investigator then reports the results of the investigation, and the transaction is considered closed. It is important that investigations be closed rapidly, preferably within the same day. The number of new investigations and the number and proportion closed on the same day that the inquiry was made are stored in FundTran .
a. Construct a control chart for these data.
b. Is the process in a state of statistical control? Explain.
c. Based on the results of (a) and (b), what should management do next to improve the process?

9.27 A branch manager of a brokerage company has the business objective of reducing the number of undesirable trades made by her sales staff. A trade is considered undesirable if there is an error on the trade ticket. Trades with errors are canceled and resubmitted. The cost of correcting errors is billed to the brokerage company. The branch manager wants to know whether the proportion of undesirable trades is in a state of statistical control so she can plan the next step in a quality improvement process. Data were collected for a 30-day period and stored in `Trade`.
a. Construct a control chart for these data.
b. Is the process in control? Explain.
c. Based on the results of (a) and (b), what should the manager do next to improve the process?

9.28 As chief operating officer of a local community hospital, you have just returned from a three-day seminar on quality and productivity. It is your intention to implement many of the ideas that you learned at the seminar. You have decided to construct control charts for the upcoming month for the proportion of rework in the laboratory (based on 1,000 daily samples) and time (in hours) between receipt of a specimen at the laboratory and completion of the work (based on a subgroup of 10 specimens per day). The data collected are summarized and stored in `HospAdm`. You are to make a presentation to the chief executive officer of the hospital and the board of directors. Prepare a report that summarizes the conclusions drawn from analyzing control charts for these variables. In addition, recommend additional variables to measure and monitor by using control charts.

9.29 A team working at a cat food company had the business objective of reducing nonconformance in the cat food canning process. As the team members began to investigate the current process, they found that, in some instances, production needed expensive overtime costs to meet the requirements requested by the market forecasting team. They also realized that data were not available concerning the stability and magnitude of the rate of nonconformance and the production volume throughout the day. Their previous study of the process indicated that output could be nonconforming for a variety of reasons. The reasons broke down into two categories: quality characteristics due to the can and characteristics concerning the fill weight of the container. Because these nonconformities stemmed from different sets of underlying causes, they decided to study them separately. The group assigned to study and reduce the nonconformities due to the

can decided that at 15-minute intervals during each shift the number of nonconforming cans would be determined along with the total number of cans produced during the time period. The results for a single day's production of kidney cat food and a single day's production of shrimp cat food for each shift are stored in `CatFood3`. You want to study the process of producing cans of cat food for the two shifts and the two types of food. Completely analyze the data.

9.30 Refer to Problem 9.29. The production team at the cat food company investigating nonconformities due to the fill weight of the cans determined that at 15-minute intervals during each shift, a subgroup of five cans would be selected, and the contents of the selected cans would be weighed. The results for a single day's production of kidney cat food and a single day's production of shrimp cat food are stored in `CatFood4`. You want to study the process of producing cans of cat food for the two shifts and the two types of food. Completely analyze the data.

9.31 For a period of four weeks, record your pulse rate (in beats per minute) just after you get out of bed in the morning and then again before you go to sleep at night. Construct $\overline{X}$ and R charts and determine whether your pulse rate is in a state of statistical control. Discuss.

9.32 (Class Project) Use the table of random numbers (Table E.1) to simulate the selection of different-colored balls from an urn, as follows:
1. Start in the row corresponding to the day of the month in which you were born plus the last two digits of the year in which you were born. For example, if you were born October 3, 1990, you would start in row 93 (3 + 90). If your total exceeds 100, subtract 100 from the total.
2. Select two-digit random numbers.
3. If you select a random number from 00 to 94, consider the ball to be white; if the random number is from 95 to 99, consider the ball to be red.

Each student is to select 100 two-digit random numbers and report the number of "red balls" in the sample. Construct a control chart for the proportion of red balls. What conclusions can you draw about the system of selecting red balls? Are all the students part of the system? Is anyone outside the system? If so, what explanation can you give for someone who has too many red balls? If a bonus were paid to the top 10% of the students (the 10% with the fewest red balls), what effect would that have on the rest of the students? Discuss.

THE HARNSWELL SEWING MACHINE COMPANY CASE

Phase 1

For more than 40 years, the Harnswell Sewing Machine Company has manufactured industrial sewing machines. The company specializes in automated machines called pattern tackers that sew repetitive patterns on such mass-produced products as shoes, garments, and seat belts. Aside from the sales of machines, the company sells machine parts. Because the company's products have a reputation for being superior, Harnswell is able to command a price premium for its product line.

Recently, the operations manager, Natalie York, purchased several books related to quality. After reading them, she considered the feasibility of beginning a quality program at the company. At the current time, the company has no formal quality program. Parts are 100% inspected at the time of shipping to a customer or installation in a machine, yet Natalie has always wondered why inventory of certain parts (in particular, the half-inch cam rollers) invariably falls short before a full year lapses, even though 7,000 pieces have been produced for a demand of 5,000 pieces per year.

After a great deal of reflection and with some apprehension, Natalie has decided that she will approach John Harnswell, the owner of the company, about the possibility of beginning a program to improve quality in the company, starting with a trial project in the machine parts area. As she is walking to Mr. Harnswell's office for the meeting, she has second thoughts about whether this is such a good idea. After all, just last month, Mr. Harnswell told her, "Why do you need to go to graduate school for your master's degree in business? That is a waste of your time and will not be of any value to the Harnswell Company. All those professors are just up in their ivory towers and don't know a thing about running a business, like I do."

As she enters his office, Mr. Harnswell invites Natalie to sit down across from him. "Well, what do you have on your mind this morning?" Mr. Harnswell asks her in an inquisitive tone. She begins by starting to talk about the books that she has just completed reading and about how she has some interesting ideas for making production even better than it is now and improving profits. Before she can finish, Mr. Harnswell has started to answer: "Look, everything has been fine since I started this company in 1968. I have built this company up from nothing to one that employs more than 100 people. Why do you want to make waves? Remember, if it ain't broke, don't fix it." With that, he ushers her from his office with the admonishment of, "What am I going to do with you if you keep coming up with these ridiculous ideas?"

EXERCISES

1. Based on what you have read, which of Deming's 14 points of management are most lacking at the Harnswell Sewing Machine Company? Explain.
2. What changes, if any, do you think that Natalie York might be able to institute in the company? Explain.

Phase 2

Natalie slowly walks down the hall after leaving Mr. Harnswell's office, feeling rather downcast. He just won't listen to anyone, she thinks. As she walks, Jim Murante, the shop foreman, comes up beside her. "So," he says, "did you really think that he would listen to you? I've been here more than 25 years. The only way he listens is if he is shown something that worked after it has already been done. Let's see what we can plan together."

Natalie and Jim decide to begin by investigating the production of the cam rollers, which are precision-ground parts. The last part of the production process involves the grinding of the outer diameter. After grinding, the part mates with the cam groove of the particular sewing pattern. The half-inch rollers technically have an engineering specification for the outer diameter of the roller of 0.5075 inch (the specifications are actually metric, but in factory floor jargon, they are referred to as half-inch), plus a tolerable error of 0.0003 inch on the lower side. Thus, the outer diameter is allowed to be between 0.5072 and 0.5075 inch. Anything larger is reclassified into a different and less costly category, and anything smaller is unusable for anything other than scrap.

The grinding of the cam roller is done on a single machine with a single tool setup and no change in the grinding wheel after initial setup. The operation is done by Dave Martin, the head machinist, who has 30 years of experience in the trade and specific experience producing the cam roller part. Because production occurs in batches, Natalie and Jim sample five parts produced from each batch. Table HS9.1 presents data collected over 30 batches (stored in `Harnswell`).

EXERCISE

3. **a.** Is the process in control? Why?
   b. What recommendations do you have for improving the process?

Phase 3

Natalie examines the $\bar{X}$ and R charts developed from the data presented in Table HS9.1. The R chart indicates that the process is in control, but the $\bar{X}$ chart reveals that the

TABLE HS9.1

Diameter of Cam Rollers (in Inches)

Batch	Cam Roller 1	2	3	4	5
1	.5076	.5076	.5075	.5077	.5075
2	.5075	.5077	.5076	.5076	.5075
3	.5075	.5075	.5075	.5075	.5076
4	.5075	.5076	.5074	.5076	.5073
5	.5075	.5074	.5076	.5073	.5076
6	.5076	.5075	.5076	.5075	.5075
7	.5076	.5076	.5076	.5075	.5075
8	.5075	.5076	.5076	.5075	.5074
9	.5074	.5076	.5075	.5075	.5076
10	.5076	.5077	.5075	.5075	.5075
11	.5075	.5075	.5075	.5076	.5075
12	.5075	.5076	.5075	.5077	.5075
13	.5076	.5076	.5073	.5076	.5074
14	.5075	.5076	.5074	.5076	.5075
15	.5075	.5075	.5076	.5074	.5073
16	.5075	.5074	.5076	.5075	.5075
17	.5075	.5074	.5075	.5074	.5072
18	.5075	.5075	.5076	.5075	.5076
19	.5076	.5076	.5075	.5075	.5076
20	.5075	.5074	.5077	.5076	.5074
21	.5075	.5074	.5075	.5075	.5075
22	.5076	.5076	.5075	.5076	.5074
23	.5076	.5076	.5075	.5075	.5076
24	.5075	.5076	.5075	.5076	.5075
25	.5075	.5075	.5075	.5075	.5074
26	.5077	.5076	.5076	.5074	.5075
27	.5075	.5075	.5074	.5076	.5075
28	.5077	.5076	.5075	.5075	.5076
29	.5075	.5075	.5074	.5075	.5075
30	.5076	.5075	.5075	.5076	.5075

mean for batch 17 is outside the LCL. This immediately gives her cause for concern because low values for the roller diameter could mean that parts have to be scrapped. Natalie goes to see Jim Murante, the shop foreman, to try to find out what had happened to batch 17. Jim looks up the production records to determine when this batch was produced. "Aha!" he exclaims. "I think I've got the answer! This batch was produced on that really cold morning we had last month. I've been after Mr. Harnswell for a long time to let us install an automatic thermostat here in the shop so that the place doesn't feel so cold when we get here in the morning. All he ever tells me is that people aren't as tough as they used to be."

Natalie is almost in shock. She realizes that what happened is that, rather than standing idle until the environment and the equipment warmed to acceptable temperatures, the machinist opted to manufacture parts that might have to be scrapped. In fact, Natalie recalls that a major problem occurred on that same day, when several other expensive parts had to be scrapped. Natalie says to Jim, "We just have to do something. We can't let this go on now that we know what problems it is potentially causing." Natalie and Jim decide to take enough money out of petty cash to get the thermostat without having to fill out a requisition requiring Mr. Harnswell's signature. They install the thermostat and set the heating control so that the heat turns on a half hour before the shop opens each morning.

EXERCISES

4. What should Natalie do now concerning the cam roller data? Explain.
5. Explain how the actions of Natalie and Jim to avoid this particular problem in the future have resulted in quality improvement.

PHASE 4

Because corrective action was taken to eliminate the special cause of variation, Natalie removes the data for batch 17 from the analysis. The control charts for the remaining days indicate a stable system, with only common causes of variation operating on the system. Then, Natalie and Jim sit down with Dave Martin and several other machinists to try to determine all the possible causes for the existence of oversized and scrapped rollers. Natalie is still troubled by the data. After all, she wants to find out whether the process is giving oversizes (which are downgraded) and undersizes (which are scrapped). She thinks about which tables and charts might be most helpful.

EXERCISE

6. a. Construct a frequency distribution and a stem-and-leaf display of the cam roller diameters. Which do you prefer in this situation?
   b. Based on your results in (a), construct all appropriate charts of the cam roller diameters.
   c. Write a report, expressing your conclusions concerning the cam roller diameters. Be sure to discuss the diameters as they relate to the specifications.

PHASE 5

Natalie notices immediately that the overall mean diameter with batch 17 eliminated is 0.507527, which is higher than the specification value. Thus, the mean diameter of the rollers produced is so high that many will be downgraded in value. In fact, 55 of the 150 rollers sampled (36.67%) are above the specification value. If this percentage is extrapolated to the full year's production, 36.67% of the 7,000 pieces manufactured, or 2,567, could not be sold as half-inch rollers, leaving only 4,433 available for sale. "No wonder we often have shortages that require costly emergency runs," she thinks. She also notes that not one diameter is below the lower specification of 0.5072, so not one of the rollers had to be scrapped.

Natalie realizes that there has to be a reason for all this. Along with Jim Murante, she decides to show the results to Dave Martin, the head machinist. Dave says that the results don't surprise him that much. "You know," he says, "there is only 0.0003 inch variation in diameter that I'm allowed. If I aim for exactly halfway between 0.5072 and 0.5075, I'm afraid that I'll make a lot of short pieces that will have to be scrapped. I know from way back when I first started here that Mr. Harnswell and everybody else will come down on my head if they start seeing too many of those scraps. I figure that if I aim at 0.5075, the worst thing that will happen will be a bunch of downgrades, but I won't make any pieces that have to be scrapped."

EXERCISES

7. What approach do you think the machinist should take in terms of the diameter he should aim for? Explain.
8. What do you think that Natalie should do next? Explain.

MANAGING ASHLAND MULTICOMM SERVICES

The AMS technical services team has embarked on a quality improvement effort. Its first project relates to maintaining the target upload speed for its Internet service subscribers. Upload speeds are measured on a device that records the results on a standard scale in which the target value is 1.0. Each day five uploads are randomly selected, and the speed of each upload is measured. Table AMS9.1 below presents the results for 25 days (stored in **AMS9**).

EXERCISE

1. a. Construct the appropriate control charts for these data.
   b. Is the process in a state of statistical control? Explain.
   c. What should the team recommend as the next step to improve the process?

TABLE AMS9.1

Upload Speeds for 25 Consecutive Days

Day	Upload 1	Upload 2	Upload 3	Upload 4	Upload 5
1	0.96	1.01	1.12	1.07	0.97
2	1.06	1.00	1.02	1.16	0.96
3	1.00	0.90	0.98	1.18	0.96
4	0.92	0.89	1.01	1.16	0.90
5	1.02	1.16	1.03	0.89	1.00
6	0.88	0.92	1.03	1.16	0.91
7	1.05	1.13	1.01	0.93	1.03
8	0.95	0.86	1.14	0.90	0.95
9	0.99	0.89	1.00	1.15	0.92
10	0.89	1.18	1.03	0.96	1.04
11	0.97	1.13	0.95	0.86	1.06
12	1.00	0.87	1.02	0.98	1.13
13	0.96	0.79	1.17	0.97	0.95
14	1.03	0.89	1.03	1.12	1.03
15	0.96	1.12	0.95	0.88	0.99
16	1.01	0.87	0.99	1.04	1.16
17	0.98	0.85	0.99	1.04	1.16
18	1.03	0.82	1.21	0.98	1.08
19	1.02	0.84	1.15	0.94	1.08
20	0.90	1.02	1.10	1.04	1.08
21	0.96	1.05	1.01	0.93	1.01
22	0.89	1.04	0.97	0.99	0.95
23	0.96	1.00	0.97	1.04	0.95
24	1.01	0.98	1.04	1.01	0.92
25	1.01	1.00	0.92	0.90	1.11

REFERENCES

1. Arndt, M., "Quality Isn't Just for Widgets," *Business-Week*, July 22, 2002, pp. 72–73.
2. Automotive Industry Action Group (AIAG), *Statistical Process Control Reference Manual* (Chrysler, Ford, and General Motors Quality and Supplier Assessment Staff, 1995).
3. Cyger, M., "The Last Word—Riding the Bandwagon," *iSixSigma Magazine*, November/December 2006.
4. Davis, R. B., and T. C. Krehbiel, "Shewhart and Zone Control Charts Under Linear Trend," *Communications in Statistics: Simulation and Computation*, 31 (2002), 91–96.

5. Deming, W. E., *The New Economics for Business, Industry, and Government* (Cambridge, MA: MIT Center for Advanced Engineering Study, 1993).

6. Deming, W. E., *Out of the Crisis* (Cambridge, MA: MIT Center for Advanced Engineering Study, 1986).

7. Gabor, A., *The Man Who Discovered Quality* (New York: Time Books, 1990).

8. Gitlow, H., and D. Levine, *Six Sigma for Green Belts and Champions* (Upper Saddle River, NJ: Financial Times/Prentice Hall, 2005).

9. Gitlow, H., D. Levine, and E. Popovich, *Design for Six Sigma for Green Belts and Champions* (Upper Saddle River, NJ: Financial Times/Prentice Hall, 2006).

10. Hahn, G. J., N. Doganaksoy, and R. Hoerl, "The Evolution of Six Sigma," *Quality Engineering*, 12 (2000), 317–326.

11. Lemak, D. L., N. P. Mero, and R. Reed, "When Quality Works: A Premature Post-Mortem on TQM," *Journal of Business and Management*, 8 (2002), 391–407.

12. Levine, D. M., *Statistics for Six Sigma for Green Belts with Minitab and JMP* (Upper Saddle River, NJ: Financial Times/Prentice Hall, 2006).

13. *Microsoft Excel 2010* (Redmond, WA: Microsoft Corp., 2010).

14. *Minitab Release 16* (State College, PA: Minitab Inc., 2010).

15. Scherkenbach, W. W., *The Deming Route to Quality and Productivity: Road Maps and Roadblocks* (Washington, DC: CEEP Press, 1987).

16. Shewhart, W. A., *Economic Control of the Quality of Manufactured Product* (New York: Van Nostrand-Reinhard, 1931, reprinted by the American Society for Quality Control, Milwaukee, 1980).

17. Snee, R. D., "Impact of Six Sigma on Quality," *Quality Engineering*, 12 (2000), ix–xiv.

18. Vardeman, S. B., and J. M. Jobe, *Statistical Methods for Quality Assurance: Basics, Measurement, Control, Capability and Improvement* (New York: Springer-Verlag, 2009).

19. Walton, M., *The Deming Management Method* (New York: Perigee Books, 1986).

CHAPTER 9 EXCEL GUIDE

EG9.1 The Theory of Control Charts

There are no Excel Guide instructions for this section.

EG9.2 Type of Control Charts

PHStat2 Use **p Chart** to create a *p* chart and supporting worksheets that compute the control limits and plot points. For example, to create the Figure 9.2 *p* chart for the Table 9.1 nonconforming hotel room data, open to the **DATA worksheet** of the **Hotel1 workbook**. Select **PHStat → Control Charts → p Chart** and in the procedure's dialog box (shown at right):

1. Enter **C1:C29** as the **Nonconformances Cell Range.**

2. Check **First cell contains label.**

3. Click **Size does not vary** and enter **200** as the **Sample/Subgroup Size.**

4. Enter a **Title** and click **OK.**

The procedure creates a *p* chart on its own chart sheet and two supporting worksheets: one that computes the control limits and one that computes the values to be plotted. For more information about these two worksheets, read the following *In-Depth Excel* instructions.

For problems in which the sample/subgroup sizes vary, replace step 3 with this step: Click **Size varies**, enter the cell range that contains the sample/subgroup sizes as the **Sample/Subgroup Cell Range**, and click **First cell contain label**.

In-Depth Excel Use the **pChartDATA** and **COMPUTE worksheets** of the **p Chart workbook** as a template for computing control limits and plot points. The pChartDATA worksheet uses formulas in column D that divide the column C number of nonconformances value by the column B subgroup/sample size value to compute the proportion (p_i) and uses formulas in columns E through G to display the values for the LCL, $\bar{p}$, and UCL that are computed in cells B12 through B14 of the COMPUTE worksheet. In turn, the COMPUTE worksheet (shown below) uses the subgroup sizes and the proportion values found in the pChartDATA worksheet to compute the control limits.

	A	B	
1	p Chart Summary		
2			
3	Intermediate Calculations		
4	Sum of Subgroup Sizes	5600	=SUM(pChartDATA!B:B)
5	Number of Subgroups Taken	28	=COUNT(pChartDATA!B:B)
6	Average Sample/Subgroup Size	200	=B4/B5
7	Average Proportion of Nonconforming Items	0.0827	=SUM(pChartDATA!C:C)/B4
8	Three Standard Deviations	0.0584	=3 * SQRT(B7 * (1 - B7)/B6)
9	Preliminary Lower Control Limit	0.0243	=B7 - B8
10			
11	p Chart Control Limits		
12	Lower Control Limit	0.0243	=IF(B9 > 0, B9, 0)
13	Center	0.0827	=B7
14	Upper Control Limit	0.1411	=B7 + B8

Computing control limits and plotting points for other problems requires changes to the **pChartDATA worksheet** of the **p Chart workbook**. First, paste the time period, subgroup/sample size, and number of nonconformances data into columns A through C of the pChartDATA worksheet. If there are more than 28 time periods, select cell range **D29:G29** and copy the range down through all the rows. If there are fewer than 28 time periods, delete the extra rows from the bottom up, starting with row 29.

Use the pChartDATA worksheet as the basis for creating a *p* chart. For example, to create the Figure 9.2 *p* chart for the nonconforming hotel room data, open to the pChartDATA worksheet which contains the Table 9.1 nonconforming hotel room data. Select the cell range **A1:A29** and while holding down the **Ctrl** key, select the cell range **D1:G29**. (This operation selects the cell range **A1:A29, D1:G29**.) Then:

1. Select **Insert ➔ Scatter** and select the fourth choice from the **Scatter** gallery (**Scatter with Straight Lines and Markers**).
2. Relocate the chart to a chart sheet and adjust chart formatting by using the instructions in Appendix Section F.4.

At this point, a recognizable chart begins to take shape, but the control limit and center lines are improperly formatted and are not properly labeled. Use the following three sets of instructions to correct these formatting errors:

To reformat each control limit line:

1. Right-click the control limit line and select **Format Data Series** from the shortcut menu.
2. In the Format Data Series dialog box left pane, click **Marker Options** and in the **Marker Options** right panel, click **None**.
3. In the left pane, click **Line Style** and in the **Line Style** right panel, select the sixth choice (a dashed line) from the **Dash type** drop-down gallery list.
4. In the left pane, click **Line Color** and in the **Line Color** right panel, select the black color from the **Color** drop-down gallery list.
5. Click **Close**.

To reformat the center line:

1. Right-click the center line and select **Format Data Series** from the shortcut menu.
2. In the Format Data Series dialog box left pane, click **Marker Options** and in the **Marker Options** right panel, click **None**.
3. In the left pane, click **Line Color** and in the **Line Color** right panel, click **Solid line** and then select a red color from the **Color** drop-down gallery.
4. Click **Close**.

To label a control limit line or the center line:

1. Select **Layout ➔ Text Box** (in Insert group) and starting slightly above and to the right of the line, drag the special cursor diagonally to form a new text box.
2. Enter the line label in the text box and then click on the chart background.

EG9.4 Control Charts for the Range and the Mean

The *R* Chart and the *X* Chart

PHStat2 Use **R and XBar Charts** to create *R* and $\bar{X}$ charts and supporting worksheets that compute the control limits and plot points. For example, to create the Figure 9.5 *R* chart and the Figure 14.6 $\bar{X}$ chart for the Table 14.4 luggage delivery times, open to the **DATA worksheet** of the **Hotel2 workbook**. Because the PHStat2 procedure requires column cell ranges that contain either means or ranges, first add two columns that compute the mean and ranges on this worksheet. Enter the column heading **Mean** in cell **G1** and the heading **Range** in cell **H1**. Enter the formula =AVERAGE(B2:F2) in cell **G2** and the formula =MAX(B2:F2) - MIN(B2:F2) in cell **H2**. Select the cell range **G2:H2** and copy the range down through row 29.

With the two columns created, select **PHStat → Control Charts → R and XBar Charts**. In the procedure's dialog box (shown below):

1. Enter 5 as the **Subgroup/Sample Size**.
2. Enter **H1:H29** as the **Subgroup Ranges Cell Range**.
3. Check **First cell contains label**.
4. Click **R and XBar Charts**. Enter **G1:G29** as the **Subgroup Means Cell Range** and check **First cell contains label**.
5. Enter a **Title** and click **OK**.

The procedure creates the two charts on separate chart sheets and two supporting worksheets: one that computes the control limits and one that computes the values to be plotted. For more information about these two worksheets, read the following *In-Depth Excel* section.

In-Depth Excel Use the **DATA**, **RXChartDATA**, and **COMPUTE worksheets** of the **R and XBar Chart workbook** as a template for computing control limits and plotting points. The RXChartDATA worksheet uses formulas in columns B and C to compute the mean and range values for the Table 14.4 luggage delivery times stored in the DATA worksheet. The worksheet uses formulas in columns D through I to display the values for the control limit and center lines, using values that are computed in the COMPUTE worksheet. Formulas in columns D and G use IF functions that will omit the lower control limit if the LCL value computed is less than 0. (To examine the formulas used in the worksheet, open to the **RXChartDATA_FORMULAS worksheet**.)

The COMPUTE worksheet (shown below) uses the computed means and ranges to compute $\bar{R}$ and $\bar{\bar{X}}$, the mean of the subgroup means. Unlike the COMPUTE worksheets for other control charts, you must manually enter the **Sample/Subgroup Size** in cell **B4** (5, as shown below) in addition to the D_3, D_4, and A_2 factors in cells **B8**, **B9**, and **B18** (0, 2.114, and 0.577, as shown).

Use Table E.8 to look up the values for the D_3, D_4, and A_2 factors.

	A	B	
1	R and XBar Chart Summary		
2			
3	**Data**		
4	Sample/Subgroup Size	5	
5			
6	**R Chart Intermediate Calculations**		
7	RBar	3.4821	=AVERAGE(RXChartDATA!C:C)
8	D_3 Factor	0	
9	D_4 Factor	2.114	
10			
11	**R Chart Control Limits**		
12	Lower Control Limit	0.0000	=B8 * B7
13	Center	3.4821	=B7
14	Upper Control Limit	7.3613	=B9 * B7
15			
16	**XBar Chart Intermediate Calculations**		
17	Average of Subgroup Averages	9.4779	=AVERAGE(RXChartDATA!B:B)
18	A_2 Factor	0.577	
19	A_2 Factor * RBar	2.0092	=B18 * B7
20			
21	**XBar Chart Control Limits**		
22	Lower Control Limit	7.4687	=B17- B19
23	Center	9.4779	=B17
24	Upper Control Limit	11.4871	=B17 + B19

Computing control limits and plotting points for other problems requires changes to the RXChartDATA or the DATA worksheet, depending on whether means and ranges have been previously computed. If the means and ranges have been previously computed, paste these values into column B and C of the RXChartDATA worksheet. If there are more than 28 time periods, select cell range **D29:I29** and copy the range down through all the rows. If there are fewer than 28 time periods, delete the extra rows from the bottom up, starting with row 29.

If the means and ranges have not been previously computed, changes must be made to the DATA worksheet. First, determine the subgroup size. If the subgroup size is less than 5, delete the extra columns, right-to-left, starting with column F. If the subgroup size is greater than 5, select column F, right-click, and click **Insert** from the short-cut menu. (Repeat as many times as necessary.) With the DATA worksheet so adjusted, paste the time and subgroup data into the worksheet, starting with cell A1. Then open to the RXChartDATA worksheet, and if the number of time periods is not equal to 28, adjust the number of rows using the instructions of the previous paragraph.

Use the RXChartDATA worksheet as the basis for creating R and $\bar{X}$ charts. For example, open to the **RXChartDATA worksheet** of the **R and XBar Chart workbook** which contains Table 14.4 luggage delivery times data. To create the Figure 14.5 R chart for Excel, select the cell range **C1:F29**. To create the Figure 14.6 $\bar{X}$ chart, select the cell range **B1:B29, G1:I29** (while holding down the **Ctrl key**, select the cell range **B1:B29** and then the cell range **G1:I29**). In either case:

1. Select **Insert → Scatter** and select the fourth choice from the **Scatter** gallery **(Scatter with Straight Lines and Markers)**.

2. Relocate the chart to a chart sheet and adjust the chart formatting by using the instructions in Appendix Section F.4.

At this point, a recognizable chart begins to take shape, but the control limit and center lines are improperly formatted and are not properly labeled. To correct these formatting errors, use the three sets of instructions given in the Section EG9.2 *In-Depth Excel* instructions.

Appendices

APPENDIX A Basic Math Concepts and Symbols

A.1 Rules for Arithmetic Operations

RULE	EXAMPLE
1. $a + b = c$ and $b + a = c$	$2 + 1 = 3$ and $1 + 2 = 3$
2. $a + (b + c) = (a + b) + c$	$5 + (7 + 4) = (5 + 7) + 4 = 16$
3. $a - b = c$ but $b - a \neq c$	$9 - 7 = 2$ but $7 - 9 \neq 2$
4. $(a)(b) = (b)(a)$	$(7)(6) = (6)(7) = 42$
5. $(a)(b + c) = ab + ac$	$(2)(3 + 5) = (2)(3) + (2)(5) = 16$
6. $a \div b \neq b \div a$	$12 \div 3 \neq 3 \div 12$
7. $\dfrac{a + b}{c} = \dfrac{a}{c} + \dfrac{b}{c}$	$\dfrac{7 + 3}{2} = \dfrac{7}{2} + \dfrac{3}{2} = 5$
8. $\dfrac{a}{b + c} \neq \dfrac{a}{b} + \dfrac{a}{c}$	$\dfrac{3}{4 + 5} \neq \dfrac{3}{4} + \dfrac{3}{5}$
9. $\dfrac{1}{a} + \dfrac{1}{b} = \dfrac{b + a}{ab}$	$\dfrac{1}{3} + \dfrac{1}{5} = \dfrac{5 + 3}{(3)(5)} = \dfrac{8}{15}$
10. $\left(\dfrac{a}{b}\right)\left(\dfrac{c}{d}\right) = \left(\dfrac{ac}{bd}\right)$	$\left(\dfrac{2}{3}\right)\left(\dfrac{6}{7}\right) = \left(\dfrac{(2)(6)}{(3)(7)}\right) = \dfrac{12}{21}$
11. $\dfrac{a}{b} \div \dfrac{c}{d} = \dfrac{ad}{bc}$	$\dfrac{5}{8} \div \dfrac{3}{7} = \left(\dfrac{(5)(7)}{(8)(3)}\right) = \dfrac{35}{24}$

A.2 Rules for Algebra: Exponents and Square Roots

RULE	EXAMPLE
1. $(X^a)(X^b) = X^{a+b}$	$(4^2)(4^3) = 4^5$
2. $(X^a)^b = X^{ab}$	$(2^2)^3 = 2^6$
3. $(X^a/X^b) = X^{a-b}$	$\dfrac{3^5}{3^3} = 3^2$
4. $\dfrac{X^a}{X^a} = X^0 = 1$	$\dfrac{3^4}{3^4} = 3^0 = 1$
5. $\sqrt{XY} = \sqrt{X}\sqrt{Y}$	$\sqrt{(25)(4)} = \sqrt{25}\sqrt{4} = 10$
6. $\sqrt{\dfrac{X}{Y}} = \dfrac{\sqrt{X}}{\sqrt{Y}}$	$\sqrt{\dfrac{16}{100}} = \dfrac{\sqrt{16}}{\sqrt{100}} = 0.40$

A.3 Rules for Logarithms

Base 10

Log is the symbol used for base-10 logarithms:

RULE	EXAMPLE
1. $\log(10^a) = a$	$\log(100) = \log(10^2) = 2$
2. If $\log(a) = b$, then $a = 10^b$	If $\log(a) = 2$, then $a = 10^2 = 100$
3. $\log(ab) = \log(a) + \log(b)$	$\log(100) = \log[(10)(10)] = \log(10) + \log(10)$
	$\qquad = 1 + 1 = 2$
4. $\log(a^b) = (b)\log(a)$	$\log(1{,}000) = \log(10^3) = (3)\log(10) = (3)(1) = 3$
5. $\log(a/b) = \log(a) - \log(b)$	$\log(100) = \log(1{,}000/10) = \log(1{,}000) - \log(10)$
	$\qquad = 3 - 1 = 2$

EXAMPLE

Take the base-10 logarithm of each side of the following equation:

$$Y = \beta_0 \beta_1^X \varepsilon$$

SOLUTION: Apply rules 3 and 4:

$$\log(Y) = \log(\beta_0 \beta_1^X \varepsilon)$$
$$= \log(\beta_0) + \log(\beta_1^X) + \log(\varepsilon)$$
$$= \log(\beta_0) + X\log(\beta_1) + \log(\varepsilon)$$

Base e

ln is the symbol used for base e logarithms, commonly referred to as natural logarithms. e is Euler's number, and $e \cong 2.718282$:

RULE	EXAMPLE
1. $\ln(e^a) = a$	$\ln(7.389056) = \ln(e^2) = 2$
2. If $\ln(a) = b$, then $a = e^b$	If $\ln(a) = 2$, then $a = e^2 = 7.389056$
3. $\ln(ab) = \ln(a) + \ln(b)$	$\ln(100) = \ln[(10)(10)]$
	$= \ln(10) + \ln(10) = 2.302585 + 2.302585 = 4.605170$
4. $\ln(a^b) = (b)\ln(a)$	$\ln(1{,}000) = \ln(10^3) = 3\ln(10) = 3(2.302585) = 6.907755$
5. $\ln(a/b) = \ln(a) - \ln(b)$	$\ln(100) = \ln(1{,}000/10) = \ln(1{,}000) - \ln(10)$
	$= 6.907755 - 2.302585 = 4.605170$

EXAMPLE

Take the base e logarithm of each side of the following equation:

$$Y = \beta_0 \beta_1^X \varepsilon$$

SOLUTION: Apply rules 3 and 4:

$$\ln(Y) = \ln(\beta_0 \beta_1^X \varepsilon)$$
$$= \ln(\beta_0) + \ln(\beta_1^X) + \ln(\varepsilon)$$
$$= \ln(\beta_0) + X\ln(\beta_1) + \ln(\varepsilon)$$

A.4 Summation Notation

The symbol Σ, the Greek capital letter sigma, represents "taking the sum of." Consider a set of n values for variable X. The expression $\sum_{i=1}^{n} X_i$ means to take the sum of the n values for variable X. Thus:

$$\sum_{i=1}^{n} X_i = X_1 + X_2 + X_3 + \cdots + X_n$$

The following problem illustrates the use of the symbol Σ. Consider five values of a variable X: $X_1 = 2, X_2 = 0, X_3 = -1, X_4 = 5$, and $X_5 = 7$. Thus:

$$\sum_{i=1}^{5} X_i = X_1 + X_2 + X_3 + X_4 + X_5 = 2 + 0 + (-1) + 5 + 7 = 13$$

In statistics, the squared values of a variable are often summed. Thus:

$$\sum_{i=1}^{n} X_i^2 = X_1^2 + X_2^2 + X_3^2 + \cdots + X_n^2$$

and, in the example above:

$$\sum_{i=1}^{5} X_i^2 = X_1^2 + X_2^2 + X_3^2 + X_4^2 + X_5^2$$
$$= 2^2 + 0^2 + (-1)^2 + 5^2 + 7^2$$
$$= 4 + 0 + 1 + 25 + 49$$
$$= 79$$

$\sum_{i=1}^{n} X_i^2$, the summation of the squares, is *not* the same as $\left(\sum_{i=1}^{n} X_i \right)^2$, the square of the sum:

$$\sum_{i=1}^{n} X_i^2 \neq \left(\sum_{i=1}^{n} X_i \right)^2$$

In the example given above, the summation of squares is equal to 79. This is not equal to the square of the sum, which is $13^2 = 169$.

Another frequently used operation involves the summation of the product. Consider two variables, X and Y, each having n values. Then:

$$\sum_{i=1}^{n} X_i Y_i = X_1 Y_1 + X_2 Y_2 + X_3 Y_3 + \cdots + X_n Y_n$$

Continuing with the previous example, suppose there is a second variable, Y, whose five values are $Y_1 = 1, Y_2 = 3, Y_3 = -2, Y_4 = 4$, and $Y_5 = 3$. Then,

$$\sum_{i=1}^{n} X_i Y_i = X_1 Y_1 + X_2 Y_2 + X_3 Y_3 + X_4 Y_4 + X_5 Y_5$$
$$= (2)(1) + (0)(3) + (-1)(-2) + (5)(4) + (7)(3)$$
$$= 2 + 0 + 2 + 20 + 21$$
$$= 45$$

In computing $\sum_{i=1}^{n} X_i Y_i$, you need to realize that the first value of X is multiplied by the first value of Y, the second value of X is multiplied by the second value of Y, and so on. These products are then summed in order to compute the desired result. However, the summation of products is *not* equal to the product of the individual sums:

$$\sum_{i=1}^{n} X_i Y_i \neq \left(\sum_{i=1}^{n} X_i \right)\left(\sum_{i=1}^{n} Y_i \right)$$

In this example,

$$\sum_{i=1}^{5} X_i = 13$$

and

$$\sum_{i=1}^{5} Y_i = 1 + 3 + (-2) + 4 + 3 = 9$$

so that

$$\left(\sum_{i=1}^{5} X_i \right)\left(\sum_{i=1}^{5} Y_i \right) = (13)(9) = 117$$

However,

$$\sum_{i=1}^{5} X_i Y_i = 45$$

The following table summarizes these results:

VALUE	X_i	Y_i	$X_i Y_i$
1	2	1	2
2	0	3	0
3	−1	−2	2
4	5	4	20
5	7	3	21
	$\sum_{i=1}^{5} X_i = 13$	$\sum_{i=1}^{5} Y_i = 9$	$\sum_{i=1}^{5} X_i Y_i = 45$

Rule 1   The summation of the values of two variables is equal to the sum of the values of each summed variable:

$$\sum_{i=1}^{n} (X_i + Y_i) = \sum_{i=1}^{n} X_i + \sum_{i=1}^{n} Y_i$$

Thus,

$$\sum_{i=1}^{5} (X_i + Y_i) = (2 + 1) + (0 + 3) + (-1 + (-2)) + (5 + 4) + (7 + 3)$$

$$= 3 + 3 + (-3) + 9 + 10$$

$$= 22$$

$$\sum_{i=1}^{5} X_i + \sum_{i=1}^{5} Y_i = 13 + 9 = 22$$

Rule 2 The summation of a difference between the values of two variables is equal to the difference between the summed values of the variables:

$$\sum_{i=1}^{n}(X_i - Y_i) = \sum_{i=1}^{n}X_i - \sum_{i=1}^{n}Y_i$$

Thus,

$$\sum_{i=1}^{5}(X_i - Y_i) = (2 - 1) + (0 - 3) + (-1 - (-2)) + (5 - 4) + (7 - 3)$$

$$= 1 + (-3) + 1 + 1 + 4$$

$$= 4$$

$$\sum_{i=1}^{5}X_i - \sum_{i=1}^{5}Y_i = 13 - 9 = 4$$

Rule 3 The sum of a constant times a variable is equal to that constant times the sum of the values of the variable:

$$\sum_{i=1}^{n}cX_i = c\sum_{i=1}^{n}X_i$$

where c is a constant. Thus, if $c = 2$,

$$\sum_{i=1}^{5}cX_i = \sum_{i=1}^{5}2X_i = (2)(2) + (2)(0) + (2)(-1) + (2)(5) + (2)(7)$$

$$= 4 + 0 + (-2) + 10 + 14$$

$$= 26$$

$$c\sum_{i=1}^{5}X_i = 2\sum_{i=1}^{5}X_i = (2)(13) = 26$$

Rule 4 A constant summed n times will be equal to n times the value of the constant.

$$\sum_{i=1}^{n}c = nc$$

where c is a constant. Thus, if the constant $c = 2$ is summed 5 times,

$$\sum_{i=1}^{5}c = 2 + 2 + 2 + 2 + 2 = 10$$

$$nc = (5)(2) = 10$$

EXAMPLE

Suppose there are six values for the variables X and Y, such that $X_1 = 2, X_2 = 1, X_3 = 5$, $X_4 = -3, X_5 = 1, X_6 = -2$ and $Y_1 = 4, Y_2 = 0, Y_3 = -1, Y_4 = 2, Y_5 = 7$, and $Y_6 = -3$. Compute each of the following:

(a) $\sum_{i=1}^{6}X_i$ (d) $\sum_{i=1}^{6}Y_i^2$

(b) $\sum_{i=1}^{6}Y_i$ (e) $\sum_{i=1}^{6}X_iY_i$

(c) $\sum_{i=1}^{6}X_i^2$ (f) $\sum_{i=1}^{6}(X_i + Y_i)$

(g) $\sum_{i=1}^{6}(X_i - Y_i)$ (i) $\sum_{i=1}^{6}(cX_i)$, where $c = -1$

(h) $\sum_{i=1}^{6}(X_i - 3Y_i + 2X_i^2)$ (j) $\sum_{i=1}^{6}(X_i - 3Y_i + c)$, where $c = +3$

Answers

(a) 4   (b) 9   (c) 44   (d) 79   (e) 10   (f) 13   (g) −5   (h) 65   (i) −4   (j) −5

References

1. Bashaw, W. L., *Mathematics for Statistics* (New York: Wiley, 1969).
2. Lanzer, P., *Basic Math: Fractions, Decimals, Percents* (Hicksville, NY: Video Aided Instruction, 2006).
3. Levine, D. and A. Brandwein, *The MBA Primer: Business Statistics*, 3rd ed. (Cincinnati, OH: Cengage Publishing, 2011).
4. Levine, D., *Statistics* (Hicksville, NY: Video Aided Instruction, 2006).
5. Shane, H., *Algebra 1* (Hicksville, NY: Video Aided Instruction, 2006).

A.5 Statistical Symbols

+	add	×	multiply
−	subtract	÷	divide
=	equal to	≠	not equal to
≅	approximately equal to	<	less than
>	greater than	≤	less than or equal to
≥	greater than or equal to		

A.6 Greek Alphabet

GREEK LETTER		LETTER NAME	ENGLISH EQUIVALENT	GREEK LETTER		LETTER NAME	ENGLISH EQUIVALENT
A	α	Alpha	a	N	ν	Nu	n
B	β	Beta	b	Ξ	ξ	Xi	x
Γ	γ	Gamma	g	O	o	Omicron	ŏ
Δ	δ	Delta	d	Π	π	Pi	p
E	ε	Epsilon	ĕ	P	ρ	Rho	r
Z	ζ	Zeta	z	Σ	σ	Sigma	s
H	η	Eta	ē	T	τ	Tau	t
Θ	θ	Theta	th	Y	υ	Upsilon	u
I	ι	Iota	i	Φ	ϕ	Phi	ph
K	κ	Kappa	k	X	χ	Chi	ch
Λ	λ	Lambda	l	Ψ	ψ	Psi	ps
M	μ	Mu	m	Ω	ω	Omega	ō

APPENDIX E Tables

Row	Column 00000 12345	00001 67890	11111 12345	11112 67890	22222 12345	22223 67890	33333 12345	33334 67890
01	49280	88924	35779	00283	81163	07275	89863	02348
02	61870	41657	07468	08612	98083	97349	20775	45091
03	43898	65923	25078	86129	78496	97653	91550	08078
04	62993	93912	30454	84598	56095	20664	12872	64647
05	33850	58555	51438	85507	71865	79488	76783	31708
06	97340	03364	88472	04334	63919	36394	11095	92470
07	70543	29776	10087	10072	55980	64688	68239	20461
08	89382	93809	00796	95945	34101	81277	66090	88872
09	37818	72142	67140	50785	22380	16703	53362	44940
10	60430	22834	14130	96593	23298	56203	92671	15925
11	82975	66158	84731	19436	55790	69229	28661	13675
12	30987	71938	40355	54324	08401	26299	49420	59208
13	55700	24586	93247	32596	11865	63397	44251	43189
14	14756	23997	78643	75912	83832	32768	18928	57070
15	32166	53251	70654	92827	63491	04233	33825	69662
16	23236	73751	31888	81718	06546	83246	47651	04877
17	45794	26926	15130	82455	78305	55058	52551	47182
18	09893	20505	14225	68514	47427	56788	96297	78822
19	54382	74598	91499	14523	68479	27686	46162	83554
20	94750	89923	37089	20048	80336	94598	26940	36858
21	70297	34135	53140	33340	42050	82341	44104	82949
22	85157	47954	32979	26575	57600	40881	12250	73742
23	11100	02340	12860	74697	96644	89439	28707	25815
24	36871	50775	30592	57143	17381	68856	25853	35041
25	23913	48357	63308	16090	51690	54607	72407	55538
26	79348	36085	27973	65157	07456	22255	25626	57054
27	92074	54641	53673	54421	18130	60103	69593	49464
28	06873	21440	75593	41373	49502	17972	82578	16364
29	12478	37622	99659	31065	83613	69889	58869	29571
30	57175	55564	65411	42547	70457	03426	72937	83792
31	91616	11075	80103	07831	59309	13276	26710	73000
32	78025	73539	14621	39044	47450	03197	12787	47709
33	27587	67228	80145	10175	12822	86687	65530	49325
34	16690	20427	04251	64477	73709	73945	92396	68263
35	70183	58065	65489	31833	82093	16747	10386	59293
36	90730	35385	15679	99742	50866	78028	75573	67257
37	10934	93242	13431	24590	02770	48582	00906	58595
38	82462	30166	79613	47416	13389	80268	05085	96666
39	27463	10433	07606	16285	93699	60912	94532	95632
40	02979	52997	09079	92709	90110	47506	53693	49892
41	46888	69929	75233	52507	32097	37594	10067	67327
42	53638	83161	08289	12639	08141	12640	28437	09268
43	82433	61427	17239	89160	19666	08814	37841	12847
44	35766	31672	50082	22795	66948	65581	84393	15890
45	10853	42581	08792	13257	61973	24450	52351	16602
46	20341	27398	72906	63955	17276	10646	74692	48438
47	54458	90542	77563	51839	52901	53355	83281	19177
48	26337	66530	16687	35179	46560	00123	44546	79896
49	34314	23729	85264	05575	96855	23820	11091	79821
50	28603	10708	68933	34189	92166	15181	66628	58599
51	66194	28926	99547	16625	45515	67953	12108	57846
52	78240	43195	24837	32511	70880	22070	52622	61881
53	00833	88000	67299	68215	11274	55624	32991	17436
54	12111	86683	61270	58036	64192	90611	15145	01748
55	47189	99951	05755	03834	43782	90599	40282	51417
56	76396	72486	62423	27618	84184	78922	73561	52818
57	46409	17469	32483	09083	76175	19985	26309	91536

TABLE E.1
Table of Random
Numbers (continued)

Row	00000 12345	00001 67890	11111 12345	11112 67890	22222 12345	22223 67890	33333 12345	33334 67890
58	74626	22111	87286	46772	42243	68046	44250	42439
59	34450	81974	93723	49023	58432	67083	36876	93391
60	36327	72135	33005	28701	34710	49359	50693	89311
61	74185	77536	84825	09934	99103	09325	67389	45869
62	12296	41623	62873	37943	25584	09609	63360	47270
63	90822	60280	88925	99610	42772	60561	76873	04117
64	72121	79152	96591	90305	10189	79778	68016	13747
65	95268	41377	25684	08151	61816	58555	54305	86189
66	92603	09091	75884	93424	72586	88903	30061	14457
67	18813	90291	05275	01223	79607	95426	34900	09778
68	38840	26903	28624	67157	51986	42865	14508	49315
69	05959	33836	53758	16562	41081	38012	41230	20528
70	85141	21155	99212	32685	51403	31926	69813	58781
71	75047	59643	31074	38172	03718	32119	69506	67143
72	30752	95260	68032	62871	58781	34143	68790	69766
73	22986	82575	42187	62295	84295	30634	66562	31442
74	99439	86692	90348	66036	48399	73451	26698	39437
75	20389	93029	11881	71685	65452	89047	63669	02656
76	39249	05173	68256	36359	20250	68686	05947	09335
77	96777	33605	29481	20063	09398	01843	35139	61344
78	04860	32918	10798	50492	52655	33359	94713	28393
79	41613	42375	00403	03656	77580	87772	86877	57085
80	17930	00794	53836	53692	67135	98102	61912	11246
81	24649	31845	25736	75231	83808	98917	93829	99430
82	79899	34061	54308	59358	56462	58166	97302	86828
83	76801	49594	81002	30397	52728	15101	72070	33706
84	36239	63636	38140	65731	39788	06872	38971	53363
85	07392	64449	17886	63632	53995	17574	22247	62607
86	67133	04181	33874	98835	67453	59734	76381	63455
87	77759	31504	32832	70861	15152	29733	75371	39174
88	85992	72268	42920	20810	29361	51423	90306	73574
89	79553	75952	54116	65553	47139	60579	09165	85490
90	41101	17336	48951	53674	17880	45260	08575	49321
91	36191	17095	32123	91576	84221	78902	82010	30847
92	62329	63898	23268	74283	26091	68409	69704	82267
93	14751	13151	93115	01437	56945	89661	67680	79790
94	48462	59278	44185	29616	76537	19589	83139	28454
95	29435	88105	59651	44391	74588	55114	80834	85686
96	28340	29285	12965	14821	80425	16602	44653	70467
97	02167	58940	27149	80242	10587	79786	34959	75339
98	17864	00991	39557	54981	23588	81914	37609	13128
99	79675	80605	60059	35862	00254	36546	21545	78179
100	72335	82037	92003	34100	29879	46613	89720	13274

Source: Partially extracted from the Rand Corporation, *A Million Random Digits with 100,000 Normal Deviates* (Glencoe, IL, The Free Press, 1955).

TABLE E.2
The Cumulative Standardized Normal Distribution

Entry represents area under the cumulative standardized
normal distribution from $-\infty$ to Z

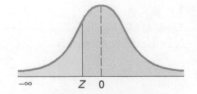

					Cumulative Probabilities					
Z	0.00	0.01	0.02	0.03	0.04	0.05	0.06	0.07	0.08	0.09
−6.0	0.000000001									
−5.5	0.000000019									
−5.0	0.000000287									
−4.5	0.000003398									
−4.0	0.000031671									
−3.9	0.00005	0.00005	0.00004	0.00004	0.00004	0.00004	0.00004	0.00004	0.00003	0.00003
−3.8	0.00007	0.00007	0.00007	0.00006	0.00006	0.00006	0.00006	0.00005	0.00005	0.00005
−3.7	0.00011	0.00010	0.00010	0.00010	0.00009	0.00009	0.00008	0.00008	0.00008	0.00008
−3.6	0.00016	0.00015	0.00015	0.00014	0.00014	0.00013	0.00013	0.00012	0.00012	0.00011
−3.5	0.00023	0.00022	0.00022	0.00021	0.00020	0.00019	0.00019	0.00018	0.00017	0.00017
−3.4	0.00034	0.00032	0.00031	0.00030	0.00029	0.00028	0.00027	0.00026	0.00025	0.00024
−3.3	0.00048	0.00047	0.00045	0.00043	0.00042	0.00040	0.00039	0.00038	0.00036	0.00035
−3.2	0.00069	0.00066	0.00064	0.00062	0.00060	0.00058	0.00056	0.00054	0.00052	0.00050
−3.1	0.00097	0.00094	0.00090	0.00087	0.00084	0.00082	0.00079	0.00076	0.00074	0.00071
−3.0	0.00135	0.00131	0.00126	0.00122	0.00118	0.00114	0.00111	0.00107	0.00103	0.00100
−2.9	0.0019	0.0018	0.0018	0.0017	0.0016	0.0016	0.0015	0.0015	0.0014	0.0014
−2.8	0.0026	0.0025	0.0024	0.0023	0.0023	0.0022	0.0021	0.0021	0.0020	0.0019
−2.7	0.0035	0.0034	0.0033	0.0032	0.0031	0.0030	0.0029	0.0028	0.0027	0.0026
−2.6	0.0047	0.0045	0.0044	0.0043	0.0041	0.0040	0.0039	0.0038	0.0037	0.0036
−2.5	0.0062	0.0060	0.0059	0.0057	0.0055	0.0054	0.0052	0.0051	0.0049	0.0048
−2.4	0.0082	0.0080	0.0078	0.0075	0.0073	0.0071	0.0069	0.0068	0.0066	0.0064
−2.3	0.0107	0.0104	0.0102	0.0099	0.0096	0.0094	0.0091	0.0089	0.0087	0.0084
−2.2	0.0139	0.0136	0.0132	0.0129	0.0125	0.0122	0.0119	0.0116	0.0113	0.0110
−2.1	0.0179	0.0174	0.0170	0.0166	0.0162	0.0158	0.0154	0.0150	0.0146	0.0143
−2.0	0.0228	0.0222	0.0217	0.0212	0.0207	0.0202	0.0197	0.0192	0.0188	0.0183
−1.9	0.0287	0.0281	0.0274	0.0268	0.0262	0.0256	0.0250	0.0244	0.0239	0.0233
−1.8	0.0359	0.0351	0.0344	0.0336	0.0329	0.0322	0.0314	0.0307	0.0301	0.0294
−1.7	0.0446	0.0436	0.0427	0.0418	0.0409	0.0401	0.0392	0.0384	0.0375	0.0367
−1.6	0.0548	0.0537	0.0526	0.0516	0.0505	0.0495	0.0485	0.0475	0.0465	0.0455
−1.5	0.0668	0.0655	0.0643	0.0630	0.0618	0.0606	0.0594	0.0582	0.0571	0.0559
−1.4	0.0808	0.0793	0.0778	0.0764	0.0749	0.0735	0.0721	0.0708	0.0694	0.0681
−1.3	0.0968	0.0951	0.0934	0.0918	0.0901	0.0885	0.0869	0.0853	0.0838	0.0823
−1.2	0.1151	0.1131	0.1112	0.1093	0.1075	0.1056	0.1038	0.1020	0.1003	0.0985
−1.1	0.1357	0.1335	0.1314	0.1292	0.1271	0.1251	0.1230	0.1210	0.1190	0.1170
−1.0	0.1587	0.1562	0.1539	0.1515	0.1492	0.1469	0.1446	0.1423	0.1401	0.1379
−0.9	0.1841	0.1814	0.1788	0.1762	0.1736	0.1711	0.1685	0.1660	0.1635	0.1611
−0.8	0.2119	0.2090	0.2061	0.2033	0.2005	0.1977	0.1949	0.1922	0.1894	0.1867
−0.7	0.2420	0.2388	0.2358	0.2327	0.2296	0.2266	0.2236	0.2206	0.2177	0.2148
−0.6	0.2743	0.2709	0.2676	0.2643	0.2611	0.2578	0.2546	0.2514	0.2482	0.2451
−0.5	0.3085	0.3050	0.3015	0.2981	0.2946	0.2912	0.2877	0.2843	0.2810	0.2776
−0.4	0.3446	0.3409	0.3372	0.3336	0.3300	0.3264	0.3228	0.3192	0.3156	0.3121
−0.3	0.3821	0.3783	0.3745	0.3707	0.3669	0.3632	0.3594	0.3557	0.3520	0.3483
−0.2	0.4207	0.4168	0.4129	0.4090	0.4052	0.4013	0.3974	0.3936	0.3897	0.3859
−0.1	0.4602	0.4562	0.4522	0.4483	0.4443	0.4404	0.4364	0.4325	0.4286	0.4247
−0.0	0.5000	0.4960	0.4920	0.4880	0.4840	0.4801	0.4761	0.4721	0.4681	0.4641

TABLE E.2

The Cumulative Standardized Normal Distribution (*continued*)

Entry represents area under the cumulative standardized
normal distribution from $-\infty$ to Z

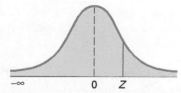

	Cumulative Probabilities									
Z	**0.00**	**0.01**	**0.02**	**0.03**	**0.04**	**0.05**	**0.06**	**0.07**	**0.08**	**0.09**
0.0	0.5000	0.5040	0.5080	0.5120	0.5160	0.5199	0.5239	0.5279	0.5319	0.5359
0.1	0.5398	0.5438	0.5478	0.5517	0.5557	0.5596	0.5636	0.5675	0.5714	0.5753
0.2	0.5793	0.5832	0.5871	0.5910	0.5948	0.5987	0.6026	0.6064	0.6103	0.6141
0.3	0.6179	0.6217	0.6255	0.6293	0.6331	0.6368	0.6406	0.6443	0.6480	0.6517
0.4	0.6554	0.6591	0.6628	0.6664	0.6700	0.6736	0.6772	0.6808	0.6844	0.6879
0.5	0.6915	0.6950	0.6985	0.7019	0.7054	0.7088	0.7123	0.7157	0.7190	0.7224
0.6	0.7257	0.7291	0.7324	0.7357	0.7389	0.7422	0.7454	0.7486	0.7518	0.7549
0.7	0.7580	0.7612	0.7642	0.7673	0.7704	0.7734	0.7764	0.7794	0.7823	0.7852
0.8	0.7881	0.7910	0.7939	0.7967	0.7995	0.8023	0.8051	0.8078	0.8106	0.8133
0.9	0.8159	0.8186	0.8212	0.8238	0.8264	0.8289	0.8315	0.8340	0.8365	0.8389
1.0	0.8413	0.8438	0.8461	0.8485	0.8508	0.8531	0.8554	0.8577	0.8599	0.8621
1.1	0.8643	0.8665	0.8686	0.8708	0.8729	0.8749	0.8770	0.8790	0.8810	0.8830
1.2	0.8849	0.8869	0.8888	0.8907	0.8925	0.8944	0.8962	0.8980	0.8997	0.9015
1.3	0.9032	0.9049	0.9066	0.9082	0.9099	0.9115	0.9131	0.9147	0.9162	0.9177
1.4	0.9192	0.9207	0.9222	0.9236	0.9251	0.9265	0.9279	0.9292	0.9306	0.9319
1.5	0.9332	0.9345	0.9357	0.9370	0.9382	0.9394	0.9406	0.9418	0.9429	0.9441
1.6	0.9452	0.9463	0.9474	0.9484	0.9495	0.9505	0.9515	0.9525	0.9535	0.9545
1.7	0.9554	0.9564	0.9573	0.9582	0.9591	0.9599	0.9608	0.9616	0.9625	0.9633
1.8	0.9641	0.9649	0.9656	0.9664	0.9671	0.9678	0.9686	0.9693	0.9699	0.9706
1.9	0.9713	0.9719	0.9726	0.9732	0.9738	0.9744	0.9750	0.9756	0.9761	0.9767
2.0	0.9772	0.9778	0.9783	0.9788	0.9793	0.9798	0.9803	0.9808	0.9812	0.9817
2.1	0.9821	0.9826	0.9830	0.9834	0.9838	0.9842	0.9846	0.9850	0.9854	0.9857
2.2	0.9861	0.9864	0.9868	0.9871	0.9875	0.9878	0.9881	0.9884	0.9887	0.9890
2.3	0.9893	0.9896	0.9898	0.9901	0.9904	0.9906	0.9909	0.9911	0.9913	0.9916
2.4	0.9918	0.9920	0.9922	0.9925	0.9927	0.9929	0.9931	0.9932	0.9934	0.9936
2.5	0.9938	0.9940	0.9941	0.9943	0.9945	0.9946	0.9948	0.9949	0.9951	0.9952
2.6	0.9953	0.9955	0.9956	0.9957	0.9959	0.9960	0.9961	0.9962	0.9963	0.9964
2.7	0.9965	0.9966	0.9967	0.9968	0.9969	0.9970	0.9971	0.9972	0.9973	0.9974
2.8	0.9974	0.9975	0.9976	0.9977	0.9977	0.9978	0.9979	0.9979	0.9980	0.9981
2.9	0.9981	0.9982	0.9982	0.9983	0.9984	0.9984	0.9985	0.9985	0.9986	0.9986
3.0	0.99865	0.99869	0.99874	0.99878	0.99882	0.99886	0.99889	0.99893	0.99897	0.99900
3.1	0.99903	0.99906	0.99910	0.99913	0.99916	0.99918	0.99921	0.99924	0.99926	0.99929
3.2	0.99931	0.99934	0.99936	0.99938	0.99940	0.99942	0.99944	0.99946	0.99948	0.99950
3.3	0.99952	0.99953	0.99955	0.99957	0.99958	0.99960	0.99961	0.99962	0.99964	0.99965
3.4	0.99966	0.99968	0.99969	0.99970	0.99971	0.99972	0.99973	0.99974	0.99975	0.99976
3.5	0.99977	0.99978	0.99978	0.99979	0.99980	0.99981	0.99981	0.99982	0.99983	0.99983
3.6	0.99984	0.99985	0.99985	0.99986	0.99986	0.99987	0.99987	0.99988	0.99988	0.99989
3.7	0.99989	0.99990	0.99990	0.99990	0.99991	0.99991	0.99992	0.99992	0.99992	0.99992
3.8	0.99993	0.99993	0.99993	0.99994	0.99994	0.99994	0.99994	0.99995	0.99995	0.99995
3.9	0.99995	0.99995	0.99996	0.99996	0.99996	0.99996	0.99996	0.99996	0.99997	0.99997
4.0	0.999968329									
4.5	0.999996602									
5.0	0.999999713									
5.5	0.999999981									
6.0	0.999999999									

TABLE E.3
Critical Values of t

*For a particular number of degrees of freedom, entry represents
the critical value of t corresponding to the cumulative probability
$(1 - \alpha)$ and a specified upper-tail area (α).*

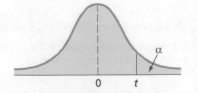

Degrees of Freedom	Cumulative Probabilities					
	0.75	0.90	0.95	0.975	0.99	0.995
	Upper-Tail Areas					
	0.25	0.10	0.05	0.025	0.01	0.005
1	1.0000	3.0777	6.3138	12.7062	31.8207	63.6574
2	0.8165	1.8856	2.9200	4.3027	6.9646	9.9248
3	0.7649	1.6377	2.3534	3.1824	4.5407	5.8409
4	0.7407	1.5332	2.1318	2.7764	3.7469	4.6041
5	0.7267	1.4759	2.0150	2.5706	3.3649	4.0322
6	0.7176	1.4398	1.9432	2.4469	3.1427	3.7074
7	0.7111	1.4149	1.8946	2.3646	2.9980	3.4995
8	0.7064	1.3968	1.8595	2.3060	2.8965	3.3554
9	0.7027	1.3830	1.8331	2.2622	2.8214	3.2498
10	0.6998	1.3722	1.8125	2.2281	2.7638	3.1693
11	0.6974	1.3634	1.7959	2.2010	2.7181	3.1058
12	0.6955	1.3562	1.7823	2.1788	2.6810	3.0545
13	0.6938	1.3502	1.7709	2.1604	2.6503	3.0123
14	0.6924	1.3450	1.7613	2.1448	2.6245	2.9768
15	0.6912	1.3406	1.7531	2.1315	2.6025	2.9467
16	0.6901	1.3368	1.7459	2.1199	2.5835	2.9208
17	0.6892	1.3334	1.7396	2.1098	2.5669	2.8982
18	0.6884	1.3304	1.7341	2.1009	2.5524	2.8784
19	0.6876	1.3277	1.7291	2.0930	2.5395	2.8609
20	0.6870	1.3253	1.7247	2.0860	2.5280	2.8453
21	0.6864	1.3232	1.7207	2.0796	2.5177	2.8314
22	0.6858	1.3212	1.7171	2.0739	2.5083	2.8188
23	0.6853	1.3195	1.7139	2.0687	2.4999	2.8073
24	0.6848	1.3178	1.7109	2.0639	2.4922	2.7969
25	0.6844	1.3163	1.7081	2.0595	2.4851	2.7874
26	0.6840	1.3150	1.7056	2.0555	2.4786	2.7787
27	0.6837	1.3137	1.7033	2.0518	2.4727	2.7707
28	0.6834	1.3125	1.7011	2.0484	2.4671	2.7633
29	0.6830	1.3114	1.6991	2.0452	2.4620	2.7564
30	0.6828	1.3104	1.6973	2.0423	2.4573	2.7500
31	0.6825	1.3095	1.6955	2.0395	2.4528	2.7440
32	0.6822	1.3086	1.6939	2.0369	2.4487	2.7385
33	0.6820	1.3077	1.6924	2.0345	2.4448	2.7333
34	0.6818	1.3070	1.6909	2.0322	2.4411	2.7284
35	0.6816	1.3062	1.6896	2.0301	2.4377	2.7238
36	0.6814	1.3055	1.6883	2.0281	2.4345	2.7195
37	0.6812	1.3049	1.6871	2.0262	2.4314	2.7154
38	0.6810	1.3042	1.6860	2.0244	2.4286	2.7116
39	0.6808	1.3036	1.6849	2.0227	2.4258	2.7079
40	0.6807	1.3031	1.6839	2.0211	2.4233	2.7045
41	0.6805	1.3025	1.6829	2.0195	2.4208	2.7012
42	0.6804	1.3020	1.6820	2.0181	2.4185	2.6981
43	0.6802	1.3016	1.6811	2.0167	2.4163	2.6951
44	0.6801	1.3011	1.6802	2.0154	2.4141	2.6923
45	0.6800	1.3006	1.6794	2.0141	2.4121	2.6896
46	0.6799	1.3002	1.6787	2.0129	2.4102	2.6870
47	0.6797	1.2998	1.6779	2.0117	2.4083	2.6846
48	0.6796	1.2994	1.6772	2.0106	2.4066	2.6822

	Cumulative Probabilities					
	0.75	0.90	0.95	0.975	0.99	0.995
Degrees of Freedom	Upper-Tail Areas					
	0.25	0.10	0.05	0.025	0.01	0.005
49	0.6795	1.2991	1.6766	2.0096	2.4049	2.6800
50	0.6794	1.2987	1.6759	2.0086	2.4033	2.6778
51	0.6793	1.2984	1.6753	2.0076	2.4017	2.6757
52	0.6792	1.2980	1.6747	2.0066	2.4002	2.6737
53	0.6791	1.2977	1.6741	2.0057	2.3988	2.6718
54	0.6791	1.2974	1.6736	2.0049	2.3974	2.6700
55	0.6790	1.2971	1.6730	2.0040	2.3961	2.6682
56	0.6789	1.2969	1.6725	2.0032	2.3948	2.6665
57	0.6788	1.2966	1.6720	2.0025	2.3936	2.6649
58	0.6787	1.2963	1.6716	2.0017	2.3924	2.6633
59	0.6787	1.2961	1.6711	2.0010	2.3912	2.6618
60	0.6786	1.2958	1.6706	2.0003	2.3901	2.6603
61	0.6785	1.2956	1.6702	1.9996	2.3890	2.6589
62	0.6785	1.2954	1.6698	1.9990	2.3880	2.6575
63	0.6784	1.2951	1.6694	1.9983	2.3870	2.6561
64	0.6783	1.2949	1.6690	1.9977	2.3860	2.6549
65	0.6783	1.2947	1.6686	1.9971	2.3851	2.6536
66	0.6782	1.2945	1.6683	1.9966	2.3842	2.6524
67	0.6782	1.2943	1.6679	1.9960	2.3833	2.6512
68	0.6781	1.2941	1.6676	1.9955	2.3824	2.6501
69	0.6781	1.2939	1.6672	1.9949	2.3816	2.6490
70	0.6780	1.2938	1.6669	1.9944	2.3808	2.6479
71	0.6780	1.2936	1.6666	1.9939	2.3800	2.6469
72	0.6779	1.2934	1.6663	1.9935	2.3793	2.6459
73	0.6779	1.2933	1.6660	1.9930	2.3785	2.6449
74	0.6778	1.2931	1.6657	1.9925	2.3778	2.6439
75	0.6778	1.2929	1.6654	1.9921	2.3771	2.6430
76	0.6777	1.2928	1.6652	1.9917	2.3764	2.6421
77	0.6777	1.2926	1.6649	1.9913	2.3758	2.6412
78	0.6776	1.2925	1.6646	1.9908	2.3751	2.6403
79	0.6776	1.2924	1.6644	1.9905	2.3745	2.6395
80	0.6776	1.2922	1.6641	1.9901	2.3739	2.6387
81	0.6775	1.2921	1.6639	1.9897	2.3733	2.6379
82	0.6775	1.2920	1.6636	1.9893	2.3727	2.6371
83	0.6775	1.2918	1.6634	1.9890	2.3721	2.6364
84	0.6774	1.2917	1.6632	1.9886	2.3716	2.6356
85	0.6774	1.2916	1.6630	1.9883	2.3710	2.6349
86	0.6774	1.2915	1.6628	1.9879	2.3705	2.6342
87	0.6773	1.2914	1.6626	1.9876	2.3700	2.6335
88	0.6773	1.2912	1.6624	1.9873	2.3695	2.6329
89	0.6773	1.2911	1.6622	1.9870	2.3690	2.6322
90	0.6772	1.2910	1.6620	1.9867	2.3685	2.6316
91	0.6772	1.2909	1.6618	1.9864	2.3680	2.6309
92	0.6772	1.2908	1.6616	1.9861	2.3676	2.6303
93	0.6771	1.2907	1.6614	1.9858	2.3671	2.6297
94	0.6771	1.2906	1.6612	1.9855	2.3667	2.6291
95	0.6771	1.2905	1.6611	1.9853	2.3662	2.6286
96	0.6771	1.2904	1.6609	1.9850	2.3658	2.6280
97	0.6770	1.2903	1.6607	1.9847	2.3654	2.6275
98	0.6770	1.2902	1.6606	1.9845	2.3650	2.6269
99	0.6770	1.2902	1.6604	1.9842	2.3646	2.6264
100	0.6770	1.2901	1.6602	1.9840	2.3642	2.6259
110	0.6767	1.2893	1.6588	1.9818	2.3607	2.6213
120	0.6765	1.2886	1.6577	1.9799	2.3578	2.6174
∞	0.6745	1.2816	1.6449	1.9600	2.3263	2.5758

TABLE E.4

Critical Values of χ^2

For a particular number of degrees of freedom, entry represents the critical value of χ^2
corresponding to the cumulative probability $(1 - \alpha)$ and a specified upper-tail area (α).

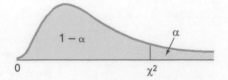

Degrees of Freedom	Cumulative Probabilities											
	0.005	0.01	0.025	0.05	0.10	0.25	0.75	0.90	0.95	0.975	0.99	0.995
	Upper-Tail Areas (α)											
	0.995	0.99	0.975	0.95	0.90	0.75	0.25	0.10	0.05	0.025	0.01	0.005
1			0.001	0.004	0.016	0.102	1.323	2.706	3.841	5.024	6.635	7.879
2	0.010	0.020	0.051	0.103	0.211	0.575	2.773	4.605	5.991	7.378	9.210	10.597
3	0.072	0.115	0.216	0.352	0.584	1.213	4.108	6.251	7.815	9.348	11.345	12.838
4	0.207	0.297	0.484	0.711	1.064	1.923	5.385	7.779	9.488	11.143	13.277	14.860
5	0.412	0.554	0.831	1.145	1.610	2.675	6.626	9.236	11.071	12.833	15.086	16.750
6	0.676	0.872	1.237	1.635	2.204	3.455	7.841	10.645	12.592	14.449	16.812	18.548
7	0.989	1.239	1.690	2.167	2.833	4.255	9.037	12.017	14.067	16.013	18.475	20.278
8	1.344	1.646	2.180	2.733	3.490	5.071	10.219	13.362	15.507	17.535	20.090	21.955
9	1.735	2.088	2.700	3.325	4.168	5.899	11.389	14.684	16.919	19.023	21.666	23.589
10	2.156	2.558	3.247	3.940	4.865	6.737	12.549	15.987	18.307	20.483	23.209	25.188
11	2.603	3.053	3.816	4.575	5.578	7.584	13.701	17.275	19.675	21.920	24.725	26.757
12	3.074	3.571	4.404	5.226	6.304	8.438	14.845	18.549	21.026	23.337	26.217	28.299
13	3.565	4.107	5.009	5.892	7.042	9.299	15.984	19.812	22.362	24.736	27.688	29.819
14	4.075	4.660	5.629	6.571	7.790	10.165	17.117	21.064	23.685	26.119	29.141	31.319
15	4.601	5.229	6.262	7.261	8.547	11.037	18.245	22.307	24.996	27.488	30.578	32.801
16	5.142	5.812	6.908	7.962	9.312	11.912	19.369	23.542	26.296	28.845	32.000	34.267
17	5.697	6.408	7.564	8.672	10.085	12.792	20.489	24.769	27.587	30.191	33.409	35.718
18	6.265	7.015	8.231	9.390	10.865	13.675	21.605	25.989	28.869	31.526	34.805	37.156
19	6.844	7.633	8.907	10.117	11.651	14.562	22.718	27.204	30.144	32.852	36.191	38.582
20	7.434	8.260	9.591	10.851	12.443	15.452	23.828	28.412	31.410	34.170	37.566	39.997
21	8.034	8.897	10.283	11.591	13.240	16.344	24.935	29.615	32.671	35.479	38.932	41.401
22	8.643	9.542	10.982	12.338	14.042	17.240	26.039	30.813	33.924	36.781	40.289	42.796
23	9.260	10.196	11.689	13.091	14.848	18.137	27.141	32.007	35.172	38.076	41.638	44.181
24	9.886	10.856	12.401	13.848	15.659	19.037	28.241	33.196	36.415	39.364	42.980	45.559
25	10.520	11.524	13.120	14.611	16.473	19.939	29.339	34.382	37.652	40.646	44.314	46.928
26	11.160	12.198	13.844	15.379	17.292	20.843	30.435	35.563	38.885	41.923	45.642	48.290
27	11.808	12.879	14.573	16.151	18.114	21.749	31.528	36.741	40.113	43.194	46.963	49.645
28	12.461	13.565	15.308	16.928	18.939	22.657	32.620	37.916	41.337	44.461	48.278	50.993
29	13.121	14.257	16.047	17.708	19.768	23.567	33.711	39.087	42.557	45.722	49.588	52.336
30	13.787	14.954	16.791	18.493	20.599	24.478	34.800	40.256	43.773	46.979	50.892	53.672

For larger values of degrees of freedom (df) the expression $Z = \sqrt{2\chi^2} - \sqrt{2(df) - 1}$ may be used and the resulting upper-tail area can be found from the cumulative standardized normal distribution (Table E.2).

TABLE E.5
Critical Values of F

For a particular combination of numerator and denominator degrees of freedom, entry represents the critical values of F corresponding to the cumulative probability $(1 − α)$ and a specified upper-tail area $(α)$.

α = 0.05

Cumulative Probabilities = 0.95

Upper-Tail Areas = 0.05

Numerator, df_1

Denominator, df_2	1	2	3	4	5	6	7	8	9	10	12	15	20	24	30	40	60	120	∞
1	161.40	199.50	215.70	224.60	230.20	234.00	236.80	238.90	240.50	241.90	243.90	245.90	248.00	249.10	250.10	251.10	252.20	253.30	254.30
2	18.51	19.00	19.16	19.25	19.30	19.33	19.35	19.37	19.38	19.40	19.41	19.43	19.45	19.45	19.46	19.47	19.48	19.49	19.50
3	10.13	9.55	9.28	9.12	9.01	8.94	8.89	8.85	8.81	8.79	8.74	8.70	8.66	8.64	8.62	8.59	8.57	8.55	8.53
4	7.71	6.94	6.59	6.39	6.26	6.16	6.09	6.04	6.00	5.96	5.91	5.86	5.80	5.77	5.75	5.72	5.69	5.66	5.63
5	6.61	5.79	5.41	5.19	5.05	4.95	4.88	4.82	4.77	4.74	4.68	4.62	4.56	4.53	4.50	4.46	4.43	4.40	4.36
6	5.99	5.14	4.76	4.53	4.39	4.28	4.21	4.15	4.10	4.06	4.00	3.94	3.87	3.84	3.81	3.77	3.74	3.70	3.67
7	5.59	4.74	4.35	4.12	3.97	3.87	3.79	3.73	3.68	3.64	3.57	3.51	3.44	3.41	3.38	3.34	3.30	3.27	3.23
8	5.32	4.46	4.07	3.84	3.69	3.58	3.50	3.44	3.39	3.35	3.28	3.22	3.15	3.12	3.08	3.04	3.01	2.97	2.93
9	5.12	4.26	3.86	3.63	3.48	3.37	3.29	3.23	3.18	3.14	3.07	3.01	2.94	2.90	2.86	2.83	2.79	2.75	2.71
10	4.96	4.10	3.71	3.48	3.33	3.22	3.14	3.07	3.02	2.98	2.91	2.85	2.77	2.74	2.70	2.66	2.62	2.58	2.54
11	4.84	3.98	3.59	3.36	3.20	3.09	3.01	2.95	2.90	2.85	2.79	2.72	2.65	2.61	2.57	2.53	2.49	2.45	2.40
12	4.75	3.89	3.49	3.26	3.11	3.00	2.91	2.85	2.80	2.75	2.69	2.62	2.54	2.51	2.47	2.43	2.38	2.34	2.30
13	4.67	3.81	3.41	3.18	3.03	2.92	2.83	2.77	2.71	2.67	2.60	2.53	2.46	2.42	2.38	2.34	2.30	2.25	2.21
14	4.60	3.74	3.34	3.11	2.96	2.85	2.76	2.70	2.65	2.60	2.53	2.46	2.39	2.35	2.31	2.27	2.22	2.18	2.13
15	4.54	3.68	3.29	3.06	2.90	2.79	2.71	2.64	2.59	2.54	2.48	2.40	2.33	2.29	2.25	2.20	2.16	2.11	2.07
16	4.49	3.63	3.24	3.01	2.85	2.74	2.66	2.59	2.54	2.49	2.42	2.35	2.28	2.24	2.19	2.15	2.11	2.06	2.01
17	4.45	3.59	3.20	2.96	2.81	2.70	2.61	2.55	2.49	2.45	2.38	2.31	2.23	2.19	2.15	2.10	2.06	2.01	1.96
18	4.41	3.55	3.16	2.93	2.77	2.66	2.58	2.51	2.46	2.41	2.34	2.27	2.19	2.15	2.11	2.06	2.02	1.97	1.92
19	4.38	3.52	3.13	2.90	2.74	2.63	2.54	2.48	2.42	2.38	2.31	2.23	2.16	2.11	2.07	2.03	1.98	1.93	1.88
20	4.35	3.49	3.10	2.87	2.71	2.60	2.51	2.45	2.39	2.35	2.28	2.20	2.12	2.08	2.04	1.99	1.95	1.90	1.84
21	4.32	3.47	3.07	2.84	2.68	2.57	2.49	2.42	2.37	2.32	2.25	2.18	2.10	2.05	2.01	1.96	1.92	1.87	1.81
22	4.30	3.44	3.05	2.82	2.66	2.55	2.46	2.40	2.34	2.30	2.23	2.15	2.07	2.03	1.98	1.94	1.89	1.84	1.78
23	4.28	3.42	3.03	2.80	2.64	2.53	2.44	2.37	2.32	2.27	2.20	2.13	2.05	2.01	1.96	1.91	1.86	1.81	1.76
24	4.26	3.40	3.01	2.78	2.62	2.51	2.42	2.36	2.30	2.25	2.18	2.11	2.03	1.98	1.94	1.89	1.84	1.79	1.73
25	4.24	3.39	2.99	2.76	2.60	2.49	2.40	2.34	2.28	2.24	2.16	2.09	2.01	1.96	1.92	1.87	1.82	1.77	1.71
26	4.23	3.37	2.98	2.74	2.59	2.47	2.39	2.32	2.27	2.22	2.15	2.07	1.99	1.95	1.90	1.85	1.80	1.75	1.69
27	4.21	3.35	2.96	2.73	2.57	2.46	2.37	2.31	2.25	2.20	2.13	2.06	1.97	1.93	1.88	1.84	1.79	1.73	1.67
28	4.20	3.34	2.95	2.71	2.56	2.45	2.36	2.29	2.24	2.19	2.12	2.04	1.96	1.91	1.87	1.82	1.77	1.71	1.65
29	4.18	3.33	2.93	2.70	2.55	2.43	2.35	2.28	2.22	2.18	2.10	2.03	1.94	1.90	1.85	1.81	1.75	1.70	1.64
30	4.17	3.32	2.92	2.69	2.53	2.42	2.33	2.27	2.21	2.16	2.09	2.01	1.93	1.89	1.84	1.79	1.74	1.68	1.62
40	4.08	3.23	2.84	2.61	2.45	2.34	2.25	2.18	2.12	2.08	2.00	1.92	1.84	1.79	1.74	1.69	1.64	1.58	1.51
60	4.00	3.15	2.76	2.53	2.37	2.25	2.17	2.10	2.04	1.99	1.92	1.84	1.75	1.70	1.65	1.59	1.53	1.47	1.39
120	3.92	3.07	2.68	2.45	2.29	2.17	2.09	2.02	1.96	1.91	1.83	1.75	1.66	1.61	1.55	1.50	1.43	1.35	1.25
∞	3.84	3.00	2.60	2.37	2.21	2.10	2.01	1.94	1.88	1.83	1.75	1.67	1.57	1.52	1.46	1.39	1.32	1.22	1.00

Cumulative Probabilities = 0.975

Upper-Tail Areas = 0.025

Denominator, df_2	Numerator, df_1																		
	1	2	3	4	5	6	7	8	9	10	12	15	20	24	30	40	60	120	∞
1	647.80	799.50	864.20	899.60	921.80	937.10	948.20	956.70	963.30	968.60	976.70	984.90	993.10	997.20	1,001.00	1,006.00	1,010.00	1,014.00	1,018.00
2	38.51	39.00	39.17	39.25	39.30	39.33	39.36	39.39	39.39	39.40	39.41	39.43	39.45	39.46	39.46	39.47	39.48	39.49	39.50
3	17.44	16.04	15.44	15.10	14.88	14.73	14.62	14.54	14.47	14.42	14.34	14.25	14.17	14.12	14.08	14.04	13.99	13.95	13.90
4	12.22	10.65	9.98	9.60	9.36	9.20	9.07	8.98	8.90	8.84	8.75	8.66	8.56	8.51	8.46	8.41	8.36	8.31	8.26
5	10.01	8.43	7.76	7.39	7.15	6.98	6.85	6.76	6.68	6.62	6.52	6.43	6.33	6.28	6.23	6.18	6.12	6.07	6.02
6	8.81	7.26	6.60	6.23	5.99	5.82	5.70	5.60	5.52	5.46	5.37	5.27	5.17	5.12	5.07	5.01	4.96	4.90	4.85
7	8.07	6.54	5.89	5.52	5.29	5.12	4.99	4.90	4.82	4.76	4.67	4.57	4.47	4.42	4.36	4.31	4.25	4.20	4.14
8	7.57	6.06	5.42	5.05	4.82	4.65	4.53	4.43	4.36	4.30	4.20	4.10	4.00	3.95	3.89	3.84	3.78	3.73	3.67
9	7.21	5.71	5.08	4.72	4.48	4.32	4.20	4.10	4.03	3.96	3.87	3.77	3.67	3.61	3.56	3.51	3.45	3.39	3.33
10	6.94	5.46	4.83	4.47	4.24	4.07	3.95	3.85	3.78	3.72	3.62	3.52	3.42	3.37	3.31	3.26	3.20	3.14	3.08
11	6.72	5.26	4.63	4.28	4.04	3.88	3.76	3.66	3.59	3.53	3.43	3.33	3.23	3.17	3.12	3.06	3.00	2.94	2.88
12	6.55	5.10	4.47	4.12	3.89	3.73	3.61	3.51	3.44	3.37	3.28	3.18	3.07	3.02	2.96	2.91	2.85	2.79	2.72
13	6.41	4.97	4.35	4.00	3.77	3.60	3.48	3.39	3.31	3.25	3.15	3.05	2.95	2.89	2.84	2.78	2.72	2.66	2.60
14	6.30	4.86	4.24	3.89	3.66	3.50	3.38	3.29	3.21	3.15	3.05	2.95	2.84	2.79	2.73	2.67	2.61	2.55	2.49
15	6.20	4.77	4.15	3.80	3.58	3.41	3.29	3.20	3.12	3.06	2.96	2.86	2.76	2.70	2.64	2.59	2.52	2.46	2.40
16	6.12	4.69	4.08	3.73	3.50	3.34	3.22	3.12	3.05	2.99	2.89	2.79	2.68	2.63	2.57	2.51	2.45	2.38	2.32
17	6.04	4.62	4.01	3.66	3.44	3.28	3.16	3.06	2.98	2.92	2.82	2.72	2.62	2.56	2.50	2.44	2.38	2.32	2.25
18	5.98	4.56	3.95	3.61	3.38	3.22	3.10	3.01	2.93	2.87	2.77	2.67	2.56	2.50	2.44	2.38	2.32	2.26	2.19
19	5.92	4.51	3.90	3.56	3.33	3.17	3.05	2.96	2.88	2.82	2.72	2.62	2.51	2.45	2.39	2.33	2.27	2.20	2.13
20	5.87	4.46	3.86	3.51	3.29	3.13	3.01	2.91	2.84	2.77	2.68	2.57	2.46	2.41	2.35	2.29	2.22	2.16	2.09
21	5.83	4.42	3.82	3.48	3.25	3.09	2.97	2.87	2.80	2.73	2.64	2.53	2.42	2.37	2.31	2.25	2.18	2.11	2.04
22	5.79	4.38	3.78	3.44	3.22	3.05	2.93	2.84	2.76	2.70	2.60	2.50	2.39	2.33	2.27	2.21	2.14	2.08	2.00
23	5.75	4.35	3.75	3.41	3.18	3.02	2.90	2.81	2.73	2.67	2.57	2.47	2.36	2.30	2.24	2.18	2.11	2.04	1.97
24	5.72	4.32	3.72	3.38	3.15	2.99	2.87	2.78	2.70	2.64	2.54	2.44	2.33	2.27	2.21	2.15	2.08	2.01	1.94
25	5.69	4.29	3.69	3.35	3.13	2.97	2.85	2.75	2.68	2.61	2.51	2.41	2.30	2.24	2.18	2.12	2.05	1.98	1.91
26	5.66	4.27	3.67	3.33	3.10	2.94	2.82	2.73	2.65	2.59	2.49	2.39	2.28	2.22	2.16	2.09	2.03	1.95	1.88
27	5.63	4.24	3.65	3.31	3.08	2.92	2.80	2.71	2.63	2.57	2.47	2.36	2.25	2.19	2.13	2.07	2.00	1.93	1.85
28	5.61	4.22	3.63	3.29	3.06	2.90	2.78	2.69	2.61	2.55	2.45	2.34	2.23	2.17	2.11	2.05	1.98	1.91	1.83
29	5.59	4.20	3.61	3.27	3.04	2.88	2.76	2.67	2.59	2.53	2.43	2.32	2.21	2.15	2.09	2.03	1.96	1.89	1.81
30	5.57	4.18	3.59	3.25	3.03	2.87	2.75	2.65	2.57	2.51	2.41	2.31	2.20	2.14	2.07	2.01	1.94	1.87	1.79
40	5.42	4.05	3.46	3.13	2.90	2.74	2.62	2.53	2.45	2.39	2.29	2.18	2.07	2.01	1.94	1.88	1.80	1.72	1.64
60	5.29	3.93	3.34	3.01	2.79	2.63	2.51	2.41	2.33	2.27	2.17	2.06	1.94	1.88	1.82	1.74	1.67	1.58	1.48
120	5.15	3.80	3.23	2.89	2.67	2.52	2.39	2.30	2.22	2.16	2.05	1.94	1.82	1.76	1.69	1.61	1.53	1.43	1.31
∞	5.02	3.69	3.12	2.79	2.57	2.41	2.29	2.19	2.11	2.05	1.94	1.83	1.71	1.64	1.57	1.48	1.39	1.27	1.00

continued

TABLE E.5

Critical Values of F (continued)

Cumulative Probabilities = 0.99

Upper-Tail Areas = 0.01

$\alpha = 0.01$

Numerator: df_1

Denominator, df_2	1	2	3	4	5	6	7	8	9	10	12	15	20	24	30	40	60	120	∞
1	4,052.00	4,999.50	5,403.00	5,625.00	5,754.00	5,859.00	5,928.00	5,982.00	6,022.00	6,056.00	6,106.00	6,157.00	6,209.00	6,235.00	6,261.00	6,287.00	6,313.00	6,339.00	6,366.00
2	98.50	99.00	99.17	99.25	99.30	99.33	99.36	99.37	99.39	99.40	99.42	99.43	99.45	99.46	99.47	99.47	99.48	99.49	99.50
3	34.12	30.82	29.46	28.71	28.24	27.91	27.67	27.49	27.35	27.23	27.05	26.87	26.69	26.60	26.50	26.41	26.32	26.22	26.13
4	21.20	18.00	16.69	15.98	15.52	15.21	14.98	14.80	14.66	14.55	14.37	14.20	14.02	13.93	13.84	13.75	13.65	13.56	13.46
5	16.26	13.27	12.06	11.39	10.97	10.67	10.46	10.29	10.16	10.05	9.89	9.72	9.55	9.47	9.38	9.29	9.20	9.11	9.02
6	13.75	10.92	9.78	9.15	8.75	8.47	8.26	8.10	7.98	7.87	7.72	7.56	7.40	7.31	7.23	7.14	7.06	6.97	6.88
7	12.25	9.55	8.45	7.85	7.46	7.19	6.99	6.84	6.72	6.62	6.47	6.31	6.16	6.07	5.99	5.91	5.82	5.74	5.65
8	11.26	8.65	7.59	7.01	6.63	6.37	6.18	6.03	5.91	5.81	5.67	5.52	5.36	5.28	5.20	5.12	5.03	4.95	4.86
9	10.56	8.02	6.99	6.42	6.06	5.80	5.61	5.47	5.35	5.26	5.11	4.96	4.81	4.73	4.65	4.57	4.48	4.40	4.31
10	10.04	7.56	6.55	5.99	5.64	5.39	5.20	5.06	4.94	4.85	4.71	4.56	4.41	4.33	4.25	4.17	4.08	4.00	3.91
11	9.65	7.21	6.22	5.67	5.32	5.07	4.89	4.74	4.63	4.54	4.40	4.25	4.10	4.02	3.94	3.86	3.78	3.69	3.60
12	9.33	6.93	5.95	5.41	5.06	4.82	4.64	4.50	4.39	4.30	4.16	4.01	3.86	3.78	3.70	3.62	3.54	3.45	3.36
13	9.07	6.70	5.74	5.21	4.86	4.62	4.44	4.30	4.19	4.10	3.96	3.82	3.66	3.59	3.51	3.43	3.34	3.25	3.17
14	8.86	6.51	5.56	5.04	4.69	4.46	4.28	4.14	4.03	3.94	3.80	3.66	3.51	3.43	3.35	3.27	3.18	3.09	3.00
15	8.68	6.36	5.42	4.89	4.56	4.32	4.14	4.00	3.89	3.80	3.67	3.52	3.37	3.29	3.21	3.13	3.05	2.96	2.87
16	8.53	6.23	5.29	4.77	4.44	4.20	4.03	3.89	3.78	3.69	3.55	3.41	3.26	3.18	3.10	3.02	2.93	2.81	2.75
17	8.40	6.11	5.18	4.67	4.34	4.10	3.93	3.79	3.68	3.59	3.46	3.31	3.16	3.08	3.00	2.92	2.83	2.75	2.65
18	8.29	6.01	5.09	4.58	4.25	4.01	3.84	3.71	3.60	3.51	3.37	3.23	3.08	3.00	2.92	2.84	2.75	2.66	2.57
19	8.18	5.93	5.01	4.50	4.17	3.94	3.77	3.63	3.52	3.43	3.30	3.15	3.00	2.92	2.84	2.76	2.67	2.58	2.49
20	8.10	5.85	4.94	4.43	4.10	3.87	3.70	3.56	3.45	3.37	3.23	3.09	2.94	2.86	2.78	2.69	2.61	2.52	2.42
21	8.02	5.78	4.87	4.37	4.04	3.81	3.64	3.51	3.40	3.31	3.17	3.03	2.88	2.80	2.72	2.64	2.55	2.46	2.36
22	7.95	5.72	4.82	4.31	3.99	3.76	3.59	3.45	3.35	3.26	3.12	2.98	2.83	2.75	2.67	2.58	2.50	2.40	2.31
23	7.88	5.66	4.76	4.26	3.94	3.71	3.54	3.41	3.30	3.21	3.07	2.93	2.78	2.70	2.62	2.54	2.45	2.35	2.26
24	7.82	5.61	4.72	4.22	3.90	3.67	3.50	3.36	3.26	3.17	3.03	2.89	2.74	2.66	2.58	2.49	2.40	2.31	2.21
25	7.77	5.57	4.68	4.18	3.85	3.63	3.46	3.32	3.22	3.13	2.99	2.85	2.70	2.62	2.54	2.45	2.36	2.27	2.17
26	7.72	5.53	4.64	4.14	3.82	3.59	3.42	3.29	3.18	3.09	2.96	2.81	2.66	2.58	2.50	2.42	2.33	2.23	2.13
27	7.68	5.49	4.60	4.11	3.78	3.56	3.39	3.26	3.15	3.06	2.93	2.78	2.63	2.55	2.47	2.38	2.29	2.20	2.10
28	7.64	5.45	4.57	4.07	3.75	3.53	3.36	3.23	3.12	3.03	2.90	2.75	2.60	2.52	2.44	2.35	2.26	2.17	2.06
29	7.60	5.42	4.54	4.04	3.73	3.50	3.33	3.20	3.09	3.00	2.87	2.73	2.57	2.49	2.41	2.33	2.23	2.14	2.03
30	7.56	5.39	4.51	4.02	3.70	3.47	3.30	3.17	3.07	2.98	2.84	2.70	2.55	2.47	2.39	2.30	2.21	2.11	2.01
40	7.31	5.18	4.31	3.83	3.51	3.29	3.12	2.99	2.89	2.80	2.66	2.52	2.37	2.29	2.20	2.11	2.02	1.92	1.80
60	7.08	4.98	4.13	3.65	3.34	3.12	2.95	2.82	2.72	2.63	2.50	2.35	2.20	2.12	2.03	1.94	1.84	1.73	1.60
120	6.85	4.79	3.95	3.48	3.17	2.96	2.79	2.66	2.56	2.47	2.34	2.19	2.03	1.95	1.86	1.76	1.66	1.53	1.38
∞	6.63	4.61	3.78	3.32	3.02	2.80	2.64	2.51	2.41	2.32	2.18	2.04	1.88	1.79	1.70	1.59	1.47	1.32	1.00

Cumulative Probabilities = 0.995

Upper-Tail Areas = 0.005

$\alpha = 0.005$

Numerator, df_1

Denominator, df_2	1	2	3	4	5	6	7	8	9	10	12	15	20	24	30	40	60	120	∞
1	16,211.00	20,000.00	21,615.00	22,500.00	23,056.00	23,437.00	23,715.00	23,925.00	24,091.00	24,224.00	24,426.00	24,630.00	24,836.00	24,910.00	25,044.00	25,148.00	25,253.00	25,359.00	25,465.00
2	198.50	199.00	199.20	199.20	199.30	199.30	199.40	199.40	199.40	199.40	199.40	199.40	199.40	199.50	199.50	199.50	199.50	199.50	199.50
3	55.55	49.80	47.47	46.19	45.39	44.84	44.43	44.13	43.88	43.69	43.39	43.08	42.78	42.62	42.47	42.31	42.15	41.99	41.83
4	31.33	26.28	24.26	23.15	22.46	21.97	21.62	21.35	21.14	20.97	20.70	20.44	20.17	20.03	19.89	19.75	19.61	19.47	19.32
5	22.78	18.31	16.53	15.56	14.94	14.51	14.20	13.96	13.77	13.62	13.38	13.15	12.90	12.78	12.66	12.53	12.40	12.27	12.11
6	18.63	14.54	12.92	12.03	11.46	11.07	10.79	10.57	10.39	10.25	10.03	9.81	9.59	9.47	9.36	9.24	9.12	9.00	8.88
7	16.24	12.40	10.88	10.05	9.52	9.16	8.89	8.68	8.51	8.38	8.18	7.97	7.75	7.65	7.53	7.42	7.31	7.19	7.08
8	14.69	11.04	9.60	8.81	8.30	7.95	7.69	7.50	7.34	7.21	7.01	6.81	6.61	6.50	6.40	6.29	6.18	6.06	5.95
9	13.61	10.11	8.72	7.96	7.47	7.13	6.88	6.69	6.54	6.42	6.23	6.03	5.83	5.73	5.62	5.52	5.41	5.30	5.19
10	12.83	9.43	8.08	7.34	6.87	6.54	6.30	6.12	5.97	5.85	5.66	5.47	5.27	5.17	5.07	4.97	4.86	4.75	4.61
11	12.23	8.91	7.60	6.88	6.42	6.10	5.86	5.68	5.54	5.42	5.24	5.05	4.86	4.75	4.65	4.55	4.44	4.34	4.23
12	11.75	8.51	7.23	6.52	6.07	5.76	5.52	5.35	5.20	5.09	4.91	4.72	4.53	4.43	4.33	4.23	4.12	4.01	3.90
13	11.37	8.19	6.93	6.23	5.79	5.48	5.25	5.08	4.94	4.82	4.64	4.46	4.27	4.17	4.07	3.97	3.87	3.76	3.65
14	11.06	7.92	6.68	6.00	5.56	5.26	5.03	4.86	4.72	4.60	4.43	4.25	4.06	3.96	3.86	3.76	3.66	3.55	3.41
15	10.80	7.70	6.48	5.80	5.37	5.07	4.85	4.67	4.54	4.42	4.25	4.07	3.88	3.79	3.69	3.58	3.48	3.37	3.26
16	10.58	7.51	6.30	5.64	5.21	4.91	4.69	4.52	4.38	4.27	4.10	3.92	3.73	3.64	3.54	3.44	3.33	3.22	3.11
17	10.38	7.35	6.16	5.50	5.07	4.78	4.56	4.39	4.25	4.14	3.97	3.79	3.61	3.51	3.41	3.31	3.21	3.10	2.98
18	10.22	7.21	6.03	5.37	4.96	4.66	4.44	4.28	4.14	4.03	3.86	3.68	3.50	3.40	3.30	3.20	3.10	2.99	2.87
19	10.07	7.09	5.92	5.27	4.85	4.56	4.34	4.18	4.04	3.93	3.76	3.59	3.40	3.31	3.21	3.11	3.00	2.89	2.78
20	9.94	6.99	5.82	5.17	4.76	4.47	4.26	4.09	3.96	3.85	3.68	3.50	3.32	3.22	3.12	3.02	2.92	2.81	2.69
21	9.83	6.89	5.73	5.09	4.68	4.39	4.18	4.02	3.88	3.77	3.60	3.43	3.24	3.15	3.05	2.95	2.84	2.73	2.61
22	9.73	6.81	5.65	5.02	4.61	4.32	4.11	3.94	3.81	3.70	3.54	3.36	3.18	3.08	2.98	2.88	2.77	2.66	2.55
23	9.63	6.73	5.58	4.95	4.54	4.26	4.05	3.88	3.75	3.64	3.47	3.30	3.12	3.02	2.92	2.82	2.71	2.60	2.48
24	9.55	6.66	5.52	4.89	4.49	4.20	3.99	3.83	3.69	3.59	3.42	3.25	3.06	2.97	2.87	2.77	2.66	2.55	2.43
25	9.48	6.60	5.46	4.84	4.43	4.15	3.94	3.78	3.64	3.54	3.37	3.20	3.01	2.92	2.82	2.72	2.61	2.50	2.38
26	9.41	6.54	5.41	4.79	4.38	4.10	3.89	3.73	3.60	3.49	3.33	3.15	2.97	2.87	2.77	2.67	2.56	2.45	2.33
27	9.34	6.49	5.36	4.74	4.34	4.06	3.85	3.69	3.56	3.45	3.28	3.11	2.93	2.83	2.73	2.63	2.52	2.41	2.29
28	9.28	6.44	5.32	4.70	4.30	4.02	3.81	3.65	3.52	3.41	3.25	3.07	2.89	2.79	2.69	2.59	2.48	2.37	2.25
29	9.23	6.40	5.28	4.66	4.26	3.98	3.77	3.61	3.48	3.38	3.21	3.04	2.86	2.76	2.66	2.56	2.45	2.33	2.21
30	9.18	6.35	5.24	4.62	4.23	3.95	3.74	3.58	3.45	3.34	3.18	3.01	2.82	2.73	2.63	2.52	2.42	2.30	2.18
40	8.83	6.07	4.98	4.37	3.99	3.71	3.51	3.35	3.22	3.12	2.95	2.78	2.60	2.50	2.40	2.30	2.18	2.06	1.93
60	8.49	5.79	4.73	4.14	3.76	3.49	3.29	3.13	3.01	2.90	2.74	2.57	2.39	2.29	2.19	2.08	1.96	1.83	1.69
120	8.18	5.54	4.50	3.92	3.55	3.28	3.09	2.93	2.81	2.71	2.54	2.37	2.19	2.09	1.98	1.87	1.75	1.61	1.43
∞	7.88	5.30	4.28	3.72	3.35	3.09	2.90	2.74	2.62	2.52	2.36	2.19	2.00	1.90	1.79	1.67	1.53	1.36	1.00

TABLE E.6

Critical Values of the Studentized Range, Q

Upper 5% Points ($\alpha = 0.05$)

Denominator, df	Numerator, df																		
	2	3	4	5	6	7	8	9	10	11	12	13	14	15	16	17	18	19	20
1	17.97	26.98	32.82	37.08	40.41	43.12	45.40	47.36	49.07	50.59	51.96	53.20	54.33	55.36	56.32	57.22	58.04	58.83	59.56
2	6.09	8.33	9.80	10.88	11.74	12.44	13.03	13.54	13.99	14.39	14.75	15.08	15.38	15.65	15.91	16.14	16.37	16.57	16.77
3	4.50	5.91	6.83	7.50	8.04	8.48	8.85	9.18	9.46	9.72	9.95	10.15	10.35	10.53	10.61	10.84	10.98	11.11	11.24
4	3.93	5.04	5.76	6.29	6.71	7.05	7.35	7.60	7.83	8.03	8.21	8.37	8.53	8.66	8.79	8.91	9.03	9.13	9.23
5	3.64	4.60	5.22	5.67	6.03	6.33	6.58	6.80	7.00	7.17	7.32	7.47	7.60	7.72	7.83	7.93	8.03	8.12	8.21
6	3.46	4.34	4.90	5.31	5.63	5.90	6.12	6.32	6.49	6.65	6.79	6.92	7.03	7.14	7.24	7.34	7.43	7.51	7.59
7	3.34	4.17	4.68	5.06	5.36	5.61	5.82	6.00	6.16	6.30	6.43	6.55	6.66	6.76	6.85	6.94	7.02	7.10	7.17
8	3.26	4.04	4.53	4.89	5.17	5.40	5.60	5.77	5.92	6.05	6.18	6.29	6.39	6.48	6.57	6.65	6.73	6.80	6.87
9	3.20	3.95	4.42	4.76	5.02	5.24	5.43	5.60	5.74	5.87	5.98	6.09	6.19	6.28	6.36	6.44	6.51	6.58	6.64
10	3.15	3.88	4.33	4.65	4.91	5.12	5.31	5.46	5.60	5.72	5.83	5.93	6.03	6.11	6.20	6.27	6.34	6.41	6.47
11	3.11	3.82	4.26	4.57	4.82	5.03	5.20	5.35	5.49	5.61	5.71	5.81	5.90	5.98	6.06	6.13	6.20	6.27	6.33
12	3.08	3.77	4.20	4.51	4.75	4.95	5.12	5.27	5.40	5.51	5.62	5.71	5.80	5.88	5.95	6.02	6.09	6.15	6.21
13	3.06	3.74	4.15	4.45	4.69	4.89	5.05	5.19	5.32	5.43	5.53	5.63	5.71	5.79	5.86	5.93	6.00	6.06	6.11
14	3.03	3.70	4.11	4.41	4.64	4.83	4.99	5.13	5.25	5.36	5.46	5.55	5.64	5.71	5.79	5.85	5.92	5.97	6.03
15	3.01	3.67	4.08	4.37	4.60	4.78	4.94	5.08	5.20	5.31	5.40	5.49	5.57	5.65	5.72	5.79	5.85	5.90	5.96
16	3.00	3.65	4.05	4.33	4.56	4.74	4.90	5.03	5.15	5.26	5.35	5.44	5.52	5.59	5.66	5.73	5.79	5.84	5.90
17	2.98	3.63	4.02	4.30	4.52	4.71	4.86	4.99	5.11	5.21	5.31	5.39	5.47	5.54	5.61	5.68	5.73	5.79	5.84
18	2.97	3.61	4.00	4.28	4.50	4.67	4.82	4.96	5.07	5.17	5.27	5.35	5.43	5.50	5.57	5.63	5.69	5.74	5.79
19	2.96	3.59	3.98	4.25	4.47	4.65	4.79	4.92	5.04	5.14	5.23	5.32	5.39	5.46	5.53	5.59	5.65	5.70	5.75
20	2.95	3.58	3.96	4.23	4.45	4.62	4.77	4.90	5.01	5.11	5.20	5.28	5.36	5.43	5.49	5.55	5.61	5.66	5.71
24	2.92	3.53	3.90	4.17	4.37	4.54	4.68	4.81	4.92	5.01	5.10	5.18	5.25	5.32	5.38	5.44	5.49	5.55	5.59
30	2.89	3.49	3.85	4.10	4.30	4.46	4.60	4.72	4.82	4.92	5.00	5.08	5.15	5.21	5.27	5.33	5.38	5.43	5.48
40	2.86	3.44	3.79	4.04	4.23	4.39	4.52	4.64	4.74	4.82	4.90	4.98	5.04	5.11	5.16	5.22	5.27	5.31	5.36
60	2.83	3.40	3.74	3.98	4.16	4.31	4.44	4.55	4.65	4.73	4.81	4.88	4.94	5.00	5.06	5.11	5.15	5.20	5.24
120	2.80	3.36	3.69	3.92	4.10	4.24	4.36	4.47	4.56	4.64	4.71	4.78	4.84	4.90	4.95	5.00	5.04	5.09	5.13
∞	2.77	3.31	3.63	3.86	4.03	4.17	4.29	4.39	4.47	4.55	4.62	4.68	4.74	4.80	4.85	4.89	4.93	4.97	5.01

continued

TABLE E.6
Critical Values of the Studentized Range, Q

Upper 1% Points ($\alpha = 0.01$)

Denominator, df	Numerator, df																		
	2	3	4	5	6	7	8	9	10	11	12	13	14	15	16	17	18	19	20
1	90.03	135.00	164.30	185.60	202.20	215.80	227.20	237.00	245.60	253.20	260.00	266.20	271.80	277.00	281.80	286.30	290.40	294.30	298.00
2	14.04	19.02	22.29	24.72	26.63	28.20	29.53	30.68	31.69	32.59	33.40	34.13	34.81	35.43	36.00	36.53	37.03	37.50	37.95
3	8.26	10.62	12.17	13.33	14.24	15.00	15.64	16.20	16.69	17.13	17.53	17.89	18.22	18.52	18.81	19.07	19.32	19.55	19.77
4	6.51	8.12	9.17	9.96	10.58	11.10	11.55	11.93	12.27	12.57	12.84	13.09	13.32	13.53	13.73	13.91	14.08	14.24	14.40
5	5.70	6.98	7.80	8.42	8.91	9.32	9.67	9.97	10.24	10.48	10.70	10.89	11.08	11.24	11.40	11.55	11.68	11.81	11.93
6	5.24	6.33	7.03	7.56	7.97	8.32	8.61	8.87	9.10	9.30	9.49	9.65	9.81	9.95	10.08	10.21	10.32	10.43	10.54
7	4.95	5.92	6.54	7.01	7.37	7.68	7.94	8.17	8.37	8.55	8.71	8.86	9.00	9.12	9.24	9.35	9.46	9.55	9.65
8	4.75	5.64	6.20	6.63	6.96	7.24	7.47	7.68	7.86	8.03	8.18	8.31	8.44	8.55	8.66	8.76	8.85	8.94	9.03
9	4.60	5.43	5.96	6.35	6.66	6.92	7.13	7.33	7.50	7.65	7.78	7.91	8.03	8.13	8.23	8.33	8.41	8.50	8.57
10	4.48	5.27	5.77	6.14	6.43	6.67	6.87	7.06	7.21	7.36	7.49	7.60	7.71	7.81	7.91	7.99	8.08	8.15	8.23
11	4.39	5.15	5.62	5.97	6.25	6.48	6.67	6.84	6.99	7.13	7.25	7.36	7.47	7.56	7.65	7.73	7.81	7.88	7.95
12	4.32	5.04	5.50	5.84	6.10	6.32	6.51	6.67	6.81	6.94	7.06	7.17	7.26	7.36	7.44	7.52	7.59	7.66	7.73
13	4.26	4.96	5.40	5.73	5.98	6.19	6.37	6.53	6.67	6.79	6.90	7.01	7.10	7.19	7.27	7.35	7.42	7.49	7.55
14	4.21	4.90	5.32	5.63	5.88	6.09	6.26	6.41	6.54	6.66	6.77	6.87	6.96	7.05	7.13	7.20	7.27	7.33	7.40
15	4.17	4.84	5.25	5.56	5.80	5.99	6.16	6.31	6.44	6.56	6.66	6.76	6.85	6.93	7.00	7.07	7.14	7.20	7.26
16	4.13	4.79	5.19	5.49	5.72	5.92	6.08	6.22	6.35	6.46	6.56	6.66	6.74	6.82	6.90	6.97	7.03	7.09	7.15
17	4.10	4.74	5.14	5.43	5.66	5.85	6.01	6.15	6.27	6.38	6.48	6.57	6.66	6.73	6.81	6.87	6.94	7.00	7.05
18	4.07	4.70	5.09	5.38	5.60	5.79	5.94	6.08	6.20	6.31	6.41	6.50	6.58	6.66	6.73	6.79	6.85	6.91	6.97
19	4.05	4.67	5.05	5.33	5.55	5.74	5.89	6.02	6.14	6.25	6.34	6.43	6.51	6.59	6.65	6.72	6.78	6.84	6.89
20	4.02	4.64	5.02	5.29	5.51	5.69	5.84	5.97	6.09	6.19	6.29	6.37	6.45	6.52	6.59	6.65	6.71	6.77	6.82
24	3.96	4.55	4.91	5.17	5.37	5.54	5.69	5.81	5.92	6.02	6.11	6.19	6.26	6.33	6.39	6.45	6.51	6.56	6.61
30	3.89	4.46	4.80	5.05	5.24	5.40	5.54	5.65	5.76	5.85	5.93	6.01	6.08	6.14	6.20	6.26	6.31	6.36	6.41
40	3.83	4.37	4.70	4.93	5.11	5.27	5.39	5.50	5.60	5.69	5.76	5.84	5.90	5.96	6.02	6.07	6.12	6.17	6.21
60	3.76	4.28	4.60	4.82	4.99	5.13	5.25	5.36	5.45	5.53	5.60	5.67	5.73	5.79	5.84	5.89	5.93	5.97	6.02
120	3.70	4.20	4.50	4.71	4.87	5.01	5.12	5.21	5.30	5.38	5.44	5.51	5.56	5.61	5.66	5.71	5.75	5.79	5.83
∞	3.64	4.12	4.40	4.60	4.76	4.88	4.99	5.08	5.16	5.23	5.29	5.35	5.40	5.45	5.49	5.54	5.57	5.61	5.65

Source: Extracted from H. L. Harter and D. S. Clemm, "The Probability Integrals of the Range and of the Studentized Range—Probability Integral, Percentage Points, and Moments of the Range," *Wright Air Development Technical Report 58–484*, Vol. 1, 1959.

Critical Values, d_L and d_U, of the Durbin-Watson Statistic, D (Critical Values Are One-Sided)[a]

$\alpha = 0.05$

n	k=1 d_L	k=1 d_U	k=2 d_L	k=2 d_U	k=3 d_L	k=3 d_U	k=4 d_L	k=4 d_U	k=5 d_L	k=5 d_U
15	1.08	1.36	.95	1.54	.82	1.75	.69	1.97	.56	2.21
16	1.10	1.37	.98	1.54	.86	1.73	.74	1.93	.62	2.15
17	1.13	1.38	1.02	1.54	.90	1.71	.78	1.90	.67	2.10
18	1.16	1.39	1.05	1.53	.93	1.69	.82	1.87	.71	2.06
19	1.18	1.40	1.08	1.53	.97	1.68	.86	1.85	.75	2.02
20	1.20	1.41	1.10	1.54	1.00	1.68	.90	1.83	.79	1.99
21	1.22	1.42	1.13	1.54	1.03	1.67	.93	1.81	.83	1.96
22	1.24	1.43	1.15	1.54	1.05	1.66	.96	1.80	.86	1.94
23	1.26	1.44	1.17	1.54	1.08	1.66	.99	1.79	.90	1.92
24	1.27	1.45	1.19	1.55	1.10	1.66	1.01	1.78	.93	1.90
25	1.29	1.45	1.21	1.55	1.12	1.66	1.04	1.77	.95	1.89
26	1.30	1.46	1.22	1.55	1.14	1.65	1.06	1.76	.98	1.88
27	1.32	1.47	1.24	1.56	1.16	1.65	1.08	1.76	1.01	1.86
28	1.33	1.48	1.26	1.56	1.18	1.65	1.10	1.75	1.03	1.85
29	1.34	1.48	1.27	1.56	1.20	1.65	1.12	1.74	1.05	1.84
30	1.35	1.49	1.28	1.57	1.21	1.65	1.14	1.74	1.07	1.83
31	1.36	1.50	1.30	1.57	1.23	1.65	1.16	1.74	1.09	1.83
32	1.37	1.50	1.31	1.57	1.24	1.65	1.18	1.73	1.11	1.82
33	1.38	1.51	1.32	1.58	1.26	1.65	1.19	1.73	1.13	1.81
34	1.39	1.51	1.33	1.58	1.27	1.65	1.21	1.73	1.15	1.81
35	1.40	1.52	1.34	1.58	1.28	1.65	1.22	1.73	1.16	1.80
36	1.41	1.52	1.35	1.59	1.29	1.65	1.24	1.73	1.18	1.80
37	1.42	1.53	1.36	1.59	1.31	1.66	1.25	1.72	1.19	1.80
38	1.43	1.54	1.37	1.59	1.32	1.66	1.26	1.72	1.21	1.79
39	1.43	1.54	1.38	1.60	1.33	1.66	1.27	1.72	1.22	1.79
40	1.44	1.54	1.39	1.60	1.34	1.66	1.29	1.72	1.23	1.79
45	1.48	1.57	1.43	1.62	1.38	1.67	1.34	1.72	1.29	1.78
50	1.50	1.59	1.46	1.63	1.42	1.67	1.38	1.72	1.34	1.77
55	1.53	1.60	1.49	1.64	1.45	1.68	1.41	1.72	1.38	1.77
60	1.55	1.62	1.51	1.65	1.48	1.69	1.44	1.73	1.41	1.77
65	1.57	1.63	1.54	1.66	1.50	1.70	1.47	1.73	1.44	1.77
70	1.58	1.64	1.55	1.67	1.52	1.70	1.49	1.74	1.46	1.77
75	1.60	1.65	1.57	1.68	1.54	1.71	1.51	1.74	1.49	1.77
80	1.61	1.66	1.59	1.69	1.56	1.72	1.53	1.74	1.51	1.77
85	1.62	1.67	1.60	1.70	1.57	1.72	1.55	1.75	1.52	1.77
90	1.63	1.68	1.61	1.70	1.59	1.73	1.57	1.75	1.54	1.78
95	1.64	1.69	1.62	1.71	1.60	1.73	1.58	1.75	1.56	1.78
100	1.65	1.69	1.63	1.72	1.61	1.74	1.59	1.76	1.57	1.78

$\alpha = 0.01$

n	k=1 d_L	k=1 d_U	k=2 d_L	k=2 d_U	k=3 d_L	k=3 d_U	k=4 d_L	k=4 d_U	k=5 d_L	k=5 d_U
15	.81	1.07	.70	1.25	.59	1.46	.49	1.70	.39	1.96
16	.84	1.09	.74	1.25	.63	1.44	.53	1.66	.44	1.90
17	.87	1.10	.77	1.25	.67	1.43	.57	1.63	.48	1.85
18	.90	1.12	.80	1.26	.71	1.42	.61	1.60	.52	1.80
19	.93	1.13	.83	1.26	.74	1.41	.65	1.58	.56	1.77
20	.95	1.15	.86	1.27	.77	1.41	.68	1.57	.60	1.74
21	.97	1.16	.89	1.27	.80	1.41	.72	1.55	.63	1.71
22	1.00	1.17	.91	1.28	.83	1.40	.75	1.54	.66	1.69
23	1.02	1.19	.94	1.29	.86	1.40	.77	1.53	.70	1.67
24	1.04	1.20	.96	1.30	.88	1.41	.80	1.53	.72	1.66
25	1.05	1.21	.98	1.30	.90	1.41	.83	1.52	.75	1.65
26	1.07	1.22	1.00	1.31	.93	1.41	.85	1.52	.78	1.64
27	1.09	1.23	1.02	1.32	.95	1.41	.88	1.51	.81	1.63
28	1.10	1.24	1.04	1.32	.97	1.41	.90	1.51	.83	1.62
29	1.12	1.25	1.05	1.33	.99	1.42	.92	1.51	.85	1.61
30	1.13	1.26	1.07	1.34	1.01	1.42	.94	1.51	.88	1.61
31	1.15	1.27	1.08	1.34	1.02	1.42	.96	1.51	.90	1.60
32	1.16	1.28	1.10	1.35	1.04	1.43	.98	1.51	.92	1.60
33	1.17	1.29	1.11	1.36	1.05	1.43	1.00	1.51	.94	1.59
34	1.18	1.30	1.13	1.36	1.07	1.43	1.01	1.51	.95	1.59
35	1.19	1.31	1.14	1.37	1.08	1.44	1.03	1.51	.97	1.59
36	1.21	1.32	1.15	1.38	1.10	1.44	1.04	1.51	.99	1.59
37	1.22	1.32	1.16	1.38	1.11	1.45	1.06	1.51	1.00	1.59
38	1.23	1.33	1.18	1.39	1.12	1.45	1.07	1.52	1.02	1.58
39	1.24	1.34	1.19	1.39	1.14	1.45	1.09	1.52	1.03	1.58
40	1.25	1.34	1.20	1.40	1.15	1.46	1.10	1.52	1.05	1.58
45	1.29	1.38	1.24	1.42	1.20	1.48	1.16	1.53	1.11	1.58
50	1.32	1.40	1.28	1.45	1.24	1.49	1.20	1.54	1.16	1.59
55	1.36	1.43	1.32	1.47	1.28	1.51	1.25	1.55	1.21	1.59
60	1.38	1.45	1.35	1.48	1.32	1.52	1.28	1.56	1.25	1.60
65	1.41	1.47	1.38	1.50	1.35	1.53	1.31	1.57	1.28	1.61
70	1.43	1.49	1.40	1.52	1.37	1.55	1.34	1.58	1.31	1.61
75	1.45	1.50	1.42	1.53	1.39	1.56	1.37	1.59	1.34	1.62
80	1.47	1.52	1.44	1.54	1.42	1.57	1.39	1.60	1.36	1.62
85	1.48	1.53	1.46	1.55	1.43	1.58	1.41	1.60	1.39	1.63
90	1.50	1.54	1.47	1.56	1.45	1.59	1.43	1.61	1.41	1.64
95	1.51	1.55	1.49	1.57	1.47	1.60	1.45	1.62	1.42	1.64
100	1.52	1.56	1.50	1.58	1.48	1.60	1.46	1.63	1.44	1.65

[a]n = number of observations; k = number of independent variables.

Source: Computed from TSP 4.5 based on R. W. Farebrother, "A Remark on Algorithms AS106, AS153, and AS155: The Distribution of a Linear Combination of Chi-Square Random Variables," *Journal of the Royal Statistical Society, Series C (Applied Statistics)*, 1984, 29, p. 323–333.

TABLE E.8
Control Chart Factors

Number of Observations in Sample/Subgroup (n)	d_2	d_3	D_3	D_4	A_2
2	1.128	0.853	0	3.267	1.880
3	1.693	0.888	0	2.575	1.023
4	2.059	0.880	0	2.282	0.729
5	2.326	0.864	0	2.114	0.577
6	2.534	0.848	0	2.004	0.483
7	2.704	0.833	0.076	1.924	0.419
8	2.847	0.820	0.136	1.864	0.373
9	2.970	0.808	0.184	1.816	0.337
10	3.078	0.797	0.223	1.777	0.308
11	3.173	0.787	0.256	1.744	0.285
12	3.258	0.778	0.283	1.717	0.266
13	3.336	0.770	0.307	1.693	0.249
14	3.407	0.763	0.328	1.672	0.235
15	3.472	0.756	0.347	1.653	0.223
16	3.532	0.750	0.363	1.637	0.212
17	3.588	0.744	0.378	1.622	0.203
18	3.640	0.739	0.391	1.609	0.194
19	3.689	0.733	0.404	1.596	0.187
20	3.735	0.729	0.415	1.585	0.180
21	3.778	0.724	0.425	1.575	0.173
22	3.819	0.720	0.435	1.565	0.167
23	3.858	0.716	0.443	1.557	0.162
24	3.895	0.712	0.452	1.548	0.157
25	3.931	0.708	0.459	1.541	0.153

Source: Reprinted from *ASTM-STP 15D* by kind permission of the American Society for Testing and Materials.

TABLE E.9
The Standardized Normal Distribution

Entry represents area under the standardized normal distribution from the mean to Z

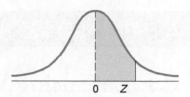

Z	.00	.01	.02	.03	.04	.05	.06	.07	.08	.09
0.0	.0000	.0040	.0080	.0120	.0160	.0199	.0239	.0279	.0319	.0359
0.1	.0398	.0438	.0478	.0517	.0557	.0596	.0636	.0675	.0714	.0753
0.2	.0793	.0832	.0871	.0910	.0948	.0987	.1026	.1064	.1103	.1141
0.3	.1179	.1217	.1255	.1293	.1331	.1368	.1406	.1443	.1480	.1517
0.4	.1554	.1591	.1628	.1664	.1700	.1736	.1772	.1808	.1844	.1879
0.5	.1915	.1950	.1985	.2019	.2054	.2088	.2123	.2157	.2190	.2224
0.6	.2257	.2291	.2324	.2357	.2389	.2422	.2454	.2486	.2518	.2549
0.7	.2580	.2612	.2642	.2673	.2704	.2734	.2764	.2794	.2823	.2852
0.8	.2881	.2910	.2939	.2967	.2995	.3023	.3051	.3078	.3106	.3133
0.9	.3159	.3186	.3212	.3238	.3264	.3289	.3315	.3340	.3365	.3389
1.0	.3413	.3438	.3461	.3485	.3508	.3531	.3554	.3577	.3599	.3621
1.1	.3643	.3665	.3686	.3708	.3729	.3749	.3770	.3790	.3810	.3830
1.2	.3849	.3869	.3888	.3907	.3925	.3944	.3962	.3980	.3997	.4015
1.3	.4032	.4049	.4066	.4082	.4099	.4115	.4131	.4147	.4162	.4177
1.4	.4192	.4207	.4222	.4236	.4251	.4265	.4279	.4292	.4306	.4319
1.5	.4332	.4345	.4357	.4370	.4382	.4394	.4406	.4418	.4429	.4441
1.6	.4452	.4463	.4474	.4484	.4495	.4505	.4515	.4525	.4535	.4545
1.7	.4554	.4564	.4573	.4582	.4591	.4599	.4608	.4616	.4625	.4633
1.8	.4641	.4649	.4656	.4664	.4671	.4678	.4686	.4693	.4699	.4706
1.9	.4713	.4719	.4726	.4732	.4738	.4744	.4750	.4756	.4761	.4767
2.0	.4772	.4778	.4783	.4788	.4793	.4798	.4803	.4808	.4812	.4817
2.1	.4821	.4826	.4830	.4834	.4838	.4842	.4846	.4850	.4854	.4857
2.2	.4861	.4864	.4868	.4871	.4875	.4878	.4881	.4884	.4887	.4890
2.3	.4893	.4896	.4898	.4901	.4904	.4906	.4909	.4911	.4913	.4916
2.4	.4918	.4920	.4922	.4925	.4927	.4929	.4931	.4932	.4934	.4936
2.5	.4938	.4940	.4941	.4943	.4945	.4946	.4948	.4949	.4951	.4952
2.6	.4953	.4955	.4956	.4957	.4959	.4960	.4961	.4962	.4963	.4964
2.7	.4965	.4966	.4967	.4968	.4969	.4970	.4971	.4972	.4973	.4974
2.8	.4974	.4975	.4976	.4977	.4977	.4978	.4979	.4979	.4980	.4981
2.9	.4981	.4982	.4982	.4983	.4984	.4984	.4985	.4985	.4986	.4986
3.0	.49865	.49869	.49874	.49878	.49882	.49886	.49889	.49893	.49897	.49900
3.1	.49903	.49906	.49910	.49913	.49916	.49918	.49921	.49924	.49926	.49929
3.2	.49931	.49934	.49936	.49938	.49940	.49942	.49944	.49946	.49948	.49950
3.3	.49952	.49953	.49955	.49957	.49958	.49960	.49961	.49962	.49964	.49965
3.4	.49966	.49968	.49969	.49970	.49971	.49972	.49973	.49974	.49975	.49976
3.5	.49977	.49978	.49978	.49979	.49980	.49981	.49981	.49982	.49983	.49983
3.6	.49984	.49985	.49985	.49986	.49986	.49987	.49987	.49988	.49988	.49989
3.7	.49989	.49990	.49990	.49990	.49991	.49991	.49992	.49992	.49992	.49992
3.8	.49993	.49993	.49993	.49994	.49994	.49994	.49994	.49995	.49995	.49995
3.9	.49995	.49995	.49996	.49996	.49996	.49996	.49996	.49996	.49997	.49997

F.1 Enhancing Workbook Presentation

You can enhance workbook presentation by using common formatting commands and rearranging the order of the worksheets and chart sheets in a workbook.

Table F.1 presents the shortcuts for worksheet formatting operations used to create the Excel Guide workbooks and the results shown throughout this book. These shortcuts can be found in the Home tab of the Excel Office Ribbon (see Figure F.1 on page 813).

TABLE F.1

Shortcuts to Common Formatting Operations

Number	Operation Name	Use
❶	Font Face and Font Size	Changes the text font face and size for cell entries and chart labels. Worksheets shown in this book have been formatted as **Calibri 11**. Many DATA worksheets have been formatted as **Arial 10**.
❷	Boldface	Toggles on (or off) boldface text style for the currently selected object.
❸	Italic	Toggles on (or off) italic text style for the currently selected object.
❹	Borders	Displays a gallery of choices that permit drawing lines (borders) around a cell or cell range.
❺	Fill Color	Displays a gallery of choices for the background color of a cell. Immediately to the right of **Fill Color** is the related **Font Color** (not used in any example in this book).
❻	Align Text	Aligns the display of the contents of a worksheet cell. Three buttons are available: **Align Text Left**, **Center**, and **Align Text Right**.
❼	Merge & Center	Merges (combines) adjacent cells into one cell and centers the display of the contents of that cell. In Excel 2007, this button is also a drop-down list that offers additional **Merge** and **Unmerge** choices.
❽	Percent	Formats the display of a number value in a cell as a percentage. The value 1 displays as 100%, the value 0.01 displays as 1%. To the immediate left of **Percent** is **Currency**, which formats values as dollars and cents. Do not confuse **Currency** formatting with the symbol used to identify absolute cell references.
❾	Increase Decimal and Decrease Decimal	Adjusts the number of decimal places to display a number value in a cell.
❿	Format	Displays a gallery of choices that affect the row height and column width of a cell. The most common usage is to select a column and then select **Format → AutoFit Column Width**.

FIGURE F.1

Home tab of the Excel Office Ribbon (with number labels keyed to Table F.1)

Use the **Move or Copy** command to rearrange the order of the worksheets and chart sheets in a workbook. To move or copy a worksheet, right-click the worksheet sheet tab and click **Move or Copy** in the shortcut menu that appears. In the Move or Copy dialog box, select the destination workbook from the **To book** drop-down list—select **(new book)** to place the worksheet in a new workbook—and select a position for the worksheet in the **Before sheet** list. If making a copy, also check **Create a copy**. Click **OK** to complete the move or copy operation.

Worksheet cell formatting can also be done through the **Format Cells** command. When editing a worksheet, right-click a cell and then click **Format Cells** from the shortcut menu. In the Format Cells dialog box that appears, you can perform all the formatting operations discussed in Table F.1 and more.

F.2 Useful Keyboard Shortcuts

In Excel, certain keys or keystroke combinations (one or more keys held down as you press another key) are keyboard shortcuts that act as alternate means of executing common operations. Table F.2 presents some common shortcuts that represent some of the common Excel operations described in this book. (Keystroke combinations are shown using a plus sign, as in **Ctrl+C**, which means "while holding down the **Ctrl** key, press the **C** key.")

TABLE F.2

Useful Keyboard Shortcuts

Key	Operation
Backspace	Erases typed characters to the left of the current position, one character at a time.
Delete	Erases characters to the right of the cursor, one character at a time.
Enter or Tab	Finalizes an entry typed into a worksheet cell. Implied by the use of the verb *enter* in the Excel Guides.
Esc	Cancels an action or a dialog box. Equivalent to the dialog box **Cancel** button.
F1	Displays the Excel help system.
Ctrl+C	Copies the currently selected worksheet entry or chart label.
Ctrl+V	Pastes the currently copied object into the currently selected worksheet cell or chart label.
Ctrl+X	Cuts the currently selected worksheet entry or chart label. You cut, and not delete, something in order to paste it somewhere else.
Ctrl+B	Toggles on (or off) boldface text style for the currently selected object.
Ctrl+I	Toggles on (or off) italic text style for the currently selected object.
Ctrl+F	Finds a **Find what** value.
Ctrl+H	Replaces a **Find what** value with the **Replace with** value.
Ctrl+Z	Undoes the last operation.
Ctrl+Y	Redoes the last operation.
Ctrl+`	Toggles on (or off) formulas view of worksheet.
Ctrl+Shift+Enter	Enters an array formula.

Note: Using the copy-and-paste keyboard shortcut, Ctrl+C and Ctrl+V, to copy formulas from one worksheet cell to another is subject to the same type of adjustment.

F.3 Verifying Formulas and Worksheets

If you use formulas in your worksheets, you should review and verify formulas before you use their results. To view the formulas in a worksheet, press Ctrl+` (grave accent key). To restore the original view, the results of the formulas, press Ctrl+` a second time.

As you create and use more complicated worksheets, you might want to visually examine the relationships among a formula and the cells it uses (called the *precedents*) and the cells that use the results of the formula (the *dependents*). Select **Formulas ➔ Trace Precedents** (or **Trace Dependents**). When you are finished, clear all trace arrows by selecting **Formulas ➔ Remove Arrows**.

F.4 Chart Formatting

Excel incorrectly formats the charts created by the *In-Depth Excel* instructions. Use the formatting adjustments in Table F.3 to properly format charts you create. Before applying these adjustments, relocate a chart to its own chart sheet. To do so, right-click the chart background and click **Move Chart** from the shortcut menu. In the Move Chart dialog box, click **New Sheet**, enter a name for the new chart sheet, and click **OK**.

TABLE F.3

Excel Chart Formatting Adjustments

Layout Tab Selection	Notes
Chart Title ➔ Above Chart	In the box that is added to the chart, double-click **Chart Title** and enter an appropriate title.
Axes Titles ➔ Primary Horizontal Axis Title ➔ Title Below Axis	In the box that is added to the chart, double-click **Axis Title** and enter an appropriate title.
Axes Titles ➔ Primary Vertical Axis Title ➔ Rotated Title	In the box that is added to the chart, double-click **Axis Title** and enter an appropriate title.
Axes Titles ➔ Secondary Horizontal ➔ Axis Title ➔ None and **Axes Titles ➔ Secondary Vertical Axis Title ➔ Rotated Title**	Only for charts that contain secondary axes.
Legend ➔ None	Turns off the chart legend.
Data Labels ➔ None	Turns off the display of values at plotted points or bars in the charts.
Data Table ➔ None	Turns off the display of a summary table on the chart sheet.
Axes ➔ Primary Horizontal Axis ➔ Show Left to Right Axis (or Show Default Axis, if listed)	Turns on the display of the X axis.
Axes ➔ Primary Vertical Axis ➔ Show Default Axis	Turns on the display of the Y axis.
Gridlines ➔ Primary Horizontal Gridlines ➔ None	Turns off the improper horizontal gridlines.
Gridlines ➔ Primary Vertical Gridlines ➔ None	Turns off the improper vertical gridlines.

Use all of the adjustments in Table F.3, unless a particular set of charting instructions tells you otherwise. To apply the adjustments, you must be open to the chart sheet that contains the chart to be adjusted. All adjustments are made by first selecting the **Layout** tab (under the Chart Tools heading). If a Layout tab selection cannot be made, the adjustment does not apply to the type of chart being adjusted. (Excel hides or disables chart formatting choices that do not apply to a particular chart type.)

Occasionally, when you open to a chart sheet, the chart is either too large to be fully seen or too small, surrounded by a chart frame mat that is too large. Click the **Zoom Out** or **Zoom In** buttons, located in the lower-right portion of the Excel window frame, to adjust the display.

F.5 Creating Histograms for Discrete Probability Distributions

You can create a histogram for a discrete probability distribution based on a discrete probabilities table. For example, to create a histogram based on the Figure 6.2 binomial probabilities worksheet on page 256, open to the **COMPUTE worksheet** of the **Binomial workbook**. Select the cell range **B14:B18**, the probabilities in the Binomial Probabilities Table, and:

1. Select **Insert → Column** and select the first **2-D Column** gallery choice (**Clustered Column**).

2. Right-click the chart background and click **Select Data**.

In the Select Data Source dialog box:

3. Click **Edit** under the **Horizontal (Categories) Axis Labels** heading.

4. In the Axis Labels dialog box, enter **=COMPUTE!A14:A18** the cell range of the X axis values. (This cell range must be entered as a formula in the form **=*SheetName!CellRange*.**) Then, click **OK** to return to the Select Data Source dialog box.

5. Click **OK**.

In the chart:

6. Right-click inside a bar and click **Format Data Series** in the shortcut menu.

In the Format Data Series dialog box:

7. Click **Series Options** in the left pane. In the Series Options right pane, change the **Gap Width** slider to **Large Gap**. Click **Close**.

Relocate the chart to a chart sheet and adjust the chart formatting by using the instructions in Section F.4.

F.6 Pasting with Paste Special

Pasting data from one worksheet to another can sometimes cause unexpected side effects. When the two worksheets are in different workbooks, a simple paste creates an external link to the original workbook. This can lead to errors later if the first workbook is unavailable when the second one is being used. Even pasting between worksheets in the same workbook can lead to problems if what is being pasted is a cell range of formulas.

To avoid such side effects, use **Paste Special** in these special situations. To use this operation, copy the original cell range as you would do normally and select the cell or cell range to be the target of the paste. Right-click the target and click **Paste Special** from the shortcut menu. In the Paste Special dialog box (shown on page 816), click **Values** and then click **OK**. For the first case, Paste Special Values pastes the current values of the cells in the first workbook and not formulas that use cell references to the first workbook. For the second case, Paste Special Values pastes the current evaluation of the formulas copied and not the formulas themselves.

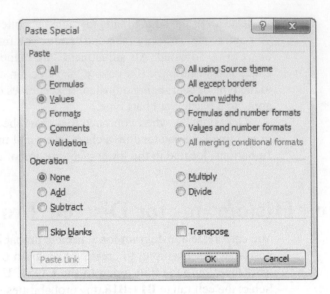

If you use PHStat2 and have data for a procedure in the form of formulas, use Paste Special Values to create columns of equivalent values before using the procedure. (PHStat2 will not work properly if data for a procedure are in the form of formulas.) Paste Special can paste other types of information, including cell formatting information. For a full discussion of Paste Special, see the Excel help system.

Answers to Selected Problems

CHAPTER 1

1.1 **(a)** ordinal **(b)** ordinal **(c)** nominal **(d)** ordinal **(e)** nominal **(f)** nominal **(g)** ordinal **(h)** nominal **(i)** ordinal **(j)** nominal

1.2

Question	Measurement Scale	Discrete/Continuous
What is your age?	Ratio	Discrete
Do you have a driver's license?	Nominal	
What is your gender?	Nominal	
Do you have any medical conditions?	Nominal	

1.3 (I) Question 1: Which year did the registered nurse employed in Nursing?

Question 2: How old are you?

(II) Year = Interval.

(III) Age = Ratio discrete.

1.4

QUESTION	Measurement Scale
1. What is your household income?	Ratio-discrete
2. What is your gender (sex)?	Nominal
3. Where is your place of birth?	Nominal
4. What is your religious observation?	Ordinal
5. Did you volunteer in the past?	Nominal
6. What is your sense of belonging to community?	Ordinal
7. Which region did you come from?	Nominal
8. What is your educational level?	Ordinal

1.5 Ratio-discrete.

CHAPTER 2

2.1 (b) The Pareto chart is best for portraying these data because it not only sorts the frequencies in descending order but also provides the cumulative line on the same chart. **(c)** You can conclude that friends/family account for the largest percentage, 45%. When other, news media, and online user reviews are added to friends/family, this accounts for 83%.

2.3 (b) 88%. **(d)** The Pareto chart allows you to see which sources account for most of the electricity.

2.5 (b) Since electricity consumption is spread over many types of appliances, a bar chart may be best in showing which types of appliances used the most electricity. **(c)** Air conditioning, lighting, and clothes washers/other accounted for 58% of the residential electricity use in the United States.

2.7 (b) A higher percentage of females enjoy shopping for clothing.

2.9 The percentage of online retailers who require three or more clicks to be removed from an e-mail list has increased drastically from 2008 to 2009.

CHAPTER 3

3.1 (a) $L = 3$ and $H = 574$; Stem: 0, 1, 2, 3, 4, 5; Stem Unit: 100

(b) $L = 1$ and $H = 48$; Stem: 0, 0, 1, 1, 2, 2, 3, 3, 4, 4; Stem Unit: 10

(c) $L = 13,002,000$ and $H = 37,000,000$; Stem: 1, 1, 2, 2, 3, 3; Stem Unit: 10,000,000

(d) $L = 11,398,000$ and $H = 376,956,000$; Stem: 0, 0, 1, 1, 2, 2, 3, 3; Stem Unit: 100,000,000

(e) $L = 6,460$ and $H = 139,000$; Stem: 0, 0, 0, 0, 0, 1, 1; Stem Unit: 100,000

(f) $L = -81.1$ and $H = 9.2$; Stem: −8, −7, −6, −5, −4, −3, −2, −1, −0, 0; Stem Unit: 10

(g) $L = -19.9$ and $H = 10.7$; Stem: −1, −1, −0, −0, 0, 0, 1; Stem Unit: 10

(h) $L = -106.6$ and $H = 25.1$; Stem: −1, −0, −0, −0, −0, −0, 0, 0; Stem Unit: 100

3.2 (a)

Stem (10)	Leaf
0	6 6 7
0	9
1	0 0 0 0 0 0 1
1	2
1	5
1	6
1	8
2	0
2	3
2	
2	
2	9

(b) $L = -0.04$ and $H = 0.09$; Stem: −0.0, −0.0, −0.0, 0.0, 0.0, 0.0, 0.0, 0.0; Stem Unit: face value

(c) $L = -0.24$ and $H = 0.84$; Stem: −0.2, −0.1, −0.0, 0.0, 0.1, 0.2, 0.3, 0.4, 0.5, 0.6, 0.7, 0.8; Stem Unit: face value

(d) $L = -0.06$ and $H = 0$; Stem: −0.06, −0.05, −0.04, −0.03, −0.02, −0.01, −0.00; Stem Unit: face value

3.4 (a) $L = 5,613$ and $H = 93,221$; Stem: 0, 1, 2, 3, 4, 5, 6, 7, 8, 9; Stem Unit: 10,000

(b) $L = -1,370$ and $H = 7,356$; Stem: −1, −0, 0, 1, 2, 3, 4, 5, 6, 7 with a total of 10 stems

(c) $L = -234$ and $H = 323$; Stem: −2, −1, −0, 0, 1, 2, 3;

(d) $L = 0$ and $H = 83$; Stem: 0, 1, 2, 3, 4, 5, 6, 7, 8; Stem Unit: 10

(e) $L = 13$ and $H = 409$; Stem: 0, 0, 1, 1, 2, 2, 3, 3, 4; Stem Unit: 100

3.6 (a)

Revenue Rank	Number of Companies
0 and under 20	14
20 and under 40	8
40 and under 60	7
60 and under 80	2
80 and under 100	0
100 and under 120	1
Total	32

cw = 25 is feasible
First class = 0 and under 25
Last class = 100 and under 125

(b)

Market Capitalization	Number of Companies
0 and under 5,000	2
5,000 and under 10,000	8
10,000 and under 15,000	11
15,000 and under 20,000	4
20,000 and under 25,000	2
25,000 and under 30,000	2
30,000 and under 35,000	0
35,000 and under 40,000	1
Total	30

(c)

P/E Ratio	Number of Companies
7.5 and under 10.0	3
10.0 and under 12.5	5
12.5 and under 15.0	12
15.0 and under 17.5	3
17.5 and under 20.0	1
20.0 and under 22.5	1
22.5 and under 25.0	2
25.0 and under 27.5	1
27.5 and under 30.0	2
Total	30

cw = 5 is feasible
First class = 5.00 and under 10.00
Last class = 25.00 and under 30.00

(d)

Per Share Data–Price/Sales	Number of Companies
0.00 and under 0.50	2
0.50 and under 1.00	8
1.00 and under 1.50	11
1.50 and under 2.00	4
2.00 and under 2.50	4
2.50 and under 3.00	0
3.00 and under 3.50	0
3.50 and under 4.00	1
Total	30

(e)

Debt/Equity Ratio	Number of Companies
0.0 and under 0.2	2
0.2 and under 0.4	9
0.4 and under 0.6	8
0.6 and under 0.8	2
0.8 and under 1.0	4
1.0 and under 1.2	2
1.2 and under 1.4	1
1.4 and under 1.6	1
1.6 and under 1.8	2
1.8 and under 2.0	1
Total	32

(f)

Revenue % Change	Number of Companies
-25 and under 0	10
0 and under 25	20
25 and under 50	1
50 and under 75	0
75 and under 100	0
100 and under 125	1
Total	32

(g)

Earnings per Share–Latest Year	Number of Companies
1.00 and under 1.50	1
1.50 and under 2.00	5
2.00 and under 2.50	1
2.50 and under 3.00	9
3.00 and under 3.50	5
3.50 and under 4.00	5
4.00 and under 4.50	1
4.50 and under 5.00	0
5.00 and under 5.50	1
Total	28

cw = 1 is feasible
First class = 1.00 and under 2.00
Last class = 5.00 and under 6.00

(h)

Number of Employees	Number of Companies
0 and under 25,000	22
25,000 and under 50,000	5
50,000 and under 75,000	3
75,000 and under 100,000	0
100,000 and under 125,000	1
125,000 and under 150,000	1
Total	32

3.7 (a)

Revenue Amount 2007($)	Number of Companies
15,000,000 and under 20,000,000	4
20,000,000 and under 22,000,000	7
25,000,000 and under 30,000,000	6
30,000,000 and under 35,000,000	3
35,000,000 and under 40,000,000	0
40,000,000 and under 45,000,000	1
Total	21

(b)

Profit Amount 2007($)	Number of Companies
0 and under 1,000,000	4
1,000,000 and under 2,000,000	1
2,000,000 and under 3,000,000	5
3,000,000 and under 4,000,000	4
4,000,000 and under 5,000,000	4
5,000,000 and under 6,000,000	1
Total	19

(c)

Revenue Change (%)	Number of Companies
-15.0 and under -10.0	1
-10.0 and under -5.0	0
-5.0 and under 0.0	3
0.0 and under 5.0	5
5.0 and under 10.0	1
10.0 and under 15.0	5
15.0 and under 20.0	2
20.0 and under 25.0	3
25.0 and under 30.0	1
Total	21

CW = 10 is feasible
First class = −20.0 and under −10.0
Last class = 20.0 and under 30.0

(d)

Profit Change (%)	Number of Companies
-250 and under 0	5
0 and under 250	12
250 and under 500	1
500 and under 750	0
750 and under 1,000	0
1,000 and under 1,250	1
Total	19

3.8 (a)

Volume	Number of Companies
0 and under 200,000	16
200,000 and under 400,000	3
400,000 and under 600,000	0
600,000 and under 800,000	0
800,000 and under 1,000,000	1
Total	20

(b)

High/Ask Price	Number of Companies
0.00 and under 10.00	11
10.00 and under 20.00	3
20.00 and under 30.00	4
30.00 and under 40.00	1
40.00 and under 50.00	0
50.00 and under 60.00	1
Total	20

(c)

Low/Bid Price	Number of Companies
0.00 and under 10.00	11
10.00 and under 20.00	4
20.00 and under 30.00	3
30.00 and under 40.00	1
40.00 and under 50.00	0
50.00 and under 60.00	1
Total	20

(d)

Close/Previous Price	Number of Companies
0.00 and under 10.00	11
10.00 and under 20.00	4
20.00 and under 30.00	3
30.00 and under 40.00	1
40.00 and under 50.00	0
50.00 and under 60.00	1
Total	20

(e)

Net Change	Number of Companies
-0.50 and under 0.00	4
0.00 and under 0.50	10
0.50 and under 1.00	2
1.00 and under 1.50	2
1.50 and under 2.00	2
Total	20

(f)

52 Week High Price	Number of Companies
0.00 and under 10.00	5
10.00 and under 20.00	5
20.00 and under 30.00	6
30.00 and under 40.00	1
40.00 and under 50.00	1
50.00 and under 60.00	2
Total	20

(g)

52 Week Low Price	Number of Companies
0.00 and under 5.00	12
5.00 and under 10.00	1
10.00 and under 15.00	4
15.00 and under 20.00	2
20.00 and under 25.00	1
Total	20

3.9 (a) Manulife Mix Funds   L = 10.21   H = 14.38

Valuation ($)	# of Funds
10.00 and under 11.00	6
11.00 and under 12.00	9
12.00 and under 13.00	12
13.00 and under 14.00	2
14.00 and under 15.00	1
Total	30

(b) Manulife Mix Funds   L = −0.12   H = 0.04

Change ($)	# of Funds
−0.12 and under −0.10	1
−0.10 and under −0.08	0
−0.08 and under −0.06	2
−0.06 and under −0.04	4
−0.04 and under −0.02	9
−0.02 and under 0.00	10
0.00 and under 0.02	2
0.02 and under 0.04	1
0.04 and under 0.06	1
Total	30

(c) Manulife Mix Funds   L = −0.94   H = 0.35

Percent Change	# of Funds
−1.00 and under −0.75	1
−0.75 and under −0.50	3
−0.50 and under −0.25	11
−0.25 and under 0.00	11
0.00 and under 0.25	3
0.25 and under 0.50	1
Total	30

(d) CI-Clarica Mutual Funds   L = 8.44   H = 21.02

Valuation ($)	# of Funds
7.50 and under 10.00	5
10.00 and under 12.50	12
12.50 and under 15.00	12
15.00 and under 17.50	5
17.50 and under 20.00	1
20.00 and under 22.50	1
Total	36

(e) Transamerica Growsafe 75/100   L = 2.86   H = 6.12

Valuation ($)	# of Funds
2.00 and under 3.00	1
3.00 and under 4.00	5
4.00 and under 5.00	15
5.00 and under 6.00	13
6.00 and under 7.00	1
Total	35

(f) Transamerica Growsafe 75/100   L = −1.19   H = 0.75

Valuation ($)	# of Funds
−1.50 and under −1.00	1
−1.00 and under −0.50	1
−0.50 and under 0.00	16
0.00 and under 0.50	16
0.50 and under 1.00	1
Total	35

3.10 (a) 32% **(b)** $22,000) **(c)** $29,000

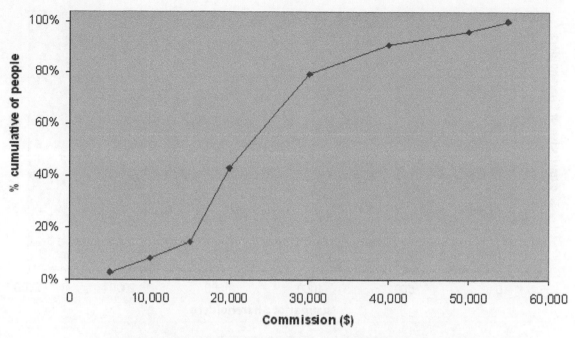

3.11 (a) 51 **(b)** 16%

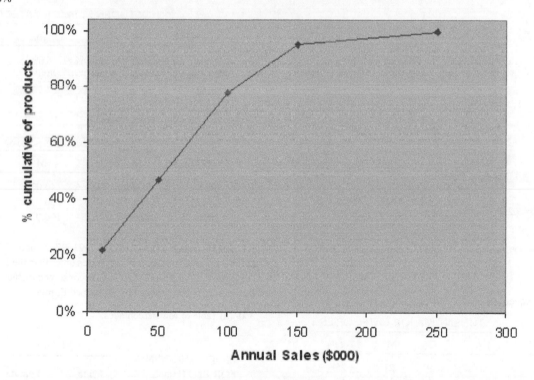

3.12 (a) 46% **(b)** 450 sharesz

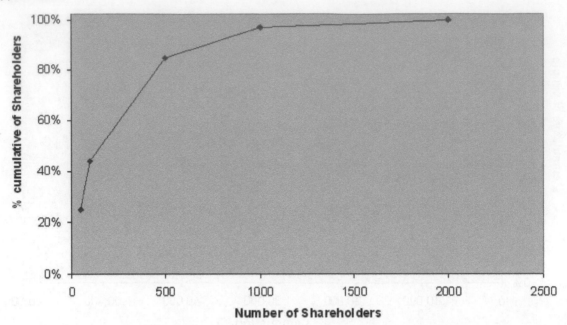

3.13 (a)

(a) $\left[10\left(\dfrac{25}{100}\right)+\dfrac{1}{2}\right] = 3;\ x_3 = 2990$

(b) $\left[10\left(\dfrac{50}{100}\right)+\dfrac{1}{2}\right] = 5.5;\ \dfrac{x_5+x_6}{2} = \dfrac{3461+3959}{2} = 3710$

(c) $\left[10\left(\dfrac{75}{100}\right)+\dfrac{1}{2}\right] = 8;\ x_8 = 6499$

(d) $\left[10\left(\dfrac{80}{100}\right)+\dfrac{1}{2}\right] = 8.5;\ \dfrac{x_8+x_9}{2} = \dfrac{6499+9291}{2} = 7895$

(e) $\left[10\left(\dfrac{43}{100}\right)+\dfrac{1}{2}\right] = 4.8 \Rightarrow 5;\ x_5 = 3461$

(f) $\left[10\left(\dfrac{67}{100}\right)+\dfrac{1}{2}\right] = 7.2 \Rightarrow 7;\ x_7 = 6170$

3.15 (a) Table of frequencies for all student responses:

| GENDER | STUDENT MAJOR CATEGORIES | | | |
	A	C	M	Totals
Male	14	9	2	25
Female	6	6	3	15
Totals	20	15	5	40

(b) Table based on total percentages:

| GENDER | STUDENT MAJOR CATEGORIES | | | |
	A	C	M	Totals
Male	35.0%	22.5%	5.0%	62.5%
Female	15.0	15.0	7.5	37.5
Totals	50.0	37.5	12.5	100.0

Table based on row percentages:

| GENDER | STUDENT MAJOR CATEGORIES | | | |
	A	C	M	Totals
Male	56.0%	36.0%	8.0%	100.0%
Female	40.0	40.0	20.0	100.0
Totals	50.0	37.5	12.5	100.0

Table based on column percentages;

| GENDER | STUDENT MAJOR CATEGORIES | | | |
	A	C	M	Totals
Male	70.0%	60.0%	40.0%	62.5%
Female	30.0	40.0	60.0	37.5
Totals	100.0	100.0	100.0	100.0

3.17 (a) The percentages are 17.18, 5.21, 22.28, and 55.33. **(b)** More than half the oil consumed is from countries other than the U.S., Japan, and developed Europe. More than 20% is consumed by the U.S. and slightly less than 20% is consumed by developed Europe.

3.19 (a) Table of row percentages:

| ENJOY SHOPPING FOR CLOTHING | GENDER | | |
	Male	Female	Total
Yes	46%	54%	100%
No	53	47	100
Total	50	50	100

Table of column percentages:

| ENJOY SHOPPING FOR CLOTHING | GENDER | | |
	Male	Female	Total
Yes	44%	51%	47%
No	56	49	53
Total	100	100	100

Table of total percentages:

ENJOY SHOPPING FOR CLOTHING	GENDER		
	Male	Female	Total
Yes	22%	25%	47%
No	28	25	53
Total	50	50	100

(b) A higher percentage of females enjoy shopping for clothing.

3.21 The percentage of online retailers who require three or more clicks to be removed from an e-mail list has increased drastically from 2008 to 2009.

3.22 (b) Yes, there is a strong positive relationship between X and Y. As X increases, so does Y.

3.24 (c) There appears to be very little relationship between the first weekend gross and either the U.S. gross or the worldwide gross of Harry Potter movies.

3.26 (a) and (c) There appears to be a positive relationship between the coaches' salary and revenue. Yes, this is borne out by the data.

3.28 (b) There is a great deal of variation in the returns from decade to decade. Most of the returns are between 5% and 15%. The 1950s, 1980s, and 1990s had exceptionally high returns, and only the 1930s and 2000s had negative returns.

3.30 (b) There has been a slight decline in movie attendance between 2001 and 2010. During that time, movie attendance increased from 2002 to 2004 but then decreased to a level below that in 2001.

3.48 (c) The publisher gets the largest portion (64.8%) of the revenue. About half (32.3%) of the revenue received by the publisher covers manufacturing costs. The publisher's marketing and promotion account for the next largest share of the revenue, at 15.4%. Author, bookstore employee salaries and benefits, and publisher administrative costs and taxes each account for around 10% of the revenue, whereas the publisher after-tax profit, bookstore operations, bookstore pretax profit, and freight constitute the "trivial few" allocations of the revenue. Yes, the bookstore gets twice the revenue of the authors.

3.50 (b) The pie chart may be best since with only three categories, it enables you to see the portion of the whole in each category. **(d)** The pie chart may be best since, with only four categories it enables you to see the portion of the whole in each category. **(e)** The online content is not copy-edited or fact-checked as carefully as print content. Only 41% of the online content is copy-edited as carefully as print content and only 57% of the online content is fact-checked as carefully as the print content.

3.52 (a)

DESSERT ORDERED	GENDER		
	Male	Female	Total
Yes	71%	29%	100%
No	48	52	100
Total	53	47	100

DESSERT ORDERED	GENDER		
	Male	Female	Total
Yes	30%	14%	23%
No	70	86	77
Total	100	100	100

DESSERT ORDERED	GENDER		
	Male	Female	Total
Yes	16%	7%	23%
No	37	40	77
Total	53	47	100

DESSERT ORDERED	BEEF ENTRÉE		
	Yes	No	Total
Yes	52%	48%	100%
No	25	75	100
Total	31	69	100

DESSERT ORDERED	BEEF ENTRÉE		
	Yes	No	Total
Yes	38%	16%	23%
No	62	84	77
Total	100	100	100

DESSERT ORDERED	BEEF ENTRÉE		
	Yes	No	Total
Yes	12%	11%	23%
No	19	58	77
Total	31	69	100

(b) If the owner is interested in finding out the percentage of males and females who order dessert or the percentage of those who order a beef entrée and a dessert among all patrons, the table of total percentages is most informative. If the owner is interested in the effect of gender on ordering of dessert or the effect of ordering a beef entrée on the ordering of dessert, the table of column percentages will be most informative. Because dessert is usually ordered after the main entrée, and the owner has no direct control over the gender of patrons, the table of row percentages is not very useful here. **(c)** 30% of the men ordered desserts, compared to 14% of the women; men are more than twice as likely to order dessert as women. Almost 38% of the patrons ordering a beef entrée ordered dessert, compared to 16% of patrons ordering all other entrées. Patrons ordering beef are more than 2.3 times as likely to order dessert as patrons ordering any other entrée.

3.54 (a) 23575R15 accounts for over 80% of the warranty claims. **(b)** 91.82% of the warranty claims are from the ATX model. **(c)** Tread separation accounts for 73.23% of the warranty claims among the ATX model. **(d)** The number of claims is evenly distributed among the three incidents; other/unknown incidents account for almost 40% of the claims, tread separation accounts for about 35% of the claims, and blowout accounts for about 25% of the claims.

3.56 (c) The alcohol percentage is concentrated between 4% and 6%, with the largest concentration between 4% and 5%. The calories are concentrated between 140 and 160. The carbohydrates are concentrated between 12 and 15. There are outliers in the percentage of alcohol in both tails. The outlier in the lower tail is due to the non-alcoholic beer O'Doul's with only a 0.4% alcohol content. There are a few beers with alcohol content as high as around 11.5%. There are a few beers with calorie content as high as 330 and carbohydrates as high as 32.1. There is a strong positive relationship between percentage alcohol and calories, and calories and carbohydrates and a moderately positive relationship between percentage alcohol and carbohydrates.

3.58 (c) The one-year CD rate is concentrated above 1.20. The five-year CD rate is concentrated between 2.2 and 2.5. In general, the five-year CD has the higher yield. There does not appear to be any relationship between the one-year CD rate and the five-year CD rate at the various banks.

3.60 (a)

Frequency (Boston)		
Weight (Boston)	**Frequency**	**Percentage**
3,015 but less than 3,050	2	0.54%
3,050 but less than 3,085	44	11.96
3,085 but less than 3,120	122	33.15
3,120 but less than 3,155	131	35.60
3,155 but less than 3,190	58	15.76
3,190 but less than 3,225	7	1.90
3,225 but less than 3,260	3	0.82
3,260 but less than 3,295	1	0.27

(b)

Frequency (Vermont)		
Weight (Vermont)	**Frequency**	**Percentage**
3,550 but less than 3,600	4	1.21%
3,600 but less than 3,650	31	9.39
3,650 but less than 3,700	115	34.85
3,700 but less than 3,750	131	39.70
3,750 but less than 3,800	36	10.91
3,800 but less than 3,850	12	3.64
3,850 but less than 3,900	1	0.30

(d) 0.54% of the Boston shingles pallets are underweight, and 0.27% are overweight. 1.21% of the Vermont shingles pallets are underweight, and 3.94% are overweight.

3.62 (c)

Calories	Frequency	Percentage	Limit	Percentage Less Than
50 but less than 100	3	12%	100	12%
100 but less than 150	3	12	150	24
150 but less than 200	9	36	200	60
200 but less than 250	6	24	250	84
250 but less than 300	3	12	300	96
300 but less than 350	0	0	350	96
350 but less than 400	1	4	400	100

Cholesterol	Frequency	Percentage	Limit	Percentage Less Than
0 but less than 50	2	8%	50	8%
50 but less than 100	17	68	100	76
100 but less than 150	4	16	150	92
150 but less than 200	1	4	200	96
200 but less than 250	0	0	250	96
250 but less than 300	0	0	300	96
300 but less than 350	0	0	350	96
350 but less than 400	0	0	400	96
400 but less than 450	0	0	450	96
450 but less than 500	1	4	500	100

The sampled fresh red meats, poultry, and fish vary from 98 to 397 calories per serving, with the highest concentration between 150 to 200 calories. One protein source, spareribs, with 397 calories, is more than 100 calories above the next-highest-caloric food. The protein content of the sampled foods varies from 16 to 33 grams, with 68% of the values falling between 24 and 32 grams. Spareribs and fried liver are both very different from other foods sampled—the former on calories and the latter on cholesterol content.

3.64 (b) There is a downward trend in the amount filled. **(c)** The amount filled in the next bottle will most likely be below 1.894 liter. **(d)** The scatter plot of the amount of soft drink filled against time reveals the trend of the data, whereas a histogram only provides information on the distribution of the data.

CHAPTER 4

4.1 (a) $1295 per office **(b)** $410 per person

4.2 (a) 21.78 **(b)** $76.17 **(c)** $21.56 **(d)** 89.4

4.3 40.2%

4.4 $1.50

4.5 $0.94

4.6 $16.67

4.7 (a) 10.5 hours **(b)** $29.0 **(c)** 28.90

4.8 (a) $2,639.03 **(b)** 422,245.25 **(c)** 22.25%

4.9 (a) $24,752.21 **(b)** 7,989.35

4.10 (a) mean = 375, median = 350, Mean is a better measure. **(b)** $450

4.11 (a) $398 **(b)** $5.88 million **(c)** Median **(d)** $5.2 million. Illinois and Pennsylvania

4.12 33 days

4.13 (a) 2 star: mean = $23,200 per room, 3-star:mean = $53,500 per room **(b)** Median = 201 rooms **(c)** $8.5 million

4.14 (a) $29,353.441 **(b)** 3.02%

4.15 (a) $1509.14 **(b)** 126 people

4.16 12,202 students

4.17 17.49 hours

4.18 $210,303.41

4.19 (a) Mean = $4.14 billion US **(b)** $64,150 US **(c)** 61,497.33

Section 4.2
All answers assume that each data set represents a sample.

4.20 (a)

$$\bar{x} = \frac{0+0+173+378+441+733+759+857+958+985+1{,}434+2{,}063}{12} = 731.75$$

The mean travel expenditure is $731.75 per member.

(b)

Position of median: $i = \frac{12+1}{2} = 6.5, \tilde{x} = \frac{733+759}{2} = 746$

The median travel expenditure is $746 per member.

(c) Position of the 80th percentile is $r = Half\,Round\left[12 \cdot \frac{80}{100} + \frac{1}{2}\right] = 10. P_{80} = 985$

The 80th percentile is $985 per member.

(d) $R = 2{,}063 - 0 = 2{,}063$

$$r_{Q_1} = Half\ Round\left[12 \cdot \frac{1}{4} + \frac{1}{2}\right] = 3.5$$

$$Q_1 = \frac{173+378}{2} = 275.5$$

$$r_{Q_3} = Half\ Round\left[12 \cdot \frac{3}{4} + \frac{1}{2}\right] = 9.5$$

$$Q_3 = \frac{958+985}{2} = 971.5$$

$$IQR = Q_3 - Q_1 = 971.5 - 275.5 = 696$$

(e)

$$s = 602.2632, \bar{x} = 731.75$$

$$CV = \frac{602.2632}{731.75} \cdot 100\% = 82.3\%$$

The coefficient of variation is 82%.

4.21 Corresponding data array in ascending order:

0	0	0	1	1	1	2	2	3	4	5	21

(a)

$$\bar{x} = \frac{0+0+0+1+1+1+2+2+3+4+5+21}{12} = 3.3333$$

There are 3.333 defective items per lot.

(b) There are $16(3.5) = 56$ total defective items.

(c) Position of median $i = \frac{12+1}{2} = 6.5, \tilde{x} = \frac{1+2}{2} = 1.5$

The median number of defects is 1.5.

(d) There is an outlier of 21 defects; this outlier affects the mean much more than the median.

(e) It is impossible to determine the total number of defects for Plant C since the median does not give any information regarding the other da
sample, only that the average of the tenth and eleventh data points is 4.

(f)

$$s = \sqrt{\frac{3\cdot(0-3.333)^2 + 3\cdot(1-3.333)^2 + 2\cdot(2-3.333)^2 + (3-3.333)^2 + (4-3.333)^2 + (5-3.333)^2 + (21-3.333)^2}{12-1}} = 5.7892$$

4.22 (a)

$$\bar{x} = \frac{-614 + (-103) + 41 + 258 + 313 + 387 + 490}{7} = 110.2857.$$

The mean change in enrollment is 110.29. The combined change in enrollment is also positive because the combined change is equal to the mean change multiplied by 7.

(b) Position of median $i = \dfrac{7+1}{2} = 4, \tilde{x} = 258.$

The median change in enrollment is 258 students.

(c) $s = \sqrt{\dfrac{(-614 - 110.2857)^2 + \dots + (490 - 110.2857)^2}{7-1}} = 378.2740$

Since the standard deviation is an absolute measure of variability, the standard deviation is always a positive value and does not correspond to the sign of the mean.

4.23 $S = \$10.61$

4.24 $S = \$2,733$ thousand

4.25 $S = \$319$

4.26 $S = \$1967$

4.27 $S = 0.919$ hours

4.28 $S = \$3.41$ billions

4.29 $S = 0.7018$

4.30

	Revenue	Volume
Wheat	CV = 32%	CV = 30%
Barley	CV = 41%	CV = 33%

For wheat, revenue is more variable than volume.

For barley, revenue is more variable than volume.

4.31 (a) $7091.471 **(b)** approximately $4 million

4.32 Mean = 18.99 and s = 2.90 (assume sample data)

4.33 Average Hour Worked: CV = 11%
GDP: CV=16%
GDP is more variable than average hour worked

4.35 (a) Mean = 7, median = 7, mode = 7. **(b)** Range = 9, $S^2 = 10.8$, $S = 3.286$, $CV = 46.948\%$. **(c)** Z scores: 0, −0.913, 0.609, 0, −1.217, 1.522. None of the Z scores are larger than 3.0 or smaller than −3.0. There is no outlier. **(d)** Symmetric because mean = median.

4.37 (a) Mean = 2, median = 7, mode = 7. **(b)** Range = 17, $S^2 = 62$ $S = 7.874$, $CV = 393.7\%$. **(c)** 0.635, −0.889, −1.270, 0.635, 0.889. There are no outliers.
(d) Left-skewed because mean < median.

4.39

(a)

	Grade X	Grade Y
Mean	575	575.4
Median	575	575
Standard deviation	6.40	2.07

(b) If quality is measured by central tendency, Grade X tires provide slightly better quality because X's mean and median are both equal to the expected value, 575 mm. If, however, quality is measured by consistency, Grade Y provides better quality because, even though Y's mean is only slightly larger than the mean for Grade X, Y's standard deviation is much smaller. The range in values for Grade Y is 5 mm compared to the range in values for Grade X, which is 16 mm.

(c)

	Grade X	Grade Y, Altered
Mean	575	577.4
Median	575	575
Standard deviation	6.40	6.11

When the fifth Y tire measures 588 mm rather than 578 mm, Y's mean inner diameter becomes 577.4 mm, which is larger than X's mean inner diameter, and Y's standard deviation increases from 2.07 mm to 6.11 mm. In this case, X's tires are providing better quality in terms of the mean inner diameter, with only slightly more variation among the tires than Y's.

4.41 (a) ,Mean $= \dfrac{63.26}{9} = 7.0289$

Median $= 5th$ ranked value $= 7.38$

(b) Variance $= (4.20 - 7.0289)^2 + (5.03 - 7.0289)^2 + (5.86 - 7.0289)^2$

$+ (6.45 - 7.0289)^2 + (7.38 - 7.0289)^2$

$+ (7.54 - 7.0289)^2 + (8.46 - 7.0289)^2$

$+ (8.47 - 7.0289)^2 + (9.87 - 7.0289)^2$

$= \dfrac{26.2809}{9 - 1} = 3.2851,$

Standard deviation $= \sqrt{3.2851} = 1.8125,$ range $= 9.87 - 4.20 = 5.67,$

Coefficient of variation $= \dfrac{1.8125}{7.0289} \times 100\% = 25.79\%$

(c) The mean is only slightly smaller than the median, so the data are only slightly left-skewed. **(d)** The mean cost is $7.03, and the median cost is $7.38. The average scatter of cost around the mean is $1.81. The difference between the highest cost and the lowest cost is $5.67.

4.43 (a) Mean $= 21.12,$ median $= 22,$ mode $= 22$ **(b)** $S^2 = 5.2767,$

$S = 2.2971,$ range $= 10,$ coefficient of variation $= 10.88\%,$ and Z scores are $-0.49, 1.25, 0.38, 0.82, -0.49, 0.38, -0.05, 0.38, 0.38, -0.92,$ $0.38, 0.38, 2.12, -0.93, -0.93, 0.82, 1.25, -0.05, -0.05, -0.93, -0.05, 0.38,$ $0.38, -2.23, -2.23.$ **(c)** Because the mean is slightly less than the median, the data are slightly left-skewed. **(d)** The distributions of MPG of the sedans is right-skewed, while the MPG of the SUVs is slightly right-skewed. The mean MPG of sedans is 4.66 higher than that of SUVs. The average scatter and the range of the MPG of sedans is much higher than that for SUVs.

4.45 (a) Mean $= 0.9257,$ median $= 0.88$ **(b)** Variance $= 0.1071,$ standard deviation $= 0.3273,$ range $= 0.96,$ $CV = 35.36\%.$ There is no outlier because none of the Z scores has an absolute value that is greater than 3.0. **(c)** The data appear to be right-skewed because the mean is greater than the median.

4.47 (a) Mean $= 82.3333,$ median $= 77.0.$ **(b)** Range $= 48,$ variance $= 327.0667,$ standard deviation $= 18.085$ **(c)** The price paid by U.S. travelers is right-skewed because the mean is greater than the median. **(d) (a)** Mean $= 90.6667,$ median $= 77.$ **(b)** Range $= 98,$

variance $= 1,297.0667,$ standard deviation $= 36.0148.$ **(c)** The price is now more skewed because the mean is much greater than the median due to the higher price in the first city (160).

4.49 (a) Mean $= 7.11,$ median $= 6.68.$ **(b)** Variance $= 4.336,$ standard deviation $= 2.082,$ range $= 6.67,$ $CV = 29.27\%.$

(c) Because the mean is greater than the median, the distribution is right-skewed. **(d)** The mean and median are both greater than 5 minutes. The distribution is right-skewed, meaning that there are some unusually high values. Further, 13 of the 15 bank customers sampled (or 86.7%) had waiting times greater than 5 minutes. So the customer is likely to experience a waiting time in excess of 5 minutes. The manager overstated the bank's service record in responding that the customer would "almost certainly" not wait longer than 5 minutes for service.

4.55 (a) 4, 9, 5. **(b)** 3, 4, 7, 9, 12. **(c)** The distances between the median and the extremes are close, 4 and 5, but the differences in the tails are different (1 on the left and 3 on the right), so this distribution is slightly right-skewed. **(d)** In Problem 3.2 (d), because mean $=$ median, the distribution is symmetric. The box part of the graph is symmetric, but the tails show right-skewness.

4.57 (a) $-6.5, 8, 14.5.$ **(b)** $-8, -6.5, 7, 8, 9.$ **(c)** The shape is left-skewed. **(d)** This is consistent with the answer in Problem 3.4 (d).

4.59 (a) $Q_1 = \dfrac{14 + 1}{4} = 3.75$ ranked value $=$ 4th ranked value $= \$0.68,$

$Q_3 = \dfrac{3(14 + 1)}{4} = \dfrac{45}{4} = 11.25$ ranked value $=$ 11th ranked value $= \$1.14,$

Interquartile range $= 1.14 - 0.68 = \$0.46.$ **(b)** Five-number summary: 0.55 0.68 0.88 1.14 1.51. **(c)** The distribution is right-skewed.

4.61 (a) $Q_1 = 19.5, Q_3 = 22,$ interquartile range $= 2.5.$ **(b)** Five-number summary: 16 19.5 22 22 26. **(c)** The MPG of SUVs is left skewed since the distance from the smallest value to the median is greater than the distance from the median to the largest value, the distance from the smallest value to the first quartile is greater than the distance from third quartile to the largest value, and the distance from the first quartile to the median is greater than the distance from the median to the third quartile.

4.63 (a) Commercial district five-number summary: 0.38 3.2 4.5 5.55 6.46. Residential area five-number summary: 3.82 5.64 6.68 8.73 10.49. **(b)** Commercial district: The distribution is left-skewed. Residential area: The distribution is slightly right-skewed. **(c)** The central tendency of the waiting times for the bank branch located in the commercial district of a city is lower than that of the branch located in the residential area. There are a few long waiting times for the branch located in the residential area, whereas there are a few exceptionally short waiting times for the branch located in the commercial area.

4.65 (a)

Average of 3-Year Return	Risk			
Type	Above Average	Average	Below Average	Grand Total
Intermediate government	5.6515	5.7862	4.8214	5.4367
Short-term corporate	−0.0440	2.6355	3.2294	2.1156
Grand total	3.1966	4.1583	3.9484	3.7761

(b)

StdDev of 3-Year Return	Risk			
Type	Above Average	Average	Below Average	Grand Total
Intermediate government	2.4617	1.1457	1.2784	1.8066
Short-term corporate	3.6058	1.7034	1.4886	2.6803
Grand total	4.1197	2.1493	1.6001	2.8227

(c) Across the three different risk levels, intermediate government funds have the highest average three-year returns but the lowest standard deviation. **(d)** Similarly to the 2006–2008 three-year returns, intermediate government funds have the highest average three-year returns but the lowest standard deviation across the three different risk levels.

4.67 (a)

Average of Return 2008		Risk			
Type	Fees	Above Average	Average	Below Average	Grand Total
Intermediate government	No	9.0294	6.9053	4.0368	6.5709
	Yes	3.8863	7.1700	4.5444	4.9937
Intermediate government total		6.5358	6.99656	4.200	5.9576
Short-term corporate	No	10.7315	−1.6174	0.4600	−3.2607
	Yes	−10.2000	−1.6250	0.7250	−3.5941
Short-term corporate total		−10.6252	−1.6140	0.492	−3.3237
Grand total		−0.8612	2.5450	2.1661	1.316

(b)

StdDev of Return 2008		Risk			
Type	Fees	Above Average	Average	Below Average	Grand Total
Intermediate government	No	5.6635	3.6998	3.5178	4.7322
	Yes	6.5778	2.8744	3.2055	5.0712
Intermediate government total		6.5675	3.3870	3.3694	4.8999
Short-term corporate	No	8.6070	4.0613	3.3503	7.1587
	Yes	7.2928	5.4013	3.5790	6.9786
Short-term corporate total		8.2199	4.3480	3.3220	7.0874
Grand total		11.2319	5.8231	3.8020	7.6530

(c) The intermediate government funds have the highest average 2008 returns but the lowest standard deviation among all different combinations of risk level and whether there is a fee charged with the exception that they have the highest average 2008 returns and the highest standard deviation among the below average risk funds that do not charge a fee. **(d)** In contrast to the 2008 returns, the intermediate government funds have the lowest average 2009 returns for all combinations of risk level and whether the funds charged a fee with the except of the below average risk funds that do not charge a fee where the intermediate government funds have the highest average 2008 returns. Unlike the 2008 returns, the intermediate government funds have the lowest standard deviations only among the above average risk funds that do not charge a fee, the average risk funds that either charge a fee or do not charge a fee, and the below average risk funds that charge a fee.

4.74 41.6 years

4.75 $1370

4.76 (a) 28.4 **(b)** 27.5 **(c)** 8.84

4.77 (a) 6.67 **(b)** Mean = $124 and s = $21.43 **(c)** Mean = 3.1 and s = 1.4

4.78 (a) Mean = 79.4% and s = 5.79% **(b)** Mean = 88.9% and s = 5.37%, The average grades of Queen's are higher

4.79

Statistics	Mayor's Salary	Councillor's Salary
Mean	60022.77	24251.82
Median	54758	22640
s	15251.82	13122.07
Min	45000	10664
Q1	50684.5	13750
Q3	65906	28764
Max	101084	63915
CV	25%	54%

4.80

Statistics	Cable Revenue	Advertising Revenue
Mean	0.339	0.175
Median	0.3	0.145
s	0.313	0.177
Min	0.05	0.02
Q1	0.165	0.06
Q3	0.365	0.21
Max	1.25	0.66
CV	92%	101%

c)

Statistics	2000	1989
Mean	$16.96 million	$17.54 million

4.81

	1995	1996
CV	71%	80%

4.82 Mean = 5.7172
S = 4.249

4.83

	Revenue	Net Income
CV	56%	60%

4.84

	March	April
CV	102%	73%

4.85 $28.32 million

4.86 (a) Mean = 6.15 and s = 1.68 **(b)** Men: Mean = 267.14 Women: Mean = 280 **(c)** 48.07

4.87 (a) Mean = 15.37 **(b)** 120.51

4.88 (a)

	1993	1994
Median	504.5	754

b)

	1994	1995
CV	47%	40%

CHAPTER 5

5.2 (a) Simple events include selecting a red ball. **(b)** Selecting a white ball. **(c)** The sample space consists of the 12 red balls and the 8 white balls.

5.4 (a) 60/100 = 3/5 = 0.6. **(b)** 10/100 = 1/10 = 0.1. **(c)** 35/100 = 7/20 = 0.35. **(d)** 9/10 = 0.9.

5.6 (a) Mutually exclusive, not collectively exhaustive. **(b)** Not mutually exclusive, not collectively exhaustive. **(c)** Mutually exclusive, not collectively exhaustive. **(d)** Mutually exclusive, collectively exhaustive.

5.8 (a) Needs three or more clicks to be removed from an email list. **(b)** Needs three or more clicks to be removed from an email list in 2009. **(c)** Does not need three or more clicks to be removed from an email list. **(d)** "Needs three or more clicks to be removed from an email list in 2009" is a joint event because it consists of two characteristics.

5.10 (a) A respondent who answers quickly. **(b)** A respondent who answers quickly who is over 70 years old. **(c)** A respondent who does not answer quickly. **(d)** A respondent who answers quickly and is over 70 years old is a joint event because it consists of two characteristics, answering quickly and being over 70 years old.

5.12 (a) $796/3,790 = 0.21$. **(b)** $1,895/3,790 = 0.50$. **(c)** $796/3,790 + 1,895/3,790 - 550/3,790 = 2,141/3790 = 0.5649$. **(d)** The probability of "is engaged with their workplace *or* is a U.S. worker" includes the probability of "is engaged with their workplace" plus the probability of "is a U.S. worker" minus the joint probability of "is engaged with their workplace *and* is a U.S. worker."

5.14 (a) $514/1,085$. **(b)** $76/1,085$. **(c)** $781/1,085$ **(d)** $1,085/1,085 = 1.00$.

5.16 (a) $10/30 = 1/3 = 0.33$. **(b)** $20/60 = 1/3 = 0.33$. **(c)** $40/60 = 2/3 = 0.67$. **(d)** Because $P(A/B) = P(A) = 1/3$, events A and B are independent.

5.18 $\frac{1}{2} = 0.5$.

5.20 Because $P(A \text{ and } B) = 0.20$ and $P(A)P(B) = 0.12$, events A and B are not independent.

5.22 (a) $536/1,000 = 0.536$. **(b)** $707/1,000 = 0.707$. **(c)** $P(\text{Answers quickly}) = 1,243/2,000 = 0.6215$ which is not equal to $P(\text{Answers quickly} \mid \text{between 12 and 50}) = 0.536$. Therefore, answers quickly and age are not independent.

5.24 (a) $550/1,895 = 0.2902$. **(b)** $1,345/1,895 = 0.7098$. **(c)** $246/1,895 = 0.1298$. **(d)** $1,649/1,895 = 0.8702$.

5.26 (a) $0.025/0.6 = 0.0417$. **(b)** $0.015/0.4 = 0.0375$. **(c)** Because $P(\text{Needs warranty repair} \mid \text{Manufacturer based in U.S.}) = 0.0417$ and $P(\text{Needs warranty repair}) = 0.04$, the two events are not independent.

5.28 (a) 0.0045. **(b)** 0.012. **(c)** 0.0059. **(d)** 0.0483.

5.30 0.095.

5.32 (a) 0.736. **(b)** 0.997.

5.34 (a) $P(B' \mid O) = \dfrac{(0.5)(0.3)}{(0.5)(0.3) + (0.25)(0.7)} = 0.4615$.

(b) $P(O) = 0.175 + 0.15 = 0.325$.

5.36 (a) $P(\text{Huge success} \mid \text{Favorable review}) = 0.099/0.459 = 0.2157$; $P(\text{Moderate success} \mid \text{Favorable review}) = 0.14/0.459 = 0.3050$; $P(\text{Break even} \mid \text{Favorable review}) = 0.16/0.459 = 0.3486$; $P(\text{Loser} \mid \text{Favorable review}) = 0.06/0.459 = 0.1307$. **(b)** $P(\text{Favorable review}) = 0.459$.

5.38 $3^{10} = 59,049$.

5.40 (a) $2^7 = 128$. **(b)** $6^7 = 279,936$. **(c)** There are two mutually exclusive and collectively exhaustive outcomes in (a) and six in (b).

5.42 $(8)(4)(3)(3) = 288$.

5.44 $5! = (5)(4)(3)(2)(1) = 120$. Not all the orders are equally likely because the teams have a different probability of finishing first through fifth.

5.46 $n! = 6! = 720$.

5.48 $\dfrac{10!}{4!6!} = 210$.

5.50 $4,950$.

5.60 (a)

Goals	Age		
	18–25	26–40	Total
Getting Rich	405	310	715
Other	95	190	285
Total	500	500	1,000

(b) Simple event: "Has a goal of getting rich." Joint event: "Has a goal of getting rich and is between 18–25 years old." **(c)** $P(\text{Has a goal of getting rich}) = 715/1,000 = 0.715$. **(d)** $P(\text{Has a goal of getting rich and is in the 26–40-year-old group}) = 310/1000 = 0.31$. **(e)** Not independent.

5.62 (a) $99/200$. **(b)** $127/200$. **(c)** $129/200$. **(d)** $29/200$. **(f)** $10/100$.

5.64 (a) 0.4712. **(b)** Because the probability that a fatality involved a rollover, given that the fatality involved an SUV, a van, or a pickup is 0.4712, which is almost twice the probability that a fatality involved a rollover with any vehicle type, at 0.24, SUVs, vans, and pickups are generally more prone to rollover accidents.

CHAPTER 6

6.2 (a) $\mu = 0(0.10) + 1(0.20) + 2(0.45) + 3(0.15) + 4(0.05) + 5(0.05) = 2.0$.

(b) $\sigma = \sqrt{\begin{array}{c}(0 - 2)^2(0.10) + (1 - 2)^2(0.20) + (2 - 2)^2(0.45) + \\ (3 - 2)^2(0.15) + (4 - 2)^2(0.05) + (5 - 2)^2(0.05)\end{array}}$
$= 1.183$.

6.4 (a)

X	P(X)
$-1	21/36
$+1	15/36

(b)

X	P(X)
$-1	21/36
$+1	15/36

(c)

X	P(X)
$-1	30/36
$+4	6/36

(d) $-\$0.167$ for each method of play.

6.6 (a) 2.1058. **(b)** 1.4671.

6.8 (a) $E(X) = \$66.20$; $E(Y) = \$63.01$. **(b)** $\sigma_X = \$57.22$; $\sigma_Y = \$195.22$. **(c)** Based on the expected value criteria, you would choose the common stock fund. However, the common stock fund also has a standard deviation more than three times higher than that for the corporate bond fund. An investor should carefully weigh the increased risk. **(d)** If you chose the common stock fund, you would need to assess your reaction to the small possibility that you could lose virtually all of your entire investment.

6.9 Probability distribution

P	X
0.02	50,000
0.12	35,000
0.5	20,000
0.25	10,000
0.08	0
0.03	−10,000

$E(X) = 50,000(0.02) + 35,000(0.12) + 20,000(0.5) + 10,000(0.25) + 0(0.8) - 10,000(0.03) = 17,400$

6.10 $80,000

6.11 (a)

# years	X	P(X)
1	$2.00	0.5
2	3.50	0.2
3	4.50	0.2
5	6.50	0.1

(b) $406.25 for 125 subscribers

6.12 (a) Project 3 **(b)** Project 3 has the lowest relative variability

6.13 Country C: $E(X) = $2,000$

6.14 Tire C: $E(X) = $282,000$

6.15 QMS should order 11 units: $E(X) = 67$

6.16 (a) 0.2770. **(b)** 0.0936. **(c)** 1.75 children.

6.17 (a) 0.0601. **(b)** 0.9 def. chips. **(c)** 0.1920.

6.18 (a) 0.9981. **(b)** 0.0135.

6.19 0.1495.

6.20 (a) 0.9254. **(b)** 0.5489.

6.22 (a) 0.2128. **(b)** 0.3153. **(c)** 0.9294. **(d)** $\mu = 4.95$ $\sigma = 0.9307$. **(e)** that a flight is on time or not on time and each flight is independent of all other flights.

6.24 (a) 0.0834. **(b)** 0.2351. **(c)** 0.6169. **(d)** 0.3831.

6.26 Given $\pi = 0.848$ and $n = 3$,

(a) $P(X = 3) = \dfrac{n!}{x!(n-x)!}\pi^x(1-\pi)^{n-x} = \dfrac{3!}{3!0!}(0.848)^3(0.152)^0 = 0.6098.$

(b) $P(X = 0) = \dfrac{n!}{x!(n-x)!}\pi^x(1-\pi)^{n-x} = \dfrac{3!}{0!3!}(0.848)^0(0.152)^3 = 0.0035.$

(c) $P(X \geq 2) = P(X = 2) + P(X = 3)$

$= \dfrac{3!}{2!1!}(0.848)^2(0.152)^1 + \dfrac{3!}{3!0!}(0.848)^3(0.152)^0 = 0.9377.$

(d) $E(X) = n\pi = 3(0.848) = 2.544$ $\sigma_X = \sqrt{n\pi(1-\pi)}$

$= \sqrt{3(0.848)(0.152)} = 0.6218$

6.28 0.0527.

6.29 (a) 0.1353. **(b)** 0.3712.

6.30 (a) 0.2231. **(b)** 0.3423.

6.31 (a) 0.0174. **(b)** 0.9975.

6.32 (a) 0.2707. **(b)** 0.2149.

6.33 (a) 0.6310. **(b)** 0.8488.

6.35 (a) $P(X < 5) = P(X = 0) + P(X = 1) + P(x = 2) + P(X = 3)$
$+ P(X = 4)$

$= \dfrac{e^{-6}(6)^0}{0!} + \dfrac{e^{-6}(6)^1}{1!} + \dfrac{e^{-6}(6)^2}{2!} + \dfrac{e^{-6}(6)^3}{3!} + \dfrac{e^{-6}(6)^4}{4!}$

$= 0.002479 + 0.014873 + 0.044618 + 0.089235$
$+ 0.133853$

$= 0.2851.$

(b) $P(X = 5) = \dfrac{e^{-6}(6)^5}{5!} = 0.1606.$

(c) $P(X \geq 5) = 1 - P(X < 5) = 1 - 0.2851 = 0.7149.$

(d) $P(X = 4 \text{ or } X = 5) = P(X = 4) + P(X = 5) = \dfrac{e^{-6}(6)^4}{4!} + \dfrac{e^{-6}(6)^5}{5!}$

$= 0.2945.$

6.37 (a) $P(X = 0) = 0.0296.$ **(b)** $P(X \geq 1) = 0.9704.$
(c) $P(X \geq 2) = 0.8662.$

6.39 (a) 0.0176. **(b)** 0.9093. **(c)** 0.9220.

6.41 (a) 0.2618. **(b)** 0.8478. **(c)** Because Ford had a lower mean rate of problems per car in 2009 compared to Dodge, the probability of a randomly selected Ford having zero problems and the probability of no more than two problems are both higher than Dodge.

6.43 (a) 0.2441. **(b)** 0.8311. **(c)** Because Dodge had a lower mean rate of problems per car in 2009 compared to 2008, the probability of a randomly selected Dodge having zero problems and the probability of no more than two problems are both lower in 2009 than in 2008.

6.49 (a) 0.64. **(b)** 0.64. **(c)** 0.3020. **(d)** 0.0060. **(e)** The assumption of independence may not be true.

6.51 (a) If $\pi = 0.50$ and $n = 12$, $P(X \geq 9) = 0.0730.$
(b) If $\pi = 0.75$ and $n = 12$, $P(X \geq 9) = 0.6488.$

6.53 (a) 0.1074. **(b)** 0.2684. **(c)** 0.6242. **(d)** Mean = 2.0, standard deviation = 1.2649. **(e)** Since the percentage of bills containing an error is lower in this problem, the probability is higher in (a) and (b) of this problem and lower in (c).

6.55 (a) $\mu = n\pi = 13.6$ **(b)** $\sigma = \sqrt{n\pi(1-\rho)} = 2.0861.$
(c) $P(X = 15) = 0.1599.$ **(d)** $P(X \leq 10) = 0.0719.$
(e) $P(X \geq 10) = 0.9721.$

6.57 (a) If $\pi = 0.50$ and $n = 39$, $P(X \geq 34) = 0.00000121.$
(b) If $\pi = 0.70$ and $n = 39$, $P(X \geq 34) = 0.0109.$ **(c)** If $\pi = 0.90$ and $n = 39$, $P(X \geq 34) = 0.8097.$ **(d)** Based on the results in (a)–(c), the probability that the Standard & Poor's 500 Index will increase if there is an early gain in the first five trading days of the year is very likely to be close to 0.90 because that yields a probability of 80.97% that at least 34 of the 39 years the Standard & Poor's 500 Index will increase the entire year.

6.59 (a) The assumptions needed are (i) the probability that a golfer loses a golf ball in a given interval is constant, (ii) the probability that a golfer loses more than one golf ball approaches 0 as the interval gets smaller, and (iii) the probability that a golfer loses a golf ball is independent from interval to interval. **(b)** 0.0067. **(c)** 0.6160. **(d)** 0.3840.

CHAPTER 7

7.1 (a) 0.1056 **(b)** 10.56% **(c)** 75,995 km

7.2 (a) 0.9522 **(b)** 0.9902 **(c)** 0.3829 **(d)** $2.9 million

7.3 (a) 0.7340 **(b)** 92 papers

7.4 (a) 0.8944 **(b)** IQ = 74

7.5 (a) Stocks: P(lose) = 0.2736   Bonds: P(lose) = 0.2727
(b) Stocks: 0.4498   Bonds: 0.1272 **(c)** 29.7%

7.6 (a) 0.7430 **(b)** 2.42% **(c)** GPA = 3.59

7.8 (a) $P(34 < X < 50) = P(-1.33 < Z < 0) = 0.4082.$
(b) $P(X < 30) + P(X > 60) = P(Z < -1.67) + P(Z > 0.83) = 0.0475 + (1.0 - 0.7967) = 0.2508.$ **(c)** $P(Z < -0.84) \cong 0.20,$

$Z = -0.84 = \dfrac{X - 50}{12}, X = 50 - 0.84(12) = 39.92$ thousand miles, or

39,920 miles. **(d)** The smaller standard deviation makes the absolute
Z values larger. **(a)** $P(34 < X < 50) = P(-1.60 < Z < 0) = 0.4452.$
(b) $P(X < 30) + P(X > 60) = P(Z < -2.00) + P(Z > 1.00) = 0.0228 + (1.0 - 0.8413) = 0.1815.$ **(c)** $X = 50 - 0.84(10) = 41.6$
thousand miles, or 41,600 miles.

7.10 (a) 0.9878. **(b)** 0.8185. **(c)** 86.16%. **(d)** Option 1: Because your score
of 81% on this exam represents a Z score of 1.00, which is below the
minimum Z score of 1.28, you will not earn an A grade on the exam
under this grading option. Option 2: Because your score of 68% on this
exam represents a Z score of 2.00, which is well above the minimum
Z score of 1.28, you will earn an A grade on the exam under this grading
option. You should prefer Option 2.

7.12 (a) 0.9461. **(b)** 0.0032. **(c)** 0.0045. **(d)** 29.6714.

7.27 With 39 values, the smallest of the standard normal quantile values
covers an area under the normal curve of 0.025. The corresponding
Z value is -1.96. The middle (20th) value has a cumulative area of 0.50
and a corresponding Z value of 0.0. The largest of the standard normal
quantile values covers an area under the normal curve of 0.975, and its
corresponding Z value is $+1.96$.

7.29 (a) Mean $= 21.12$, median $= 22$, $S = 2.2971$, range $= 10$,
$6S = 6(2.2971) = 13.7826$, interquartile range $- 2.5, 1.33(2.2971) = 3.0551$. The mean is slightly less than the median. The range is much less
than $6S$, and the interquartile range is less than $1.33S$. **(b)** The normal
probability plot does not appear to be highly skewed. The data may be
symmetrical but not normally distributed.

7.31 (a) Mean $= 1,040.863$, median $= 981$, range $= 1,732$,
$6(S) = 2,571.2310$, interquartile range $= 593, 1.33(S) = 569.9562$.
There are 62.75%, 78.43%, and 94.12% of the observations that
fall within 1, 1.28, and 2 standard deviations of the mean,
respectively, as compared to the approximate theoretical 66.67%, 80%,
and 95%. Because the mean is slightly larger than the median, the
interquartile range is slightly larger than 1.33 times the standard
deviation, and the range is much smaller than 6 times the standard
deviation, the data appear to deviate slightly from the normal distribution.
(b) The normal probability plot suggests that the data appear to be slightly
right-skewed.

7.33 (a) Interquartile range $= 0.0025$, $S = 0.0017$, range $= 0.008, 1.33(S) = 0.0023, 6(S) = 0.0102$. Because the interquartile range is close to
$1.33S$ and the range is also close to $6S$, the data appear to be
approximately normally distributed. **(b)** The normal probability
plot suggests that the data appear to be approximately normally
distributed.

7.35 (a) Five-number summary: 82 127 148.5 168 213; mean $= 147.06$, mode $= 130$, range $= 131$, interquartile range $= 41$, standard
deviation $= 31.69$. The mean is very close to the median. The five-number
summary suggests that the distribution is approximately symmetric
around the median. The interquartile range is very close to $1.33S$.
The range is about $50 below $6S$. In general, the distribution of the data
appears to closely resemble a normal distribution. **(b)** The normal
probability plot confirms that the data appear to be approximately normally
distributed.

7.43 (a) 0.4772. **(b)** 0.9544. **(c)** 0.0456. **(d)** 1.8835. **(e)** 1.8710
and 2.1290.

7.45 (a) 0.2734. **(b)** 0.2038. **(c)** 4.404 ounces. **(d)** 4.188 ounces and 5.212
ounces.

7.47 (a) Waiting time will more closely resemble an exponential
distribution. **(b)** Seating time will more closely resemble a
normal distribution. **(c)** Both the histogram and normal probability
plot suggest that waiting time more closely resembles an
exponential distribution. **(d)** Both the histogram and normal probability
plot suggest that seating time more closely resembles a normal
distribution.

7.49 (a) 0.999968 **(b)** 0.0668 **(c)** 0.0013 **(d)** 1.6653 **(e)** 0.8080
to 1.592 .

CHAPTER 8

8.2 Sample without replacement: Read from left to right in three-digit
sequences and continue unfinished sequences from the end of the row to
the beginning of the next row:
Row 05: 338 505 855 551 438 855 077 186 579 488 767 833 170
Rows 05–06: 897
Row 06: 340 033 648 847 204 334 639 193 639 411 095 924
Rows 06–07: 707
Row 07: 054 329 776 100 871 007 255 980 646 886 823 920 461
Row 08: 893 829 380 900 796 959 453 410 181 277 660 908 887
Rows 08–09: 237
Row 09: 818 721 426 714 050 785 223 801 670 353 362 449
Rows 09–10: 406
Note: All sequences above 902 and duplicates are discarded.

8.4 A simple random sample would be less practical for personal
interviews because of travel costs (unless interviewees are paid to go to a
central interviewing location).

8.6 Here all members of the population are equally likely to be selected,
and the sample selection mechanism is based on chance. But selection of
two elements is not independent; for example, if A is in the sample, we
know that B is also and that C and D are not.

8.8 (a)

Row 16: 2323 6737 5131 8888 1718 0654 6832 4647 6510 4877
Row 17: 4579 4269 2615 1308 2455 7830 5550 5852 5514 7182
Row 18: 0989 3205 0514 2256 8514 4642 7567 8896 2977 8822
Row 19: 5438 2745 9891 4991 4523 6847 9276 8646 1628 3554
Row 20: 9475 0899 2337 0892 0048 8033 6945 9826 9403 6858
Row 21: 7029 7341 3553 1403 3340 4205 0823 4144 1048 2949
Row 22: 8515 7479 5432 9792 6575 5760 0408 8112 2507 3742
Row 23: 1110 0023 4012 8607 4697 9664 4894 3928 7072 5815
Row 24: 3687 1507 7530 5925 7143 1738 1688 5625 8533 5041
Row 25: 2391 3483 5763 3081 6090 5169 0546
Note: All sequences above 5,000 are discarded. There were no repeating
sequences.

(b) 089 189 289 389 489 589 689 789 889 989
1089 1189 1289 1389 1489 1589 1689 1789 1889 1989
2089 2189 2289 2389 2489 2589 2689 2789 2889 2989
3089 3189 3289 3389 3489 3589 3689 3789 3889 3989
4089 4189 4289 4389 4489 4589 4689 4789 4889 4989
(c) With the single exception of invoice 0989, the invoices selected in the
simple random sample are not the same as those selected in the

systematic sample. It would be highly unlikely that a simple random sample would select the same units as a systematic sample.

8.10 Before accepting the results of a survey of college students, you might want to know, for example: Who funded the survey? Why was it conducted? What was the population from which the sample was selected? What sampling design was used? What mode of response was used: a personal interview, a telephone interview, or a mail survey? Were interviewers trained? Were survey questions field-tested? What questions were asked? Were the questions clear, accurate, unbiased, and valid? What operational definition of "vast majority" was used? What was the response rate? What was the sample size?

8.12 (a) The four types of survey errors are coverage error, nonresponse error, sampling error, and measurement error. **(b)** When people who answer the survey tell you what they think you want to hear, rather than what they really believe, this is the halo effect, which is a source of measurement error. Also, every survey will have sampling error that reflects the chance differences from sample to sample, based on the probability of particular individuals being selected in the particular sample.

8.14 Before accepting the results of the survey, you might want to know, for example: Who funded the study? Why was it conducted? What was the population from which the sample was selected? What sampling design was used? What mode of response was used: a personal interview, a telephone interview, or a mail survey? Were interviewers trained? Were survey questions field-tested? What other questions were asked? Were the questions clear, accurate, unbiased, and valid? What was the response rate? What was the margin of error? What was the sample size? What frame was used?

8.16 (a) Virtually 0. **(b)** 0.1587. **(c)** 0.0139. **(d)** 50.195.

8.18 (a) Both means are equal to 6. This property is called unbiasedness. **(c)** The distribution for $n = 3$ has less variability. The larger sample size has resulted in sample means being closer to μ.

8.20 (a) When $n = 2$, because the mean is larger than the median, the distribution of the sales price of new houses is skewed to the right, and so is the sampling distribution of $\overline{X}$ although it will be less skewed than the population. **(b)** If you select samples of $n = 100$, the shape of the sampling distribution of the sample mean will be very close to a normal distribution, with a mean of $272,400 and a standard deviation of $9,000. **(c)** 0.9989. **(d)** 0.3611

8.22 (a) $P(\overline{X} > 3) = P(Z > -1.00) = 1.0 - 0.1587 = 0.8413$. **(b)** $P(Z < 1.04) = 0.85; \overline{X} = 3.10 + 1.04(0.1) = 3.204$. **(c)** To be able to use the standardized normal distribution as an approximation for the area under the curve, you must assume that the population is approximately symmetrical. **(d)** $P(Z < 1.04) = 0.85; \overline{X} = 3.10 + 1.04(0.05) = 3.152$.

8.23 (a) 0.8351 **(b)** 108.4 kw

8.24 0.2424

8.25 4 years

8.26 (a) 0.2195 **(b)** 0.0933 **(c)** 4.2 proposals

8.27 (a) 0.0008 **(b)** 0.1030

8.28 74.6%

8.29 (a) 451 hours **(b)** 0.3085

8.30 (a) 0.9608 **(b)** 0.9802

8.31 (a) 50 managers **(b)** $252,802

8.32 (a) 0.8571 **(b)** 0.2084

8.33A 2.28%

8.33B (a) 0.8781 **(b)** 0.8943

8.34 (a) 0.2375 **(b)** 0.0766 **(c)** 0.000003 **(d)** 0.0032

8.35 399 bags

8.36 1072 days

8.37 (a) 0.0938 **(b)** 1692 drills

8.38 9.52%

8.39 0.0002

8.40 (a) 0.0004 **(b)** 40.8 minutes

8.41 (a) 0.2051 **(b)** $60,702

8.42 (a) 0.3366 **(b)** 21%

8.51 (a) 0.40. **(b)** 0.0704.

8.53 (a) $\pi = 0.501, \sigma_p = \sqrt{\dfrac{\pi(1 - \pi)}{n}} = \sqrt{\dfrac{0.501(1 - 0.501)}{100}} = 0.05$

$P(p > 0.55) = P(Z > 0.98) = 1.0 - 0.8365 = 0.1635.$

(b) $\pi = 0.60, \sigma_p = \sqrt{\dfrac{\pi(1 - \pi)}{n}} = \sqrt{\dfrac{0.6(1 - 0.6)}{100}} = 0.04899.$

$P(p > 0.55) = P(Z > -1.021) = 1.0 - 0.1539 = 0.8461.$

(c) $\pi = 0.49, \sigma_p = \sqrt{\dfrac{\pi(1 - \pi)}{n}} = \sqrt{\dfrac{0.49(1 - 0.49)}{100}} = 0.05$

$P(p > 0.55) = P(Z > 1.20) = 1.0 - 0.8849 = 0.1151.$

(d) Increasing the sample size by a factor of 4 decreases the standard error by a factor of 2.

(a) $P(p > 0.55) = P(Z > 1.96) = 1.0 - 0.9750 = 0.0250.$
(b) $P(p > 0.55) = P(Z > -2.04) = 1.0 - 0.0207 = 0.9793.$
(c) $P(p > 0.55) = P(Z > 2.40) = 1.0 - 0.9918 = 0.0082.$

8.55 (a) 0.7889. **(b)** 0.6746. **(c)** 0.8857. **(d) (a)** 0.9458. **(b)** 0.9377. **(c)** 0.9920.

8.57 (a) 0.8422 **(b)** The probability is 90% that the sample percentage will be contained within 5.58% (0.3042 to 0.4158) symmetrically around the population percentage. **(c)** The probability is 95% that the sample percentage will be contained within 6.65% (0.2935 to 0.4265) symmetrically around the population percentage.

8.59 (a) 0.0336. **(b)** 0.0000. **(c)** Increasing the sample size by a factor of 5 decreases the standard error by a factor of $\sqrt{5}$. The sampling distribution of the proportion becomes more concentrated around the true proportion of 0.59 and, hence, the probability in (b) becomes smaller than that in (a).

8.71 (a) 0.4999. **(b)** 0.00009. **(c)** 0. **(d)** 0. **(e)** 0.7518.

8.73 (a) 0.8944. **(b)** 4.617; 4.783. **(c)** 4.641.

8.75 (a) 0.5319. **(b)** 0.9538. **(c)** 0.9726.

CHAPTER 9

9.1 $\overline{R} = 0.67$
$UCL_R = D_4\overline{R} = 2.282(0.67) = 1.53$
$LCL_R = D_3\overline{R} = 0(0.67) = 0$

$\overline{\overline{X}} = 75.448$

$UCL_X = \overline{\overline{X}} + A_2\overline{R} = 75.448 + (0.729)(0.67) = 75.936$

$LCL_X = \overline{\overline{X}} - A_2\overline{R} = 75.448 - (0.729)(0.67) = 74.960$

9.2 $\overline{R} = 0.338$

$UCL_R = D_4\overline{R} = 2.004(0.338) = 0.677$

$LCL_R = D_3\overline{R} = 0(0.338) = 0$

$\overline{\overline{X}} = 35.399$

$UCL_X = \overline{\overline{X}} + A_2\overline{R} = 35.399 + (0.483)(0.338) = 35.562$

$LCL_X = \overline{\overline{X}} - A_2\overline{R} = 35.399 - (0.483)(0.338) = 35.236$

9.3 $\overline{R} = 23.7$

$UCL_R = D_4\overline{R} = 2.114(23.7) = 50.1$

$LCL_R = D_3\overline{R} = 0(23.7) = 0$

$\overline{\overline{X}} = 104$

$UCL_X = \overline{\overline{X}} + A_2\overline{R} = 104 + (0.577)(23.7) = 117.7$

$LCL_X = \overline{\overline{X}} - A_2\overline{R} = 104 - (0.577)(23.7) = 90.3$

9.4 $\overline{R} = 25.3$

$UCL_R = D_4\overline{R} = 2.282(25.3) = 57.7$

$LCL_R = D_3\overline{R} = 0(25.0) = 0$

$\overline{\overline{X}} = 382.33$

$UCL_X = \overline{\overline{X}} + A_2\overline{R} = 382.33 + (0.729)(25.3) = 400.77$

$LCL_X = \overline{\overline{X}} - A_2\overline{R} = 382.33 - (0.729)(25.3) = 363.89$

9.5 $\overline{R} = 2.71$

$UCL_R = D_4R = 2.114(2.71) = 5.73$

$LCL_R = D_3\overline{R} = 0(2.71) = 0$

$\overline{\overline{X}} = 15.53$

$UCL_X = \overline{\overline{X}} + A_2\overline{R} = 15.53 + (0.577)(2.71) = 17.09$

$LCL_X = \overline{\overline{X}} - A_2\overline{R} = 15.53 - (0.577)(2.71) = 13.97$

9.6 $\overline{R} = 1.36$

$UCL_R = D_4\overline{R} = 2.004(1.36) = 2.73$

$LCL_R = D_3\overline{R} = 0(1.36) = 0$

$\overline{\overline{X}} = 200.47$

$UCL_X = \overline{\overline{X}} + A_2\overline{R} = 200.47 + (0.483)(1.36) = 201.13$

$LCL_X = \overline{\overline{X}} - A_2\overline{R} = 200.47 - (0.483)(1.36) = 199.81$

9.8 (a) Day 4, Day 3. **(b)** LCL = 0.0397, UCL = 0.2460. **(c)** No, proportions are within control limits.

9.10 (a) $n = 500$, $p = 761/16,000 = 0.0476$.

$$UCL = \overline{p} + 3\sqrt{\frac{\overline{p}(1-\overline{p})}{n}}$$

$$= 0.0476 + 3\sqrt{\frac{0.0476(1-0.0476)}{500}} = 0.0761$$

$$LCL = \overline{p} - 3\sqrt{\frac{\overline{p}(1-\overline{p})}{n}}$$

$$= 0.0476 - 3\sqrt{\frac{0.0476(1-0.0476)}{500}} = 0.0190$$

(b) Because the individual points are distributed around $\overline{p}$ without any pattern and all the points are within the control limits, the process is in a state of statistical control.

9.12 (a) UCL = 0.0176, LCL = 0.0082. The proportion of unacceptable cans is below the LCL on Day 4. There is evidence of a pattern over time because the last eight points are all above the mean, and most of the earlier points are below the mean. Therefore, this process is out of control.

9.14 (a) UCL = 0.1431, LCL = 0.0752. Days 9, 26, and 30 are above the UCL. Therefore, this process is out of control.

9.21 (a) The main reason that service quality is lower than product quality is because the former involves human interaction, which is prone to variation. Also, the most critical aspects of a service are often timeliness and professionalism, and customers can always perceive that the service could be done more quickly and with greater professionalism. For products, customers often cannot perceive a better or more ideal product than the one they are getting. For example, a new laptop is better and contains more interesting features than any laptop the owner has ever imagined. **(b)** Both services and products are the results of processes. However, measuring services is often harder because of the dynamic variation due to the human interaction between the service provider and the customer. Product quality is often a straightforward measurement of a static physical characteristic such as the amount of sugar in a can of soda. Categorical data are also more common in service quality. **(c)** Yes. **(d)** Yes.

9.23 (a) $\overline{p} = 0.2702$, LCL = 0.1700, UCL = 0.3703. **(b)** Yes, RudyBird's market share is in control before the in-store promotion. **(c)** All seven days of the in-store promotion are above the UCL. The promotion increased market share.

9.25 (a) $\overline{p} = 0.75175$, LCL = 0.62215, UCL = 0.88135. Although none of the points are outside the control limits, there is a clear pattern over time, with the last 13 points above the center line. Therefore, this process is not in control. **(b)** Because the increasing trend begins around Day 20, this change in method would be the assignable cause. **(c)** The control chart would have been developed using the first 20 days, and then a different control chart would be used for the final 20 points because they represent a different process.

9.27 (a) $\overline{p} = 0.1198$, LCL = 0.0205, UCL = 0.2191. **(b)** Day 24 is below the LCL; therefore, the process is out of control. **(c)** Special causes of variation should be investigated to improve the process. Next, the process should be improved to decrease the proportion of undesirable trades.

9.29 Separate p charts should be developed for each food for each shift:

Kidney—Shift 1: $\overline{p} = 0.01395$, UCL = 0.02678, LCL = 0.00112. Although there are no points outside the control limits, there is a strong increasing trend in nonconformances over time.

Kidney—Shift 2: $\overline{p} = 0.01829$, UCL = 0.03329, LCL = 0.00329. Although there are no points outside the control limits, there is a strong increasing trend in nonconformances over time.

Shrimp—Shift 1: $\overline{p} = 0.006995$, UCL = 0.01569, LCL = 0. There are no points outside the control limits, and there is no pattern over time.

Shrimp—Shift 2: $\overline{p} = 0.01023$, UCL = 0.021, LCL = 0. There are no points outside the control limits, and there is no pattern over time.

The team needs to determine the reasons for the increase in nonconformances for the kidney product. The production volume for kidney is clearly decreasing for both shifts. This can be observed from a plot of the production volume over time. The team needs to investigate the reasons for this.